NATIVE ORCHIDS

of

NORTH AMERICA

Cypripedium acaule. Plant, natural size.

Drawn by Blanche Ames.

NATIVE ORCHIDS
of
NORTH AMERICA
NORTH of MEXICO

BY

DONOVAN STEWART CORRELL

WITH ILLUSTRATIONS BY
BLANCHE AMES AMES and GORDON WINSTON DILLON
CULTURAL NOTES CONTRIBUTED BY
EDGAR THEODORE WHERRY and JOHN VERTREES WATKINS

Foreword by CHARLES SCHWEINFURTH

STANFORD UNIVERSITY PRESS

Stanford, California

Stanford University Press
Stanford, California
Copyright © 1950, 1978 by the Board of Trustees of the
Leland Stanford Junior University
Printed in the United States of America
ISBN 0-8047-0999-8   LC 78-62270
First published in 1950 by the Chronica Botanica Company
Reissued in 1978 by Stanford University Press
Last figure below indicates year of this printing:
87 86 85 84 83 82 81 80 79 78

FOREWORD

To be a specialist in a difficult family of plants as well as an experienced and successful collector of that group is a fortunate and rather rare combination. And it is even rarer for that scientist to be able, in committing his thoughts to the written page, to reconcile the scientific and popular elements — in other words to produce a scientifically satisfying treatise which has a wide appeal and utility to the average naturalist. Such a task has been achieved by Dr. CORRELL in the present work.

In addition there are at least three other outstanding features of this volume. Most important of all, it assembles for the first time an account of all of the North American orchids north of Mexico yet recorded. It gives a detailed description and discussion of each species based not only upon the author's extensive collections in many representative regions but also upon the carefully verified records of the numerous outstanding herbaria in the United States and Canada.

As a result of this prolonged and minute study, there is included the latest of our scientific knowledge concerning the limits of all of the species involved and their principal nomenclature.

Furthermore, it adds to the usual scope of an orchid flora detailed cultural notes by two specialists in that sphere — Dr. EDGAR T. WHERRY of the University of Pennsylvania and Mr. JOHN V. WATKINS of the University of Florida.

Finally, and what is the most valuable and useful feature to the average person, every species is beautifully illustrated by line drawings, both artistically and scientifically, as is possible only to those masters of botanical delineation, Mrs. OAKES AMES and Mr. GORDON W. DILLON.

It is evident, therefore, that this interesting, complete and stimulating publication will inspire extensive observations and collecting, will enable more exact determinations and thus increase our understanding of North American orchidology.

CHARLES SCHWEINFURTH

Wellesley Farms,
Massachusetts.

AUTHOR'S PREFACE, 1978

Up until the time this book was published in 1950, no work was available that covered all of the orchids of North America found north of Mexico. There were, however, regional and state floras available that included these plants. There were also several regional and state treatments that dealt solely with orchids. The most recent of the latter was *Our Wild Orchids* by FRANK MORRIS and EDWARD A. EAMES, published in 1929. This book, which was illustrated with black-and-white photographs, was concerned primarily with the orchids of the northeastern United States and eastern Canada.

The present book treats 157 species, 16 varieties, and 3 hybrids in 46 genera. It was based on the combined taxonomic opinions of a consortium of orchid scholars in the OAKES AMES Orchid Herbarium of Harvard University. When it was published, the book was well received by specialists and laymen alike, and remained in print until 1962, when its publisher, Chronica Botanica, went out of business.

Since that time there has been a steady demand for secondhand copies, and some have changed hands at prices over ten times the original selling price. Deciding whether to reissue the book, however, was difficult, owing in particular to the publication of two magnificently illustrated volumes by CARLYLE A. LUER, *The Native Orchids of Florida* (1972) and *The Native Orchids of the United States and Canada Excluding Florida* (1975). LUER's two books added 4 genera and 13 species to our North American orchid flora — as was to be expected, coming 25 years after the publication of my work.

Yet a comparison of this book with the LUER books persuaded Stanford University Press, who in turn persuaded me, that there is room for both works on the orchid-lover's bookshelf. No color photographs of orchids could be more beautiful than DR. LUER's, yet there are particulars in the classic line drawings of BLANCHE AMES, GORDON W. DILLON, and E. W. SMITH that photographs cannot represent as clearly. DR. LUER's short taxonomic descriptions are sufficient for most purposes, but my more detailed descriptions and keys will be welcomed by more exacting users, as will the notes on cultivation by EDGAR T. WHERRY and JOHN V. WATKINS. Finally, there are the usual differences in nomenclature that one finds, which are often based on the personal interpretation of the author. But as it happens, the nomenclature of DR. LUER's first book is very close to mine; most of the differences arise in his second volume.

After considering whether revisions or an addendum might be in order, I concluded that the book could stand without change. It is a book that has stood the test of time, and I hope that it may find favor still with the present generation of orchid enthusiasts.

DONOVAN S. CORRELL

Fairchild Tropical Garden
Miami, Florida
June 1, 1978

AUTHOR'S PREFACE, 1950

Much has been written about the orchids of North America, and there are a number of regional treatments of the family, the most important of which are cited in the Bibliography. The present work, however, brings together for the first time information concerning all of the orchids of North America, north of Mexico, and an effort has been made to include the pertinent data regarding them. The species and some of the varieties are illustrated, many for the first time. North America is not only vast but exceedingly diverse, especially in regard to geology, topography and climate — all of which factors greatly influence a flora. Further botanical collecting and study will doubtless produce much additional knowledge concerning our orchids. This work, consequently, must be considered only as a foundation upon which more elaborate and detailed work in the future may rest.

The arrangement of the text has been made as simple as possible and the format follows the same pattern throughout. An effort has been made to organize and present the material for popular interest as well as for scientific usefulness, without unduly detracting from the value of either. Although it is difficult to describe clearly a plant in everyday vernacular, I have tried to make the descriptions as nontechnical as possible, with a minimum of botanical terms.

The arrangement of the genera follows RUDOLF SCHLECHTER's system, and the arrangement of the species (where there is more than one) within a genus is alphabetical.

Without the unselfish assistance of many individuals and institutions this work would have been impossible. To enumerate all of those who have in any way lightened or advanced my work would include many of our professional botanists and amateurs. To all of these individuals, especially those concerned with the various herbaria, I wish to express my sincerest appreciation for their cooperation and for the many courtesies extended to me during the course of this work.

To the late Professor OAKES AMES, of the Botanical Museum of Harvard University, I am especially indebted. His generosity in permitting me the use of the illustrations is gratefully acknowledged, and his constructive criticisms of the manuscript have been of immeasurable value. The privilege of using the unsurpassed OAKES AMES Orchid Herbarium and Library at the Botanical Museum of Harvard University is also greatly appreciated.

My profound appreciation is extended to the artists, BLANCHE AMES AMES (Mrs. OAKES AMES) and Mr. GORDON WINSTON DILLON, of the Botanical Museum of Harvard University, for the privilege of including their fine drawings. Most of these illustrations are here published for the first time. Others have appeared in various publications, some of which were produced in exceedingly limited editions. The illustration of *Epidendrum conopseum* is of unique and historical interest in that it is symbolic of almost a half century of illustrating by Mrs. AMES. For, having made a rough draft in 1902, Mrs. AMES completed the illustration in 1946. I am grateful to Mrs. AMES for donating plates 93, 94, and 101, and to the artist, Mr. E. W. SMITH, who executed the drawings. PLATES 92 (FIGS. 4-6) and 143 were drawn by Professor AMES. Except for the above five plates, all of the illustrations were made by Mrs. AMES and MR. DILLON.

I am indebted for the contribution of the cultural notes to Professor EDGAR THEODORE WHERRY, of the University of Pennsylvania, and to Mr. JOHN VERTREES WATKINS, of the University of Florida. The horticultural sections written by each contributor bear his initials after the last paragraph. I am personally responsible for any additional notes.

To my colleague, Mr. CHARLES SCHWEINFURTH, of the Botanical Museum of Harvard University, I owe my deepest appreciation for his tireless and sympathetic assistance in clarifying many of the details involved in this work, and for his having read and constructively criticized the entire manuscript. To Professor HUGO LEANDER BLOMQUIST, of Duke University, I owe my interest in this great family of plants. His understanding of the many problems and sympathetic guidance was an early impetus to this present publication.

To Professor ELMER DREW MERRILL, Director Emeritus of the Arnold Arboretum, Harvard University, I am indebted for valued advice and generous support, especially of field exploration.

I wish to extend my sincere thanks to Dr. ALBERT FREDERICK HILL, of the Botanical Museum of Harvard University, and to the late Mr. CHARLES ALFRED WEATHERBY, of the Gray Herbarium of Harvard University, who have offered many helpful suggestions; and to Dr. WALTER MARDIN BUSWELL, of the University of Miami (Coral Gables, Florida), and to Mr. HENRY MOUSLEY, of Montreal, Canada, for supplying me with special materials concerning certain native orchids.

Miss MARJORIE WILLIAMS STONE, Bibliographer, and Miss RUTH DEXTER SANDERSON, Librarian, of the Gray Herbarium of Harvard University, have been extremely helpful to me in the progress of this work.

To the Milton Fund of Harvard University, I wish to express my gratitude for the Grant of 1943, awarded me for the purpose of having many of the line-cuts of the illustrations made.

I wish to acknowledge my obligation to the John Simon Guggenheim Memorial Foundation for the privilege of holding one of its Post-service Fellowships for the period 1946-47. Through this Fellowship I was enabled to bring this work to completion.

Finally, I wish to express my appreciation to my wife, Dr. HELEN BUTTS CORRELL, for her assistance in all phases of this work and for her excellent field aid which has furthered this undertaking.

To

Hugo Leander Blomquist

Friend and Teacher

CONTENTS

Orchids — xiii — **Contents**

ILLUSTRATIONS

"These kinds of Orchis haue not been much written of by the ancients, neither by the late writers to any purpose, so that it may content you for this time to receiue the names set downe in their seuerall titles, ...

"The nature and vertues of these kindes of Orchis are referred vnto the others, namely to those of the Fox stones: notwithstanding there is no great vse of these in Phisicke, but regarded for the pleasant and beautifull flowers, wherewith nature hath seemed to plaie and disport hir selfe."

JOHN GERARDE, The Herball or Generall Historie of Plantes, page 167 (1597).

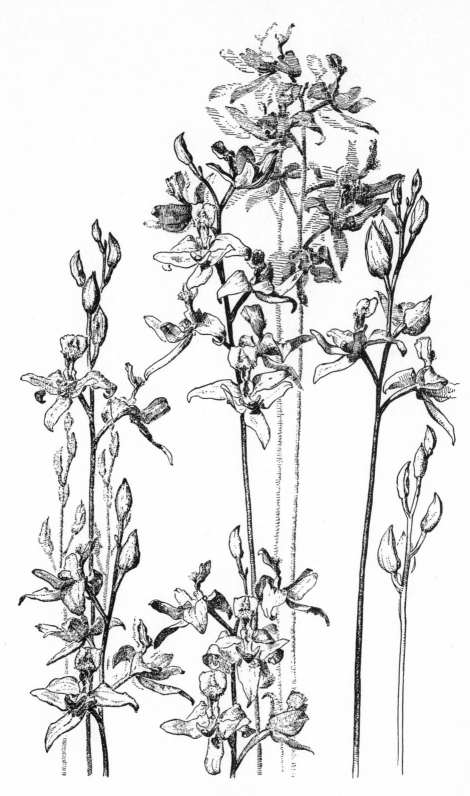

Calopogon

Drawn by Blanche Ames

INTRODUCTION

From where I stood on the edge of a forest of giant spruces, I could look far across the broad valley to distant massive slate-gray mountains. Above the emerald sweep of grasses and sedges spreading before me, the burnished lips of the Yellow Lady's-slipper stood like solitary nuggets of orient gold and the fluffy lavender blossoms of a fragile aster dotted the lush green fields. A tiny rare bellflower, with flaring blue petals, grew here and there among deeply embedded stones, while farther down the valley scattered islets of meadowland were aflame with the intense pink-purple flowers of the Broad-leaved Fireweed.

It is not, however, only northern British Columbia that can offer such a scene; it can be duplicated or simulated wherever orchids may grow. For one who seeks to find these regal flowers in their native haunts, refreshing adventure waits. Through the ages man has sought orchids, not only for their satisfying beauty, but also for their once fancied value in alleviating suffering and for their supposed restorative and procreative powers.

At first their supposed medicinal properties were of primary concern; the Greeks THEOPHRASTUS and DIOSCORIDES, more than two thousand years ago, advanced the belief that most plants, including a species of *Orchis,* could be used for curative purposes. Throughout Europe, especially during the Renaissance, these ancient Greek concepts were adhered to and consequently interest centered in those plants which were thought to be of medicinal value. Even today in some parts of the world primitive peoples use some orchids in their therapeutic practices. However, the singular beauty of the flowers and the bizarre forms which many of them assume are the primary reasons for most of the present-day interest in orchids.

Although mention of the word "orchid" usually brings to mind sweltering jungles of far-off lands, shrouded in mystery and romance, such need not be the case, for perhaps the small patch of woodland lying within a stone's throw of one's home may harbor several species of these much sought-for plants. And, although the flowers may not, at first glance, resemble those exotics displayed in a florist shop-window, a close examination will reveal that they are just as alluring and attractive in their way as any of their cousins which are native to dense tropical forests.

The Orchidaceae, a cosmopolitan family attaining its highest development in the tropics and subtropics of both hemispheres, is one of the largest families of flowering plants in the world, consisting of several hundred genera and fifteen thousand or more species and varieties. It is probably exceeded in number of species only by the Compositae. The orchid family, which is considered to have originated from the Liliaceae, is perhaps the most advanced in the Monocotyledoneae. Some other closely allied families, besides the Liliaceae, are the Burmanniaceae, Iridaceae, Amaryllidaceae and Hypoxidaceae. Although the family is thought to be rather ancient in respect to geologic time, no fossil remains have been found. While there is enormous variation in the form and structure of the various genera and species, all orchids have a distinctive feature in common which, for our convenience, superficially separates them from other plants in our flora. This feature is the column, an elongation of the floral axis which bears the sexual organs. According to PFITZER's observations (1889), the technical and only real difference which separates the orchids from all other plants is the absence of an embryonic root.

Besides its wide distribution and its large number of species, the orchid family is unusual among the higher plants for several reasons, namely — the extreme variations of its complex and highly specialized flowers; its great variety of habit and diversity of ·habitat; the enormous number of seeds produced in a single capsule. Very few, if any, plant families possess the floral and vegetative variations which are to be found in the Orchidaceae. Because of this extreme variability and the consequent singularity of the flowers, orchids have acquired numerous descriptive common names. It is also quite possible that the physiological adaptations of the genera have no equal in any other family. Parasitism on higher plants and carnivorism are perhaps the only physiological functions not definitely known to occur in the Orchidaceae.

The number of seeds produced in an orchid capsule is in many cases phenomenal. The astronomers at the Greenwich Observatory, England, made an accurate count of the seeds in a capsule of the tropical American orchid, *Cycnoches chlorochilon*, and found that it contained 3,770,000 seeds. For a tropical species of *Maxillaria*, DARWIN (1877) accepted FRITZ MUELLER's computation that a single capsule yields 1,756,440 seeds, and DARWIN, himself, estimated that the European *Orchis maculata* produces approximately 6,200 seeds in a single capsule. Many of our native orchids produce large numbers of seeds, and it may be noted here that the seeds exhibit distinct features for each species. In spite of this prolific seed production, however, orchids remain a comparatively inconspicuous feature of any flora. Although a number of theories have been advanced, no completely satisfactory explanation has ever been arrived at in regard to the rarity of orchids. Perhaps a fundamental reason is the fact that for the most part they depend upon external aid for pollination, and because of faulty pollination, economy of vitality on the part of the plant, etc. very few seed-pods are formed. Also, the period of time elapsing between pollination and fecundation is often of long duration, sometimes as much as several weeks. In the meantime, the orchid is apt to lose its inflorescence through injury (with consequent loss of fruit production) or succumb to some one of its many natural enemies. Even so, considering the huge production of seeds in a single capsule, it stands to reason that only a few fruits are necessary for the survival of a given species. Hence, this delicate biological balance in the Orchidaceae remains in the realm of speculation.

The microscopic seeds apparently contain no endosperm or stored food and thus they are thought to be entirely dependent upon external aid for germination and the growth of the seedling. In nature, fungi are considered to furnish this assistance and, if the seed is not destroyed, a compatible relationship is established between the fungus and the orchid. This phenomenon, called symbiosis, is discussed in detail under *Goodyera pubescens*. The delicate balance between the orchid seedling and the fungus, which may easily be upset to the detriment of the seedling, is another reason for the rarity of orchids. Perhaps in nature most, if not all, species of orchids contain within their roots and rootstocks an endotrophic fungus which occupies the cellular structure and remains in harmony with the orchid.

From an artistic and aesthetic point of view orchids are universally accorded first place in nature. Their extraordinary beauty makes them the basis of a multimillion dollar floral industry in the United States alone. However, the family is otherwise of little economic importance. Vanilla, the extract from the cured unripened pods of various species of the genus *Vanilla*, especially *V. planifolia* in the Western Hemisphere, is the most important commercial product of this large family. A few Asiatic species have tubers and tuberoids which contain a nutritive starch associated with a peculiar gum. These tubers are collected and dried, and are placed on the market where they are sold as salep. This drug is extensively used in oriental countries as a demulcent, nerve tonic, for paralysis and as a food similar to tapioca. The leaves of *Angraecum fragrans* (*Jumellea fragrans*), of the

Seychelles Islands, are used for making faham tea. Although for centuries some orchids were considered efficacious in the healing of the sick, they have fallen into disrepute, and not a single species has been retained in modern medicine as an indispensable source of any drug. A few North American species have miscellaneous household uses as a source of glue and resin.

Surprisingly, in recent years orchids have received political recognition. Minnesota has adopted the queenly *Cypripedium reginae* as its state flower. Brazil, Colombia, Costa Rica, Guatemala and Honduras have all issued postage stamps commemorating outstanding species prevalent in their respective geographical regions. Guatemala has designated the exceptionally beautiful *Lycaste virginalis* (*L. Skinneri*), commonly known as "Monja Blanca," as its national flower. Likewise, Costa Rica has adopted *Cattleya Skinneri,* commonly known as "Guaria morada" or "Flor de San Sebastian," as its national flower.

A most interesting natural phenomenon in the Orchidaceae is insect-pollination. Although many plants are wind-pollinated, with few exceptions orchids are pollinated by insects. Each individual species seems to have its own peculiar mechanism to insure its receiving pollen from another plant of the same species. The column is so formed and placed in the flower that, in order to reach the nectary, the visiting insect must touch the stigmas and deposit there any pollen which it may be carrying. Upon leaving, the insect must first come in contact with the anther and thus become burdened with another load of pollen or an entire pollinium which it carries to the stigmas of the next flower visited. In this manner cross-pollination is effected and self-pollination of the species is prevented or made unnecessary. This phenomenon is taken up in more detail under *Cypripedium acaule* and *Calopogon pulchellus.*

It is believed that many orchids can be pollinated only by a single specific insect, such as a bumble bee. The pollinating agents in the Orchidaceae include bees, wasps, various flies and ants as well as butterflies, moths, beetles and snails.

There is always the possibility that irregular flowers, such as those found in orchids, may revert to a regular structure — the ancestral and more primitive condition. This reversion of irregular to regular floral parts is known as "peloria." This condition may also result from an increase in the number of the modified segments (*cf. Cypripedium reginae*). Peloria is often hereditary. Although peloric plants are sometimes frequent, as exhibited by *Spiranthes cernua* in the southwestern United States, I have not given distinctive names to these plants since it seemed best to recognize them only as abnormalities.

Although it would be of value to include an exhaustive historical study of the orchids in our flora, such has not been undertaken. To evaluate properly all the contributions to our knowledge of this great and interesting family would involve more time and space than can be allowed. A selected Bibliography of the more important publications replaces to some extent an historical treatment.

Distribution of our Native Orchids:— To attempt to discuss fully the geological, topographical and climatic factors in the region under consideration and their influence upon the Orchidaceae would be a major undertaking in itself, and perhaps would lead only to confusion instead of clarity. Briefly, North America, as here considered, comprises Greenland, Canada (including the outlying islands), Alaska (including the Aleutian Islands) and the United States. This vast area may be best characterized in contrasting terms. From the Arctic icecap, continually swept by frigid storms, to warm Florida strands, often devastated by tropical hurricanes, sprawls this Gargantuan land-mass. Now its surface is flattened by tundra, prairies, plains, deserts, lakes and plateaus, now roughened by rugged chains of mountains. Its chameleon complexion imperceptibly changes from perpetual whiteness in the Arctic, through bluish green conifers, bright-colored hardwoods and grasslands to multicolored coastal shores. Underlying all this region may be found igneous, sedimentary and metamorphic rocks, the parent materials of a diversified soil-covering. Extensive areas have been or still are under the influence of glaciation.

Our present-day knowledge of the distribution and abundance of any species of plant is relative to the amount of botanical collecting which has been carried on in a given area. As a result of the personal idiosyncrasies of field botanists and the general limitations of plant collecting, distribution, at best, must be tentative and an approximation. The fact that plants are living things means that they are plastic and potentially dynamic. Their behavior is, however, controlled by external as well as internal factors. The extent of their distribution depends largely upon their resistance or adjustment to these factors. For example, temperature plays an important role. In mild and favorable years a given species may advance northward some distance beyond its usual range, and then it may be destroyed in all the invaded area by a return of normal cold temperature. Therefore, unless some individuals develop sufficient cold-resistance the species will remain definitely limited in its distribution. Consequently, plant records are often misleading. There may be a record of a species from a given area, while actually that species may have been exterminated in the area soon after its collection or even by that very collection. A species may also be limited in its distribution by soil-moisture and, like many of our northern orchids, will not occur or survive unless a bog is available — a dry sandy area or even a moist forested slope will not suffice for these "bog-loving" plants.

Colonies of plants may be found at great distances from the normal range of the species. These so-called disjunct stations may be the result of wind-borne or bird-transported seeds lodging in a habitat congenial to their germination and growth where they are able to establish themselves. Plants may frequently occur in what appears to be an entirely uncongenial environment, due to some special factor which accounts for their survival. For instance, the few orchids that grow in Greenland and elsewhere in the extreme North are covered by deep snow in the severest weather. Thus, they are protected from the intense cold and high winds and are able to exist far beyond the Arctic tree-line.

Although some of the plant families represented in North America have relict and endemic species, there apparently are few in the Orchidaceae in our flora.

The environmental adaptability of orchids, as a group, is phenomenal, even though the specific requirements of an orchid may be exacting and allow for little or no variation. For example, I have collected *Spiranthes vernalis* in tidal salt flats in North Carolina and Florida, and *S. Romanzoffiana* in alkaline flats of northern British Columbia. In stunted cedar-oak groves of dusty semiarid Texas I have found richly luxuriant plants of the saprophyte, *Hexalectris Warnockii.* In deep sphagnum bogs in Vermont I have gathered *Calopogon pulchellus* and *Pogonia ophioglossoides.* From frigid alpine meadows in the Yukon I have taken clusters of *Habenaria obtusata,* and in the spongy moss of spruce forests in the same region I have found slender long-stemmed plants of *Listera cordata.* From the gnarled branches of a sweet gum tree overhanging the shores of Lake Waccamaw in eastern North Carolina I have taken specimens of the epiphyte, *Epidendrum conopseum,* thriving there at the northernmost station for an epiphytic orchid in the Western Hemisphere. In verdant jungle-like palm hammocks of the southern Florida Everglades, I have gathered from small grassy floating islands the semi-aquatic *Habenaria repens,* while on nearby rotting stumps grew plants of *Liparis elata.*

Although soil and topography have a definite influence upon terrestrial species, there is little doubt that temperature and moisture are the most essential factors which control the distribution and survival of all orchids, both terrestrial and epiphytic.

In tropical and subtropical regions the greatest number of orchids occur as epiphytes in rain-forests on moderately cool mountain slopes. Very few species are found in arid regions, and, of these, most are epiphytic or lithophytic with specially adapted tissues for storing water.

In subtropical southern peninsular Florida most of the epiphytes are confined to the moist Everglades, the Big Cypress Swamp or to the numerous peculiar hammock formations found throughout the pinelands and Everglades. In the hammocks, which are slightly elevated areas supporting a broad-leaved vegetation, not only are epiphytes found but many terrestrial orchids which are more or less confined to these areas. Each individual hammock usually has its distinctive flora. When a species is frequent in one hammock it may be rare or entirely absent in others.

In temperate and boreal regions, in which most of North America lies, orchids may be roughly divided into those which occur in open bogs, meadows, fields, prairies, and similar habitats, and those which grow in wooded areas. Some few, as several species of *Spiranthes, Habenaria* and *Hexalectris,* seem to thrive under exceptionally dry and competitive conditions.

In the arid and semiarid regions of the West and Southwest, dependence of the orchid flora on moisture is especially noticeable. With few exceptions, the species are confined to canyons, mountain ravines and valleys, depressions along water-courses or about springs. *Spiranthes* and *Hexalectris* may occasionally spread into open dry country, but on the whole the species are to be found in the more moist areas. In the Arctic and above tree-line on high mountains, where the icebound water is unavailable to plants and the habitat is physiologically dry, orchids are restricted to the few localities where moisture is readily available.

By far the greatest number of orchid species occurs in the mesophytic areas of the eastern United States and Canada — which includes the most ancient part of the continent. Of the nearly two hundred species and variants in our orchid flora, about one hundred and ten are to be found in the southeastern United States alone, while in the Lake States and New England there are about fifty. In Vermont, thirty-three species have been collected in a space of five square miles; HENRY MOUSLEY (1920) found thirty species within a space of four square miles in the vicinity of Hatley, Stanstead County, Quebec.

Orchids often occur so abundantly in a favorable habitat that they constitute the dominant members of a plant community. In Henderson County, in the mountains of North Carolina, I have observed fourteen species and varieties in and about a sphagnum bog of less than an acre in size. FULLER (1933), over a period of eight years, collected twenty species of orchids in a single large tamarack swamp in eastern Wisconsin. In balsam-spruce-tamarack associations in the Lake States, *Cypripedium reginae* occasionally occurs in colonies of several thousand plants, while in some bogs in the same region CURTIS (1941A) found an average of fifteen plants of *Habenaria clavellata* per square foot over an area of forty square feet. In Louisiana, I have seen hundreds of plants of *Habenaria flava* in an alluvial woodland in which it was the principal herbaceous species.

The most showy displays of our native orchids are often to be found on the broad open savannahs and in the shrubby pocosins in the Coastal Plain and along the Gulf Coast in the southeastern United States. In such places *Calopogon* spp., *Pogonia ophioglossoides, Cleistes divaricata, Habenaria nivea, H. ciliaris, H. integra* and several species of *Spiranthes* abound. They are often locally abundant and together with various species of pitcher plants (*Sarracenia* spp.), white-top sedges (*Dichromena* spp.), and other plants they help to create a beautiful scene across the flat far-flung savannah lands.

The areas which support the fewest species of orchids are the prairies and Great Plains of the Mississippi Basin. No orchid is restricted to the prairies. The most abundant of the species in these areas are also rather widespread in other plant communities. Such species are *Cypripedium Calceolus* var. *pubescens, C. candidum, Habenaria leucophaea, H. lacera, H. psycodes* and *Spiranthes cernua.*

The rarest species in our area are those which barely enter the region from the South or from other continents. Some of these have been collected only once, while others have been collected or observed only a few times. The points of interest concerning these unique plants are discussed in the text. Intrusions into Florida from the West Indies and into the southwestern states from Mexico have occurred in the past; future exploration will doubtless result in the discovery of other such introduced orchids. The most recent addition to our orchid flora was the finding of *Galeandra Beyrichii* in southern Florida in November 1946. The last previous discovery of an orchid new to our flora was that of *Zeuxine strateumatica* in Florida in 1936, a most striking introduction from Asia. Within the past fifteen years six species of orchids have been added to our flora.

A few instances of extremes in distribution may be of interest. Among those orchids known to science for more than fifty years, perhaps the rarest in our region is the Asiatic *Habenaria Chorisiana,* found in Alaska and British Columbia. *Polystachya luteola* of southern Florida is perhaps the most widely distributed, being found throughout the tropics and subtropics of both hemispheres. *Ionopsis utricularioides,* also of southern Florida, is one of the most widely dispersed species in the Western Hemisphere extending south to Argentina and occurring on the Galapagos Islands. Several species of *Habenaria, Listera cordata* and *Corallorhiza trifida* may well be our most northern orchids. About six species occur beyond the tree-line within the Arctic Circle.

Few data are available in regard to the ecology of orchids, but scattered notes exist in papers and on herbarium sheets. Although it is not possible to include much ecological information, it may be of interest to note some field observations concerning a few of our species. Even though most of our orchids appear to be intolerant of competition a few of them are exceedingly aggressive. In the shallow depressions along roadsides in savannahs and flatwoods of the Coastal Plain where earth has been excavated, the soil is consistently more moist and boggy than that of the surrounding terrain. Soon after their excavation, these depressions are rapidly invaded by bog plants, among which are *Calopogon* spp., *Pogonia ophioglossoides* and *Spiranthes* spp. These delicate orchids more than hold their own against the sedges and grasses and often become a conspicuous part of the association. Abandoned farm lands throughout the South are frequently invaded within a few years by *Spiranthes gracilis* and *S. Grayi*. In Alabama, I have seen *S. gracilis* successfully competing with broom-sedges (*Andropogon* spp.) and various species of legumes and composites.

In his study of some native orchids of the Lake States, especially the Lake Superior region, CURTIS (1941A) reported that an area which had been planted to potatoes forty years before and was now covered with rather large maples and hemlocks, had been successfully invaded by *Habenaria orbiculata, Malaxis unifolia, Cypripedium acaule, Corallorhiza maculata, Goodyera oblongifolia, G. tesselata* and *G. repens* var. *ophioides.* He also found that cut-over areas which had been protected from fire were repopulated with a considerable orchid flora within a few years providing that stands of virgin timber remained nearby. In accordance with the observations of others, CURTIS found that *Spiranthes gracilis* is a pioneer species in the invasion of wornout soils, wastelands and old fields, and that *Habenaria lacera* is an unusually tolerant species, occurring in tamarack bogs in the Lake States and in meadows and sedge-bogs in the South.

Perhaps the most rugged terrestrial orchid in our region, especially in the South, is *Habenaria ciliaris*. There it is almost ubiquitous and has been appropriately designated the "gentle brute" because of its extreme hardiness and competitive ability. In the mountains of North Carolina I have seen this species growing luxuriantly in a dry abandoned roadbed over which oxen and wagons had traveled only ten years before. Nearby, on a dry cut-over pine slope its deep orange plumes towered well above a thick growth of broom-sedge. It not only thrives in these dry hot habitats, but does equally well in dense wet forests or in open bogs.

The drainage of savannahs, bogs, swamps and meadows, as well as lands which are periodically inundated is usually disastrous to orchids indigenous to such places. In Mississippi, I saw hundreds of blackened plants of the beautiful *Habenaria nivea* which had been killed while still in bud as the result of the recent ditching and draining of the savannahs on which they grew. Furthermore, the draining of naturally wet regions with consequent lowering of the water level is conducive to fire, as in the case of parts of the Florida Everglades which have from time to time been burned over by destructive fires with the elimination of the native flora. It may be of interest to note that grass-pinks, especially *Calopogon multiflorus,* are quite able to survive surface fires in pinelands.

There are many extra-limital tropical and subtropical species which are cultivated out-of-doors in Florida and southern California. It is reasonable to assume that some of the more aggressive of these may in time become introduced to form a part of the flora of these two states, particularly in subtropical Florida. This type of introduction is somewhat exemplified by the Asiatic *Zeuxine strateumatica,* which was introduced into Florida apparently through the medium of grass-seed and found conditions suitable to its needs. Since its introduction it has assumed the character of a weed-species, occurring in many counties throughout Florida. Additional West Indian and Middle American species may be found in the southern and southeastern States when more extensive collecting is undertaken. Similarly, there is the possibility that other Asiatic species may be discovered in Alaska and the Aleutian Islands. There is always the chance of discovering species and varieties new to science within our relatively well-known region. In June 1935, the rather striking *Hexalectris Warnockii* was discovered in Texas and described in 1943; the extent to which new concepts may appear will be governed by the specific and varietal delimitations which we place upon them.

General Characteristics of Orchids:— Orchids are perennials and are either terrestrial, epiphytic, lithophytic, semiaquatic or very rarely subterranean. Most of the species found in the temperate zone are terrestrial while the greater number of tropical and subtropical orchids are epiphytic or lithophytic. The subterranean genera, of which there are two (*Rhizanthella* and *Cryptanthemis*), are confined to Australia.

Two distinctive types of vegetative growth are found in the Orchidaceae — sympodial and monopodial. All terrestrial and many epiphytic orchids have a sympodial main axis, in which growth of the original main axis ceases at the end of the flowering season to be resumed the next year by the development of a different axis, resulting in a series of successive annual axes. In this type of growth the inflorescence may be either terminal on the shoot or borne on the side of the shoot on a short leafless branch. The other form of growth, monopodial, occurs when the main axis grows steadily onward year after year, producing new leaves at the apex (rarely leafless) and bearing flowers on lateral shoots which arise in the axils of the older leaves.

In respect to the flowers, orchid plants may be hermaphroditic, dioecious or monoecious, depending upon the genus.

Terrestrial orchids, in general, have an erect or ascending stout or slender stem bearing one or more radical or cauline leaves or both and is terminated by one or more flowers. The leaves are either present at flowering time or appear separately at a different season. When present, the leaf is entire and varies from a bract-like sheathing leaf to a slender or broad lamina which is filiform to orbicular, membranaceous to coriaceous or fleshy and is often plicate or duplicate.

The roots are fibrous, fleshy or tuberous. Many species have prominent rhizomes upon which adventitious roots are borne; others produce corms or tubers.

A few of the terrestrial species are saprophytic; that is, they grow in and derive their nourishment from humus. These plants are commonly small and inconspicuous. They usually develop a coralloid rhizome, are more or less lacking or apparently lacking in chlorophyll, and have an essentially naked or bracteate greenish, yellowish or reddish purple stem terminated by a raceme of flowers.

Epiphytic and most lithophytic orchids have no permanent main roots. Instead, there are adventitious roots which arise mainly from the nodes of the stem and sometimes form a mat over the substratum, penetrating into the surrounding medium or hanging free from the substratum for a considerable length. The aerial roots of epiphytic orchids have a special development of the epidermis, called the velamen, which consists of a spongy tissue of several layers of cells which rapidly absorbs moisture from the atmosphere. When these roots are moist they are usually green, but when dry they are whitish, brownish or ash-colored. When present, the leaves are similar to those of terrestrial orchids.

Many epiphytic sympodial forms have pseudobulbs. These are thickened secondary stems, composed of one to several internodes, which serve as reservoirs of water and food. They are variously shaped, being mostly globose, pyriform or fusiform, and bear leaves either throughout their entire length or only at the apex. The leaves are one or more, simple and entire, and are often thick and fleshy, being usually well adapted for storing water because of a thick cuticle.

The inflorescence of the Orchidaceae consists of one or more flowers and is a spike, simple raceme or panicle. The zygomorphic flowers (*cf.* PLATE 1) are either unisexual or bisexual and have an inferior 1- or 3-celled ovary. They may be small and inconspicuous or large and showy. Occasionally polymorphic, cleistogamous, peloric or teratologic flowers are produced. The three sepals are generally colored as well as the petals instead of being green as in most flowers. They may be free from one another or more or less united, sometimes forming a tube. The symmetrical dorsal sepal usually differs somewhat in shape from the lateral sepals which are more or less oblique. The lateral sepals are either free from each other or somewhat coherent and are often united at the base, occasionally forming a mentum, or chin, with the foot of the column. Of the inner segments, the petals, two are regular and identical, and the third, called the lip, or labellum, is more or less modified. The lip is properly the uppermost petal of the flower, but in most species it assumes the lower position in the perianth as a result of the twisting of the pedicel or pedicel and ovary. It usually differs markedly in shape, size and coloration from the other two petals and is commonly by far the most conspicuous feature of the flower. The lip is either simple or variously lobed; flat or more or less saccate; entire, fringed or variously toothed and notched; and its disc, or upper surface, is frequently adorned with calli, papillae or lamellae. It may be only slightly or greatly extended at the base to form a spur, or nectary.

The column (*cf.* PLATE 1), which represents a union of carpels and is, in part, an elongation of the floral axis, bears at or near the summit, or laterally, one to rarely three mobile or rigidly attached anthers and in front on the ventral surface the more or less confluent stigmas or stigma. In many species a modified stigma, called the rostellum, projects out over the stigmatic surface and serves to affix the pollinia to insects. The anther, or anthers, situated behind the rostellum and often lying upon it, rests in a shallow cavity, called the clinandrium. It is more or less distinctly 2-celled and contains a mass of pollen or two, four, six or eight distinct pollen masses, or pollinia — the number present sometimes being used in the differentiation of genera. The pollen is either powdery, granular-mealy (sometimes composed of groups of grains), waxy or cartilaginous. The columns of the various genera and species exhibit a wide range of variation, and are of basic importance in classification. The column is often produced into a more or less distinct foot.

A detailed discussion of the various parts of the column and their morphological origin would doubtless be of interest, especially in relation to their dramatic significance to insect-pollination. However, in a primarily taxonomic work such as this, space will not permit too lengthy a discussion of this subject. If detailed information concerning this subject is desired, an excellent account may be found

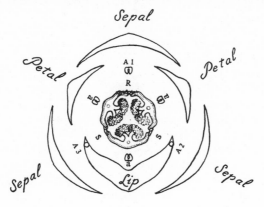

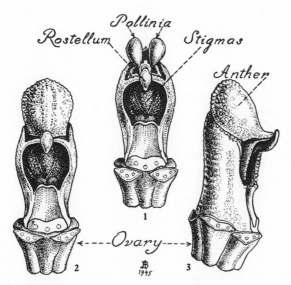

PLATE 1.— The diagram represents a cross section of an orchid flower at a time in its age-long evolution when all of the organs were distinct. A1-A3 show the three stamens of the outer whorl; a, a, a, show the stamens of the inner whorl; S, S, indicate the position of the fertile stigmas; R, is the sterile stigma which has become the rostellum. The central figure shows the fruit in cross section with its three rows of dust-like seeds. Below the diagram a typical column is shown. In figs. 1-3 stamens and stigmas and the central axis of the flower have combined to form the column—the diagnostic structure of the vast orchid family. The *pollinia* represent A1 of the diagram. *Drawn by Blanche Ames.*

in DARWIN's *Various Contrivances by which Orchids are Fertilized by Insects* (1877). Briefly, in many genera, as *Listera, Orchis, Oncidium,* etc., part of the rostellum forms a disc to which the pollinia are attached by a caudicle or stalk.

On its under surface this disc secretes, or there collects, a sticky fast-setting cement. When an insect enters the flower in search of nectar, the rostellum becomes ruptured. The viscid disc is exposed and is so situated that it comes in contact with the proboscis, head, thorax or abdomen of the insect and thus becomes attached to the little pollinator.

The fruits of orchids, with few exceptions, are dry capsules, and are variously shaped, being commonly ovoid, ellipsoid or cylindrical. They are frequently strongly 3-angled, and the angles may be winged. *Vanilla,* however, has a more or less cylindrical fleshy pod or "bean." In many species the withered flower persists at the apex of the fruit. When ripe, the dry capsule dehisces along one, two, three or six longitudinal sutures, with the valves usually, but not always, remaining united above and below. The minute seeds, composed of undifferentiated cells, are produced in enormous quantities and are well adapted for dispersal by wind.

Cultural Notes on Extra-Tropical Orchids:— The cultivation of terrestrial orchids involves two factors which need especial attention — the soil-reaction and the soil-temperature. Before any transplanting is attempted one of the commercial soil-testing sets should be obtained, and the reactions of the soils to be used be determined by its aid. If the soil should prove to be too acid for the species which is to be introduced, neutralization must be produced. This is best accomplished by the addition of crushed limestone, which can be obtained from dealers in agricultural supplies. One pound should be applied to each square yard and thoroughly mixed with the soil to a depth of about six inches. Tests should be repeated every three months and successive applications of the limestone be made until the indicator dye shows the color for neutrality. What this color is will presumably be stated in the directions accompanying the outfit; if the pH system is used, 7 corresponds to neutrality.

On the other hand, if the observed reaction is deficient in acidity which a species requires more elaborate preparations are needed. The native soil should be dug out to a depth of at least two feet over as great an area as practicable. A layer of cinders may well be placed on the bottom to discourage earthworms. Then the excavation should be filled with a mixture of sterile lime-free sand and acid humus. The latter may consist of partially decomposed pine or hemlock needles, rotten wood, weathered sawdust, etc.; or of peat-moss, provided that it is strongly acid. Avoid at all costs rotted leaf mold or manure, muck, and lime-rich commercial humus, as these will rapidly neutralize the acidity which is being sought. Any such material should always be tested and its high acidity established before it is introduced, and tests should be repeated at intervals of every few months. In any case, an annual top-dressing of one of the types of acid humus will be desirable.

In connection with keeping the bed acid, it must be borne in mind that the common garden earthworms (*Eisenia, Lumbricus,* etc.) bring up much lime from the subsoil and rapidly neutralize the acidity of the surface soil. Accordingly, earthworms must be kept out of the bed. Lining the bed with cinders or slabs of bark may aid, and watering the bed with weak tannic acid solutions is usually sufficient to discourage them.

In transplanting orchids the "ball-of-earth" method often gives good results, at least when the block of soil containing the roots is set into a well-prepared bed. Often, however, no matter how carefully the plant is dug up, in an attempt to prevent disturbing its roots, alterations will be caused in the delicate equilibrium between the orchid and the soil micro-organisms, with resulting injury to the plant. If the "ball-of-earth" method is not used it is usually preferable to wash all of the original soil from the roots and then to keep them moist by a covering of sterile sphagnum moss during transportation.

When watering the bed into which native orchids have been set, attention must be given to the reaction of the water used. Repeated drenching of a bed of acid soil with lime-rich hard water will soon neutralize the necessary acidity. If practicable, rain-water should be collected and stored in wooden casks until needed; but care must be taken that this water does not flow for considerable distances through gutters or pipes of lead, copper or zinc, as enough of these metals may dissolve to injure plants as delicate as our native orchids. The lime-content of the ground water can be reduced by adding fresh sphagnum moss or other acid humus material to the water in the storage tank from time to time.

From the temperature standpoint, the chief problem is to prevent heating of the soil when northern or high-mountain species have been moved to lower latitudes or altitudes. Rocks or stumps, so placed that they shade the soil immediately around the roots, will help in this respect. However, Nature's plan of keeping soil cool is to have an unfailing supply of water which rises to the surface and evaporates there. This can be attained artificially, although the reaction of the water to be used must be taken into account. In extreme cases, it may be necessary for pipes carrying cooled brine from a refrigerating system to be run through the bed. A long thermometer (with the temperature readings indicated on the glass tube) should be used freely in the culture-beds.

Finally, there is the problem of destructive organisms. Orchids are especially susceptible to attack by parasitic fungi, many species succumbing if a single root is cut or broken. Moreover, the plants are preyed upon by various insects, by slugs, and by rodents such as short-tailed mice. Fortunately the chemical metaldehyde (commercially "Meta") has proved successful in combatting pests of the snail or slug type. The burrowing mice can be kept away by surrounding the plants individually with masses of crushed rock — quartz or siliceous rock being preferable because of its chemical inertness. They can also be prevented from attacking bog species by a moat of open water.

The goal of cultivation is not merely to transplant an individual orchid from its native haunts to a garden where it may continue to exist for a few seasons, only to weaken gradually and finally die. To be classed as really successful, cultivation should mean the transplanting of the plant to its new habitat and having it thrive there indefinitely, ultimately reproducing its kind. (E.T.W.)

The cultivation of our subtropical species, most of which are epiphytic, will be discussed at some length in the text.

All of the tropical and subtropical species which have been introduced into regions with a temperate or boreal climate, such as that of England and the northern portion of North America, must be grown in greenhouses where temperature and moisture conditions are easily controlled. The hardier northern species can be grown out-of-doors in wild gardens.

The accumulation and cultivation of large collections of tropical and subtropical orchids began in England the early part of the nineteenth century. It was not until about 1865, however, that interest in orchids was awakened in the United States. Once started, however, the craze for possessing rare and exotic specimens took hold of the wealthy amateur horticulturists, and the search for and importation of plants from their native haunts and from European greenhouses soon assumed large proportions. Today, in the United States alone, commercial orchid establishments are estimated to be worth millions of dollars.

Explanation of the Text:— As stated in the Preface, the arrangement of the text has been made as simple as possible and the method of treatment is uniform throughout.

The species concepts have been treated rather broadly. However, it would be unethical as well as unscientific to ignore all of the varieties and forms which have been proposed. If a variety or a form is considered to have a sufficiently pronounced characteristic whereby it might be separated from the typical form it has been included. There are, however, infinite minor variations, as in some species of *Spiranthes* and *Habenaria*. To give names to these would be of little or no value and it would lead to even greater confusion in the nomenclature of our native orchids.

The arrangement of the genera follows the recent phylogenetic system of classification of the Orchidaceae proposed by RUDOLF SCHLECHTER in 1926 (*Notizblatt des Botanischen Gartens und Museums Berlin-Dahlem*, Bd. 9, No. 88, pp. 563-591). In this system the simple and primitive genera are followed by the more complex and advanced. The arrangement of the species within a genus is alphabetical.

The scientific names are in accord with the definite regulations prescribed by the *International Rules of Botanical Nomenclature* (1935) for the publication and treatment of botanical names. The name of the plant is followed in each case by the name (often abbreviated) of the author who proposed it together with a bibliographical reference to the place of publication and the type locality (or in some instances the type collection) cited by the author. For some names two authorities are cited, one in parenthesis. This indicates that the specific epithet was used by the author in parenthesis in a different genus. In the case of *Habenaria ciliaris* (L.) R. Br., for example, CAROLUS LINNAEUS described a plant from "Virginia and Canada" as *Orchis ciliaris* in 1753. Later, in 1813, ROBERT BROWN transferred this species to the genus *Habenaria* and thus made the proper nomenclatural change. For convenience in identifying the authors of the names of our native orchids, a section has been included which gives their full name.

When the name of a plant is preceded by a × this signifies that the plant is a hybrid or putative hybrid.

The type locality is the place where the type specimen was collected or where the species was thought to be indigenous. This type specimen served as the basis for the original description.

The correct name may be followed by the citation of synonyms, incorrect names for the same plant which were used earlier or later. The synonym which was responsible for the specific epithet (*Orchis ciliaris* in the example cited above) is always given. Additional synonyms which are found in standard Floras have been included, but their places of publication are omitted. If this information is desired, it may be obtained from AMES' *Enumeration of the Orchids of the United States and Canada* (1924), where most of our orchid synonymy is to be found.

The meaning of the names has been included not only because they may not be self explanatory but with the hope that if the derivation of the terms were explained it would be a simpler matter to use them. The scientific names have been derived from Greek or Latin words of a descriptive nature or from the latinized names of people or localities. For convenience, those common names which are found in literature or are in use within the area covered have been incorporated. It would be far better, however, for one to associate with orchids their universally applicable scientific names, as we do for so many of our commonly cultivated plants (*Rhododendron, Begonia, Chrysanthemum*, etc.), instead of the ambiguous and often misleading or local common names.

The generic and specific descriptions have been made as non-technical as possible, but they have not been so simplified as to become unusable. The illustrations supplement the descriptions and make for a more complete understanding of the plants. Since it is realized that one of the chief difficulties in plant identification is the use of a technical vocabulary, a Glossary has been included in which the more technical terms are defined.

The sections devoted to discussion contain miscellaneous information or stress certain characters by which a species or variety may be more easily identified. The data regarding habitat and flowering season are comprehensive. As far as it has been possible to do so, the complete geographical distribution has been given for each of the entities. This information is based on personal field observations and studies of collections and literature in the herbarium and library.

The cultural notes concerning individual species are not included for the purpose of encouraging the promiscuous transplanting of the plants from their natural haunts to gardens. Indeed, the primary purpose is to discourage the removal of those orchids which are seldom successfully transplanted to an artificial environment. A few species whose cultivation may be attended with some degree of success are noted. If orchids are to be brought into the garden, it is hoped that these cultural notes will aid the grower to insure their successful cultivation.

Additional data of horticultural interest have been included for many of the species. Miscellaneous information has been pieced together in an attempt to give the recorded history of cultivation. Since the English pioneered in orchid horticulture, in nearly all instances they have been the ones to leave for posterity the earliest comments concerning the cultivation of our native species. The first record I have been able to find concerning the cultivation of any of our native orchids is that of the Queen Lady's-slipper (*Cypripedium reginae*), which was cultivated in England before 1731 by PHILIP MILLER.

Use of Keys:— Plants are classified in several categories, the more familiar ones being family, genus, species and variety. A common device by which a plant can be located in its proper category is called a "key." In this publication there is a key to the genera and keys to the species in those genera with more than one species. The keys are artificial, that is they have been constructed for utility and not for the purpose of showing relationship. Each key is made up of pairs of contrasting statements regarding certain characteristics, each bearing the same introductory number. At the end of each statement is a second number which refers to the next pair of statements to be used, or to the name of the genus or species, as the case may be. If the name of the genus or species appears, a page number immediately following it designates where it is discussed in the text. The statements in the key are true or false for any given species or group of orchids. The process of identification consists of following the true statements until the genus or species is "keyed out." If no mistake has been made in the interpretation of the characters one will arrive at the correct name for a given plant. Only those species occurring naturally in our region are included in the keys, although in the generic discussion extra-limital species may be considered.

Orchidaceae

Orchidaceae Lindl., Nat. Syst., ed. 2: 336. 1836.

(The name, *Orchidaceae,* is from the Greek word meaning "testicle," doubtless in allusion to the shape of the testiculate tuberoids in the genus *Orchis,* the type genus of the family.)

Perennial herbs, vines or shrub-like plants of various habits and habitats, terrestrial, epiphytic, lithophytic, semiaquatic or very rarely subterranean, autophytic or saprophytic, hermaphroditic, dioecious or monoecious, produced from a short or elongated or (rarely) coralloid rhizome, corm or tuber. Roots subterranean or aerial, fibrous, fleshy or tuberous, solitary, fasciculate or adventitious and scattered on the rhizome or stem. Stems terete to ancipitous, sometimes angular, much abbreviated to elongated, slender to very stout, often modified as thickened pseudobulbs, naked, bracteate or leafy. Pseudobulbs variously shaped, usually globose, pyriform or fusiform, one- or more-leaved, subtended by leaves, sheaths or cataphylls. Leaves simple, radical or cauline or both, persistent, deciduous or marcescent, occasionally altogether lacking, varying from foliaceous sheathing bracts to a broad or narrow lamina; lamina filiform to orbicular, membranaceous to fleshy or coriaceous, often duplicate or plicate. Inflorescence terminal or lateral, supported by an abbreviated to greatly elongated peduncle, consisting of one or more flowers, commonly a spike, simple raceme or panicle. Flowers small and inconspicuous to large and showy, zygomorphic, unisexual or bisexual, sometimes polymorphic; perianth composed of three outer segments (sepals) and three inner segments (petals), the segments free or more or less united, adnate to the 1- or 3-celled inferior ovary, one petal (the lip or labellum) usually complex in structure and differing only slightly to greatly in form, size and coloration from the other segments; lip often extended at the base and forming a spur or nectary. Stamens and pistils (including the filaments and styles) united to form, in part, an organ called the column in the center of the flower. Column various, formed by an elongation of the floral axis, bearing at or near its summit or laterally one, two or (very rarely) three mobile or rigidly attached anthers, producing in front on the ventral surface the somewhat confluent stigmas, with one stigma usually modified to form the rostellum, often produced below into a foot; anther situated behind the rostellum, resting in a bed or clinandrium, perfectly or imperfectly 2-celled, containing a mass of pollen or two to eight distinct pollen-masses or pollinia; pollen powdery, granular-mealy, waxy or cartilaginous. Fruit a dry capsule or fleshy pod, commonly ovoid, ellipsoid or cylindric, dehiscing along one, two, three or six longitudinal sutures; seeds numerous, scobicular (except in *Vanilla* and *Selenipedium*).

KEY TO THE GENERA

1. Lip an inflated sac or pouch which is never produced in front into an extended lamina, forming the lowermost segment of the perianth; fertile anthers two, borne laterally on the column ....*Cypripedium* (p. 18)
1. Lip simple or complex, if saccate either produced in front into a more or less expanded lamina or forming the uppermost segment of the perianth; fertile anther one....................2
  2. Plants vine-like, climbing (confined to southern peninsular Florida) ......*Vanilla* (p. 155)
  2. Plants neither vine-like nor climbing...3
    3. Leaves absent at flowering time...4
      4. Plant with a thickened corm...5
        5. Lip forming a slender or broadly conical spur at the base........................6
          6. Spur slender; lip 3-lobed with the mid-lobe linear-oblong......*Tipularia* (p. 277)
          6. Spur broadly conical; lip simple, suborbicular................*Galeandra* (p. 312)
        5. Lip not forming a distinct spur...7
          7. Lip cuneate at the base (distribution north of Florida)........................8
            8. Lip with a bearded crest, entire or at most shallowly 3-lobed..*Arethusa* (p. 164)
            8. Lip without a bearded crest, deeply 3-lobed...............*Aplectrum* (p. 315)
          7. Lip broadly rounded at the base (limited to southern Florida)....*Bletia* (p. 339)
      4. Plant not with a thickened corm...9
        9. Rhizome coralloid 10
          10. Lip usually provided near the base with a pair of short fleshy calli or keels; pollinia four ....*Corallorhiza* (p. 325)
          10. Lip usually provided at about the middle or above with three or more lamellae or with a broad fleshy plate at the base; pollinia eight.........*Hexalectris* (p. 318)

9. Rhizome not coralloid...11
  11. Lip produced into a prominent spur at the base (plants epiphytic)............12
    12. Lip deeply bifid; flowers large and showy...............*Polyrrhiza* (p. 375)
    12. Lip entire or obscurely 3-lobed, not bifid; flowers minute.................13
      13. Raceme laxly few-flowered; floral bracts obsolete.....*Harrisella* (p. 372)
      13. Raceme densely many-flowered; floral bracts conspicuous...............
      ....*Campylocentrum* (p. 370)
  11. Lip not produced into a prominent spur at the base, at most saccate (plants terrestrial) 14
    14. Lip deeply 3-lobed, conspicuously saccate at the base..*Cephalanthera* (p. 134)
    14. Lip neither deeply 3-lobed nor conspicuously saccate at the base............
    ....*Spiranthes* (p. 184)
3. Leaves present at flowering time..15
  15. Lip (not the sepals) produced into a prominent spur at the base.................16
    16. Leaves distinctly petioled, with inflated tubular sheaths; roots from the nodes of a creeping rhizome...*Erythrodes* (p. 241)
    16. Leaves neither distinctly petioled nor provided with tubular inflated sheaths; roots not from the nodes of a creeping rhizome...................................17
      17. Spur more or less tapering from a broad base, somewhat cornucopiate; viscid disc of the pollinia enclosed in a pouch-like structure of the rostellum........
      ....*Orchis* (p. 42)
      17. Spur various, not noticeably tapering from a broad base (except in *Habenaria Hookeri* and *H. obtusata*); viscid disc of the pollinia free...*Habenaria* (p. 49)
  15. Lip not produced into a prominent spur at the base, at most strongly saccate......18
    18. Lip forming the uppermost segment of the perianth........................19
      19. Leaves duplicate and coriaceous (plant epiphytic).....................20
        20. Floral bracts obsolescent; lateral sepals triangular and forming with the prominent column-foot a conspicuous mentum........*Polystachya* (p. 309)
        20. Floral bracts large, often exceeding the flowers; lateral sepals never distinctly triangular and not forming a mentum; column essentially footless......
        ....*Epidendrum* (p. 284)
      19. Leaves plicate, membranaceous or succulent, never coriaceous (plant terrestrial) 21
        21. Leaves narrow, grass-like; lip prominently bearded....*Calopogon* (p. 167)
        21. Leaves not grass-like; lip not prominently bearded.....................22
          22. Leaves one or two (rarely more), with expanded blades on the stem noticeably above the base.........................*Malaxis* (p. 255)
          22. Leaves two or more in a basal rosette.............................23
            23. Lip inserted at the base of the column or on the united sepals; floral segments 3 mm. or less long.................................24
              24. Base of lip free from the base of the lateral sepals; bracts of the stem foliaceous, usually conspicuously dilated at the apex........
              ....*Cranichis* (p. 179)
              24. Base of lip adherent to the connate lamina of the lateral sepals; bracts of the stem not conspicuously dilated at the apex..........
              ....*Prescottia* (p. 177)
             23. Lip inserted above the base of the column; floral segments 3.5 mm. or more long.................................*Ponthieva* (p. 181)
    18. Lip forming the lowermost segment of the perianth........................25
      25. Leaves plicate, prominently ribbed.......................................26
        26. Plant with a large elongated and jointed pseudobulb..*Cyrtopodium* (p. 347)
        26. Plant without a large pseudobulb.....................................27
          27. Plant arising from a small corm.................................28
             28. Flower solitary (rarely two)...................................29
              29. Lip saccate ....*Calypso* (p. 280)
              29. Lip not saccate...............................*Arethusa* (p. 164)
            28. Flowers few to many...30
              30. Lip simple, broadest above the middle............*Liparis* (p. 271)
               30. Lip 3-lobed, broadest below the middle.......................31
                31. Lip lamellate-crested; floral bracts inconspicuous.*Bletia* (p. 339)
                31. Lip papillose-crested or crestless; floral bracts conspicuous....
                ....*Eulophia* (p. 342)
          27. Plant arising from a short rhizome, without a corm.................32
             32. Inflorescence a raceme (distribution northern and western).........
             ....*Epipactis* (p. 128)

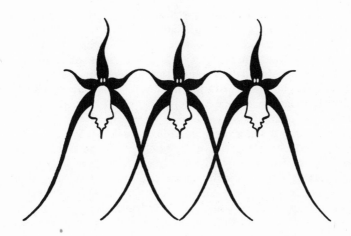

1. Cypripedium L.

Cypripedium L., Sp. Pl., ed. 1, 2:951. 1753.

(The name, *Cypripedium*, is from two Greek words meaning "Aphrodite" and "foot," interpreted here as meaning "Aphrodite's shoe," in allusion to the shape of the lip.)

Terrestrial or rarely epiphytic herbs with fibrous roots arising from a short or elongated rhizome. Leaves two or more, at the base of the plant or on the stem, plicate, prominently ribbed, sheathing the stem. Flowers one to twelve, usually showy, subtended by foliaceous bracts. Sepals spreading, free or with the lateral pair partially or wholly united. Petals spreading, free, usually smaller and narrower than the sepals. Lip sessile, inflated, saccate or pouch-shaped, horizontally inserted and variously colored. Column declined, with a pair of lateral fertile stamens (each bearing a 2-celled anther) and a thick dorsal sterile staminode; pollen granular; stigma terminal and somewhat 3-lobed. Ovary 1-celled. Capsule obovoid to ellipsoid.

This genus consists of about fifty species which are widespread in boreal, temperate and tropical regions of Europe, Asia and America. They are considered, with the other three genera of the *Cypripedieae*, to be the most primitive orchids extant and represent what appears to be a section isolated from the rest of the family, without any intermediate or connecting genera surviving today. Indeed, a good case could be argued for separating the *Cypripedieae* as a distinct family from the rest of the Orchidaceae. Some of the species are among the most attractive of the native orchids in our flora.

The European Lady's-slipper, *C. Calceolus* (the Latin for "a little shoe"), was so named by LINNAEUS because the lip resembles in shape a shoe or slipper. The early settlers of this continent found other species of *Cypripedium* to which they gave similar common names. For instance, they called *C. acaule* Pink Moccasin-flower because the lip resembles in shape and texture the footwear worn by the American Indian. In some sections of Pennsylvania any species of lady's-slipper is called "ducks," in allusion to the appearance of the flowers when the lip is partly filled with sand and the flowers placed upon water.

Of all our native orchids, the lady's-slippers are the ones most familiar to the nature-lover. They were the first to attract the attention of early European colonists in this hemisphere, especially as to the possibility of their being cultivated. The English, who were pioneers in the cultivation of tropical orchids, also introduced and cultivated in their country various species of our Cypripediums as early as the beginning of the eighteenth century. Indeed, Cypripediums are still regarded in Europe, as well as in North America, as among the most attractive hardy terrestrial orchids for either the out-of-door garden or greenhouse. Several of our lady's-slippers have been induced to produce floweis through forcing.

The species of this genus afford a most interesting example of insect-pollination. The pollinating agent for the various species does not seem to be limited to any definite insect. Since the flowers of *Cypripedium* do not develop a spur-like nectary, butterflies and moths possessing a long proboscis are not necessary for pollination in this genus as they are for *Habenaria* and *Orchis*. Instead, crushing, cutting and chewing insects, like beetles, as well as those possessing a short, piercing and sucking proboscis, as bees and various types of flies, seem to be the primary pollinating agents. Since no nectar is thought to be present in the flowers of *Cypripedium*, CHARLES DARWIN (1884) assumed that it was quite possible that insects, especially bees, visit the flowers primarily to obtain pollen for the making of "bee bread." Even though the lure of nectar is apparently lacking, the viscid drops adhering to the hairs at the base of the lip, especially if sweet or nutritious, may have some attraction. Besides, the flowers are for the most part beautifully colored and, for this reason, should attract certain kinds of insects.

The various species of *Cypripedium,* particularly the Yellow Lady's-slipper are known to have a trace of volatile oil, a volatile acid, one or more resins, tannin, sugar, starch and a fixed oil. They form the drug powder "Cypripedium" or "Fluidextract of Cypripedium, U.S.P." which has been used primarily as a diaphoretic, nerve stimulant and antispasmodic in the treatment of hysteria, neuralgia, chorea, hypochondriasis and, to some extent, epilepsy. The drug is also said to have been used in allaying pains of the joints following scarlet-fever. Although it is less powerful than valerian it has been considered valuable as a substitute for opium in the treatment of children. Very little of the drug, perhaps no more than several hundred pounds annually, is produced today.

Some species of *Cypripedium* are poisonous to the touch, especially those plants which have their vegetative parts densely covered with glandular hairs.

Several putative hybrids of *Cypripedium* have been found in our flora. According to FULLER (1933), wherever the Small White Lady's-slipper (*C. candidum*) and Yellow Lady's-slipper are found in proximity, hybrids are produced which exhibit characters intermediate between the two plants. There is every reason to believe, as Fuller points out, that in such a hybrid population interhybridization and variations of all types may occur. Two hybrids, × *C. Andrewsii* Fuller (1932) and × *C. Favillianum* Curtis (1932), based primarily on color, have been described in this complex group. Andrews' Lady's-slipper (× *C. Andrewsii*) is characterized by having a "white-cream colored lip" and the flowers are said to be more fragrant than either of its putative parents. The lip of Faville's Lady's-slipper (× *C. Favillianum*) is said to be "yellowish in bud," later "cream-colored" and when in prime "nearly pure white," and is marked on the interior with violet-purple.

KEY FOR THE IDENTIFICATION OF THE SPECIES OF CYPRIPEDIUM

1. Plant scapose; leaves entirely basal; lip fissured in front..................*C. acaule* (p. 20)
1. Plant not scapose; leaves produced on the stem above the base; lip not fissured in front, provided above with an orifice..2
  2. Leaves two, subopposite 3
    3. Lip white, blotched throughout with purple; petals subpandurate-ligulate, obtuse....
    ....*C. guttatum* (p. 33)
    3. Lip yellow or green-yellow, not blotched with purple; petals ovate-lanceolate to linear-lanceolate, acuminate 4
      4. Flowers usually two to four in a short corymbose raceme; lip green-yellow with purple on margin of orifice; leaves near summit of stem..........*C. fasciculatum* (p. 31)
      4. Flowers one or two; lip deep yellow to almost white, often marked with purple on the inner surface; leaves near base of stem.........*C. Calceolus* var. *pubescens* (p. 24)
  2. Leaves three or more, scattered on the stem...5
    5. Lateral sepals free almost to the base..6
      6. Lip obovoid; petals white, linear-elliptic, rounded at the apex, flat; dorsal sepal suborbicular, apiculate..*C. passerinum* (p. 37)
      6. Lip saccate at base, prolonged downward into a blunt conical pouch; petals purplish, linear, acute, undulate-twisted; dorsal sepal elliptic to ovate-lanceolate, acute to subacuminate..*C. arietinum* (p. 22)
    5. Lateral sepals united to form an entire or shortly bifid lamina.......................7
      7. Petals usually (but not always) twisted and undulate, pendent, linear to linear-lanceolate when spread out, acuminate...8
        8. Lip deep or pale yellow, veined or spotted with magenta-purple on the inner surface ....*C. Calceolus* var. *pubescens* (p. 24)
        8. Lip white, tinged or veined with purple..9
          9. Plant large, usually more than 3.5 dm. tall; sepals much longer than the lip, 3 cm. or more long...*C. montanum* (p. 35)
          9. Plant small, 3 dm. or less tall; sepals scarcely exceeding the lip, less than 3 cm. long...*C. candidum* (p. 29)
      7. Petals flat, not twisted, spreading, varying from ovate-lanceolate to linear-elliptic or linear-oblong, rounded to obtuse or rarely acute at the apex........................10

10. Sepals white; dorsal sepal 3 cm. or more long; essentially eastern in distribution ....*C. reginae* (p. 39)

10. Sepals greenish, yellowish or brownish; dorsal sepal 2 cm. or less long; essentially northern and western in distribution...11

11. Plant large, usually much more than 3.5 dm. tall; flowers three to twelve in a leafy-bracted raceme.................................*C. californicum* (p. 27)

11. Plant small, usually less than 2.5 dm. tall; flowers one or two terminating a naked peduncle.. *C. passerinum* (p. 37)

1. **Cypripedium acaule** Ait., Hort. Kew., ed. 1, 3:303. 1789. Type locality: North America. (*Fissipes acaulis* (Ait.) Small). FRONTISPIECE

(The name, *acaule,* is a Latin adjective meaning "stemless," in allusion to the leafless peduncle arising between the pair of radical leaves from a short underground rhizome or stem.)

COMMON NAMES: Pink Moccasin-flower, Pink Lady's-slipper, Stemless Lady's-slipper, Two-leaved Lady's-slipper, Dwarf Umbil, Noah's Ark, Valerian, Whippoor-will-shoe, Squirrel-shoes, Purple-slipper, Rose-vein Moccasin, Hare's Lip, Brown Lady's-slipper, Old Goose, Camel's-foot.

Plant rising from a short underground rhizome and consisting of an erect scape and two basal leaves, somewhat glandular-pubescent throughout, 2-4.5 dm. tall. Leaves two or very rarely three, opposite and sheathing the scape at the base, broadly elliptic to oblong-elliptic, silvery beneath, deep green above, strongly ribbed, 1-2.4 dm. long, 3-14 cm. wide. Inflorescence a solitary flower (very rarely two) terminating the scape, subtended by a foliaceous bract. Floral bract lanceolate, acuminate, somewhat arched over the flower, 4-5 cm. long, 1-1.5 cm. wide. Flower nodding, showy. Sepals and petals variously colored yellowish green to greenish brown, often with purple or brown striations. Dorsal sepal narrowly ovate-lanceolate to elliptic-lanceolate, acute, 3-5 cm. long, 5-17 mm. wide below the middle. Lateral sepals entirely united; lamina ovate-lanceolate to elliptic-lanceolate, obtuse to subacute, 3-4.5 cm. long, 1-2.3 cm. wide. Petals ovate-lanceolate to lanceolate, obliquely dilated at the base and tapering to the acuminate apex, more or less spirally-twisted, densely silky-pubescent on the inner surface below the middle, up to 6 cm. long and 1.7 cm. wide near the base, with translucent margins at the base. Lip an inflated obovoid pouch, crimson-pink to occasionally pure white, rose-veined on the outer surface, with a velvety appearance, fissured in front with the edges folded in and downward, densely pubescent on the inner surface at the base with the hairs directed forward, 4-6 cm. (averaging 5 cm.) long, about 3.5 cm. wide. Staminode suborbicular-rhombic to ovate-deltoid in outline, up to 1.8 cm. long and wide. Capsule ellipsoid, 3-4.5 cm. long.

Albino forms, first described as forma *albiflorum* Rand & Redfield (1894) from Mount Desert Island, Maine, are apparently uncommon. They are found mainly in the northern portion of the area of distribution of the species, but have also been observed in the mountains as far south as North Carolina (Haywood County, G. W. McDOWELL). These forms are characterized by having the lip pure white or only faintly tinged or marked with pink or green and the petals are usually greenish yellow. Practically all orchid flowers which contain a pink, pink-purple or lavender pigment give rise to albino forms, as in the grass-pinks and purple fringed-orchids. This is also true of similarly colored flowers in many other plant families.

The interesting method and means of cross-pollination of the Pink Moccasin-flower has been described by a number of observers. Since this method of pollination is essentially the same in all our lady's-slippers, a detailed account of that found in the Pink Moccasin-flower will suffice for the other species (*cf.* FIGURE 1). The insect enters the fissure in front of the lip but usually finds it impossible to leave the pouch through this fissure because of the infolded margins. The only other possible exit is through an aperture at the base of the lip. The column is so placed over this opening that the insect must first strike the stigma and deposit there any pollen which it may be carrying at the time. Then, upon leaving the lip, the insect receives a load of pollen from either of the two anthers which it happens to touch. Thus the pollen will be transported to the next flower visited, and in this way, cross-pollination is assured. If the luckless insect fails to find the opening, or if it chances to be too large for the opening, it is doomed to death in a most ornate death-chamber.

Although the Pink Moccasin-flower may be found in large colonies producing as many as one hundred flowers in a space less than seventy-five feet square, it is seldom that more than a dozen or so capsules will be produced in the colony. This low percentage of capsule formation and consequent loss of reproduction may be due to several factors, such as the lack of pollinating agents and too long a period between pollination and fecundation, during which time accidents may take place. It is of interest to note that, according to Doig (1941), "no one has as yet produced flowering plants from seed" of this species. This species is extremely variable as to habitat. It is most commonly found in moist or dry pine woods, but may also be found in dry, open, upland hardwoods, on the edge of and in swamps,

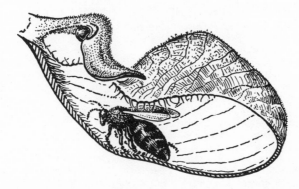

TEXTFIGURE 1. — Longitudinal section of lip of *Cypripedium acaule*, with bee, demonstrating pollination. About 1½ times natural size.

in bogs and in densely shaded woods along streams, particularly where evergreens such as pines, hemlocks, spruces and cedars occur, or in ericaceous shrub areas. It is as much at home in the sand hills of the low Coastal Plain of eastern North Carolina and in the pine barrens of New Jersey as it is on the higher mountain slopes of North Carolina, New England and Canada. The Pink Moccasin-flower is one of the earliest flowering of our eastern orchids beginning about the middle of April in the South and continuing until July in the far North.

GEOGRAPHICAL DISTRIBUTION: Newfoundland, Nova Scotia, New Brunswick, Prince Edward Island, Quebec, Ontario, west to Saskatchewan (Poplar Point and Wolverine Point on Lake Athabaska), Alberta (Sand Point on Lake Athabaska), Minnesota (Aitkin, Chisago, Clearwater and Hennepin counties), Ohio (Cuyahoga, Fairfield and Portage counties), Indiana (La Porte County) and Kentucky (Estill and Powell counties), south to South Carolina (Greenville and Oconee counties), Georgia (Bartow, Rabun and Union counties), Tennessee (west to Franklin and Williamson counties) and Alabama (Cullman and DeKalb counties).

CULTURAL NOTES: The Pink Mocccasin-flower is one of the most difficult of our native plants to cultivate. When transplanted to a garden it may bloom the first year, but usually produces only foliage the second, and fails to come up the third. Obviously, the conditions required by the species are not being satisfied.

Water supply is certainly of no significance to this plant, for it thrives alike in deep wet sphagnum bogs and in dry pine needles on the summits of sand hills. Temperature is likewise unimportant, for it ranges from South Carolina and Georgia to near the Arctic Circle in northwest Canada. It grows mostly in places where there is moderate shade and where the soil is well-provided with humus, highly sterile, strongly acid, and thoroughly aerated. Every one of these five conditions seems to be of survival value for this species; yet few indeed are the gardens in which they are supplied.

If an acid-soil bed is constructed as described in the Introduction and the clumps set into it without injury to the roots, and if all practicable efforts are made to maintain the necessary conditions, the species can sometimes be grown successfully. (E. T. W.)

According to BROWN (1813), the Pink Moccasin-flower was first introduced into England in 1786 by Sir WILLIAM HAMILTON.

2. Cypripedium arietinum R. Br. in Ait., Hort. Kew., ed. 2, 5: 222. 1813. Type locality: North America. (*Criosanthes arientina* (R. Br.) House). PLATE 2

(The name, *arietinum*, is a Latin word meaning "ram-like," in allusion to the shape, position and general appearance of the lip, in relation to the other floral segments, which simulates the head of a charging ram.)

COMMON NAMES: Ram's-head Orchid, Ram's-head Lady's-slipper, Ram's-head Cypripedium, Chandler's Cypripedium, Ram's-head, Steeple-cap.

Plant more or less glandular-pubescent throughout, 1-3.6 dm. tall. Rhizome small, slender, giving off a musky odor. Stem slender, erect or somewhat twisted, provided below with several brown tubular sheaths, leafy at about or above the middle. Leaves three to five, narrowly elliptic to elliptic-lanceolate or occasionally ovate-lanceolate, obtuse to acute, scattered, scarcely sheathing the stem, plicate, nearly glabrous, bluish green to dark green, 5-10 cm. long, 1.3-3.5 cm. wide. Floral bract ovate-lanceolate to elliptic-lanceolate, acute to acuminate, 3-6 cm. long, 1.3-2 cm. wide. Flower solitary at the summit of the slender stem, nodding, fragrant, of short duration. Sepals all free, dark purplish brown or madder-purple, margined or streaked with green, somewhat pubescent on the outer surface and margins. Dorsal sepal ellipitic to ovate-lanceolate, acute to subacuminate, concave, 1.5-2.5 cm. long, 6-10 mm. wide. Lateral sepals entirely free, linear to linear-lanceolate, acute to subacuminate, somewhat twisted, oblique, 1.5-2 cm. long, 2-4 mm. wide. Petals colored similarly to the sepals, linear, acute, somewhat undulate-twisted, oblique, 1.3-2 cm. long, 1-1.5 mm. wide. Lip saccate, much inflated at the base, prolonged downward into a blunt conical pouch, whitish or pinkish white, strongly netted with crimson or madder-purple, 1.3-2.5 cm. long, about 1.5 cm. wide and deep, with the mouth of the orifice and inner surface along the base of the sac silky-pubescent. Staminode suborbicular, with a short stalk, concave, with a central keel on the inner surface, about 5 mm. long and 4 mm. wide. Capsule obliquely ellipsoid, suberect, brown, about 2 cm. long.

The flowers of this rare species are among the most short-lived of all our native orchids, remaining in their prime for only about a day. The free, instead of fused, lateral sepals mark it as our most primitive *Cypripedium*. It is interesting to note, and is possibly of significance, that the two species of *Cypripedium,* this and *C. reginae,* which are considered to be the most primitive and supposed to represent an ancestral type, are found in proximity in China.

This species is not only an inhabitant of cold, sphagnous, cedar, tamarack and arbor-vitae swamps and bogs, but is also found in other types of damp or dry coniferous forests as well as in evergreen heath areas and wooded, rocky slopes. It thrives at an elevation of 15,000 feet in China. The Ram's-head Orchid flowers in May and June.

GEOGRAPHICAL DISTRIBUTION: Quebec (Hochelaga County) and Ontario (Bruce, Huron and Lambton counties) west to Manitoba, south to Maine, New Hampshire, Vermont, Massachusetts (Berkshire, Franklin and Hampshire counties), Connecticut (New Haven County), New York (south to Madison and Otsego counties), Michigan (south to Isabella, Gratiot and Washtenaw *(fide Hermann)* counties), Wisconsin (Door and Ozaukee counties), Illinois *(Mead)* and Minnesota (Clearwater County); also western China.

CULTURAL NOTES: Moisture conditions, usually regarded as an extremely important factor in plant growth, seem to make no difference to the Ram's-head Orchid, for it thrives alike in wet, mossy swamps and on dry, wooded, rocky slopes. Its soil is, however, always well-provided with humus and thoroughly aerated. So far as tests have shown, the soil-reaction is usually subacid or minimacid, and as in the case of most orchids, rather sterile or poor in available plant nutriments. Many woodland garden soils correspond to its needs in this respect, but not to its temperature requirements. For this is a northern plant, and throughout the region where it is native the air rarely becomes warmer than 80°F., and the soil at root-level probably never exceeds 70°F., and may be only 60°F. even

PLATE 2.— **Cypripedium arietinum.** 1, plant, one half natural size. 2, sepals and petals, spread out, natural size. 3, fruiting plant, one half natural size. *Drawn by Gordon W. Dillon.*

in midsummer. Its inability to grow in nature below central New York, Massachusetts and Connecticut clearly indicates that any attempt to cultivate it in gardens where the summer sun heats the soil to 75° or 80° for long periods is foredoomed to failure. One of the methods suggested in the Introduction for keeping surface soils cool will be required farther south. (E. T. W.)

According to Brown (1813), the Ram's-head Orchid was first introduced into England in 1808 by Messrs. Chandler and Buckingham.

3. **Cypripedium Calceolus** L. var. **pubescens** (Willd.) Correll, Bot. Mus. Leafl. Harvard Univ. 7: 14. 1938. *Cypripedium Calceolus* L., Sp. Pl., ed. 1, 2,: 951, in part. 1753. Type locality: Europe, Asia and North America. *Cypripedium pubescens* Willd., Hort. Berol. 1: pl. 13. 1804. Type locality: North America. (*C. flavescens* DC.; *C. parviflorum* Salisb.; *C. parviflorum* var. *pubescens* (Willd.) Knight; *C. parviflorum* var. *planipetalum* Fernald; *C. veganum* Cockerell & Barker; *C. hirsutum* of some authors; *C. Calceolus* var. *parviflorum* (Salisb.) Fernald).   PLATE 3

(The name, *Calceolus,* is a Latin noun meaning "a little shoe," in allusion to the shape of the lip. The name, *pubescens,* is a Latin word meaning "downy," referring to the soft, glandular hairs covering the vegetative parts of the plant.)

COMMON NAMES: Yellow Lady's-slipper, Water Stealer (*Amah Toskese*), Golden Slipper, Noah's Ark, Whippoorwill-shoe, Yellow Downy Lady's-slipper, Downy Lady's-slipper, Yellow Moccasin-flower, American Valerian, Monkey Flower, Umbil Root, Yellow Umbil, Nerve Root, Male Nervine, Yellows, Yellow Indianshoe, Venus' Cup, Venus' Shoe, Yellow Noah's Ark. The typical form is known by the following names in Europe: Common Lady's-slipper in England; *Sabot de la Vierge* and *Soulier de Nôtre Dame* in France; *Frauenschuh* and *Marienschuh* in Germany; *Pantoffala* and *Scarpa della Madonna* in Italy.

Plant erect, more or less glandular-pubescent throughout (particularly so at the nodes and on the capsules), 1-7 dm. tall. Leaves three to five, rarely two, elliptic to ovate or ovate-lanceolate, acute to acuminate, many-nerved and plicate, the lower part sheathing the stem, 5-20 cm. long, 4-10 cm. wide at the middle. Inflorescence composed of one or two flowers terminating the stem. Floral bracts ovate-lanceolate, acuminate, 1-10 cm. long, 1-4 cm. wide at the middle. Flowers showy, on slender peduncles, each subtended by a foliaceous bract. Sepals and petals greenish yellow to madder-purple. Dorsal sepal ovate to ovate-lanceolate, acuminate-attenuate, often undulate, 3-8 cm. long, 1-3.5 cm. wide. Lateral sepals united almost to the apex; lamina bidentate, broadly oblong-lanceolate, 2.5-8 cm. long, up to about 2.5 cm. wide. Petals narrowly linear-lanceolate, acuminate, spirally twisted or sometimes flat, 4-9 cm. long, up to about 1 cm. wide. Lip pouch-shaped or slipper-shaped, dull cream-color or rarely approaching white to golden-yellow, usually veined or spotted with magenta-purple on the inner surface, 1.5-6.3 cm. long. Staminode bright yellow, spotted with madder-purple, varying from spatulate or oblong-linear (with a slightly cordate base) to triangular-ovate (with a somewhat auricled base and obtuse apex), occasionally concave or conduplicate, supported by a thick fleshy stalk. Capsule ellipsoid.

Cypripedium Calceolus is one of the few circumboreal species among orchids, being found throughout Europe and extending into Asia where it is occasionally found in the Himalaya Mountains at altitudes of more than 12,000 feet. It is represented in North America by the transcontinental Yellow Lady's-slipper, var. *pubescens.* The North American Yellow Lady's-slipper differs from the typical form in its polymorphic tendency — varying in the shape of the staminode, in the size of the flowers and in the coloration of the flowers. Flowers of the more northern and intermediate forms of the Yellow Lady's-slipper approach the typical form very closely and are also strongly odoriferous as in typical *C. Calceolus.* The southern plants, particularly those of Kentucky and Louisiana, often have large lips which are occasionally more than 6 cm. long.

A large number of species and varieties have been proposed for our Yellow Lady's-slipper, based primarily on the size and color of the flowers. It is difficult to recognize one form without having to recognize several. In my opinion, this plant should be recognized only as a polymorphic variety. However, some botanists recognize the small-flowered var. *parviflorum* (Salisb.) Fernald (1946) as distinct. This is a relatively northern plant which usually grows in wetter places than the large-flowered plant. Its lip is arbitrarily considered to be 3 cm. or less long. Another segregate described as *C. parviflorum* var. *planipetalum* Fernald (1926 A),

PLATE 3.— **Cypripedium Calceolus** var. **pubescens.** Plant, about one half natural size. *Drawn by Blanche Ames.*

from Newfoundland, is distinguished "by its short and comparatively broad, flat, usually purplish petals, by the relatively shorter and broader upper sepal with less acuminate or elongate tip and with rounded rather abruptly narrowed or subcuneate base, and by the cordate staminodium; . . ."

In northern British Columbia along McDonald Creek north of Summit Lake on the Alaska Highway, I found luxuriant colonies of this plant growing on open flat gravelly outwashes in full sunlight. The soil in which the plants were growing was quite dry and supported a large number of dry-habitat species in the families Leguminosae and Compositae. This is a most unusual habitat for this variety.

The Yellow Lady's-slipper is the primary source of the drug, "Cypripedium." According to HENKEL (1907), only the rootstock and roots are used in making the drug, "and these should be collected in autumn, freed from dirt, and carefully dried in the shade."

Mrs. TAYLOR (1940) states that although the Cherokee Indians use this plant in their treatment for worms, it actually, as far as she knows, is of no value in dispelling worms. She writes: "The roots, mixed with those of *Spigelia marilandica,* are made into a decoction which is sweetened with honey or with pods of *Gleditsia triacanthos.* This is drunk to dispel worms."

The irritating action of the glandular hairs of this plant on the skin is discussed under the Queen Lady's-slipper.

According to STEVENSON (1926), one of the natural enemies which affects the Yellow Lady's-slipper is the rust, *Puccinia Cypripedii* Arth. & Holw., which sometimes results in devitalization of the plant. However, since about ten thousand seeds have been estimated to be produced in each capsule, there is little chance of this variety being exterminated in the near future.

This variety is found in open or wooded sphagnum bogs, thickets, meadows, pastures, open deciduous woods, rocky dry wooded slopes or in low moist woods and swamps. It is as much at home in the Coastal Plain of Louisiana and Texas as on the higher peaks of the Smoky Mountains of North Carolina and Tennessee or at an elevation of 9,000 feet in Colorado and New Mexico and 3,500 feet in British Columbia. The Yellow Lady's-slipper flowers from April in the South to August in the extreme North.

GEOGRAPHICAL DISTRIBUTION: From Quebec and Newfoundland, south to South Carolina (Abbeville and Greenville counties; also "Fenmah Island," *Ravenel*), Georgia (south to Spalding and Taylor counties), Alabama (Clark, Cullman, Hale and Madison counties), Mississippi (Panola and Tishomingo counties) and Louisiana (Lincoln and Natchitoches parishes), southwest to Arkansas, Kansas ("Scarboro Heights") and Texas (Bailey, Cass, Harrison and San Augustine counties), west to Yukon, British Columbia, Washington (Okanogan and Spokane counties), Oregon (Lake County), Utah (Grand County), Colorado (Custer, El Paso and Larimer counties), New Mexico (Colfax, Otero, San Miguel, Santa Fe and Socorro counties) and Arizona (Apache County).

CULTURAL NOTES: As the contributor of these cultural notes views the situation, the Yellow Ladys-slipper comprises at least four ecological entities; 1) a northern, 2) a northeastern, 3) a middleeastern, and 4) a southeastern one. Since they differ ecologically, they require individual consideration from the cultural standpoint.

Entity number one is the smallest-flowered of the group, the original *Cypripedium parviflorum.* The plants are relatively slender, and anthocyan coloring matter is especially abundant in the cells, making the conspicuous long "corkscrew" lateral petals unusually deep brown, the spots on the lip intense, the herbage dark green, and even the steles of the roots brownish. The flowers have a pungent and delightful fragrance (which, alas, is attractive not only to humans but also to slugs!). It ranges across northern North America, extending south in the Rocky Mountains to Colorado, and in the east over the Great Lake states and New England, down to northern New Jersey and Pennsylvania, and very sparingly southward along the Appalachians.

This tiny slipper-orchid is normally a plant of calcareous swamp lands; even though the surface-litter may be acid, the orchid's roots extend down to circumneutral soil layers below. It is rarely cultivated successfully in gardens south of its native range, for though the circumneutral soil-reaction is not difficult to match, the combination of continuous, though never stagnant, moisture supply and relatively low soil-temperature is not often attainable.

Entity number two is rare and little known. It is moderately small-flowered, and not notable either for abundance of anthocyan or fragrance; but its flowers have a different aspect from the first in that the petals are scarcely spirally coiled. The infraspecific name, *planipetalum* Fernald, has been applied to it, and it is apparently more closely related to the original European *Cypripedium Calceolus* than the other American entities. It occurs chiefly on limestone barrens in Newfoundland, but I have seen it also in a calcareous swamp in Keweenaw County, Michigan. It is probably impossible to cultivate it farther south.

Entity number three is the widespread and relatively common member of the group in the northeastern United States, the one to which the technical name *pubescens* belongs in one or another status. When mature, it is a more robust-looking plant than the other two, and the flowers are larger but only faintly scented. The petals are less spirally twisted, and anthocyan pigments are usually little developed so that the coloring is less intense. This plant begins to bloom even when immature, the habit being then relatively slender and the flowers small in size, so that they are often mistaken for what is here classed as entity number one. Reports by horticulturists that they have changed the one into the other in gardens are due to this situation — they obtained small-flowered, immature plants, and after a year or two in more or less rich soil these reached their mature size both as to herbage and flower.

So far as known, this is the easiest of our eastern native orchids to cultivate. There are records of plants lasting for a score of years, blooming freely, and setting abundant seed, in more than one wild flower garden. Clumps of it are offered by many dealers, and it is the orchid which should be tried first by the beginner. Ranging from southern Canada to Georgia, it is relatively indifferent to temperature. As to habitat, it is most likely to be found thriving in so-called rich woods where there is shade for at least part of the day, and the soil is rich in humus and readily available plant foods. The soil-reaction may be subacid or circumneutral, and only a moderate moisture supply is required.

Little is known, culturally, about entity number four. Miss DORMON (1934) describes it as growing in "heavy, rich, damp, but well-drained soil, in semi-shade." This suggests a circumneutral soil-reaction preference, while the occurrence of the plant in the Gulf States corresponds to a tolerance of high summer soil-temperatures. (E. T. W.)

According to BROWN (1813), the small-flowered form of the Yellow Lady's-slipper was first cultivated in England in 1759 by PHILIP MILLER. The large-flowered form was later introduced into England, in 1790, by Sir JOSEPH BANKS.

4. **Cypripedium californicum** A. Gray, Proc. Am. Acad. 7: 389. 1868. Type locality and collection: Swamps on Red Mountains, Mendocino County, California, *Bolander*. PLATE 4

(The name, *californicum*, designates California as the state in which this species was first collected.)

COMMON NAME: California Lady's-slipper.

Plant erect, more or less glandular-pubescent throughout, 2.5-12 dm. tall. Rootstock slender, creeping, woody. Stem slender or stout, green or tinged with brown, leafy, with one or several large sheaths at the base. Leaves five or more, alternate, clasping the stem at the base, erect-spreading, plicate, broadly ovate to ovate-lanceolate, obtuse to acute, slightly scabrous along the numerous nerves, 7-16 cm. long, 1.5-6.5 cm. wide; upper leaves reduced, lanceolate, acuminate, passing into the floral bracts of the inflorescence. Floral bracts large, foliaceous, exceeding the flowers. Flowers three to twelve, scattered on the upper part of the plant, with the stout somewhat arcuate pedicellate ovaries 1.2-1.5 cm. long. Sepals pale brownish yellow, glandular-pubescent on the outer surface. Dorsal sepal erect, elliptic, obtuse to subacute, concave, 1.6-2 cm. long, 7-9 mm. wide. Lateral sepals united almost to the apex; lamina broadly elliptic, boat-shaped, bifid at the apex, 1.5-1.8 cm. long, 1-1.2 cm. wide. Petals dull yellow, spreading, obliquely linear-oblong to triangular-oblong, obtuse, slightly pubescent, 1.4-1.6 cm. long, 3-5 mm. wide. Lip obovoid, with the margins of the orifice deeply

PLATE 4.— **Cypripedium californicum.** 1, plant, one half natural size. 2, flower, front view, one and one half times natural size. 3, flower, side view, one and one half times natural size. *Drawn by Gordon W. Dillon.*

infolded, white or somewhat rose-colored, spotted with pale brown, densely pubescent at the base within, 1.8-2 cm. long, about 1 cm. deep and wide. Staminode essentially sessile, suborbicular, arching, concave, somewhat auriculate on each side at the base, about 6 mm. in diameter, larger than the stigma. Capsule obovoid-ellipsoid, pendent, about 2 cm. long.

The California Lady's-slipper has the most restricted range of all our Cypripediums, being found only in Oregon and California. Two other species, *C. montanum* and *C. fasciculatum,* are also found in California.

The size and form of the flowers of *C. californicum* approach most closely those of *C. passerinum,* but the several-flowered inflorescence and differently shaped staminode, as well as several other characters, readily distinguish it from that species.

The following comments are taken from a specimen-sheet of this species collected in California by H. E. and S. T. PARKS (#24008): "This beautiful plant grows in what might be called bogs. Although found occasionally at lower levels in Smith River, it favors the higher regions around 1500 feet and above. However it is difficult to say 'bogs' without an understanding of the terrain. The canyon walls of Smith River are very steep and have been denuded of a vast amount of the soil covering. The steep hills are faced with loose broken reddish sandstone and other rock, frequently held in place only by the dense shrubby growth; again it is open and sliding. From the higher ridges much water finds its way down in brawling creeks and springs which break forth to the surface in many canyon heads. In these places and often on the open slopes there are 'bogs' in which moist earth has gathered and plants of the Darlingtonia and orchid types, grasses and sedges take root. Here Cypripedium is abundant. When this collection was made it was taken from a colony on a very steep hillside of loose rock with water gurgling through everywhere. As far as we could see above our heads the Cypripedium was in flower and we could have taken a thousand without diminishing the supply in a noticeable manner."

This species is usually found in damp soil of open woods along small streams at the base of mountains. It is sometimes found in *Darlingtonia* bogs and upland marshes. It occurs up to 5,000 feet altitude in northern California, and flowers from late May to July.

GEOGRAPHICAL DISTRIBUTION: Oregon (Curry and Josephine counties) and California (Del Norte, Lassen, Mendocino, Plumas and Siskiyou counties).

CULTURAL NOTES: I have seen this plant growing in moist, sterile, subacid humus along mountain brooks in southwestern Oregon and adjacent California. This is a region where the rainfall is high, about 75 inches per year, and the temperature mild, without marked summer or winter extremes. Although dealers sometimes offer clumps for sale, the plant can hardly be expected to thrive in regions where the habitat conditions and climates are very different from those of its native haunts. There are no records of its successful cultivation in our gardens. (E. T. W.)

The California Lady's-slipper was first introduced and cultivated in England in the latter part of the nineteenth century, at least before 1890. It is cultivated out-of-doors in England where it is grown in damp peat and leaf mold. The roots, however, must be protected in frosty weather.

5. Cypripedium candidum Muhl. ex Willd., Sp. Pl. 4: 142. 1805. Type locality: Pennsylvania.   PLATE 5

(The name, *candidum,* is a Latin adjective meaning "dazzling white," in allusion to the white-enameled color of the lip.)

COMMON NAMES: Small White Lady's-slipper, White Frauenschuh, Moccasin-flower, White Lady's-slipper, Silver Slipper, Violet-veined White Slipper.

Plant rigidly erect, sparingly glandular-pubescent throughout, 1.5-3.8 dm. or more tall. Rhizome small, creeping. Stem provided with several sheaths below the middle, concealed by the leaves above. Leaves three or four, crowded at about the middle of the stem when in full flower, nearly erect or rigidly ascending, elliptic-lanceolate to lanceolate, acute to acuminate, plicate, 7.5-19 cm. long, 1.8-4 cm. wide. Floral bract foliaceous, erect, elliptic-lanceolate, subacuminate, conduplicate, up to 6.5 cm. long and 2 cm. wide. Flower usually solitary or rarely two at the apex of the stem, small, slightly fragrant. Sepals greenish or greenish yellow, sparingly or sometimes heavily streaked or spotted with madder-purple.

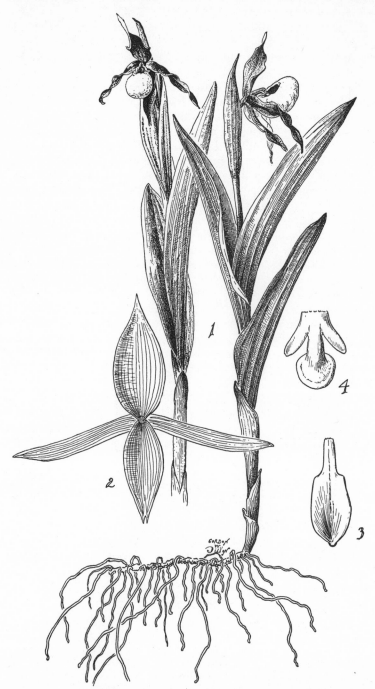

PLATE 5.— **Cypripedium candidum.** 1, plant, one half natural size. 2, sepals and petals, spread out, natural size. 3, staminode, from above, spread out, twice natural size. 4, column, with the staminode removed, front view, twice natural size. *Drawn by Gordon W. Dillon.*

Dorsal sepal ovate to ovate-lanceolate, acuminate, more or less twisted, 2.3-3 cm. long, 9-12 mm. wide. Lateral sepals united almost to the apex; lamina elliptic to elliptic-lanceolate, bidentate at the apex, 2-3 cm. long, 8-9 mm. wide. Petals colored similarly to the sepals, lanceolate to linear-lanceolate, acuminate, spirally twisted, falcate when flattened out, 2.5-4.5 cm. long, 3-4 mm. wide. Lip obovoid, waxy white, smooth and polished on the outer surface, spotted on the edge of the orifice, purple-veined within at the base, silky-pubescent on the inner surface, 1.8-2.5 cm. long, 1-1.5 cm. deep and wide. Staminode with a slender stalk, oblong-elliptic to somewhat ovate, obtuse to acute, keeled, yellow, spotted with purple, 1-1.2 cm. long including the stalk, 3.5-4.5 mm. wide. Capsule erect, ellipsoid, about 3 cm. long.

This species is known to hybridize with the Yellow Lady's-slipper. Two putative hybrids, × *C. Andrewsii* Fuller and × *C. Favillianum* Curtis have been described from this complex. Teratological forms are also known. COPELAND (1876) reported seeing three plants of the Small White Lady's-slipper whose flowers had two lips each, the extra lip taking the place of a petal.

This is the only *Cypripedium* — and one of the few orchids — which thrives on the open prairies. It is sometimes found associated with the Prairie White-fringed-orchid (*Habenaria leucophaea*). It is found commonly in limestone or marl situations in wet boggy soil of meadows and prairies, but also occurs in sheltered ravines, swamps, on the edge of thickets or occasionally on dry rocky hills and in wet woods. The Small White Lady's-slipper flowers from April to June.

GEOGRAPHICAL DISTRIBUTION: Ontario (Lambton County), New York (Genesee, Onondaga and Ontario counties), Pennsylvania and New Jersey (Morris County), through the Lake States to southern Minnesota, eastern North Dakota (Cass County), Iowa (Decatur County), northeastern Nebraska (Antelope, Custer, Kearney and Nance counties) and eastern South Dakota (Brookings County), southward to Missouri (*Bush 545*) and Kentucky ("the barrens of Ky.").

CULTURAL NOTES: Apparently surviving glaciation in Kentucky, this orchid followed the retreating ice into the Great Lakes states and eastward to the highlands of New Jersey. Its roots usually spread over circumneutral to subalkaline muck, with a more or less constant supply of cool, lime-rich water, under a fairly thick layer of litter. As to temperature, it is to be classed among the cool-climate species, for even in its more southern occurrences — Kentucky and Pennsylvania — evaporation of water keeps the soil-temperature down. If these conditions are matched, there seems no reason why it can not be grown in cultivation, although it is more delicate and easily injured by unfavorable environment and by parasitic fungi than the related Yellow Lady's-slipper. (E. T. W.)

The Small White Lady's-slipper was first introduced into England in 1826 where it has since been cultivated out-of-doors. It is grown in cool places in peat, leaf mold and moss.

6. **Cypripedium fasciculatum** Kellogg ex S. Wats., Proc. Am. Acad. 17:380. 1882. Type citations: "Washington Territory," on the White Salmon River, above the falls, May, 1880, *W. N. Suksdorf;* California, Plumas County, near Prattville, May, 1881, *Mrs. R. M. Austin;* "probably in the mountains of Del Norte County," California, *Mrs. Bradley.* (*C. pusillum* Rolfe; *C. Knightae* A. Nels.). PLATE 6

(The name, *fasciculatum,* is a Latin word meaning "gathered into a bundle," referring to the inflorescence which consists of several flowers in a cluster.)

COMMON NAMES: Clustered Lady's-slipper, Brownie Lady's-slipper.

Plant 6-40 cm. tall. Rhizome slender, often with last year's plant-stalk persistent. Stem slender, grooved, up to 15 cm. long, glandular-villous at the base, with one or more brown scarious sheaths which are up to 10 cm. long. Leaves two, subopposite, at the summit of the stem, orbicular-ovate to oblong-elliptic, broadly rounded to obtuse at the apex, membranaceous, subglabrous to puberulent, 4-11 cm. long, 2.5-7.5 cm. wide. Peduncle short when young, elongating in age, brownish, glandular-viscid, naked or sometimes. provided with one or two lanceolate bracts near the middle; bracts up to 2.5 cm. long and 6 mm. wide. Floral bracts large, foliaceous, elliptic-lanceolate, acute to shortly acuminate, up to 3.5 cm. long, 6.5-13 mm. wide. Flowers small, two to four in a short corymbose raceme, occasionally solitary, dark purple or light yellow, veined with brownish purple, with the stout arcuate glandular-pubescent pedicellate ovaries up to 1.3 cm. long. Sepals and petals conspicuously exceeding the lip. Dorsal sepal narrowly triangular-lanceolate, acuminate, 1.5-2.5 cm. long, 3-6 mm.

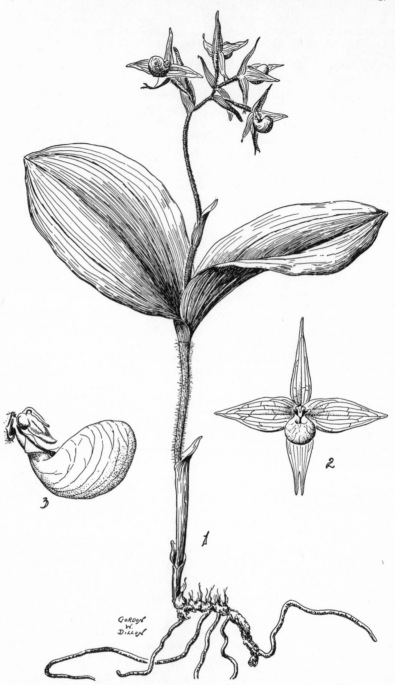

PLATE 6.— **Cypripedium fasciculatum.** 1, plant, one half natural size. 2, flower, front view, spread out, natural size. 3, lip and column, side view, three times natural size. *Drawn by Gordon W. Dillon.*

wide. Lateral sepals united to within about 5 mm. of the apex; lamina ovate-lanceolate, bifid at the apex, 1.5-2.3 cm. long, 4-8 mm. wide below the middle. Petals broadly ovate-lancelate, acuminate, not twisted, concave below the middle, 1.5-2.3 cm. long, 6-17 mm. wide near the base. Lip small, globose, green-yellow, 8-14 mm. long, with the margin of the orifice deeply infolded and purplish but abruptly turned out and reflexed at the base. Staminode smaller than the stigma, elliptic-trulliform, obtuse, 2.5-3 mm. long. Capsule obovoid-ellipsoid, 1.5-2 cm. long.

The Clustered Lady's-slipper is distinctive among our Cypripediums in that the several flowers are borne in a compact cluster. This species and *C. californicum* are the only lady's-slippers confined to the western United States.

In the original description of *C. pusillum*, ROLFE wrote (1892): "A plant was purchased for the Kew collection in May last, without any record of its origin, but shortly afterwards it was sent for determination by H. J. ELWES, Esq., of Cirencester, who had received it with the information that it came from Florida." This is without a doubt a mistake. So far as I know, no species of *Cypripedium* has ever been found in Florida. The only possibility of a lady's-slipper being found in Florida would be the occurrence of *C. acaule,* as a disjunct plant, in some of the numerous deep, wooded ravines along the Apalachicola River in western Florida.

This species is usually found in moist, or dry, open coniferous forests and sometimes in swampy places or on rocky slopes under shrubbery in mountainous regions. It flowers from late April to August on the highest mountain peaks.

GEOGRAPHICAL DISTRIBUTION: Montana, Idaho, Wyoming (Medicine Bow Mountains), Colorado (Larimer County) and Utah, west to Washington (Chelan, Kittitas and Klickitat counties), Oregon (Curry and Josephine counties) and California (Plumas and Santa Clara counties).

CULTURAL NOTES: Since this species usually grows in coniferous woods at rather high altitudes, it may perhaps be cultivated in a well-cooled and permanently acid area. (E. T. W.)

In England, the Clustered Lady's-slipper has been cultivated out-of-doors for a number of years. It is grown in damp, partially shaded places in peat and leaf mold. However, its roots must be protected from frost in winter.

7. Cypripedium guttatum Sw., Kongl. Svens. Vetens. Acad. Nya Handl. 21: 251. 1800. Type locality: East Siberia. (*C. yatabeanum* Makino). PLATE 7

(The name, *guttatum,* is a Latin adjective meaning "spotted," in allusion to the blotches of purple on the floral segments.)

COMMON NAME: Spotted Lady's-slipper.

Plant 1.3-3.5 dm. tall, softly glandular-pubescent with brownish articulated hairs, geniculate at the base. Rhizome slender, elongated, repent, flexuous, 2-4 mm. in diameter. Stem slender, more or less flexuous, provided below with about three clasping tubular sheaths and with two leaves about the middle. Leaves two, erect-spreading, usually approximate, ovate-elliptic to elliptic or elliptic-lanceolate, obtuse to subacuminate, plicate, clasping the stem at the base, sparsely pilose, ciliate, 7-15 cm. long, 2.5-6 cm. wide. Floral bract foliaceous, erect, ovate-lanceolate to lanceolate, acuminate and often strongly recurved at the apex, ciliate, up to 3 cm. long and 1.5 cm. wide. Flower solitary at the apex of the slender curved stem, white, blotched with purple (guttate). Sepals more or less pubescent on the outer surface and margins. Dorsal sepal ovate-elliptic to suborbicular-elliptic, abruptly acute or subapiculate, deeply concave, spreading over the column, 1.8-2.8 cm. long, 1.3-1.7 cm. wide. Lateral sepals united almost to the apex; lamina oblong-elliptic, bidentate at the apex, 1.3-1.8 cm. long, 6-8 mm. wide. Petals subpandurate-ligulate, minutely calyptrate at the obtuse apex, spreading, oblique, dilated below the middle, lightly undulate along the margins, glabrous, 1.3-1.8 cm. long, 7-8 mm. wide below the middle. Lip obovoid, somewhat pendent, with a broad orifice having involute margins, pilose on the inner surface, 1.8-2.5 cm. long, about 1 cm. wide and deep. Staminode oblong-quadrate to broadly elliptic, slightly retuse at the apex, somewhat curved and grooved with the margins upcurved, 8-9 mm. long.

This species and *C. passerinum* have been collected near the Arctic Circle in Alaska, and doubtless, with further exploration, they will be found to occur within that zone. Next to *C. Calceolus* and its variety *pubescens,* the Spotted Lady's-slipper is the most widely distributed of our native Cypripediums. The leaves are said to be used in Asia as a treatment for epilepsy.

This species is commonly found in meadows, grassy moors, grasslands or on the lower slopes of hills and mountains, and is sometimes found in open woods

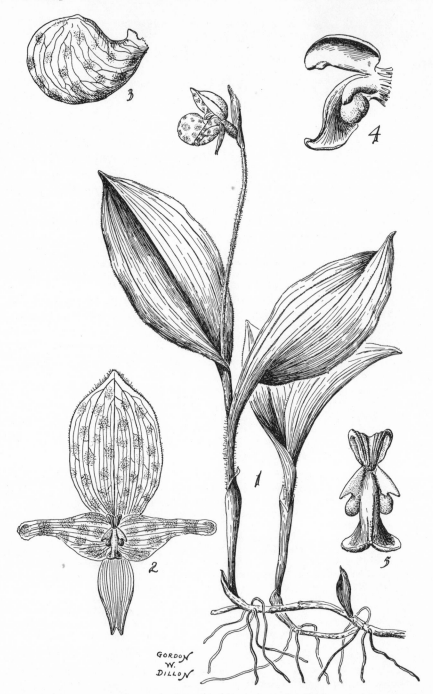

PLATE 7.—**Cypripedium guttatum.** 1, plant, one half natural size. 2, flower, with lip removed, front view, spread open, one and one half times natural size. 3, lip, side view, one and one half times natural size. 4, column, side view, four times natural size. 5, column, front view, four times natural size. *Drawn by Gordon W. Dillon.*

usually under birch trees or in thickets. It is found from about sea level in Unalaska, up to 15,000 feet altitude in China, and flowers from June to August.

GEOGRAPHICAL DISTRIBUTION: British Columbia and Yukon (Dawson and Sunnyvale) to Alaska and the Aleutian Islands; also Japan, China, Manchuria and Siberia to central Russia (Moscow).

CULTURAL NOTES: This far northwestern orchid could possibly be grown in a well-maintained acid-soil bed, but there is apparently no record of its successful cultivation in our region. (E. T. W.)

The Spotted Lady's-slipper is frequently cultivated in Asia, and it has been cultivated out-of-doors for more than fifty years in England. It is grown in cool, shady places in birch leaf mold, peat and sphagnum-moss.

8. Cypripedium montanum Dougl. ex Lindl., Gen. and Sp. Orch. Pl. 528. 1840.

Type locality and collection: Western North America, *Douglas. (C. occidentale* S. Wats.).   PLATE 8

(The name, *montanum,* is a Latin word meaning "of the mountains," in allusion to the usual habitat of this species.)

COMMON NAMES: Mountain Lady's-slipper, Large Lady's-slipper.

Plant erect, 2.5-7 dm. tall, more or less glandular-pubescent throughout. Rhizome short, stout. Stem rather stout, leafy, somewhat flexuous, provided with several long brown tubular sheaths at the base. Leaves usually four to six, clasping the stem, spreading-ascending, broadly ovate to elliptic-lanceolate, obtuse to abruptly short-acuminate, glandular-pubescent on the veins, passing into floral bracts in the inflorescence, plicate, 5-16 cm. long, 2.5-8 cm. wide. Floral bracts foliaceous, ovate-elliptic to broadly elliptic, acute to acuminate, up to 8.5 cm. long and 3.5 cm. wide. Flowers one to three, on the upper part of the stem, distant. Sepals and petals spreading, brownish purple or dark green, suffused with purple, puberulent on the outer surface. Dorsal sepal ovate-lanceolate to elliptic-lanceolate or narrowly lanceolate, long-acuminate, somewhat undulate on the margins, 3-6 cm. long, 1-1.5 cm. wide below the middle. Lateral sepals united almost to the apex; lamina elliptic-lanceolate, bidentate at the apex, concave, 3-6 cm. long, 7.5-13 mm. wide below the middle. Petals linear to linear-lanceolate, acuminate, twisted, pilose on the inner surface at the base, 4.5-7 cm. long, 3.5-6 mm. wide. Lip globose, white, tinged with purple, pilose on the inner surface, 2-3 cm. long, up to 1.5 cm. or more deep and wide. Staminode ovate-oblong to elliptic, grooved above, yellow with purple dots, 8-12 mm. long including the short stalk, about 5.5 mm. wide. Capsule suberect, ellipsoid, 2-3 cm. long.

The flowers of the Mountain Ladys'-slipper resemble very closely those of the Yellow Lady's-slipper. In the field, however, the distinctive white lip conveniently distinguishes it from the Yellow Lady's-slipper. The leaves also tend to be more open than those of the Yellow Lady's-slipper. The flowers are said to be delicately fragrant.

This species is usually found at high elevations in moist or dry open woods, and sometimes in scrub oak areas or swamps. It occurs on subalpine slopes up to 5,000 feet altitude in Alberta, British Columbia and Idaho, and flowers from May to July.

GEOGRAPHICAL DISTRIBUTION: Montana (Flathead, Mineral and Missoula counties), Idaho (south to Washington County), Wyoming (Sheridan County), California (south to Mariposa and Santa Cruz counties), Oregon, Washington, Alberta, British Columbia, Vancouver Island and Alaska.

CULTURAL NOTES: The Mountain Lady's-slipper grows on wooded mountain sides at moderate to high altitudes, the soil showing considerable range in reaction. It could possibly be cultivated in our region beyond its native haunts if a cool humus-rich bed were available, and it could be transplanted without root-injury. (E. T. W.)

The Mountain Lady's-slipper has been cultivated out-of-doors in England for more than fifty years. It is grown in sheltered, partially shaded places in damp fibrous peat, loam, and leaf mold with plenty of water added in summer.

PLATE 8.—**Cypripedium montanum.** 1, plant, one half natural size. 2, young plant shoots, one half natural size. 3, staminode, spread out, two and one half times natural size. *Drawn by Gordon W. Dillon.*

9. **Cypripedium passerinum** Richards. in Franklin, Narrative Journ. to Polar sea,
Bot. Appen., quarto, ed. 2, 762 (Separate p. 34.) 1823. Type locality
and collection: Arctic America, 1820, *Dr. Richardson*. (*Cypripedium passerinum* var. *minganense* Victorin). PLATE 9

(The name, *passerinum*, is a Latin word meaning "sparrow-like," that is "like
a house-sparrow's egg," as recorded by Dr. JOHN RICHARDSON, the Scottish sur-
geon-scientist who accompanied FRANKLIN's expedition to the Polar Sea. The
name is in allusion to the small lip which resembles superficially a sparrow's egg.)

COMMON NAMES: Sparrow's-egg Lady's-slipper, Franklin's Lady's-slipper,
Sparrow's-egg, Purple-spot White-slipper, Small White Lady's-slipper, Small
White Northern Lady's-slipper.

Plant erect from an ascending base, more or less densely villous-pubescent throughout,
1.2-3.8 dm. tall. Rhizome slender, creeping, giving rise at intervals to flowering stems, usually
with last year's fruiting stalk persisting. Stem leafy, provided at the base with two to four
short clasping sheaths. Leaves three to five, clasping and nearly concealing the stem, elliptic
to elliptic-lanceolate or ovate-lanceolate, obtuse to acute, plicate, 5-16 cm. long, 1.5-5 cm. wide.
Floral bract foliaceous, ovate-lanceolate to elliptic, acute to subacuminate, up to 8 cm. long
and 2 cm. wide. Flower solitary or rarely two at the summit of the shaggy-pubescent stem,
fragrant, suberect. Sepals greenish, olive-colored or yellowish, somewhat pubescent on the
outer surface and margins. Dorsal sepal suborbicular to suborbicular-obovate, apiculate with
the apicule recurved, concave, 1.5-2 cm. long, 1-1.5 cm. wide. Lateral sepals free almost to
the base or united almost to the apex to form a broadly elliptic lamina which is closely
appressed to the under side of the lip and has the two apical tips spreading; each sepal (when
free) obliquely elliptic, subobtuse to acute, 1-1.5 cm. long and about 6 mm. wide. Petals
white, not twisted, obliquely linear-elliptic to oblong, rounded at the apex, 1.2-2 cm. long, 3-4
mm. wide. Lip obovoid, white to pale magenta, lined and spotted with violet-purple, not
shining, more or less translucent, glandular-pubescent within and on the outside at the base,
1.2-2 cm. long, 8-12 mm. deep and wide; orifice provided with an infolded flap on each side.
Staminode yellow, spotted with reddish brown, ovate-cordate to ovate-oblong, rounded to
subcordate at the base, retuse or with a recurved tip at the apex, arcuate and dorsally grooved,
about 6 mm. long and 4 mm. wide. Capsule erect, broadly obovoid, 2-2.5 cm. long.

The Sparrow's-egg Lady's-slipper is almost transcontinental in its distribution.
It is essentially a far northern plant, and doubtless grows well within the Arctic
Circle.

VICTORIN (1929) described as var. *minganense* a plant from the Mingan
Islands, Province of Quebec, which differs from typical material only in being a
smaller plant than usual. VICTORIN stated that the plant, which grew on cobbly
beaches, was adapted in its isolated station to littoral conditions which had slightly
affected its morphological characteristics. An examination of an isotype of this
variety in the Gray Herbarium, Harvard University, reveals no outstanding difference from plants of the typical form which I have collected on the shores of Lake
Muncho in northern British Columbia. At this locality the species grew on open
gravelly outwash fans which had been disgorged from precipitous box canyons by
rainfalls of cloudburst proportion. Farther north, *C. passerinum* was found on old
open gravel-sand bars along the river which drained Summit Lake. A littoral
habitat seems to be a rather common one for this species.

This species is commonly found in rich, moist coniferous forests, in deep ravines,
and on the edge of streams and lake margins, and on gravel outwashes and talus
slopes. It occurs up to 7,000 feet altitude in British Columbia. The Sparrow's-
egg Lady's-slipper flowers in June and July.

GEOGRAPHICAL DISTRIBUTION: Quebec, northern Ontario, Manitoba, Saskatchewan (Wall-
wort), Alberta (Banff and Cypress Hills) and British Columbia, northwest to the Mackenzie
Basin, Yukon (Dawson and Lake Labarge) and Alaska (Dawson and Wiseman).

CULTURAL NOTES: The Sparrow's-egg Lady's slipper grows both in circumneutral limestone gravel and in moderately acid coniferous humus. If it is ever to
be cultivated successfully south of its native regions, special attention will have
to be given to keeping the bed cool. (E. T. W.)

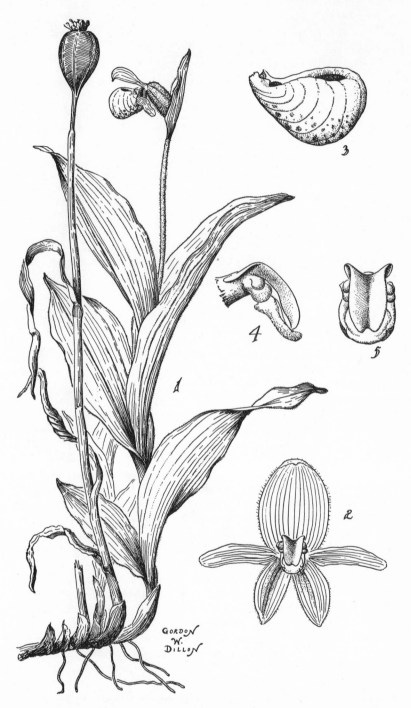

PLATE 9.—**Cypripedium passerinum.** 1, plant, one half natural size. 2, flower, with lip removed, front view, spread open, one and one half times natural size. 3, lip, side view, one and one half times natural size. 4, column, side view, one and one half times natural size. 5, column, front view, one and one half times natural size. *Drawn by Gordon W. Dillon.*

In England, *C. passerinum* has been cultivated out-of-doors for a number of years. It is grown in damp places filled with good leaf mold and quartz sand.

10. **Cypripedium reginae** Walt., Fl. Carol. 222. 1788. Type locality: Carolina. (*C. spectabile* Salisb.; *C. hirsutum* of some authors.). PLATE 10

(The name, *reginae*, is a Latin word meaning "of the queen," designating this, one of our most beautiful native orchids, as worthy of being the slipper of a "fairy queen.")

COMMON NAMES: Queen Lady's-slipper, Showy Lady's-slipper, White-petaled Lady's-slipper, Queen Slipper-orchid, Showy-slipper, White-wing Moccasin, Purple-blush, Big Pink-and-white, Pink Lady's-slipper, Large White Lady's-slipper, Royal Lady's-slipper, Pink Moccasin-flower, Female Nervine, Silver-slipper.

Plant erect, with a leafy stem which is often twisted, glandular-hirsute throughout, 3.5-8.5 dm. tall. Leaves usually three to seven, closely sheathing the stem at the base, ovate to elliptic-lanceolate, acute to acuminate, strongly ribbed and plicate, with the veins and margins strongly hirsute, 1-2.4 dm. long, 6-15 cm. wide. Inflorescence consisting of one or two (or sometimes as many as four) flowers which are supported by short pedicels in the axils of the erect floral bracts. Floral bracts foliaceous, oblong-elliptic to broadly lanceolate, acute to acuminate, 6-12 cm. long, 2.5-5 cm. wide. Flowers large, showy. Sepals and petals of a delicate waxy whiteness. Dorsal sepal ovate-orbicular, 3-4.5 cm. long, 2.3-3.5 cm. wide. Lateral sepals wholly united; lamina ovate-orbicular, 3-4 cm. long, 2-3 cm. wide. Petals oblong-elliptic to ovate-lanceolate, obtuse to acute, 2.5-4.2 cm. long, 1-1.4 cm. wide. Lip pouch-shaped, with shallow vertical and evenly distributed white furrows, white, crimson-magenta or rose-pink in front, often with purple or rose veins, 2.5-5 cm. long. Staminode cordate-ovate, on a rather stout stalk, 1-1.7 cm. long, 7-14 mm. wide at the widest point. Stigma 3-lobed. Capsule 3-4.5 cm. long, ellipsoid, about 1.5 cm. in diameter.

This species seems particularly abundant in the balsam-spruce-tamarack swamps in the Lake States region where colonies of several thousand flowering plants are occasionally to be found. It has been adopted as the state flower of Minnesota and is the only orchid so honored by any state. Nearly pure white-flowered forms have been seen at various places throughout its area of distribution. The trilobed stigma marks the Queen Lady's-slipper as an ancestral type, and consequently a primitive form in this genus.

Two instances of peloric flowers have been recorded for this species. In 1881, BASTIN found near Lake Michigan a plant which supported on a single stem two flowers, one of which was normal, the other almost regular. The regular flower had no slipper, the petals were similar to the sepals, the ovary was not twisted, and three distinct anthers were present instead of the normal pair. However, there were only two staminodes present. In 1941, CURTIS reported finding a perfectly regular flower in the Gillen Refuge in northern Michigan. Regular flowers in this species represent a reversion to an ancestral form.

The short, coarse, glandular hairs which cover the vegetative parts of this species and that of the Yellow Lady's-slipper are capable of causing severe cases of dermatitis, similar to that caused by Poison Ivy (*Rhus Toxicodendron*) and Poison Sumac (*Rhus Vernix*). According to MacDOUGAL (1895), the irritant action of the plants on the skin was found, through experiments, to increase with the degree of maturity of the plants, and a maximum effect was reached during the formation of the capsules. This increased effect, with growth and development of the plants, was found to correspond with the activity of the glandular cells and the amount of secretion present. MacDOUGAL also pointed out that the glandular secretions do not form the sole protection for the lady's-slippers but that the plant tissues are provided with a large number of cells containing needle-shaped crystals (raphides), which serve somewhat as a protection, particularly against grazing animals.

This species is usually found in wet neutral or limestone soils in cedar, larch, tamarack or arbor vitae swamps and bogs. It is also found in upland swamps, prairies and meadows, and on mossy wooded slopes or in boggy uplands. The Queen Lady's-slipper is often associated with the Yellow Lady's-slipper, and flowers from May to August or rarely September.

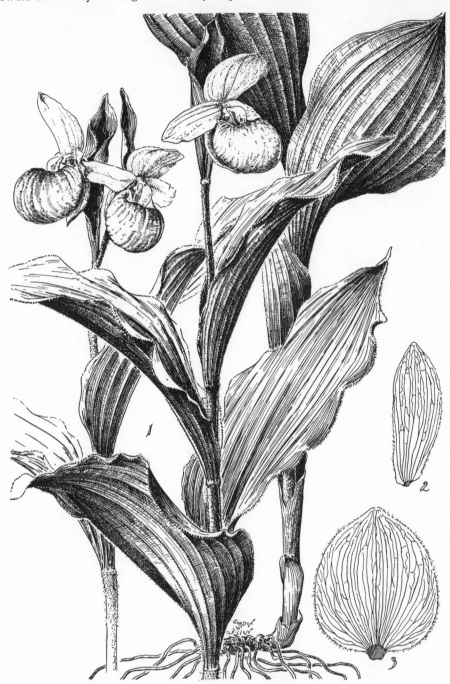

PLATE 10.— **Cypripedium reginae.** 1, plant, one half natural size. 2, petal, natural size. 3, dorsal sepal, natural size. *Drawn by Gordon W. Dillon.*

GEOGRAPHICAL DISTRIBUTION: Miquelon Island, Newfoundland, Nova Scotia, New Brunswick, Prince Edward Island, Quebec and Ontario, through New England, New York and New Jersey, south to the mountains of North Carolina (Jackson and Macon counties) and Tennessee (Polk County), westward through Michigan, Wisconsin, Minnesota and North

Dakota (Benson County) to Saskatchewan, through Ohio, Indiana and Illinois to Iowa (Fayette County) and Missouri (Shannon County) ; reported from Huntsville, Alabama (*Niles*) ; also western China.

CULTURAL NOTES: The Queen Lady's-slipper is not easy to cultivate successfully. The difficulty is apparently not a matter of temperature for, until destroyed by man, it grew at fairly low elevations in Virginia and the Carolinas where the soil becomes decidedly warm in summer. After the last ice sheet melted, the Queen Lady's-slipper migrated north into Canada, so it evidently can withstand severe cold in winter. Soil acidity is also not a factor for, contrary to the belief of some people, it is not at all an acid-loving plant. It may grow, to be sure, in swamps where sphagnum and other acidulous mosses cover the surface, but its roots penetrate down to where the reaction is neutral or essentially so. It needs a more constant supply of moisture than the average garden can afford, but even in especially moist situations it will often thrive for a year or two and then suddenly vanish. Susceptibility to attacks of parasitic fungi is the only explanation which seems to account for this behavior, and no way to prevent such attacks is known. If it must be cultivated, the only thing to do is to renew one's stock at frequent intervals. Clumps can be purchased from dealers in native plants, but its colonies are rapidly being destroyed by this practice. (E. T. W.)

According to BROWN (1813) the Queen Lady's-slipper was cultivated in England before 1731 by PHILIP MILLER.

* * * * *

Cypripedium irapeanum La Llave & Lex., Nov. Veget. Descr., Orch. Opusc. fasc.
    2 : 10. 1825.

Fox (1895) reported this species from New Mexico, based on an erroneous citation of literature. She wrongly credited BENTHAM (Plant. Hartweg. p. 72. 1839) with giving the range of *C. molle* Lindl., a synonym, as "from New Mexico to Santa Maria . . . ." This species, which superficially resembles the Queen Lady's-slipper, is known only from Mexico and Guatemala.

The first of June, when the lady's slipper [Cypripedium acaule] and wild pink have come out in sunny places on the hill-sides, then the summer is begun according to the clock of the seasons. (THOREAU: "Summer," 1884).

2. Orchis L.

Orchis L., Sp. Pl., ed. 1, 2: 939. 1753.

(The name, *Orchis,* is a Greek word meaning "testicle," in allusion to the pair of tuberoids found at the base of the stem among the roots of many of the species.)

Terrestrial, mostly succulent herbs with fibrous and tuberous-thickened roots and a leafy or scapose stem. Leaves one or more scattered on the stem or at the base of the scape. Flowers more or less showy, few or many (rarely solitary) in a congested or lax raceme, ringent. Sepals free, erect or spreading, subequal. Petals free, similar to the sepals but smaller, oblique, connivent with the dorsal sepal to form a hood over the column. Lip simple or more or less 3-lobed, shortly connate with the lower part of the column, produced at the base into a prominent spur. Column short, stout; anther-cells two, contiguous and parallel; pollen cohering in numerous coarse waxy grains which are collected on a cobwebby elastic tissue into two large masses (one filling each cell) borne on slender stalks, the bases of which are attached to the glands or viscid discs of the stigma; the two glands contained in a single little pouch or bursicle placed just above the orifice of the spur. Capsule ellipsoid to ellipsoid-fusiform, oblique.

This genus, which is the type of the family Orchidaceae, includes nearly one hundred species which are centered in the temperate regions of Europe and Asia and the boreal regions of Africa, with several species in America. The species, especially those found in Europe, are often quite difficult to define, and have been arbitrarily split into countless forms.

KEY FOR THE IDENTIFICATION OF THE SPECIES OF ORCHIS

1. Stem leafy and with leafy bracts throughout; floral bracts and sepals usually aristate......
   ....*O. aristata* (p. 42)
1. Stem naked, with a leaf or leaves at the base; floral bracts and sepals at most acuminate, not aristate 2
   2. Leaves two; lip entire, broadly ovate to lingulate, white; lateral sepals ascending and connivent with the dorsal sepal and petals........................*O. spectabilis* (p. 46)
   2. Leaf solitary; lip more or less 3-lobed, marked with magenta or purple dots or stripes; lateral sepals spreading...3
      3. Lip deeply and prominently 3-lobed, hastate; mid-lobe clawed, separated from the lateral lobes by a broad sinus..4
         4. Lip white, spotted with magenta or purple...................*O. rotundifolia* (p. 44)
         4. Lip white, with two broad longitudinal dark purplish stripes......................
            ....*O. rotundifolia* var. *lineata* (p. 46)
      3. Lip obscurely 3-lobed, not hastate; mid-lobe sessile, not separated from the lateral lobes by a broad sinus.......................................*O. rotundifolia* (form) (p. 44)

1. **Orchis aristata** Fisch. ex Lindl., Gen. and Sp. Orch. Pl. 262. 1835. Type locality and collection: Unalaska, *Fischer.* PLATE 11

(The name, *aristata,* is a Latin adjective meaning "awned," in allusion to the elongated, tapering apex of the sepals and petals.)

COMMON NAME: Fischer's Orchis.

Plant 1-4 dm. tall, glabrous throughout. Roots fibrous and tuberous; tuberoids fleshy, usually less than 2 cm. long, more or less divided with the segments tapering. Stem slender, leafy, often tinged with purple, up to 3 dm. long, enveloped at the base by three scarious tubular obtuse imbricating sheaths which are up to 7 cm. long. Leaves two or more, variable, reduced above to bracts, 4-14 cm. long, 1-4 cm. wide; lower blades oblanceolate to obovate and obtuse to rounded at the apex; upper blades lanceolate, acute to acuminate, narrowed into tubular petioles which clasp the stem. Raceme showy, ovoid to subcylindrical, few- to many-flowered, usually congested, up to 8 cm. long and 5.5 cm. in diameter. Floral bracts lanceolate, long-acuminate or aristate, cellular-ciliate on the margin, 2-4.5 cm. long, 6-13 mm. wide near the base, exceeding the flowers. Flowers usually light magenta to violet-purple, rarely almost

PLATE 11.—**Orchis aristata.** 1, plant, one half natural size. 2, flower, side view, twice natural size. 3, flower, front view, twice natural size. 4, dorsal sepal, two and one half times natural size. 5, petal, two and one half times natural size. 6, lateral sepal, two and one half times natural size. 7, lip, front view, spread out, two and one half times natural size. *Drawn by Gordon W. Dillon.*

white, with the stout pedicellate ovaries 1-1.8 cm. long. Sepals erect, ovate-lanceolate, sub-acute to acuminate or complicate and aristate at the apex, 3- to 5-nerved with some of the nerves branched, concave, 9-13 mm. long, 4-6 mm. wide near the base; dorsal sepal erect; lateral sepals very oblique, subfalcate, reflexed-spreading. Petals decurrent on the column, adherent to the dorsal sepal to form a shallow hood over the column, obliquely ovate-lanceolate, acuminate, 3-nerved with the nerves more or less branched, about 8 mm. long and 3 mm. wide near the base. Lip often spotted with deep purple, united with the lower half of the column, suborbicular to broadly subquadrate, subtruncate to broadly cuneate at the base, apiculate at the apex, subentire to erose-crenulate on the anterior margin, 8-10 mm. long, 8.5-11 mm. wide, produced at the base into a conspicuous spur; spur subhorizontal, tubular, slightly compressed, 1-1.4 cm. long, tapering from a broad base or orifice which is up to 5 mm. wide. Column short, stout, about 5 mm. long. Capsule obliquely fusiform-ellipsoid, about 1.2 cm. long.

The flowers of this species are comparatively constant in size and shape. They vary in color, however, from pale lavender or almost white to a deep violet-purple, and are often heavily spotted with deep reddish purple.

Fischer's Orchis grows in meadows and boggy places or on grassy slopes on hills and mountains. In the Aleutian Islands it is rather common and widespread, and is usually found on the lower slopes of hills near sea level where its brilliantly colored flowers often tinge the landscape. In China, however, it seems to be confined to mountainous country. It flowers from the last of May to August in various parts of its range.

GEOGRAPHICAL DISTRIBUTION: Alaska (Kukak, Barren Island, Kodiak Island, Middleton Island, Metrofania Island, etc.) and the Aleutian Islands (Akutan, Amchitka, Attu, Carlisle, Kagamil, Unalaska, etc.); also Japan and China.

CULTURAL NOTES: There is apparently no information available concerning the cultivation of this orchid.

2. Orchis rotundifolia Banks ex Pursh, Fl. Am. Sept. 2: 588. 1814. Type locality: On Hudson Bay. PLATE 12

(The name, *rotundifolia,* is a Latin word meaning "round-leaved," denoting the typical shape of the solitary leaf.)

COMMON NAMES: Small Round-leaved Orchis, Mauve-spotted Orchis, Little Round-leaf, One-leaf Orchis, Spotted Kirtle-pink.

Plant slender, stoloniferous, glabrous throughout, 9-35 cm. tall. Roots fleshy-fibrous. Scape slender, naked, slightly angled, up to 2.5 dm. tall, provided with a basal leaf, enveloped at the base by two scarious obtuse imbricating sheaths which are up to 4 cm. long. Leaf solitary, subbasal, usually about 1.5 cm. or more above the base of the scape, dull green, orbicular to oval or broadly obovate-elliptic, obtuse to rounded at the apex, 3-10 cm. long, 2.3-7 cm. wide. Inflorescence one- to several-flowered, forming a loosely flowered raceme which is up to 8 cm. long and 2-3 cm. in diameter. Floral bracts lanceolate, acuminate, 7-15 mm. long, 3-5 mm. wide near the base. Flowers showy, as many as sixteen, with the stout pedicellate ovaries 8-12 mm. long. Sepals white to pale mauve-pink, elliptic-subquadrate to ovate-elliptic, subobtuse to broadly rounded or subtruncate and usually minutely cucullate at the apex, 3- to 5-nerved, 6-10 mm. long, 3-4 mm. wide below the middle; dorsal sepal erect; lateral sepals oblique, spreading, longer than the dorsal sepal. Petals pale white to mauve, ovate-oblong, broadly obtuse, oblique, adherent to the dorsal sepal to form a hood over the column, 2- to 3-nerved, 5-6 mm. long, 2-3 mm. wide near the base. Lip white, spotted with magenta or purple, deeply 3-lobed at the base, broadly ovate in outline, 6-9.5 mm. long, produced at the base into a spur, more or less cellular-papillose throughout; lateral lobes obliquely ovate-oblong to oblong-lanceolate, obtuse, falcate, 1- to 2-nerved, about 2 mm. long; mid-lobe much larger than the lateral lobes and separated from them by a broad isthmus, irregularly oblong-spatulate to cuneate-obcordate, obliquely dilated and notched at the apex, with the apical margin somewhat undulate, 3-nerved with the lateral nerves branched, 4-6 mm. wide across the apex; spur slender, curved, 5-6.5 mm. long. Column short, stout, 3-4 mm. long. Capsule ellipsoid, about 1.5 cm. long.

While the lip of this species is usually prominently three-lobed, that of some plants is almost entire or only shallowly lobed.

In the northeastern United States the Small Round-leaved Orchis is one of the rarest orchids occurring there. It is more frequent in parts of its western range.

PLATE 12.—**Orchis rotundifolia.** 1, plants, two thirds natural size. 2, flower, front-side view, twice natural size. 3, column, front view, ten times natural size. 4, petal, five times natural size. 5, dorsal sepal, four times natural size. 6, lateral sepal, four times natural size.

Orchis rotundifolia var. **lineata.** 7, lip, two and one half times natural size. *Drawn by Gordon W. Dillon.*

Mousley (1941) described var. *lineata* (meaning "lined" in Latin) from above Elkwater Lake in the Cypress Hills of Alberta, Canada. This unusual variety differs from the typical form in that the lip (Pl. 12, Fig. 7) has two broad, dark purplish longitudinal stripes instead of the characteristic spots. It was collected again in the Cypress Hills in 1945 by Robert G. H. Cormack.

This species is an inhabitant of cold moist or wet forests, commonly in calcareous regions. It is often found in cedar, spruce or tamarack swamps and bogs, in moss of spruce-covered mountain slopes, and in peaty open soil. In Newfoundland, it occurs on turfy limestone barrens. It usually grows at considerable elevations and is found up to 3,500 feet altitude in British Columbia, and flowers from the middle of March (in Alberta) to August in various parts of its range.

Geographical distribution: Greenland (Qagssiarssuk and head of Söndre Strömfjord), Anticosti, Hudson Bay, eastern Quebec, west to Alberta, British Columbia, the Yukon (Dawson) and Alaska, south to northern Maine (Aroostook and Piscataquis counties), central Vermont (Addison County), New York (Herkimer County), Michigan (Marquette County), Wisconsin (Ozaukee and Milwaukee counties), Minnesota (Becker and Hubbard counties and Itasca Lake), Montana (Kettle Rapids) and Wyoming (Park County).

Cultural notes: The places where the Small Round-leaved Orchis grows are characterized by a cool summer climate, an unfailing supply of moisture accompanied by good drainage, and sufficient lime to keep the soil-reaction neutral or essentially so. Should anyone have a garden in which these features are present, they may succeed in cultivating it. In transplanting, the greatest care must be taken to keep its root-system intact, for it is a delicate plant and cannot stand much injury. If moved south of its native haunts, it should be shaded from direct sunlight the greater part of the day. (E. T. W.)

3. Orchis spectabilis L., Sp. Pl., ed. 1, 2: 943. 1753. Type locality: Virginia, "D. Gronovius." (*Galeorchis spectabilis* (L.) Rydb.). PLATE 13

(The name, *spectabilis,* is a Latin adjective meaning "showy," so-called because of the striking appearance of the raceme.)

Common names: Showy Orchis, Purple-hooded Orchis, Kirtle-pink, Showy American Orchis, Mauve-hood Orchis, Two-leaved Orchis.

Plant low, succulent, glabrous throughout, 7-38 cm. tall. Roots slender, fleshy, tuberous. Scape rather stout, naked, 4- to 5-angled, up to 3 dm. long, provided with two basal leaves, at the base enveloped by two scarious obtuse imbricating sheaths which are up to 6 cm. long. Leaves two, basal, subopposite, with the petioles sheathing the base of the scape, suborbicular-obovate to oblong-obovate or broadly elliptic, broadly rounded at the apex, gradually narrowed into an indistinct petiole sheathing the base, 6-21 cm. long, 3-10 cm. wide. Raceme 2- to 15-flowered (rarely a solitary flower), lax, up to 10 cm. long, 3.5-4.5 cm. in diameter. Floral bracts foliaceous, elliptic to lanceolate, obtuse to subacute, 2.5-7.5 cm. long, 1-1.8 cm. wide, usually equaling or exceeding the flowers. Flowers showy, ringent, with stout pedicellate ovaries which are 1-2 cm. long. Sepals and petals free, erect or suberect, connivent to form a hood over the column, pink to mauve, rarely almost white. Sepals elliptic to ovate-lanceolate, rounded to subacuminate and usually minutely cucullate at the apex, concave, 3- to 5-nerved with some of the nerves branched, 1.3-2 cm. long, 5.5-6.5 mm. wide below the middle; lateral sepals oblique. Petals linear-oblong to linear-lanceolate, bluntly obtuse and usually somewhat cucullate at the apex, often obliquely dilated near the base, 1.2-1.5 cm. long, 2.5-4.3 mm. wide near the base. Lip white, entire, suborbicular-ovate to broadly ovate-subquadrate or lingulate, subtruncate to broadly rounded at the apex, more or less crenate on the margin, 1-1.8 cm. long, 7-15 mm. wide, produced at the base into a conspicuous spur; spur tubular, slender-clavellate, 1.3-2 cm. long. Column stout, about 9 mm. long. Capsule ellipsoid, 1.8-2.5 cm. long.

The Showy Orchis, with its short spike of pink-mauve and white flowers rising from between two broad, basal, shining leaves, is seldom more than three decimeters tall. It is one of our earliest flowering woodland orchids, and it may frequently be found forming large, extensive colonies on forested slopes.

This species is usually found in rich hardwood forests where there is an accumulation of humus, but it occasionally occurs in coniferous forests. It also grows in clayey soil of floodplain areas of streams in rich woods, in wooded ravines along mountain streams and on low wooded slopes. In Alabama, the Showy Orchis

PLATE 13.— **Orchis spectabilis.** 1, plant, three fourths natural size. 2, flower, side view, one and one half times natural size. *Drawn by Gordon W. Dillon.*

grows in rich calcareous soils of dense forests, and in Vermont it has been found on dry roadside banks. It is found from about 300 feet altitude in the Coastal Plain of North Carolina, up to 4,000 feet or more in the southern Appalachian

Mountains of North Carolina and Tennessee, and flowers from April in Lee County, North Carolina, to July in the North.

GEOGRAPHICAL DISTRIBUTION: New Brunswick, Quebec and Ontario (Carleton County), through New England, New York, Pennsylvania, New Jersey and West Virginia, south to South Carolina (Greenville and Pickens counties), Georgia (Habersham and Rabun counties) and Alabama (Franklin and Madison counties), west through the Central and Lake States to Minnesota (Goodhue and McLeod counties), Iowa (Fayette, Johnson and Story counties), Nebraska (Otoe County), Kansas (Doniphan and Wyandotte counties), Missouri (Adair and Jackson counties) and Arkansas (Boone, Carroll and Logan counties).

CULTURAL NOTES: The favored habitat of this species is what is commonly termed a "rich woods," where its roots spread through the decomposed leaf-litter. Because of the current view that leaf mold is an acid material, it is often classed among acid-loving plants. Actual tests, however, have shown this to be erroneous. The black humus resulting from the thorough decay of vegetable debris reacts neutral or essentially so, and immediately around the plant's roots there is normally found at most a minimacid condition. Since circumneutral soils are present in many gardens, one might infer that this would be an easy species to establish. Some wild-flower gardeners do succeed with it fairly well, but others finds it difficult to grow.

Soil temperature is not an important factor, for it grows in Arkansas, Alabama and Georgia where the woods are considerably hot in summer, and winters are mild. After the last ice sheet melted, this species was able to migrate into the glaciated territory as far as Minnesota, Ontario and Quebec, where the winters are severe. It grows best where there is shade, a moderate (though not excessive) supply of moisture, and a chance for air to circulate around its roots; conditions that can be attained in any garden.

One reason for reports of its failure in gardens may be connected with the fact that the bud on the rootstock sometimes remains dormant for a year or two before sending up a leaf or flowering stalk. Native colonies correspondingly show marked variation in the number of individuals from year to year. More often, however, the roots have been injured in transplanting or the plant attacked by pests in its new situation, and failure to reappear is because of its destruction. (E. T. W.)

According to BROWN (1813), the Showy Orchis was first introduced into England in 1801 by FRANCIS MASSON.

"When we review the long history of the word 'orchis' and the genus for which it stands, we find that it has come down to us through two thousand or more years and, without too much doubt, is applied today as THEOPHRASTUS would have had us apply it. Under one of its popular names SHAKESPEARE gave the genus a place in one of the great dramas [Hamlet] of English literature. LINNAEUS retained it as the genus Orchis in his Species Plantarum of 1753. JOHN LINDLEY in 1836 modified it to form the name of the family Orchidaceae. So, beginning its career in one of the oldest botanical manuscripts, the term 'orchis' has preserved its identity in the genus Orchis and in the name of the largest family of flowering plants."

OAKES AMES, The Origin of the Term Orchis, American Orchid Society Bulletin, 1942.

3. Habenaria Willd.

Habenaria Willd., Sp. Pl. 4 : 44. 1805.

(The name, *Habenaria,* comes from the Latin *habena,* meaning "strap" or "rein," originally in allusion to the shape of the spur, but more applicable to the shape of the lip of some of our species.)

Terrestrial or semi-aquatic herbs with fleshy or tuberous roots which are ovoid to fusiform-elongated or rarely palmate. Plants erect, simple, glabrous; stem leafy or merely bracted. Leaves one or more, basal or cauline, essentially sessile, with the basal part sheathing the stem. Flowers small or medium-sized, in showy or inconspicuous racemes. Sepals free, similar or dissimilar; dorsal sepal erect or incurved to form a hood over the column; lateral sepals spreading or reflexed. Petals free, erect, usually connivent with the dorsal sepal, simple or bipartite. Lip lowermost or occasionally uppermost, simple, trilobed or tripartite (the divisions cuneate to filiform-setaceous, entire or variously toothed or fringed), entire, toothed or fringed, extended at the base into a spur. Spur rarely saccate-scrotiform to much elongated and filiform or filiform-clavellate, shorter to much longer than the pedicellate ovary. Column short; stigmas with or without papillose processes; anther-cells two, separate, relatively distant; pollen granular, attached to exposed glands (not contained in a pouch). Capsules narrowly cylindrical to ellipsoid.

This is a polymorphic genus of approximately 500 species which are native mainly of the warmer regions of the world. They are found primarily in woodlands, savannahs, meadows and swamps where they usually grow in moderate to strongly acid soils.

At various times, *Habenaria* has been divided into numerous genera based, for the most part, upon floral morphology, especially upon modifications of the column. It is my opinion, as well as that of my colleagues, that the acceptance of these numerous generic segregates over a wide range would result in hopeless confusion. Furthermore, in order to be consistent in recognizing trivial differences, one would be compelled to segregate from the genus even more concepts than have already been made. Consequently, I believe it is preferable to deal with one large, if polymorphic, genus, and to rest assured that all similar plants fall into that broad concept.

The general aspect of the various species, especially in the section *Limnorchis,* is often greatly affected by age. This is particularly true in regard to the inflorescence. Each stage — bud, anthesis, beginning of capsule enlargement, and finally fruit maturity — in the same species often appears to be separable from the preceding or following stage. The various stages of development often determine the density and size of the inflorescence. Because of these superficial and minor differences the various growth forms of some of the species have been segregated by some authors as distinct species. There is little doubt that in most of the species spur development, especially as to length, is also greatly affected by age. In several of the species, however, this does not seem to be the case. In working with such variable plants as comprise this genus, it seems best to allow for extreme variations within a given species. This has been the guiding principle in the preparation of this work.

KEY FOR THE IDENTIFICATION OF THE SPECIES OF HABENARIA

1. Lip deeply 3-parted, that is divided at least halfway to the base of the lamina............2
    2. Divisions of the lip fringed or conspicuously crenate or eroded; petals simple (not 2-parted), either crenate or fringed on the margin..3
        3. Lateral divisions of the lip capillary-fringed two-thirds or more of the distance to the base 4

4. Petals narrowly cuneate to flabellate-dilated, with the apical margin eroded or dentate; flowers white, tinged with cream-color or with green, showy...................... ....*H. leucophaea* (p. 85)
4. Petals linear-oblong to oblong-spatulate, entire (rarely denticulate)...............5
  5. Flowers pale yellowish or whitish green.........................*H. lacera* (p. 83)
  5. Flowers purple to white, tinged with lavender..............× *H. Andrewsii* (p. 54)
3. Lateral divisions of the lip fringed at most halfway to the base or merely eroded......6
  6. Divisions of the lip irregularly eroded, with the middle division deeply notched at the apex; petals coarsely eroded or entire....................*H. peramoena* (p. 95)
  6. Divisions of the lip copiously fringed; petals finely toothed.......................7
    7. Lip less than 1.3 cm. wide, with the divisions fringed to less than one-third of their length; raceme less than 3.5 cm. in diameter, densely flowered and compact; flowers purple..*H. psycodes* (p. 97)
    7. Lip more than 1.3 cm. wide, with the divisions fringed more than one-third of their length; raceme more than 4 cm. in diameter, loosely flowered; flowers lilac, rarely almost white.................................*H. psycodes* var. *grandiflora* (p. 99)
2. Divisions of the lip not fringed, entire, oblong to linear-filiform; petals simple or 2-parted..8
  8. Petals simple, not divided; divisions of the lip tooth-like, oblong to lanceolate; limited to the extreme northeast...............................*H. albida* var. *straminea* (p. 54)
  8. Petals 2-parted; divisions of the lip linear-filiform; distribution southern..............9
    9. Spur more than 4 cm. long, much longer than the pedicellate ovary (often as much as 6 times as long); lateral divisions of the lip 1.5 cm. or more long.............. ....*H. quinqueseta* (p. 100)
    9. Spur less than 2 cm. long, about as long as the pedicellate ovary; lateral divisions of the lip less than 1.3 cm. long..10
      10. Leaves essentially basal; raceme laxly few-flowered; spur slender-clavate........ ....*H. distans* (p. 72)
      10. Leaves scattered along the stem; raceme compact, many-flowered; spur filiform... .... *H. repens* (p. 103)
1. Lip simple (not 3-parted), linguiform, ligulate, linear or lanceolate, at most fringed, angled, notched or lobed...11
  11. Lip copiously ciliate-fringed...12
    12. Flowers white, occasionally tinged with cream-color; lip narrowly ovate-oblong.... ....*H. blephariglottis* (p. 57)
    12. Flowers yellow or orange; lip ovate to oblong.....................................13
      13. Lip ovate, less than 6 mm. long; spur shorter than the pedicellate ovary........14
        14. Spur less than 1 cm. long...............................*H. cristata* (p. 67)
        14. Spur more than 1.1 cm. long.........................× *H. Chapmanii* (p. 60)
      13. Lip oblong, more than 8 mm. long; spur longer than the pedicellate ovary...... ....*H. ciliaris* (p. 64)
  11. Lip not fringed, at most coarsely erose...15
    15. Lip entire or only crenate, not noticeably lobed or notched.......................16
      16. Leaves 1 or 2 (rarely 3), basal or essentially so; stem ebracteate or provided with a solitary bract (rarely more) at about the middle.......................17
        17. Spur scrotiform; lip broadly elliptic to suborbicular or obovate, deeply concave...*H. Chorisiana* (p. 62)
        17. Spur elongated, cylindrical, tapering at the apex or somewhat thickened; lip linear to linear-oblong or narrowly triangular-lanceolate, not concave........18
          18. Leaf solitary (very rarely 2), broadly obovate to linear-oblanceolate, erect-spreading; spur 1.2 cm. or less long....................................19
            19. Lip linear to narrowly triangular-lanceolate; spur tapering from a rather broad base, about as long as the lip...... ....*H. obtusata* (p. 91)
            19. Lip elliptic; spur cylindrical, usually thickened near the apex, about twice as long as the lip.................................*H. behringiana* p. 55)
          18. Leaves 2 (very rarely 3), orbicular to broadly elliptic, lying on the ground; spur more than 1.4 cm. long.......................................20
            20. Scape with a solitary bract; spur thickened at the apex; lip linear-oblong, obtuse; petals spreading free from the dorsal sepal; column with a pair of prominent arms.............................*H. orbiculata* (p. 93)
            20. Scape naked; spur tapering uniformly to a sharp point; lip lanceolate, acute to acuminate; petals connivent with the dorsal sepal; column without prominent arms.............................*H. Hookeri* (p. 76)
    16. Leaves several, cauline or subbasal; stem leafy or conspicuously bracteate......21
      21. Flowers lemon-yellow to bright orange.....................*H. integra* (p. 81)
      21. Flowers white or greenish...22
        22. Lip uppermost; flowers snowy-white.....................*H. nivea* (p. 89)
        22. Lip lowermost; flowers greenish or white...........................23

23. Lip with a small tubercle or cushion-like callus in the center at or near the base, usually strongly arcuate at the base.........................24
24. Lip subquadrate; petals usually crenulate on the margins...........
....*H. flava* (form) (p. 74)
24. Lip linear or linear-ligulate; petals entire.......................25
   25. Spur thick-cylindric, more than 1 cm. long; distribution southwestern.......................................*H. limosa* (p. 87)
   25. Spur slender-cylindric, less than 1 cm. long; distribution eastern and southern................*H. flava* var. *herbiola* (form) (p. 76)
23. Lip sometimes with a thickened keel but never with a tubercle at or near the base, pendent, spreading or upcurved..........................26
26. Lip more than 1.3 cm. long; distribution southeastern..............
........................*H. blephariglottis* var. *integrilabia* (p. 59)
26. Lip usually much less than 1.2 cm. long; distribution northern and western 27
   27. Spur scrotiform or strongly saccate to thick-cylindric, usually (but not always) less than two-thirds the length of the lip......28
      28. Raceme densely flowered, usually short, thick, congested.....29
         29. Lip narrowly elliptic to lanceolate; spur usually about as long as the lip and cylindrical, if shorter than the lip not saccate nor distinctly clavate; inflorescence characteristically less than 2 cm. in diameter; flowers greenish.................
...............................*H. hyperborea* (p. 78)
         29. Lip rhombic-lanceolate to occasionally broadly lanceolate, usually dilated at the base; spur usually about two-thirds the length of the lip and saccate to clavate; inflorescence characteristically 2 cm. or more in diameter; flowers whitish..
........................*H. dilatata* var. *albiflora* (p. 71)
      28. Raceme laxly flowered, elongated, often with the flowers scattered 30
         30. Lip rhombic-lanceolate to occasionally broadly lanceolate, usually dilated at the base; spur slender-clavate to saccate; flowers whitish............*H. dilatata* var. *albiflora* (p. 71)
         30. Lip linear to occasionally elliptic-lanceolate, never dilated at the base; spur saccate to clavate; flowers greenish........
.............................*H. saccata* (p. 103)
   27. Spur slender-cylindric, only slightly clavellate, variable in length, as long as or longer than the lip..............................31
      31. Leaves very short, ovate, less than 9 cm. long, usually reduced to clasping tubular sheaths.*H. sparsiflora* var. *brevifolia* (p. 108)
      31. Leaves ample, usually broadly elliptic to lanceolate, variable in length, never reduced entirely to sheaths....................32
         32. Leaves always clustered at or near the base of the stem, usually withering before or during anthesis; stem provided with numerous scale-like bracts; lip either somewhat truncate at the base or angled on each side at the base; sepals 1-nerved.33
           33. Spur about equal to or a little longer than the lip; raceme laxly flowered, wand-like, usually about 1 cm. or less in diameter.....................*H. unalascensis* (p. 111)
           33. Spur twice or more longer than the lip; raceme rather densely flowered, cylindrical to pyramidal, usually 1.5 cm. or more in diameter........................34
              34. Plant confined to the Pacific coastal area, typically short and stout; raceme densely flowered, thick, often pyramidal, 2 cm. or more in diameter; flowers whitish ....*H. unalascensis* var. *maritima* (p. 114)
              34. Plant widely distributed in the West, typically slender and tall; raceme cylindrical, laxly or densely flowered, not conspicuously congested, often distantly flowered, usually less than 2 cm. in diameter; flowers greenish..
.................*H. unalascensis* var. *elata* (p. 113)
         32. Leaves scattered on the stem or sometimes clustered at or near the base of the stem, usually persisting after anthesis; stem provided with a few foliaceous bracts; lip not truncate nor angled at the base; sepals 3-nerved.................35
           35. Spur one and one-half times to twice as long as the lip.36

36. Plant dwarf; flowers green and purplish; lip very fleshy, elliptic; distribution Aleutian Islands.........
......................................*H. behringiana* (p. 55)

36. Plant usually very tall; flowers white; lip rather thin, rhombic-lanceolate, prominently dilated at the base; distribution western United States and Canada......
..................*H. dilatata* var. *leucostachys* (p. 72)

35. Spur about equal to or only slightly exceeding the lip..37

37. Lip rhombic-lanceolate, prominently dilated at the base; flowers usually white, rarely greenish.........
....*H. dilatata* (p. 69)

37. Lip linear to linear-elliptic or broadly lanceolate, not prominently dilated at the base; flowers always greenish, sometimes marked with purple................38

38. Flowers usually scattered, rarely approximate or produced in an elongated raceme; lip characteristically linear..................................39

39. Flowers rather small, usually marked or suffused with purple; lip 4-7.5 mm. long, fleshy but usually without a central ridge; column small, usually with a narrow connective, about one-third the length of the dorsal sepal...........
...........*H. sparsiflora* var. *laxiflora* (p. 108)

39. Flowers rather large, light green; lip 6-14 mm. long, usually with a fleshy ridge in the center below the middle; column large, with a broad connective, usually about one-half as long as the dorsal sepal ....*H. sparsiflora* (p. 106)

38. Flowers usually in a densely or loosely flowered slender cylindrical raceme; lip characteristically lanceolate (sometimes broadly lanceolate)........
...................*H. hyperborea* (form) (p. 78)

15. Lip angled or lobed at the base (rarely entire) or trilobulate or tridentate at the apex 40

40. Lip lobed or angled (sometimes truncate) at the base........................41

41. Leaves always clustered at or near the base of the stem, usually withering before or during anthesis; stem provided with numerous scale-like bracts; lip either somewhat truncate at the base or angled on each side at the base; sepals 1-nerved 42

42. Spur about equal to or a little longer than the lip; raceme laxly flowered, wand-like, usually about 1 cm. or less in diameter...*H. unalascensis* (p. 111)

42. Spur twice as long as the lip or more; raceme rather densely flowered, cylindrical to pyramidal, usually 1.5 cm. or more in diameter.............43

43. Plant confined to the Pacific coastal area, typically short and stout; raceme congested, densely flowered, often pyramidal, 2 cm. or more in diameter; flowers whitish..................*H. unalascensis* var. *maritima* (p. 114)

43. Plant widely distributed in the West, typically slender and tall; raceme cylindrical, laxly or densely flowered, not conspicuously congested, often distantly flowered, usually less than 2 cm. in diameter; flowers greenish...
....................................*H. unalascensis* var. *elata* (p. 113)

41. Leaves scattered on the stem or sometimes clustered at or near the base of the stem, usually persisting after anthesis; stem provided with a few foliaceous bracts; lip neither truncate nor angled at the base; sepals 3 nerved.................44

44. Lip with a prominent tubercle in the center near the base, less than 6 mm. long, ovate-subquadrate to oblong-elliptic.............................45

45. Leaves borne below the middle of the stem, usually narrowly lanceolate; raceme slender, elongated, laxly flowered; floral bracts rather short, usually about as long as the flowers; lip ovate-subquadrate......*H. flava* (p. 74)

45. Leaves borne up to the inflorescence, usually elliptic-lanceolate; raceme compact, densely flowered; floral bracts usually greatly exceeding the flowers; lip oblong-elliptic...............*H. flava* var. *herbiola* (p. 76)

44. Lip without a tubercle in the center, more than 6 mm. long, linear, slender..
.....................................*H. strictissima* var. *odontopetala* (p. 109)

40. Lip neither lobed nor angled at the base, either trilobulate or tridentate at the apex 46

46. Spur slender, clavate, longer than the pedicellate ovary; lip shallowly notched at the apex with 3 short equal rounded lobules............*H. clavellata* (p. 65)
46. Spur scrotiform, much shorter than the pedicellate ovary; lip unequally 3-lobed at the apex, the acute lateral lobes prolonged beyond the obsolescent middle lobe.. ....*H. viridis* var. *bracteata* (p. 114)

PLATE 14.—**Habenaria albida** var. **straminea.** 1, plant, three fourths natural size. 2, flower, side view, three times natural size. 3, flower, front view, spread open, three times natural size. *Drawn by Gordon W. Dillon.*

1. **Habenaria albida** (L.) R. Br. var. **straminea** (Fernald) Morris & Eames, Our Wild Orchids, 69, pls. 23 & 24. 1929. *Habenaria straminea* Fernald, Rhodora 28: 174. 1926. Type locality and collection: Newfoundland, boggy depressions in limestone barrens, Cape Norman, July 18, 1925, *Wiegand, Griscom & Hotchkiss 27,892.* PLATE 14

(The name, *straminea,* is a Latin term meaning "straw-colored," referring to the color of the flowers which differ from the white-flowered typical form.)

COMMON NAME: Vanilla-scented Habenaria.

Plant erect, slender or stout, glabrous throughout, 5-35 cm. tall. Roots fusiform, fleshy, tapering. Stem leafy below the middle. Leaves two to four on the lower part of the stem, oblong-obovate to oblong-elliptic, obtuse to acute, sheathing the stem below, glaucous beneath, 2-7 cm. long, 8-35 mm. wide above the middle, reduced above to lanceolate bracts. Raceme spicate, densely many-flowered, cylindrical, 2.5-10 cm. long, 1.2-2 cm. in diameter. Floral bracts lanceolate, acuminate, up to 1.5 cm. long, exceeding the ovaries. Flowers small, greenish yellow or greenish white, vanilla-scented, with fusiform-arcuate ovaries which are 4-6 mm. long. Dorsal sepal elliptic-oblong, rounded at the apex, 3-nerved, shallowly concave, connivent with the petals to form a hood over the column, 2.7-4 mm. long, about 1.5 mm. wide. Lateral sepals obliquely ovate-lanceolate, obtuse, spreading, 3-nerved, 3.2-3.5 mm. long, about 1.8 mm. wide below the middle. Petals narrowly ovate, obtuse, oblique, connivent with the dorsal sepal, 3- to 5-nerved, about 3 mm. long and 1.5 mm. wide. Lip fleshy, broadly cuneate below, deeply cleft into three subequal tooth-like lobes at about the middle, concave at the base, 3-5 mm. long, about 2 mm. wide across the middle; lateral lobes lanceolate-falcate, acute, 2-nerved; mid-lobe oblong, obtuse, 3-nerved, slightly longer than the lateral lobes. Spur cylindric-clavellate, obtuse, 2-3 mm. long, about half as long as the ovary.

Variety *straminea* differs from typical *H. albida,* of Europe, not only in color but in its thicker spike (0.7-1.3 cm. in diameter in the typical form), longer floral bracts which exceed the ovaries (those of the typical form seldom overtop the ovaries), longer, thinner and more nervose sepals (2-3 mm. long with only the mid-nerve prominent in the typical form), and longer spur. The flowers are said to emit a very strong, agreeable odor of vanilla.

This variety is found in moist, turfy or peaty depressions in the limestone barrens of Newfoundland, and often grows in herb mats about warm springs in Greenland where it occurs up to 1,000 feet altitude on Disco Island. It flowers during July and August.

GEOGRAPHICAL DISTRIBUTION: Greenland (Kigdtussat, Disco, Neria, Julianehaab, Kuanersok, Godhavn), Newfoundland (Schooner Island, Burnt Cape and Cook Point on Pistolet Bay, Four-mile Cove and Savage Cove at Straits of Belle Isle), Iceland and Faroe Islands. The typical form is found in Europe.

CULTURAL NOTES: This orchid grows in peaty soil in limestone barrens in Newfoundland where the soil ranges from subacid to neutral. Whether it could be cultivated far south of its native haunts seems doubtful. It might be experimentally grown in a mass of sterile humus kept cool in summer by constant evaporation of neutral water. (E. T. W.)

2. × **Habenaria Andrewsii** White ex Niles, Bog-trotting for Orchids, 258, pl. 1904. — ampl. Correll, Bot. Mus. Leafl. Harvard Univ. 7: 57. 1939. *Habenaria psycodes* × *lacera* A. Andrews, Rhodora 2: 114. 1900, by inference only; Rhodora 3: 246. 1901. Type locality and collection: A very wet meadow in Pownal, Vermont, July 22, 1898, *M. W. White & A. L. Andrews,* August 5, 1901, *A. L. Andrews.* (*Habenaria fimbriata* forma *mentotonsa* Fernald.). PLATE 27

(The name, *Andrewsii,* is in honor of A. LE ROY ANDREWS (1878-   ), eminent American bryologist, who first called attention to this hybrid between *Habenaria lacera* and the purple-fringed Habenarias.

COMMON NAME: Andrews' Rose-purple-orchid.

Although most plants of × *H. Andrewsii* usually possess characters which are intermediate between the putative parents, examples occur which vegetatively resemble one parent or the other. The flowers of this hybrid are extremely variable, particularly in the median division of the lip which may be entire and spatulate-clavate to deeply fringed and broadly cuneate or narrowly flabellate. The median division, as well as the lateral divisions, of the lip of × *H. Andrewsii,* is consistently narrower than in *H. psycodes* or in *H. psycodes* var. *grandiflora,* and wider and longer than in *H. lacera.* The most constant character of the hybrid, and the one which immediately distinguishes it, is the shape of the petals. These are prevailingly linear-oblong to linear-spatulate, as in *H. lacera.* However, although they are for the most part entire, the petals are sometimes more or less denticulate, as in the purple-fringed orchids.

This putative hybrid is almost always found in the proximity of its parent species and consequently shares their boggy or damp habitat. It is found up to 5,000 feet altitude in North Carolina and flowers from June to August.

GEOGRAPHICAL DISTRIBUTION: Miquelon Island, Newfoundland (Avalon peninsula, Force le Plain and Port aux Basques), Prince Edward Island (Prince County), Nova Scotia (Cape Breton, Halifax and Pictou counties), New Brunswick (Westmoreland County), Quebec (Quebec County) and Ontario (Huron County), through New England, New York (Herkimer and Oneida counties) and New Jersey (Summit Mt.), south in the mountains to North Carolina (Buncombe County); also Michigan (Keweenaw County) and Ohio (Lorain County).

CULTURAL NOTES: While there are apparently no records of the cultivation of this hybrid, its requirements are presumably like those of its parents, especially *H. psycodes.* (E. T. W.)

3. **Habenaria behringiana** (Rydb.) Ames, Orch., fasc. 4: 91, pl. 60. 1910. *Limnorchis behringiana* Rydb., Bull. Torr. Bot. Club 28: 620. 1901. Type locality and collection: Asia, Behring Island, 1891, *British Behring Sea Commission 143.* PLATE 15

(The name, *behringiana,* is a Latin adjective for Behring Island, the place where this species was first collected.)

COMMON NAME: Behring Island Habenaria.

Plant small, 7.5-18 cm. tall, provided with a tubular bract at the base of the stem and one leaf and a foliaceous bract above the leaf. Roots tuberous, elongated-fusiform, about 5 mm. in diameter. Leaf solitary (rarely two), arising near the middle of the stem, ovate-lanceolate to elliptic-oblong or lanceolate, obtuse to subacute, 4-6 cm. long, 0.8-2 cm. wide; cauline bract foliaceous, lanceolate. Raceme short, rather densely few-flowered, with four or more flowers, 3-4 cm. long, up to 2 cm. in diameter. Floral bracts lanceolate to linear-lanceolate, subacute to acute, the lower ones about twice as long as the flowers. Flowers said to be purplish. Sepals 3-nerved; dorsal sepal suborbicular-ovate, rounded at the apex, concave, erect and connivent with the petals to form a hood over the column, 4-5 mm. long; lateral sepals elliptic, broadly obtuse, reflexed-spreading, about 5 mm. long. Petals ovate to ovate-lanceolate, obtuse, falcate, about 5 mm. long. Lip elliptic to elliptic-lanceolate, obtuse, very fleshy, 5-8 mm. long, up to 3 mm. wide. Spur slender or slightly clavellate above, about 1 cm. long.

This species is characterized by its dwarf habit and elongated spur (about 1 cm. long), which is about twice as long as the lip. The flowers are said to be purplish, and, judging from their appearance in the dried state, it is quite possible that the petals, lip and spur are suffused with this color. The plant averages about 12 cm. in height and the typically solitary leaf and single foliaceous bract on the stem are distinctive.

Habenaria behringiana is one of the rarest orchids in our region. Until recently the only collection known from North America was obtained by ERIC HULTÉN (#6831) in 1932 from Attu Island in the Aleutian Islands. However, during the recent World War, several of our men in the service made collections of this plant while stationed in the Aleutians. One of these collections, made by G. B. VAN SCHAACK (#14), bears the simple but meaningful data: "Attu Isl., Aleutians, Massacre Bay, Casco Cove, July 16, 1944."

This species is found in bogs and heaths, and flowers during July and August.

GEOGRAPHICAL DISTRIBUTION: Rare in the Aleutian Islands (Adak, Attu); also Behring Island.

PLATE 15.—**Habenaria behringiana.** 1, plants, natural size. 2, flower, front view, three times natural size. 3, petal, five times natural size. *Drawn by Blanche Ames.*

CULTURAL NOTES: There is apparently no information concerning the cultivation of this orchid. Very probably its cultivation has never been attempted.

4. **Habenaria blephariglottis** (Willd.) Hook., Exot. Fl. 2: t. 87. 1824. *Orchis blephariglottis* Willd., Sp. Pl. 4:9. 1805. Type locality: Pennsylvania. (*Blephariglottis blephariglottis* (Willd.) Rydb.; *B. conspicua* (Nash) Small; *Habenaria blephariglottis* var. *holopetala* (Lindl.) Gray). PLATE 16

(The name, *blephariglottis,* is a Greek term meaning "eyebrow-tongued," in allusion to the coarsely and deeply fringed tongue-shaped lip.)

COMMON NAMES: White Fringed-orchid, Snowy-orchid, Plume-of-Navarre.

Plant stout, leafy below, bracted above, glabrous, 0.8-11 dm. tall. Roots fleshy, tuberous-thickened. Stem strongly ribbed. Leaves ovate-lanceolate to elliptic-lanceolate or linear-lanceolate, acute to acuminate, with the lower part sheathing the stem, 5-35 cm. long, 1-5 cm. wide. Raceme densely or laxly flowered, 3-20 cm. long, 2.5-8 cm. in diameter. Floral bracts narrowly lanceolate, shorter than the pedicellate ovaries, 1.5-2.5 cm. long. Flowers white, often tinged with cream-color, with slender pedicellate ovaries which are about 2 cm. long. Dorsal sepal oblong-elliptic to orbicular, obtuse to rounded at the apex, concave, 5-10 mm. long, 4-8 mm. wide. Lateral sepals broadly ovate-orbicular, oblique, 5-11 mm. long, 4-9 mm. wide. Petals linear to narrowly oblong-spatulate or oblanceolate, truncate and retuse to denticulate at the apex, 3-8 mm. long, 1-3 mm. wide above. Lip with the undivided portion linguiform, ovate-oblong to oblong-elliptic or oblong-quadrate, rarely suborbicular, 4-13 mm. long, 2-4 mm. wide, copiously and coarsely fringed; fringes less than 8 mm. long, with the segments often branched. Spur slender, as long as or longer than the pedicellate ovary, 1.5-5 cm. long.

Lack of field experience with this species of some authors has often caused much confusion in literature regarding it. As compared with some of our species, however, *H. blephariglottis* presents a rather simple problem. Flowers of the plants found in the southern states are usually so much larger and outwardly different from those found in the northern part of its range that the two extremes have been considered by some authors as two different species. However, as is the case with most species whose area of distribution extends along the Atlantic seaboard from Canada to Florida, ecological and geographical variations are to be expected. The Florida plants of the White Fringed-orchid are characteristically more luxuriant than those found in Newfoundland. This same condition applies to several other species, such as *Calopogon pulchellus.*

The common form of the southern states has been segregated as var. *conspicua* (Nash) Ames (1908), and differs from the typical form found in the North, mainly in its more open raceme, larger flowers and longer spur (PL. 16, FIG. 6). Conversely, the typical form has a densely flowered raceme and much smaller flowers with a shorter spur than that found in the South.

After examining material from the entire range of this species, I find a gradual variation in the plants from the luxuriant southern form to the dwarf northern form. However, the extreme northern and southern forms may be arbitrarily separated from one another on the basis of the aforementioned characters.

A characteristic habitat of the White Fringed-orchid in the southeastern states is the narrow strip of wet, acid sandy muck where a pocosin bog grades into the gradually rising pine-oak sandhills. In southeastern North Carolina it is often associated with the remarkable Venus' Fly-trap (*Dionaea muscipula*) in this type of habitat. In the summer of 1938, I saw hundreds of the White Fringed-orchid in a fresh-water marsh near Bay St. Louis, Mississippi. They were extremely large plants, some being as much as 11 dm. tall. This station is of particular interest because the species was so abundant, less than twenty miles from the Louisiana State line. Yet, so far as I know, this species has not been found in Louisiana.

A frequent habitat of *H. blephariglottis* in the northern part of its range is the moist edge of cranberry bogs.

This species also occurs in meadows, marshes, sphagnum and sedge bogs, wet depressions in savannahs and prairies, low scrub land, edge of hammocks and cypress swamps, sandy soil on the edge of thickets, low flatwoods and pine barrens, wet upland woods and borders of low swampy streams. It is primarily a Coastal

PLATE 16.—**Habenaria blephariglottis.** 1, plant, one half natural size. 2, flower, side view, one and one half times natural size. 3, dorsal sepal, twice natural size. 4, petal, twice natural size. 5, lip, spread out, twice natural size.

Habenaria blephariglottis var. **conspicua.** 6, flower, side view, one and one half times natural size.

Habenaria blephariglottis var. **integrilabia.** 7, flower, side view, one and one half times natural size. *Drawn by Gordon W. Dillon.*

Plain plant, but occurs up to 2,000 feet altitude in the mountains of North Carolina. The White Fringed-orchid flowers from June (rarely earlier) to the middle of September.

GEOGRAPHICAL DISTRIBUTION: Widespread and locally abundant from Miquelon Island, Newfoundland, Nova Scotia, Prince Edward Island, Quebec and Ontario, through New England and the Atlantic States, south to Florida, along the Gulf Coast to Mississippi (Hancock, Harrison and Jackson counties), with a probable disjunct station in Texas (Galveston County), west to Ohio (Geauga and Summit counties) and Michigan (Cheboygan, Mason, Tuscola and Wexford counties).

The typical form occurs from upland North Carolina north to Miquelon Island and Newfoundland and west to Michigan and Ohio, whereas var. *conspicua* is found from eastern North Carolina south to Florida and along the Gulf Coast to Mississippi and Texas.

CULTURAL NOTES: The two variants of this species differ in their temperature requirements although they are alike as to soil-reaction. The more northern typical form is found where the soils do not become very warm in summer, but are frozen for long periods in winter. The more southern form, var. *conspicua,* occurs where the soil temperature becomes high in summer and the ground is frozen for but short periods, if at all, in winter. For successful cultivation, either of these two variants should be chosen which fits best with the existing garden temperature conditions. Both grow in habitats characterized by sandy soil with a minimum of clay colloids, but with large amounts of mediacid humus often derived from sphagnum moss. There is also required a constant supply of strongly acid water, which, however, should not stagnate around the roots for long periods. Partial shade of shrubs seems most favorable. If these conditions can be met in a garden, successful cultivation may be practical, but they are rarely attained. (E. T. W.)

This species was first introduced into the British Isles in 1822 from Canada by JOHN GOLDIE, but without success. In 1825 it was successfully grown in the garden of Dalhousie Castle.

5. **Habenaria blephariglottis** (Willd.) Hook. var. **integrilabia** Correll, Bot. Mus. Leafl. Harvard Univ. 9: 153. 1941. Type locality and collection: Kentucky, boggy sphagnum ravine three miles north of Whitley City, McCreary County, August 27, 1940, *F. T. McFarland & H. J. Rogers 97.*   PLATE 16

(The name, *integrilabia,* is a Latin adjective meaning "entire lip," referring to the fringeless condition of that organ.)

COMMON NAME: Monkey-face.

Aside from having larger flowers, this variety differs from the typical form only in the entire or nearly entire lip and petals.

All of the material from Kentucky and Tennessee which I have examined belongs to this variety. Apparently neither the typical form nor var. *conspicua* is found in these two states. It seems to be fairly common locally on the Cumberland Plateau, with two outlying stations in the Smoky Mountains of North Carolina and several scattered stations on the Piedmont Plateau and Coastal Plain of Georgia, Alabama and Mississippi.

An interesting letter regarding a collection of this variety in Tennessee was received from Dr. H. K. SVENSON dated September 15, 1938. It is, in part, as follows: "These [plants] were collected on the Cumberland Plateau near Beersheba Springs. I saw approximately two hundred specimens in grassy swamps, accompanied by *H. ciliaris* and *H. cristata.* This is undoubtedly the plant mentioned in AMES, Orchidaceae, IV, 171, 1910 — 'Tennessee (?) Cumberland Mts., 1888, Mrs. BENNETT (8) (a form with entire labellum).' It appears to be a large-flowered *H. blephariglottis,* with large petals and with a labellum which is consistently entire or practically so. It occurred in two swamps about five miles apart and is known from other places in the vicinity. Like the other species of *Habenaria* it is known locally as 'Monkey-face'."

Concerning the type station of this variety, Dr. F. T. McFARLAND wrote in a letter: "There are literally 100's of these plants in this sphagnum bog . . . " In fact, this variety is so abundant at the type station that the University of Kentucky distributed a set of isotypes in their First Century of plants.

This variety is found in sphagnum bogs, grassy swamps, marshes, ravines and along streams. It occurs up to 2,000 feet altitude in North Carolina and Tennessee. Although it usually blooms during August and September, it has been found in flower in June in Alabama.

GEOGRAPHICAL DISTRIBUTION: North Carolina (Cherokee and Henderson counties), Georgia (Cobb County), Kentucky (McCreary County), Tennessee (Fentress, Franklin, Grundy and Hamilton counties), Alabama (Butler, Culman, Jackson, Tuscaloosa and Winston counties), and Mississippi (Glendale).

CULTURAL NOTES: There is apparently no information concerning the cultivation of this orchid. Very probably its cultivation has never been attempted.

6. × **Habenaria Chapmanii** (Small) Ames, Orch., fasc. 4: 155. 1910. *Blephariglottis Chapmanii* Small, Fl. Southeast. U. S., ed. 1, 314. 1903. Type locality: In pine woods, Apalachicola, Florida. (× *Habenaria Canbyi* Ames; *Blephariglottis Canbyi* (Ames) W. Stone). FIGURE 2

(The name, *Chapmanii,* is in honor of ALVAN WENTWORTH CHAPMAN (1809-1899), distinguished American botanist who wrote a Flora of the Southern United States.)

COMMON NAME: Chapman's Orchid.

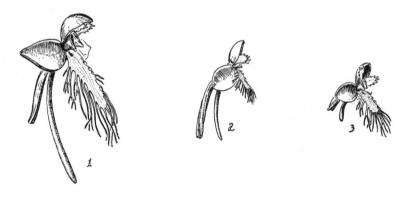

TEXTFIGURE 2.— Flowers, side-front view, all one and one half times natural size. 1, **Habenaria ciliaris**. 2, × **Habenaria Chapmanii**. 3, **Habenaria cristata**. *Drawn by Gordon W. Dillon.*

Plant glabrous, rather slender, 3-10 dm. tall. Roots fleshy, tuberous-thickened, elongated. Leaves one or two, linear-lanceolate, acuminate, abruptly diminishing into bracts above, 10-28 cm. long, 1.3-3.5 cm. wide. Raceme compact, cylindrical, 5-16 cm. long, 1.5-4.5 cm. in diameter. Floral bracts narrowly lanceolate, acuminate, 1-3 cm. long. Flowers deep orange to orange-lemon in color. Dorsal sepal suborbicular to oblong-elliptic, obtuse to acute, deeply concave, 4-6 mm. long, 3-5.5 mm. wide. Lateral sepals ovate to suborbicular, oblique, obtuse to acute, 4-5.5 mm. long, 2-5 mm. wide. Petals narrowly cuneate to oblong-cuneate, usually short-fringed at the apex, 3-4 mm. long, 1-2 mm. wide. Lip with the undivided portion ovate to ovate-oblong or elliptic, 3-6 mm. long, 1-2 mm. wide, deeply ciliate-fringed. Spur slender, 1.1-1.4 cm. long, rarely longer.

W. M. CANBY, who first collected this plant near Lewes, Delaware, in company with *H. cristata* and *H. blephariglottis,* thought that it might be a hybrid of those two species. In 1908, AMES recognized the plant as a hybrid and named it for the collector. Earlier, in 1903, SMALL described × *H. Chapmanii* (as

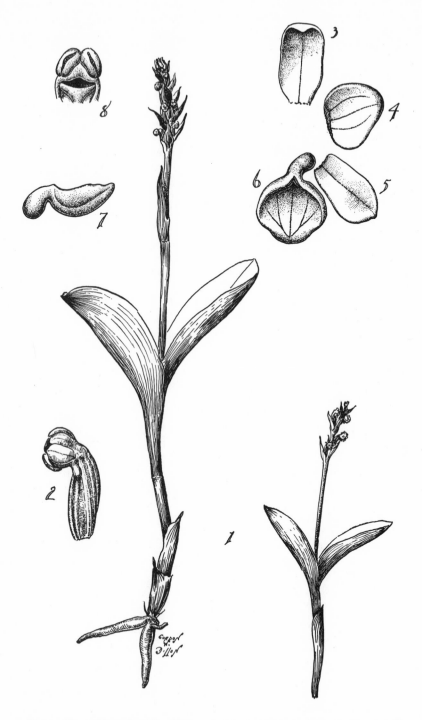

PLATE 17.—**Habenaria Chorisiana.** 1, plants, natural size. 2, flower, side view, six times natural size. 3, dorsal sepal, ten times natural size. 4, petal, ten times natural size. 5, lateral sepal, ten times natural size. 6, lip and spur, spread out, ten times natural size. 7, lip and spur, side view, ten times natural size. 8, column, front view, ten times natural size. *Drawn by Gordon W. Dillon.*

Blephariglottis Chapmanii) which he later (in 1933) considered to be a hybrid of *H. cristata* × *H. ciliaris*.

Specimens of what I consider to be typical × *H. Canbyi* were collected in Hardin County, Texas. However, so far as can be determined, *H. blephariglottis* (except for a probable disjunct station in Galveston County, Texas) has neither been reported nor collected in the South any farther west than Mississippi, whereas *H. ciliaris* occurs rather abundantly in eastern Texas. The occurrence of typical × *H. Canbyi* in Texas, in consideration of the apparent lack or rarity of *H. blephariglottis* in both Louisiana and Texas, is most disconcerting and arouses suspicion as to which species are the true parents of this hybrid. Since SMALL'S type of *Blephariglottis Chapmanii* is undoubtedly a hybrid of *H. cristata* × *H. ciliaris* or *H. cristata* × *H. blephariglottis* and it is impossible, without experimental evidence, to determine the true identity of the parent species of either of the described hybrids, I have accepted the older and valid name and consider all of the so-called hybrids exhibiting intermediate characters between the above species as × *H. Chapmanii*.

The raceme of somewhat larger flowers of the hybrid approaches most closely that of *H. cristata*. However, the spur immediately separates these two plants. The spur of *H. cristata* averages 6 mm. in length, whereas that of × *H. Chapmanii* averages 12 mm. in length.

This putative hybrid is found in low moist pinelands and swamps, acid bogs, open wet woods, margin of creeks and low moist meadows. Although it is primarily limited to the Coastal Plain, it is found up to 2,000 feet altitude in the mountains of North Carolina. It flowers during July and August.

GEOGRAPHICAL DISTRIBUTION: This distinctive but complex hybrid occurs locally from New Jersey (Camden and Cape May counties) and Delaware (Sussex County), through Virginia (Nansemond and Sussex counties) and North Carolina (Henderson County), south to Georgia (Brooks, Camden, Charlton, Glynn and Towns counties) and northern Florida (Columbia, Duval, Franklin and Taylor counties), along the Gulf Coast to Texas (Hardin and Jefferson counties).

CULTURAL NOTES: This hybrid is similar in habitat preferences to its parent, *H. cristata,* and can perhaps be grown in artificial habitats suitable for that species. (E. T. W.)

7. **Habenaria Chorisiana** Cham., Linnaea 3 : 31. 1828. Type locality : Everywhere in the mountains of Unalaska. (*Pseudodiphryllum Chorisianum* (Cham.) Nevski; *Limnorchis Chorisiana* (Cham.) J. P. Anders.).   PLATE 17

(The name, *Chorisiana,* is in honor of LOUIS CHORIS (1795-1828), Russian painter and traveller.)

COMMON NAME: Chamisso's Orchid.

Plant usually small, slender, rarely more than 15 cm. tall (one plant observed was 30 cm. tall), with several fusiform fleshy roots. Stem scapose, 1- or 2-leaved below, naked above or with a solitary (rarely two) lanceolate acute bract. Leaves subbasal (rarely midway on the stem), two or rarely one, subopposite, sheathing the stem below, ovate, lanceolate or broadly elliptic to suborbicular, obtuse to acute, often somewhat apiculate, up to 6.5 cm. long and 3.7 cm. wide. Raceme spicate, few- (rarely twenty) flowered, 1.5-5 cm. long, 5-10 mm. in diameter. Floral bracts triangular-ovate to triangular-lanceolate, acute to acuminate, up to 1.5 cm. long, mostly exceeding the flowers. Flowers minute, with the floral segments fleshy and scarcely spreading. Sepals oblong-quadrate to oblong-obovate, obtuse to broadly rounded at the apex, 1-nerved, 1.7-2.5 mm. long, about 1 mm. wide; lateral sepals slightly oblique. Petals obliquely suborbicular-ovate, rounded at the apex, 3-nerved, 1.5-2 mm. long and wide, rarely larger. Lip entire, broadly elliptic to orbicular or obovate, broadly rounded at the apex, deeply concave, very fleshy, about 1.5 mm. long (rarely up to 2.5 mm. long) and 1.2-1.7 mm. wide. Spur short, scrotiform, 0.7-1 mm. long. Column short, 1.2-1.5 mm. long.

This is our smallest *Habenaria*. The plant seldom exceeds 10 cm. in height and the floral segments are rarely as much as 2 mm. in length. The pair of subbasal leaves and the few-flowered, scapose inflorescence are distinctive.

This species and *H. behringiana* are the rarest orchids in the genus *Habenaria* within our range, and they are among the rarest plants in North America. Until recently there were but two really serviceable collections of this species in the

PLATE 18.—**Habenaria ciliaris.** Plant, natural size. *Drawn by Blanche Ames.*

herbaria of North America. These were ERIC HULTÉN's (#6540) collection from Atka Island in the Aleutian Islands and JOHN MACOUN's (#82473) collection from Ucluelet, Vancouver Island, British Columbia. However, during the recent World War several of our men in the service made collections of this plant while stationed in the Aleutians. These additional collections came from Adak, Attu and Unalaska Islands.

This species is found in heaths and swamps from near sea level up to 500 feet elevation, and flowers in July and August.

GEOGRAPHICAL DISTRIBUTION: British Columbia (Vancouver Island), Alaska (Juneau, *fide Anderson*) and the Aleutian Islands (Adak, Atka, Attu and Unalaska); also Japan.

CULTURAL NOTES: There is apparently no information concerning the cultivation of this orchid. Its cultivation has doubtless never been attempted.

8. **Habenaria ciliaris** (L.) R. Br. in Ait., Hort. Kew., ed. 2, 5: 194. 1813. *Orchis ciliaris* L., Sp. Pl., ed. 1, 2:939. 1753, excluding Gron. Fl. Virg. citation. Type locality: Virginia and Canada. (*Platanthera ciliaris* (L.) Lindl.; *Blephariglottis ciliaris* (L.) Rydb.). PLATE 18 and FIGURE 2

(The name, *ciliaris*, is a Latin term meaning "like an eyelash," in allusion to the prominently fringed lip.)

COMMON NAMES: Yellow Fringed-orchid, Orange-fringe, Orange-plume, Rattlesnake's Master.

Plant stout, glabrous, leafy below, bracted above, 2.4-10 dm. tall. Roots fleshy, tuberous-thickened; tuberoids oval, often 4 cm. long and 1.5 cm. in diameter. Leaves oblong-lanceolate to lanceolate, acuminate, with the lower portion sheathing the stem, often strongly keeled, 7-30 cm. long, 0.6-6 cm. wide. Raceme densely or laxly flowered, 3.5-20 cm. long, 4-8 cm. in diameter. Floral bracts linear-lanceolate, acuminate, shorter than the pedicellate ovaries, 1-2 cm. long. Flowers bright yellow or deep orange, with the slender pedicellate ovaries about 2 cm. long. Dorsal sepal oblong-elliptic to orbicular, rarely notched or bidentate at the broad apex, concave, 4-9 mm. long, about 4 mm. wide. Lateral sepals broadly ovate to suborbicular, abruptly obtuse, oblique, 6-9 mm. long, 5-8 mm. wide. Petals linear-oblong to linear-cuneate, acute and toothed at the apex, 6-7 mm. long, 1-2 mm. wide. Lip with the undivided portion linear-oblong to linear-cuneate, 8-12 mm. long, 2-3 mm. wide, copiously ciliate-fringed (the basal segments often branched) with the fringes usually 1 cm. or more long. Spur slender, longer than the pedicellate ovary, 2-3.3 cm. long.

Habenaria ciliaris, one of our most showy species, is closely similar in habit to *H. blephariglottis.* However, when observed in the field the two species are readily separated by the color of their flowers. The rich golden yellow flowers of *H. ciliaris* contrast vividly with the snow-white flowers of *H. blephariglottis.* Where these two orchids occur in proximity, plants with pale cream-colored flowers are often found, doubtless representing a hybrid population of these closely allied species. Although these two species are often found in the same plant community, *H. blephariglottis* is always associated with moist conditions while *H. ciliaris* is almost ubiquitous in parts of the South.

No matter how distinct the Yellow Fringed-orchid and White Fringed-orchid may be in the field, the separation of dried material (in the absence of color notes) is usually extremely trying. In separating herbarium material, I have found the following characteristics to be helpful: In *H. blephariglottis* the fringes on the lip, besides being rather coarse, appear bristly and stand out all around the margin of the lip, whereas in *H. ciliaris* the fringes are weak and slender and tend to hang parallel to the limb of the lip and are directed forward toward its apex.

This species is apparently tolerant of practically any type of habitat, being found in sphagnum and sedge bogs, swamps, marshes, in thickets on borders of streams and ponds, in low flatwoods and wet pine barrens, swampy floodplain woods, wet meadows, edge of cypress swamps and hammocks, savannahs, prairies and pocosins, in deep humus of moist upland pine and hardwood forests and in seepage of swampy wooded slopes. It is also found in the South on rocky open well-drained ridges, on dry open mountain slopes, rather dry pine barrens and in open dry grassy fields, usually in strongly acid situations. In Cherokee County, North Carolina, this species was observed to compete successfully with a dense stand of broom sedge (*Andropogon* spp.) on an open dry south-facing slope. It occurs from near sea level on the Coastal Plain, up to 1,600 feet altitude in Georgia, 2,000 feet in Alabama and 5,500 feet in the mountains of North Carolina and Tennessee. The Yellow Fringed-orchid flowers from late June to late September or rarely October.

GEOGRAPHICAL DISTRIBUTION: Rare and local in Ontario (Essex S. County), Vermont, Massachusetts, Rhode Island, Connecticut, becoming frequent through the Atlantic states to southern Florida, along the Gulf Coast to Texas (west to Milam County), west through the Central and Lake States to Michigan, Wisconsin, Illinois, Missouri and Arkansas (west to Clark, Hempstead, Hot Springs and Garland counties).

CULTURAL NOTES: Considering its wide range, this orchid is evidently rather indifferent to temperature conditions. It thrives equally well in full sun or partial shade. It is one of the more adaptable species in respect to soil, growing not only in humus-rich sands but also in dense clayey loam of more or less sterile character. Although soil-moisture may be abundant throughout the season, it is often sparse during late summer or autumn. The soil-reaction is usually mediacid to subacid. Because of its adaptability to varying habitat conditions, this is one of the easiest native orchids to cultivate, and it has been successfully grown in some wild gardens where parasites happen to be scarce. (E. T. W.)

Flowering spikes remain in good condition on the plant for about two weeks and, consequently, this species is a most desirable plant for the flower garden. Even when picked, the flowers of this species are quite hardy, and they will last for more than a week.

According to BROWN (1813), the Yellow Fringed-orchid was cultivated in England before 1796 by R. A. SALISBURY, Esq.

9. **Habenaria clavellata** (Michx.) Spreng., Syst. Veg. 3: 689. 1826. *Orchis clavellata* Michx., Fl. Bor.-am. 2:155. 1803. Type locality: Carolina. (*Habenaria tridentata* (Muhl. ex Willd.) Hook.; *H. clavellata* var. *ophioglossoides* Fernald; *Gymnadenia tridentata* (Muhl. ex Willd.) Lindl.; *Gymnadeniopsis clavellata* (Michx.) Rydb.; *Denslovia clavellata* (Michx.) Rydb.). PLATE 19

(The name, *clavellata*, is a Latin adjective meaning "like a small club," in allusion to the typical shape of the spur.)

COMMON NAMES: Small Green Wood-orchid, Frog-spike, Green Rein-orchid, Little Club-spur Orchid, Southern Rein-orchid, Wood Orchid.

Plant usually small, glabrous, 0.8-4.5 dm. tall. Roots slender, fleshy, rarely swollen near the base of the stem. Stem somewhat angled and narrowly winged. Leaves one or rarely two, at about the middle of the stem, obovate-oblanceolate to narrowly oblanceolate, obtuse, 5-18 cm. long, 1-3.5 cm. wide, reduced above to linear-lanceolate bracts. Raceme few- to many-flowered, 2-9 cm. long, 2-3.5 cm. in diameter. Floral bracts lanceolate, acuminate, 3-10 mm. long. Flowers greenish or yellowish white, with stout spreading pedicellate ovaries which are about 1 cm. long. Sepals ovate, rounded to obtuse at the apex, 4-5 mm. long, about 2.5 mm. wide; lateral sepals oblique. Petals ovate, obtuse, irregularly sinuate along the apical margin, 3-5 mm. long, about 2 mm. wide. Lip narrowly oblong-cuneate, truncate and sinuately tridentate at the apex, 3-7 mm. long, 3-4 mm. wide at the apex. Spur longer than the pedicellate ovary, slender-clavate (rarely cleft at the apex), curved upward, 8-12 (averaging less than 10) mm. long.

This little plant is one of the most abundant and easily obtainable of all our orchids in the eastern states. Due to its unobtrusive appearance, as well as to its usually secluded habitat, it has been left unmolested and has thus been able to spread and thrive. Also, it is self-pollinated, instead of having to depend upon outside agencies for this function; so it usually produces a maximum of fully ripened seed-filled capsules which thus assure it of perpetuation. Furthermore, it is unique in the genus in the usually oblique arrangement of the flowers, so that the lip and spur come from the side of the flower and give it the appearance of being askew.

PLATE 19.—**Habenaria nivea.** 1, plant, one half natural size. 2, flower, front view, spread out, two and one half times natural size. 3, flower, side view, two and one half times natural size.

Habenaria clavellata. 4, plant, one half natural size. 5, flower, front view, spread open, two and one half times natural size. 6, flower, side view, two and one half times natural size. *Drawn by Gordon W. Dillon.*

A superficial variant, var. *ophioglossoides* Fernald (1946 A), has recently been described from Nova Scotia, and is supposed to be the common form occurring north of Virginia. This plant, which represents only an extreme vegetative variation, was supposed to differ from the typical form by the following characterization: " . . . oval, oblong or broadly oblanceolate leaves rounded to tapering to an essentially sessile (not subpetiolar) base, the blade 3-17 cm. long and 1-4 cm. broad (one sixth to one half as broad as long)." In my opinion, this proposed variant is not worthy of recognition. This species commonly grows in water and on the edge of water along streams in densely wooded areas, in sheltered or open sphagnum bogs, swamps, marshes, wet meadows and pocosins, mud and sphagnum of seepage on heavily wooded slopes and alluvial soils, deep ravines, and in moist open grassy soil. It is found from near sea level on the Coastal Plain, up to 1,700 feet altitude in Georgia, 2,500 feet in Vermont and 6,500 feet in the mountains of North Carolina. The Small Green Wood-orchid flowers from June to late August or rarely September.

GEOGRAPHICAL DISTRIBUTION: Miquelon Island, Newfoundland, Anticosti, Nova Scotia, Prince Edward Island, New Brunswick, Quebec and Ontario (Sudbury and Wellington counties and Temagami), through New England and the Atlantic States, south to northern Florida (Columbia County), along the Gulf Coast to Texas (Montgomery and Nacogdoches counties), west through the Central and Lake States to Minnesota (Anoka, Chisago, Goodhue, Hennepin and Ramsay counties), Iowa (Fayette County), Missouri and Arkansas (Garland, Pulaski and Union counties); also Montana (Lewis and Clark County—probably cultivated).

CULTURAL NOTES: Ranging as it does from the Gulf of Mexico to the Great Lakes and Newfoundland, this little orchid is evidently adapted to a wide range of climatic conditions. Moreover, while requiring considerable moisture, it seems to grow equally well in sun or shade. Though not very particular as to soil acidity, it is most frequently found in rather intensely acid humus. It can be cultivated without much difficulty in a moist spot in the wild garden where the soil is rich in organic matter and the soil-reaction is mediacid or at least subacid. (E. T. W.)

This species was first introduced into the British Isles from Canada by JOHN GOLDIE about 1824.

10. **Habenaria cristata** (Michx.) R. Br. in Ait., Hort. Kew., ed. 2, 5: 194. 1813.
   Orchis cristata Michx., Fl. Bor.-am. 2:156. 1803. Type locality: In woods of Carolina. (*Platanthera cristata* (Michx.) Lindl.; *Blephariglottis cristata* (Michx.) Raf.).   PLATE. 20 and FIGURE 2

(The name, *cristata,* is a Latin term meaning "crested," in allusion to the exposed fringed tip of the petals which project from the sides of the dorsal sepal to give the flowers a crested appearance.)

COMMON NAMES: Crested Fringed-orchid, Crested Rein-orchid, Golden Fringe-orchid, Orange-crest, Crested Yellow-orchid.

Plant stout, glabrous, leafy below, bracted above, 1.8-9 dm. tall. Roots fleshy, tuberous-thickened. Leaves oblong-lanceolate to linear-lanceolate, acute to acuminate, sheathing the stem below, 7-21 cm. long, 1-2.5 cm. wide. Floral bracts narrowly lanceolate, acuminate, about as long as or shorter than the pedicellate ovary, 1-2.5 cm. long. Raceme cylindrical, densely flowered, 2-15 cm. long, 2-4 cm. in diameter. Flowers bright orange, with slender pedicellate ovaries which are 1.2-1.7 cm. long. Dorsal sepal oblong-elliptic to suborbicular, often slightly notched at the obtuse apex, concave, 3-5 mm. long, 2-3 mm. wide. Lateral sepals suborbicular to orbicular, rounded at the apex, 3-4 mm. long, 2-3 mm. wide. Petals oblong-elliptic, often narrowly cuneate, fringed at the apex, 2-4 mm. long, 1-2 mm. wide. Lip ovate to ovate-oblong, 4-6 mm. long, copiously ciliate-fringed, with the segments usually branched. Spur 5-10 (averaging 6) mm. long, slender, much shorter than the pedicellate ovary.

This is one of the typically Coastal Plain species which occur in the mountains of North Carolina, especially in the vicinity of Flat Rock in Henderson County. In and around a small sphagnum bog near Flat Rock, I collected this species together with thirteen other orchids, including the rare *H. blephariglottis* var. *integrilabia*, $\times$ *H. Chapmanii* and the less rare *Cleistes divaricata*. This part of the southern Appalachian Mountains has an extremely interesting flora

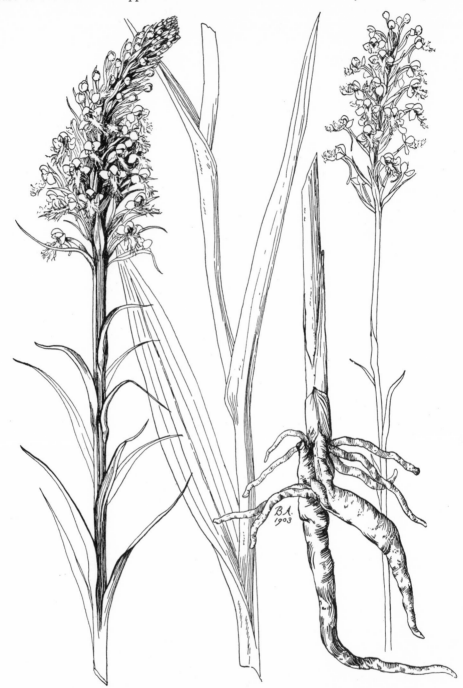

PLATE 20.—**Habenaria cristata**. Plant, natural size. *Drawn by Blanche Ames.*

in which may be found all types of plant communities from bog areas and sand-hills similar to those found on the Coastal Plain to dense northern coniferous forests. These various ecological conditions provide suitable habitats for many of our native orchids.

This species is usually found in sphagnum and sedge bogs, low moist open meadows, swamps, pocosins, low moist grassy pine barrens and flatwoods, boggy soil of prairies and savannahs, in thickets in floodplain woods and along streams, at the edge of cypress swamps, on open wooded seepage slopes, boggy places in upland woods and in depressions in pinelands. It grows from near sea level on the Coastal Plain, up to 1,000 feet altitude in Alabama and 2,500 feet in the mountains of North Carolina. The Crested Fringed-orchid flowers from June to early September throughout its range.

GEOGRAPHICAL DISTRIBUTION: This species is recorded from Massachusetts (Bristol County) and is local in New Jersey (Atlantic, Cape May, Gloucester and Middlesex counties), Pennsylvania and Delaware (Sussex County), becoming frequent in the Atlantic States, south to central Florida (south to Highlands County), along the Gulf Coast to Texas (Hardin, Harris, Montgomery and Newton counties), west to central Tennessee (Blount, Coffee, Franklin, Grundy, Putnam and Van Buren counties) and Arkansas (Pulaski County).

CULTURAL NOTES: While best developed in the southern Coastal Plain, the Crested Fringed-orchid ascends to fairly high altitudes in North Carolina and follows the coast northward to southern Massachusetts. Accordingly, it may be considered as moderately hardy. It is, however, very difficult to cultivate, for it requires a moist sandy and peaty soil of intensely acid reaction. Only if garden conditions are such that sphagnum moss really thrives, can this orchid be expected to survive for long. (E. T. W.)

According to BROWN (1813), the Crested Fringed-orchid was first introduced into England in 1806 by JOHN FRASER.

11. **Habenaria dilatata** (Pursh) Hook., Exot. Fl. 2: t. 95. 1824. *Orchis dilatata* Pursh, Fl. Am. Sept. 2: 588. 1814. Type locality and collection: Labrador, *Colmaster*. (*Limnorchis dilatata* (Pursh) Rydb.; *L. foliosa* Rydb.; *L. graminifolia* Rydb.; *L. gracilis* Rydb., in part; *L. convallariaefolia* Rydb., in part; *L. leptoceratitis* Rydb., as to type specimen and description only; *Habenaria graminifolia* (Rydb.) Henry). PLATE 21

(The name, *dilatata,* is a Latin adjective meaning "widened," in allusion to the expanded lower portion of the lip.)

COMMON NAMES: Tall White Bog-orchid, Tall White Northern-orchid, Fragrant-orchid, Boreal Bog-orchid.

Plant usually strictly erect and tall, glabrous, 1.5-12 dm. tall, sometimes taller. Stem slender or stout, leafy. Leaves linear to lanceolate or occasionally oblanceolate, obtuse to shortly acuminate, sheathing the stem below, up to 30 cm. long and 5.5 cm. wide. Raceme laxly or densely many-flowered, cylindrical, up to 45 cm. long and 3.5 cm. in diameter. Floral bracts lanceolate, acuminate, usually incurved and exceeding the flowers. Flowers white or yellowish white or greenish white. Dorsal sepal ovate to elliptic, obtuse, sometimes minutely cucullate at the apex, erect and connivent with the petals to form a hood over the column, 3-nerved, 3-7 mm. long, 2.5-4 mm. wide near the base. Lateral sepals elliptic-lanceolate to narrowly lanceolate, broadly obtuse to acuminate, 3-nerved, spreading or reflexed, 4-9 mm. long, 1-3.5 mm. wide. Petals ovate-lanceolate to linear-lanceolate, falcate, obtuse to acuminate-attenuate, obliquely dilated at the base, 1- to 2-nerved, connivent with the dorsal sepal, 4-8.2 mm. long, 1.8-4 mm. wide at the base, sometimes lightly notched at the apex and cellular-papillose on the margins. Lip variable, rhombic-lanceolate to broadly lanceolate or with a suborbicular base and linear anterior part, usually but not always strongly dilated at the base, obtuse, sometimes minutely erose-ciliate on the margins below the middle, usually projecting outward, 5-10 mm. long, 2-5 mm. wide across the base. Spur cylindrical, about equaling the lip in length.

The usually white or occasionally yellowish white or greenish white flowers, provided with a rhombic-lanceolate lip which is conspicuously dilated at the base and tapers to the apex, are characteristics of this species. The spur is about as long as the lip which typically projects outward from the rest of the flower. The floral bracts are usually incurved against the rachis, causing the raceme to appear slender and wand-like in contrast to the raceme of *H. hyperborea* with its more or

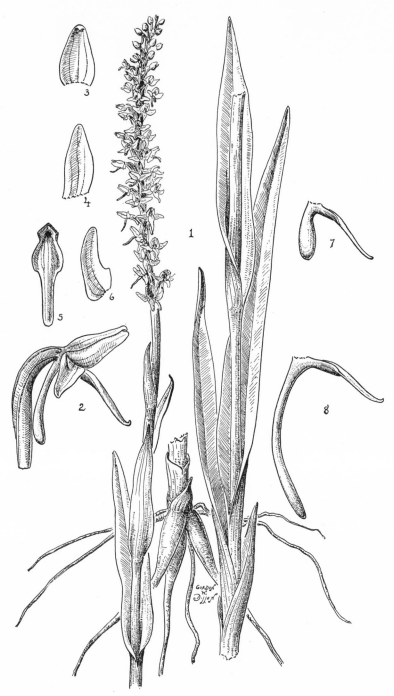

PLATE 21. — **Habenaria dilatata.** 1, plant, one half natural size. 2, flower, side view, three times natural size. 3, dorsal sepal, three times natural size. 4, lateral sepal, three times natural size. 5, lip, three times natural size. 6, petal, three times natural size.

Habenaria dilatata var. **albiflora.** 7, lip and spur, side view, three times natural size.

Habenaria dilatata var. **leucostachys.** 8, lip and spur, side view, three times natural size. *Drawn by Gordon W. Dillon.*

less spreading floral bracts. *Habenaria dilatata* is often associated with *H. hyperborea,* and there is little doubt that they freely hybridize. Some specimens of *H. dilatata* (collected in Washington) have lips which are extremely dilated at the base thus giving to the lip a three-lobed aspect. The flowers of the Tall White Bog-orchid are usually sweetly fragrant of clove or vanilla.

This species is nearly always found in moist situations in lowland or alpine meadows, swamps, bogs, marshes, coniferous forests, canyons, tidal and gravelly flats, sandy or gravelly beaches, on moist seepage slopes and in or along streams and springs, bordering lakes and rarely on dry slopes. It is found from near sea level in northern New England and the Maritime Provinces, up to 5,000 feet altitude in New Hampshire and British Columbia and 10,000 feet in Colorado, Idaho and Utah. The Tall White Bog-orchid flowers from April to September in various parts of its range.

GEOGRAPHICAL DISTRIBUTION: Greenland (Disco), Subarctic America, Newfoundland, Labrador, Ungava, Anticosti, Nova Scotia, New Brunswick, Prince Edward Island, Quebec, Ontario, west to British Columbia, Alaska and the Aleutian Islands; Maine, south to New Jersey, Pennsylvania, New York (south to Queens, Tompkins and Yates counties), Michigan (Eaton, Hillsdale, Keweenaw and Marquette counties), Wisconsin (Door and Milwaukee counties), Minnesota (Hennepin and Hubbard counties), South Dakota, Montana and Idaho, southwest to Colorado, Utah and New Mexico; also Washington, Oregon and California.

CULTURAL NOTES: A cool-climate plant, the Tall White Bog-orchid apparently survived glaciation close to the southern margin of the Pleistocene ice sheets. Then, as the ice melted, this species migrated well up into the subarctic portions of North America. On the eastern side of the continent, however, it failed to persist south of northernmost Pennsylvania and New Jersey. Farther west, however, forms differing to some extent from the eastern plant occupy swamp lands at high altitudes in the Rocky Mountains. It grows naturally in permanently moist humus-rich soil of neutral to moderately acid reaction, in sunny or but lightly shaded habitats. South of its native haunts or at lower altitudes than customary, *H. dilatata* is not at all easy to cultivate. Not only must a special effort be made to keep its soil moist and slightly acid, but also the temperature has to be maintained at a low level during the summer. Moreover, this species is very susceptible to attack by slugs and parasitic fungi. (E. T. W.)

12. **Habenaria dilatata** var. **albiflora** (Cham.) Correll, Leafl. West. Bot. 3:238. 1943. *Habenaria borealis* Cham. var. *albiflora* Cham., Linnaea 3:28. 1828. Type locality: Unalaska. (*Habenaria dilatatiformis* Rydb.; *Limnorchis dilatatiformis* Rydb.; *L. borealis* (Cham.) Rydb., exclude syn. in part.).
PLATE 21

(The name, *albiflora,* is a Latin term meaning "white-flowered," in allusion to the color of the flowers.)
COMMON NAME: None known.

This is a short-spurred variant which usually has a short, dense inflorescence of rather large flowers. However, it is represented in the Rocky Mountains by a plant (segregated by RYDBERG as *H. dilatatiformis*) which has a rather slender, lax raceme of smaller flowers. Some forms of typical *H. dilatata* approach var. *albiflora.* Such forms, however, have a slender, terete spur instead of the somewhat inflated, clavate spur characteristic of this variety.

This variety is commonly found on moist rocky slopes, in meadows, wet woods, bogs, marshes and along streams. It usually grows at high elevations in the Rocky Mountains where it occurs up to 12,000 feet altitude in Wyoming, 10,000 feet in Utah and Colorado and 5,000 feet in British Columbia. Variety *albiflora* flowers from June to September throughout its range.

GEOGRAPHICAL DISTRIBUTION: Colorado (Boulder, Gilpin, Grand and Larimer counties), Utah (Salt Lake and Summit counties), Wyoming (Albany, Teton and Yellowstone Park counties), Montana (Gallatin, Glacier, Meagher, Park and Teton counties), Idaho (Blaine, Boise and Nez Perces counties), Oregon (Baker County), Washington (Pierce County), Alberta, British Columbia and Alaska (Yakutat).

CULTURAL NOTES: See this section under the typical form.

13. **Habenaria dilatata** var. **leucostachys** (Lindl.) Ames, Orch., fasc. 4:71. 1910. *Platanthera leucostachys* Lindl., Gen. and Sp. Orch. Pl. 288. 1835. Type locality and collection: Coast of western North America, *Douglas. (Habenaria pedicellata* S. Wats.; *H. leucostachys* (Lindl.) S. Wats., excluding synonym *H. Thurberi; H. flagellans* S. Wats.; *Limnorchis leucostachys* (Lindl.) Rydb.; *L. leucostachys* var. *robusta* Rydb.; *Habenaria leptoceratitis* (Rydb.) Henry).   PLATE 21

(The name, *leucostachys,* is a combination of Greek words meaning "white spike," in allusion to the elongated inflorescence of white flowers.)

COMMON NAMES: White-flowered Bog-orchid, Sierra Rein-orchid.

This variety is identical with the typical form, except for the long spur which is 1 to 2 cm. long and varies from about one and one half times to more than twice as long as the lip. Although the lip is often narrower and longer than in typical *H. dilatata,* the shape is essentially the same in both. It is apparently confined to the western United States and Canada, although some northeastern specimens approach it very closely. There seems to be a rather definite delimitation in the length of the spur between var. *leucostachys* and the typical form and it corresponds to a similar relationship existing between *H. unalascensis* and its varieties. Variety *leucostachys* is often confused with *H. limosa* which it superficially resembles.

The habitat of var. *leucostachys* is similar to that of the typical form, but it is usually found at higher elevations. It is frequent in alpine meadows and about mountain springs from 2,000 feet altitude in Idaho and Montana, up to 11,000 feet in California and Nevada, and flowers from April to September in various parts of its range.

GEOGRAPHICAL DISTRIBUTION: Utah (Washington County and Mt. Ipabah), Nevada (northern half), California (common and widespread), Montana (western part), Idaho (western half), Oregon (widespread), Washington (Clallam, Columbia, Pierce, Snohomish and Thurston counties), British Columbia (Vancouver Island) and s. Alaska (*Anderson*).

CULTURAL NOTES: See this section under the typical form.

14. **Habenaria distans** Griseb., Cat. Pl. Cub. 270. 1866. Type locality and collection: Cuba, *Charles Wright 1481.*   PLATE 22

(The name, *distans,* is a Latin term meaning "when similar parts are not closely aggregated," doubtless referring to the few scattered flowers comprising the inflorescence.)

COMMON NAME: None known.

Plant slender, glabrous throughout, 1.4-3.3 dm. tall. Roots slender with bulbous swellings. Stem with basal leaves and clothed with bract-like leaves above. Leaves two to six, essentially basal, often forming a rosette, oblong-elliptic to rarely ovate or obovate, acute, abruptly diminishing into bracts above, 6-15 cm. long, 2-5 cm. wide. Raceme lax, composed of five to twenty-one scattered flowers, 4-13 cm. long. Floral bracts narrowly lanceolate, long-acuminate, 1-2 cm. long. Flowers greenish, with the slender pedicellate ovaries 1-1.5 cm. long. Dorsal sepal oblong-elliptic, obtuse to subacute, concave, 5-8 mm. long, 4-5 mm. wide. Lateral sepals somewhat reflexed and upcurved at the apex, obliquely elliptic to ovate-oblong, acute, 5-8 mm. long, 2-3 mm. wide at the widest point. Petals bipartite, the two divisions about equal in length, 6-8 mm. long; posterior division suberect, narrowly linear, falcate, about 1 mm. wide; anterior division filiform, usually slightly longer than the posterior division. Lip deeply tripartite; lateral divisions filiform, spreading, curved upward, 8-11 mm. long; middle division narrowly linear, pendent, 7-10 mm. long. Spur slender-clavate, recurved, about as long as the pedicellate ovary, 1.2-1.5 cm. long. Capsule ellipsoid, strongly ribbed, about 1.2 cm. long.

This species was collected for the first time in the United States in Lee County, Florida, in August 1878 by A. P. GARBER. Since then it has been very rarely

PLATE 22.—**Habenaria distans.** 1, plant, natural size. 2, flower, front view, two and one half times natural size. 3, petal, three times natural size. 4, pollen mass, highly magnified. *Redrawn from Blanche Ames by Gordon W. Dillon.*

seen. It is distinctive in that its leaves are essentially basal and commonly form a basal rosette.

Habenaria distans occurs in the southeastern United States only in Highland and Lee counties, Florida, where it presumably grows in low moist hammocks and flowers in August. In the American tropics, this species often grows up to 6,000 feet altitude, where it is found in shady damp forests and on moist grassy slopes. Under tropical conditions, the flowering season extends from July to October.

GEOGRAPHICAL DISTRIBUTION: Florida (Highlands and Lee counties); also Mexico, Guatemala, Costa Rica, Cuba, Jamaica, Santo Domingo, Haiti and Puerto Rico.

CULTURAL NOTES: This tropical and subtropical species is believed to grow in hammocks and low pinelands in southern Florida where the soil is usually intensely acid. It could perhaps be cultivated in far-southern gardens if they can be kept at a high degree of acidity. (E. T. W.)

15. **Habenaria flava** (L.) R. Br. ex Spreng., Syst. Veg. 3: 691. 1826. *Orchis flava* L., Sp. Pl., ed. 1, 2:942. 1753. Type locality: Virginia. (*Perularia bidentata* (Ell.) Small; *P. scutellata* (Nutt.) Small; *P. flava* (L.) Schltr., as to name only). PLATE 23

(The name, *flava*, is a Latin adjective meaning "yellow," and refers to the typically yellow-green flowers of this species.)

COMMON NAME: Southern Rein-orchid.

Plant 1.5-6 dm. tall; stem slender, two or occasionally three leaves below, long-bracted above. Leaves usually two, distant, oblong-elliptic to narrowly lanceolate, subobtuse to acuminate and attenuate, sheathing the stem at the base, 7-20 cm. long, 1.2-5 cm. wide. Raceme usually short-bracted, laxly flowered, cylindrical, 6-20 cm. long, 1.2-2 cm. in diameter. Floral bracts narrowly lanceolate, acuminate, usually equaling or shorter than the flowers. Sepals ovate-oblong to rhombic-ovate or suborbicular, subobtuse to rounded at the more or less crenulate apex, 2-5.5 mm. long, 1.5-2.5 mm. wide. Petals obliquely oblong to orbicular, rounded to obtuse at the more or less crenulate apex, 2-5 mm. long, 1.5-4 mm. wide. Lip ovate to suborbicular or suborbicular-quadrate, rarely oblong, with or sometimes without a tooth on each side at the base (occasionally the lateral teeth prominent), more or less crenulate on the margins, provided in the middle near the base with a tubercle, 2.2-6 mm. long, 2-5 mm. wide across the basal teeth or lobules, usually almost as wide as long. Spur cylindrical and slender or slender-clavellate, 4-9 mm. long. Capsule obliquely ellipsoid, about 8 mm. long.

The Southern Rein-orchid is an inconspicuous species, especially when it grows with tall weedy herbaceous plants. However, in Tangipahoa Parish, Louisiana, I have seen hundreds of plants which comprised the chief herbaceous element in an open-wooded floodplain forest.

The flowers of a collection from McCreary County, Kentucky, have a lip which is essentially entire. In a collection from Shannon County, Missouri, the flowers have rather large rhombic-ovate petals and a prominent lobule (instead of a tooth) on each side of the lip, the lobules are somewhat crenate and the tubercle on the surface of the lip extremely elongated and conspicuous. These two specimens represent extreme conditions of *H. flava*.

This species is primarily a plant of the Atlantic Coastal Plain and Gulf Coast, where it commonly occurs in open woods in alluvial areas of streams and in wet soil of thickets, meadows and swales. It is also found in sphagnum bogs, swamps, flatwoods, marshes, savannahs, prairies and in gravelly or muddy soil on the margin of lakes and streams. In Nova Scotia, it grows on peaty and cobbly beaches. Although the Southern Rein-orchid usually grows at low elevations, it is found at 1,000 feet altitude in De Kalb County, Georgia, and flowers from March to the last of September in various parts of its range.

GEOGRAPHICAL DISTRIBUTION: Central Florida (Orange and Seminole counties), along the Atlantic Coast to Maryland, with a disjunct station in Nova Scotia (Yarmouth County), along the Gulf Coast and Piedmont Plateau to Texas (Harris, Harrison and Upshur counties), on the Cumberland Plateau in Tennessee and Kentucky, and in the Mississippi drainage basin in Arkansas, Tennessee (Chester County), Missouri (St. Louis County), Illinois and Indiana (Posey County).

PLATE 23.—**Habenaria flava.** 1, plant, one half natural size. 2, flower, front view, spread open, five times natural size. 3, flower, side view, five times natural size. 4, lip, an entire toothless form, five times natural size.

Habenaria flava var. **herbiola.** 5, inflorescence, one half natural size. 6, flower, front view, five times natural size. 7, lip, an unusual subentire form, five times natural size. *Drawn by Gordon W. Dillon.*

CULTURAL NOTES: *Habenaria flava* is more of a shade-lover than its var. *herbiola*. It is most often found in mucky soil in swamplands where the soil-reaction ranges from neutral to subacid. This is the easier of the two forms to cultivate, for it can withstand higher summer temperatures and is fairly resistant to fungi and other pests. In cold regions, however, it needs winter protection. (E. T. W.)

16. **Habenaria flava** var. **herbiola** (R. Br.) Ames & Correll, Bot. Mus. Leafl. Harvard Univ. 11:61. 1943. *Habenaria herbiola* R. Br. in Ait., Hort. Kew., ed. 2, 5:193. 1813. Type locality: North America. (*Perularia flava* Farwell; *Habenaria flava* var. *virescens* Fernald, as to plant, not as to name). PLATE 23

(The name, *herbiola,* is a Latin term meaning "little plant," probably selected as a comparative name.)

COMMON NAMES: Tubercled Rein-orchid, Gypsy Spike.

Variety *herbiola,* a more northern variant, is distinguished from the typical form of the species by being more robust and by the usually broader leaves (which may be as many as five) extending farther up the stem. The raceme is also more compact,with the longer floral bracts often much exceeding the flowers. The characteristically oblong-quadrate, instead of ovate to suborbicular, lip of var. *herbiola* which is longer than wide is a distinctive feature by which to separate these two entities.

It is of interest to note that a collection by EZRA BRAINERD from Franklin County, Vermont, has flowers whose lip is narrowly linear-oblong and entire or with only an incipient tooth on one or both sides at the base. I consider this to be an aberrant form.

Variety *herbiola* is found in the same kind of habitat as the typical form. However, it is sometimes found in dry sterile soil, dry sedge marshes and salt meadows (in New York). It occurs from near sea level on Staten Island, New York, up to 2,100 feet altitude in Maryland and over 3,000 feet in the mountains of North Carolina. Variety *herbiola* flowers from May to August.

GEOGRAPHICAL DISTRIBUTION: Nova Scotia, New Brunswick, Quebec and Ontario, through New England, New York and Pennsylvania to Maryland (Garrett County), south along the Allegheny Mountains through West Virginia (Wayne County) and Virginia (Grayson County) to North Carolina (Buncombe County) and Tennessee, west through Ohio, Michigan, Indiana, Illinois and Wisconsin to Minnesota (Chisago and Goodhue counties) and Missouri (St. Louis County).

CULTURAL NOTES: Variety *herbiola* evidently survived glaciation in the Appalachians and, as the ice melted, the orchid spread northward and outward as far as Minnesota to the West and to Nova Scotia in the East. It is a denizen of moist meadowlands where the soil is often sandy, rich in humus and neutral to subacid in reaction. Its cultivation is rather difficult, because, although obviously winter-hardy, its soil has to be kept cool in the summer in the more southern regions. Moreover, it is highly susceptible to attack by soil fungi. (E. T. W.)

According to BROWN (1813), var. *herbiola* was cultivated in England before 1789 by JOHN FOTHERGILL.

17. **Habenaria Hookeri** Torr. ex A. Gray, Ann. Lyc. Nat. Hist. N. Y. 3 (first impression):228. 1835. Type locality: New York. (*Platanthera Hookeri* (Torr. ex A. Gray) Lindl.; *Habenaria Hookeri* var. *oblongifolia* (Paine) A. Gray; *Lysias Hookeriana* (Torr. ex A. Gray) Rydb.; *Habenaria oblongifolia* (Paine) Niles). PLATE 24

(The name, *Hookeri,* is in honor of WILLIAM JACKSON HOOKER (1785-1865), noted English botanist whose name is identified with North American botany by his Flora Boreali-Americana and other works.)

COMMON NAME: Hooker's Orchid, Hooker's Round-leaved Rein-orchid.

Plant erect, scapose, glabrous throughout, 1.8-4 dm. tall, provided with two basal leaves. Roots fusiform-elongate, fleshy. Stem naked or very rarely provided with a solitary bract about the middle. Leaves two (rarely three) at the base of the stem, subopposite, orbicular

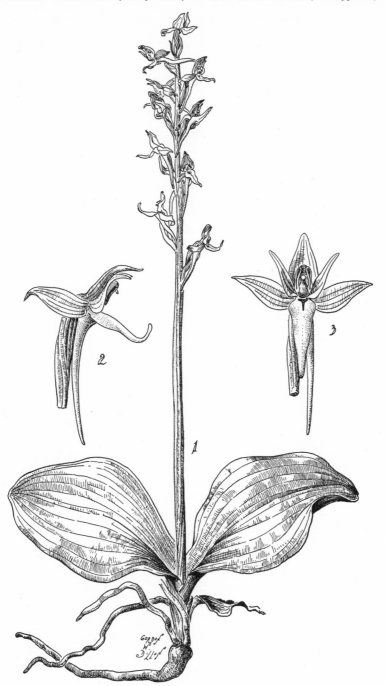

PLATE 24.— **Habenaria Hookeri.** 1, plant, one half natural size. 2, flower, side view, twice natural size. 3, flower, front view, spread open, twice natural size. *Drawn by Gordon W. Dillon.*

to suborbicular-obovate or rarely broadly elliptic, spreading flat on the ground, fleshy, shining, 6.5-15 cm. long, 4-12 cm. wide. Raceme laxly few- to many-flowered, 10-25 cm. long, 2.5-4 cm. in diameter. Floral bracts lanceolate, acuminate, shorter than the flowers, up to

2 cm. long and 6 mm. wide. Flowers yellowish green, more or less erect. Dorsal sepal triangular-ovate to elliptic-lanceolate, usually tapering to the obtuse apex, concave, 3-nerved, erect and connivent with the petals to form a hood over the column, 7-11 mm. long, 3-5 mm. wide near the base. Lateral sepals strongly reflexed, elliptic-lanceolate, oblique, acuminate or tapering to the acute somewhat conduplicate apex, 3-nerved, concave below, 8.5-13 mm. long, 3-4 mm. wide below the middle. Petals linear-lanceolate to subulate, long-attenuate at the apex, falcate, somewhat obliquely dilated and auriculate at the base, 1-nerved, connivent with the dorsal sepal, 7-9 mm. long, 1.5-2 mm. wide at the base. Lip fleshy, lanceolate to narrowly triangular-lanceolate, acuminate or tapering to the acute apex, strongly upcurved, with the lateral margins somewhat reflexed, 8-13 mm. long, 3-4 mm. wide at the base. Spur tapering uniformly from a broad base to a sharp point, directed downward or outward, 1.5-2.5 cm. long. Column large, with a small tubercle in the middle of the connective, concave, about 4 mm. long and wide. Capsule erect, obliquely ellipsoid, about 1.2 cm. long.

The greenish flowers of this species have been fancifully compared to a gargoyle—a most appropriate analogy. The arcuate dorsal sepal forms a hood above the long upcurved lip which protrudes like an abnormally elongated chin, giving to the flowers a grotesque appearance.

The tapering spur and usually bractless stem readily separate Hooker's Orchid from *H. orbiculata* which it superficially resembles.

This species is a characteristic woodland orchid. It is found in rich damp or dry coniferous or hardwood forests and occasionally swamplands. Hooker's Orchid occurs up to 1,000 feet altitude in Vermont, and flowers from May to August.

GEOGRAPHICAL DISTRIBUTION: St. Pierre Island, Nova Scotia, New Brunswick, Quebec and Ontario, south through Maine (found in every county), New Hampshire, Vermont, Massachusetts, Rhode Island, Connecticut (found in every county), New York, New Jersey (Morris County), Pennsylvania (south to Blair and Huntingdon counties), Ohio, Michigan, Wisconsin, Minnesota (Goodhue and Hubbard counties) and Iowa (Fayette County).

CULTURAL NOTES: Like many other cool-climate species, this broad-leaved orchid survived Pleistocene glaciation in the Appalachians and, after the ice melted, the orchid spread northwestward to Minnesota and northeastward to Nova Scotia. It grows most frequently in open coniferous or sugar-maple woods where the soil may become dry but is always fairly cool. The soil-reaction is usually subacid or sometimes mediacid. Cultivation of this orchid outside of its native haunts is a matter of considerable difficulty. The large leaves are very sensitive to environmental conditions, withering if allowed to get too dry and rotting if kept unduly moist. If the wild garden includes a northfacing hillside underlain by acid gravel or sand where conifer needles have accumulated to some depth, it may perhaps grow for a time in captivity. (E. T. W.)

This species was first introduced into the British Isles from Canada in 1823 by the Countess of Dalhousie. It flowered at the Glasgow Botanic Garden the following year.

18. **Habenaria hyperborea** (L.) R. Br. in Ait., Hort. Kew., ed. 2, 5: 193. 1813. *Orchis hyperborea* L., Man. Pl. 121. 1767. Type locality and collection: Iceland, *Koenig*. (*Habenaria huronensis* (Nutt.) Spreng.; *H. borealis* Cham.; *H. borealis* var. *viridiflora* Cham.; *Limnorchis hyperborea* (L.) Rydb.; *L. brachypetala* Rydb., in part; *L. viridiflora* (Cham.) Rydb.; *L. borealis* (Cham.) Rydb., exclude syn. in part; *Platanthera hyperborea* var. *dilatatoides* Hult.; *Habenaria septentrionalis* Tidestrom; *H. viridiflora* (Cham.) Henry). PLATE 25

(The name, *hyperborea*, is a Greek term meaning "beyond the north," in allusion to the far northern distribution of this species, one of the few orchids found within the Arctic Circle.)

COMMON NAMES: Tall Northern Green-orchid, Tall Leafy Green-orchid, Green-flowered Bog-orchid.

Plant erect, slender or stout, glabrous throughout, 1.5-10 dm. tall. Roots tuberous, fusiform, elongated, 5-9 mm. thick. Stem leafy throughout or only at the base. Leaves several, cauline

PLATE 25.— **Habenaria hyperborea.** 1, plant, natural size. 2, flower and floral bract, side view, twice natural size. 3, lip and spur, side view, twice natural size. 4, lip, from above, twice natural size. 5, dorsal sepal, twice natural size. 6, lateral sepal, twice natural size. 7, petal, twice natural size. *Drawn by Blanche Ames.*

or produced in a cluster near or at the base of the stem, variable, linear, oblong-elliptic, oblanceolate or linear-lanceolate, obtuse to acuminate, reduced above to bracts, 4.5-30 cm. long, 0.8-4.5 cm. wide at the widest part. Raceme spicate, extremely variable in habit, cylindrical to rarely subsecund, densely or laxly few- (rarely 3-) to many-flowered, short and stout to elongated and slender, 3-25 cm. long, 1-2.5 cm. in diameter. Floral bracts lanceolate to linear-lanceolate, acuminate, suberect to spreading, usually cellular-papillose on the margins, the lowermost bracts sometimes up to 3 cm. long and greatly exceeding the flowers. Flowers small, variable in size, often fragrant, green or yellowish green, sometimes marked or suffused with brownish purple, congested or remotely spaced on the rachis. Dorsal sepal suborbicular-ovate to ovate-elliptic, rounded to obtuse and occasionally minutely cucullate at the apex, concave, erect and connivent with the petals to form a hood over the column, 3-nerved, 3-7 mm. long, 1.3-4 mm. wide below the middle. Lateral sepals ovate to ovate-lanceolate or elliptic-lanceolate, obtuse to subacute or sometimes minutely cucullate at the apex, oblique, spreading or strongly reflexed, 3-nerved, 3-9 mm. long, 1-3.5 mm. wide below the middle. Petals usually fleshy, ovate-lanceolate to lanceolate, falcate, acute to acuminate, obliquely dilated at the base, erect and connivent with the dorsal sepal, 1- to 2-nerved, concave at the base, occasionally tinged or marked with brownish purple, more or less cellular-papillose on the margins, 3-7 mm. long, 1-3 mm. wide at the base. Lip fleshy, lanceolate to sublinear, not conspicuously dilated at the base, obtuse to acute at the tapering apex, reflexed or curved upward, 3- to 5-nerved, 3-9 mm. long, 1.5-2.5 mm. wide below the middle. Spur cylindrical, slender to somewhat clavate, 2.5-7.5 mm. long, usually shorter than the lip or at most only a little longer than the lip, occasionally only one-third as long as the lip. Column broad, thick, 1.5-3.5 mm. long. Capsule erect, obliquely ellipsoid, suberect, up to 1.5 cm. long.

In typical material of *H. hyperborea* the lip is lanceolate and not conspicuously dilated at the base. The flowers are greenish or yellowish green, rarely whitish green, and are usually in a rather dense, cylindrical, spicate raceme. The lanceolate lip often passes gradually into forms with a linear or linear-elliptic lip. The spur is commonly shorter (or occasionally only slightly longer) than the lip which is usually upcurved or projecting forward.

The more northern and northwestern plants are often small and have a rather compact, short raceme, whereas the more southern and eastern plants are usually tall and have a slender, elongated raceme. However, the flowers of this species are remarkably constant throughout the area of its distribution. Some of the specimens found in Alaska, originally described as *Habenaria borealis,* and in the Rocky Mountains have larger flowers and the spur is shorter and more clavate than in typical *H. hyperborea.* The Rocky Mountain and western form, segregated as *Limnorchis viridiflora* by RYDBERG, approaches the form found in the Great Lakes region and New England, segregated as *Orchis* [*Habenaria*] *huronensis* by NUTTALL. Both of these forms differ somewhat from the type in their characteristically lax, few-flowered inflorescence. Some forms occur which apparently represent an intermediate condition between this species and *H. saccata* or *H. dilatata.* Many of the southwestern Rocky Mountain plants grade almost imperceptibly into *H. sparsiflora* and its varieties. *Habenaria hyperborea* is doubtless the most perplexing species of *Habenaria* within our range and it is here treated as an extremely polymorphic species as to its general aspect.

POLUNIN (1943) noted that when this species grows with *H. albida* var. *straminea* in Greenland, which is often the case, there occur sterile leafy plants which may be hybrids between the two.

I have seen some plants with teratological flowers from Bruce Peninsular, Ontario and Laramie County, Wyoming, wherein some of the flowers had two lips and two spurs. The lips were normally developed but the spurs were abortive and obsolescent. Another plant from Larimer County, Colorado had a monstrous flower which had three lips, one normal spur and two abortive spurs, three columns and a number of sepals and petals. The rest of the flowers in the raceme appeared to be normally developed.

When occurring as a small few-flowered form in damp New England woods, this orchid is very inconspicuous and only the most persistent search will enable one to observe it. On the other hand, I have seen it in willow thickets on alluvial deposits along the Sikanni Chief River in northern British Columbia where it is so abundant that it is one of the dominant herbaceous plants.

This species is commonly found in moist or wet soil in meadows, turf mats, bogs, thickets, muskegs, swamps, coniferous or mixed forests, canyons, marshes, on open slopes and cliffs, along streams and on gravel bars along rivers and lakes. It grows at high elevations in the Rocky Mountains, where it occurs up to 12,500 feet altitude in Colorado, 9,000 feet in California, Utah and New Mexico and 6,000 feet in British Columbia and Idaho. It is found at 3,000 feet in Vermont, 1,500 feet in Alaska and as low as 500 feet on Kodiak Island in the Aleutian Islands. The Tall Northern Green-orchid flowers from June to September in various parts of its range.

GEOGRAPHICAL DISTRIBUTION: Greenland (Disco, Godhavn), Newfoundland, Labrador, Anticosti, Nova Scotia, New Brunswick, Prince Edward Island, Quebec and Ontario, west to British Columbia, Alaska and the Aleutian Islands; New England, New York, Pennsylvania, through the Lake States to Minnesota, west and southwest to South Dakota, Nebraska, Colorado, New Mexico, Arizona, California, Oregon and Washington; also Iceland, and Asia (*fide Hultén*).

CULTURAL NOTES: The range and temperature relations of the Tall Northern Green-orchid are much like those of its close relative *H. dilatata*. There are, however, slight environmental differences: *H. hyperborea* tolerates more shade and may grow not only in acid soil but even in slightly calcareous, circumneutral soil. This should result in its being easier to cultivate, but its requirements of permanently moist cool conditions must be satisfied, and parasites to which it is susceptible must be kept away. (E. T. W.)

According to BROWN (1813), the Tall Northern Green-orchid was first introduced into England in 1805 by CHARLES GREVILLE.

19. **Habenaria integra** (Nutt.) Spreng., Syst. Veg. 3: 689. 1826. *Orchis integra* Nutt., Gen. N. Am. Pl. 2: 188. 1818. Type locality: In the swamps of New Jersey. (*Platanthera integra* (Nutt.) Gray; *Gymnadeniopsis integra* (Nutt.) Rydb.).　　　　　　　　　　　　　　　　PLATE 26

(The name, *integra,* is a Latin adjective meaning "entire," in reference to the nearly entire, unfringed margin of the lip.)

COMMON NAMES: Yellow Fringeless-orchid, Small Southern Yellow-orchid, Golden Frog-arrow.

Plant glabrous, with several leaves below and bracted above, 3-6.2 dm. tall. Roots fleshy, tuberous, swollen near the base of the stem. Stem angled. Leaves oblong-lanceolate to narrowly lanceolate, acuminate, with the lower part sheathing the stem, 10-19 cm. long, 1-3 cm. or more wide. Raceme densely many-flowered, cylindrical, 2-10.5 cm. long, 2-3 cm. in diameter. Floral bracts narrowly lanceolate, acuminate, 1-1.7 cm. long. Flowers light lemon-orange to dull orange, with the stout pedicellate ovaries 5-10 mm. long. Dorsal sepal suborbicular to orbicular, rarely toothed at the rounded apex, concave, 3-4 mm. long, 2-3 mm. wide. Lateral sepals ovate-orbicular, subobtuse, oblique, 4-5 mm. long, 3-4 mm. wide. Petals narrowly oblong, obtuse, 3-4 mm. long, about 2 mm. wide. Lip ovate-elliptic to obovate, obtuse to acute, crenulate to rarely entire on the margins, 4-5 mm. long, 3-4 mm. wide. Spur descending, tapering from a thickened base, about 5 mm. long.

The occurrence of this typically southern Coastal Plain species in the mountains of North Carolina and the New Jersey pine barrens, both localities being apparently disjunct stations, is most unusual. The pine barrens of New Jersey, an essentially undisturbed area of alternating pine forests and sphagnous cedar swamps, is also the haven of the typically southern *H. cristata* and *H. nivea* as well as about twenty other species of orchids.

This species is found in decidedly acid soils of swamps, in boggy depressions in savannahs and prairies, low moist sandy pine barrens, swampy meadows and wet sandy soil of low flatwoods. Although it is chiefly limited to the Coastal Plain and Gulf Coast, the Small Southern Yellow-orchid occurs up to 3,000 feet altitude in North Carolina and 2,500 feet on the Cumberland Plateau in Tennessee. It flowers from July to September.

GEOGRAPHICAL DISTRIBUTION: Occurring spottily along the Atlantic Seaboard from New Jersey (Burlington and Ocean counties) to north-central Florida (south to Orange County),

PLATE 26.—**Habenaria integra.** 1, plant, one half natural size. 2, flower, front view, spread open, five times natural size. 3, flower, side view, five times natural size. *Drawn by Gordon W. Dillon.*

along the Gulf Coast to Texas (*T. Drummond 406*); also in east-central Tennessee (Coffee, Davidson, Franklin, Roane and Sumner counties) and in the mountains (Cherokee and Henderson counties) and Piedmont Plateau (Forsyth and Rowan counties) of North Carolina.

CULTURAL NOTES: While it can stand all degrees of summer heat, the Golden Frog-arrow is only moderately winter-hardy. Its requisite soil is permanently moist, sandy, rich in humus, and intensely acid in reaction. It could perhaps be cultivated in a place sufficiently moist and acid enough for sphagnum moss to thrive, but slugs will have to be kept at a distance. (E. T. W.)

20. **Habenaria lacera** (Michx.) Lodd., Bot. Cab. 3: pl. 229. 1818. *Orchis lacera* Michx., Fl. Bor.-am. 2: 156. 1803. Type locality: Carolina. (*Blephariglottis lacera* (Michx.) Farwell; *Habenaria lacera* var. *terra-novae* Fernald). PLATE 27

(The name, *lacera*, is a Latin adjective meaning "torn," referring to the deeply and irregularly fringed lip.)

COMMON NAMES: Ragged Fringed-orchid, Ragged Orchid, Green Fringed-orchid.

Plant rather stout, glabrous, 2.5-7.5 dm. tall, often propagated by means of root-shoots. Roots slender, fleshy, from thickened tuberoids. Stem somewhat ribbed, leafy below, bracted above. Leaves rather rigid, erect, linear-oblong to oblong-obovate or linear-lanceolate, with the basal part sheathing the stem, 7-21 cm. long, 1.5-5 cm. wide. Raceme loosely or densely flowered, 3-26 cm. long, 3-4.5 cm. in diameter. Floral bracts usually equaling the arcuate pedicellate ovaries, rarely exceeding the flowers, narrowly lanceolate to linear-lanceolate, acuminate, 1-4 cm. long. Flowers pale yellowish green or whitish green, with rather stout arcuate pedicellate ovaries which are 1.5-2 cm. long. Dorsal sepal ovate to elliptic, obtuse, concave, 4-5 mm. long, 3-4 mm. wide. Lateral sepals obliquely ovate, obtuse, 4-6 mm. long, about 3 mm. wide. petals linear-oblong to narrowly oblong-spatulate, entire or rarely slightly toothed at the truncate or rounded (rarely retuse) apex, somewhat oblique, 5-7 mm. long, mostly less than 2 mm. wide. Lip deeply tripartite, 1-1.6 cm. long, 1.3-1.7 cm. wide across the lateral divisions; lateral divisions deeply cut (usually to near the base) into three lobes, with the lobes again subdivided; middle division slender, clavate to narrowly cuneate or linear-spatulate, somewhat spreading above into irregular slender or coarse fringes, rarely erose to short-fringed at the apex, often laciniate halfway or more to the base. Spur curved, slender or clavellate, as long as or longer than the pedicellate ovary, 1-2.3 cm. long. Capsule ellipsoid, erect, about 1.5 cm. long.

According to FERNALD (1926), *H. lacera* is represented in Newfoundland only by his var. *terra-novae*, a plant which I consider to be only a dwarf form of this species, with flowers described as " . . . variously colored, from cream-white to crimson: . . . " Whether or not one considers these Newfoundland plants to be referable to typical *H. lacera* or to Fernald's var. *terra-novae*, there is no doubt in my mind that they hybridize with the purple fringed-orchids to produce a hybrid population referable to × *H. Andrewsii*.

The Ragged Fringed-orchid is perhaps the most frequent *Habenaria* found in the northeastern states and adjacent Canada.

This species usually grows in open sedge swamps and marshes, bogs, meadows and glades of open woods, swampy woods and wet or occasionally dry open fields and prairies, and in thickets. It is sometimes found in dry woods, on boggy sandy borders of lakes, in cranberry bogs and brackish marshes along the coast in New England and the Maritime Provinces, and in serpentine meadows in Pennsylvania. The Ragged Fringed-orchid occurs from near sea level in the northeastern states and Canada, up to 500 feet altitude in Vermont, 1,000 feet in De Kalb County, Georgia, and 3,600 feet in North Carolina and Virginia. It flowers from May (in Alabama and Arkansas) to August in the North.

GEOGRAPHICAL DISTRIBUTION: Newfoundland (Mary Ann Lake, Junction Brook), Miquelon Island, Nova Scotia, Prince Edward Island, New Brunswick and Ontario (Wellington County), through New England, New York, New Jersey and Pennsylvania, south to South Carolina (Berkeley and Oconee counties), Georgia (De Kalb, Floyd and McDuffie counties), Alabama (Autauga, Blount and Lee counties) and Mississippi (Panola County), through Tennessee (Blount and Rhea counties) and Arkansas (Drew and Pope counties), west to east Texas (Bowie County) (none seen from Louisiana), Oklahoma (Mayes County, *fide Waterfall*), Missouri (St. Louis County), Illinois (De Kalb and Ogle counties), Wisconsin (Juneau,

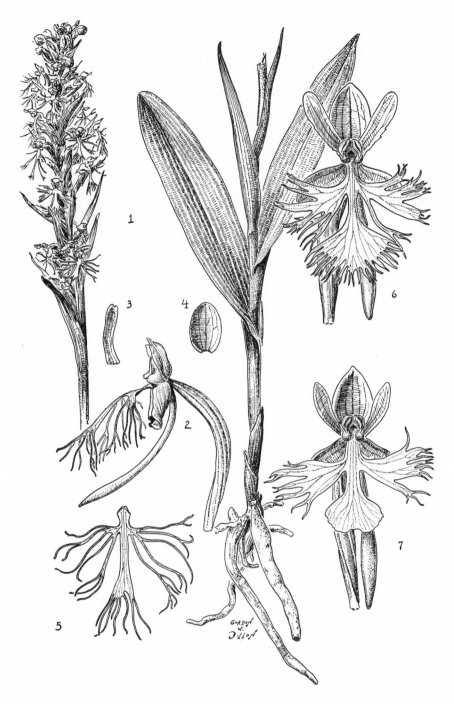

PLATE 27.—**Habenaria lacera.** 1, plant, one half natural size. 2, flower, side view, twice natural size. 3, petal, twice natural size. 4, dorsal sepal, twice natural size. 5, lip, from above, twice natural size.

✕ **Habenaria Andrewsii.** 6 and 7, flowers, front view, twice natural size. *Drawn by Gordon W. Dillon.*

Marinette, Polk and Milwaukee counties), Minnesota (Anoka and Chisago counties) and Manitoba (*fide Wherry*).

CULTURAL NOTES: The Ragged Fringed-orchid is a widespread plant, ranging from the uplands of Arkansas and Georgia to Newfoundland and Manitoba, so it is evidently indifferent to temperature conditions. As to moisture it is not especially particular, thriving alike in wet sphagnum bogs and in clayey meadows which may become dry for several months in summer. It does, however, prefer rather acid soil-reactions (mediacid to subacid). The adaptability indicated by these relations corresponds to its being somewhat more readily cultivated than are most species in the genus. It should be planted in sterile soil in a place where the moisture supply is ample and the acidity capable of being maintained at a fairly high level. In the wild state it may grow in full sun as well as in fairly dense shade, but in cultivation it favors the latter condition. The only restriction is that there must be no breeding grounds for slugs, since, attracted by its delicate fragrance, they rapidly destroy the plants. (E. T. W.)

This species was first cultivated in England by Conrad Loddiges & Sons about 1832.

21. **Habenaria leucophaea** (Nutt.) A. Gray, Man. Bot. North. U. S., ed. 5: 502. 1867. *Orchis leucophaea* Nutt., Trans. Am. Phil. Soc. n.s. 5: 161. 1834. Type locality: In moist prairies near Kiamesha, Red River. (*Blephariglottis leucophaea* (Nutt.) Farwell). PLATE 28

(The name, *leucophaea*, is a Greek derivative meaning "white-looking" or "whitish," referring to the color of the raceme of flowers.)

COMMON NAME: Prairie White-fringed-orchid.

Plant usually large and stout, glabrous throughout, rarely slender, 2-12 dm. tall. Roots coarse, fleshy, thickened near the base of the stem. Stem angled, leafy. Leaves oblong-elliptic to lanceolate, sheathing the stem below, 7-20 cm. long, 1-4 cm. wide. Raceme large, loosely flowered, 5-22 cm. long, 4-10 cm. in diameter. Floral bracts lanceolate, long-acuminate, 1.5-4 cm. long, 4-7 mm. wide below the middle. Flowers white, slightly tinged with green or cream-color, with long recurved pedicellate ovaries which are 2-3 cm. long. Sepals and petals overlapping and directed forward to form a conspicuous hood over the column. Dorsal sepal ovate to oblong-elliptic, conduplicate-concave, rarely slightly toothed at the apex, 7-16 mm. long, 5-8 mm. wide. Lateral sepals somewhat obliquely ovate to orbicular-ovate, usually narrowed toward the apex, acute to obtuse, 7-16 mm. long, 5-10 mm. wide. Petals narrowly cuneate to flabelliform, broadly rounded to truncate at the apex, eroded or coarsely toothed along the apical margin, 7-17 mm. long, 4-12 mm. wide near the apex. Lip deeply tripartite, 1.4-3.5 cm. long, 1.5-3.5 cm. wide across the lateral divisions, with the divisions coarsely fringed halfway to the base or more; lateral divisions broadly cuneate, 6-15 mm. wide near the apex; middle division narrowly cuneate to flabellate, rarely shallowly eroded or toothed, 1-2 cm. wide near the apex. Spur prominently curved and clavate, usually much longer than the pedicellate ovary, 2-5.5 cm. long.

Although this handsome plant bears the name Prairie White-fringed-orchid, in reference to its typical habitat, it attains its most luxuriant growth in the open sphagnum bogs of the Lake States. Specimens have been found with peloric flowers in which no spur is developed and the floral segments are regular or nearly so. The flowers of this species are said to be very sweet-scented after sundown — a characteristic not uncommon in many orchids, especially those found in the tropics.

This species is a characteristic prairie orchid. While commonly found in wet depressions in prairies, mossy bogs, meadows and fields, it sometimes grows on stony shores or on herb mats and in sphagnum-sedge associations around lakes. It also occurs in open coniferous forests where bog conditions exist. The Prairie White-fringed-orchid does not grow at high elevations, and flowers from the first of May (in Kansas) to August (in Iowa).

GEOGRAPHICAL DISTRIBUTION: Nova Scotia, Ontario (Bruce, Essex, Kent and Lambton counties), Maine (Aroostook County) and New York (Onondaga, Oswego, Wayne and

PLATE 28.—**Habenaria leucophaea.** 1, plant, one half natural size. 2, flower, one and one half times natural size. 3, dorsal sepal, twice natural size. 4, petal, twice natural size. 5, lateral sepal, twice natural size. 6, column, with base of spur and upper part of ovary, side view, with the floral segments removed, two and one half times natural size. 7, column, front-ventral view, two and one half times natural size. *Drawn by Gordon W. Dillon.*

Yates counties), through Michigan, Ohio, Indiana, Illinois, Missouri (Jackson County) and Arkansas (White County) to Louisiana (*J. Hale*), Kansas (Neosho, Riley and Shawnee counties), Nebraska (Kearney, Lancaster, Merrick and Otoe counties), South Dakota (Minnehaha County), North Dakota (Cass County) and Minnesota (Martin County).

CULTURAL NOTES: The Prairie White-fringed-orchid grows chiefly in the Mississippi Valley, from Louisiana north to Minnesota, though it also extends locally eastward down the St. Lawrence River to Nova Scotia and northern Maine. It is an occupant of moist spots in the prairie grasslands in open sun or partial shade of shrubs. The soil is usually rich in dark-colored humus and is circumneutral in reaction; and, although at times surrounded by sphagnum, its roots reach a zone of lower acidity below. There are reports of its having been cultivated with some degree of success in wild gardens in its native region, but it could scarcely be expected to thrive in more eastern gardens where the climate is moister and pests correspondingly more active. (E. T. W.)

22. **Habenaria limosa** (Lindl.) Hemsl. in Godm. & Salvin, Biol. Centr.-Am., Bot. 3: 305. 1884. *Platanthera limosa* Lindl., Ann. & Mag. Nat. Hist. 4: 381. 1840. Type locality and collection: Mexico, in swamps, Anganguco, near Asoleadero, September, *Hartweg*. (*Habenaria Thurberi* A. Gray; *Limnorchis Thurberi* (A. Gray) Rydb., as to name only; *L. arizonica* Rydb.).

PLATE 29

(The name, *limosa*, is a Latin adjective meaning "muddy" or "miry," doubtless referring to the habitat where this species was first found.)

COMMON NAME: Thurber's Bog-orchid.

Plant slender or stout, glabrous throughout, 3-16.5 dm. tall. Roots fibrous, from dilated tuberous bases. Stem leafy, provided at the base with tubular sheaths. Leaves lanceolate, acuminate, suberect, 9-28 cm. long, 1.2-3.5 cm. wide. Raceme cylindrical, laxly or densely flowered, with the flowers distant or approximate to compact, elongated, 6-45 cm. long, 1-2.5 cm. in diameter. Floral bracts narrowly lanceolate, the lowermost up to 4 cm. long and greatly exceeding the flowers. Flowers small, green, fragrant. Dorsal sepal ovate-oblong to elliptic, obtuse, concave, connivent with the petals to form a hood over the column, 3-nerved, 3-6 mm. long, 2-3 mm. wide below the middle. Lateral sepals strongly reflexed, ovate-lanceolate to linear-elliptic, oblique, obtuse to subacute, 3-nerved, 4-8 mm. long, 1.8-2.5 mm. wide. Petals ovate to ovate-oblong or lanceolate, more or less falcate or oblique, obtuse to subacute, obliquely dilated at the base, 3.2-6.5 mm. long, 1.5-3 mm. wide at the base. Lip linear-elliptic to somewhat elliptic-lanceolate or triangular-ovate, obtuse at the apex, tapering or rounded to somewhat angled on each side at the base, strongly arcuate-recurved in natural position, with a thick cushion-callus or tubercle in the middle near the base, often with lightly revolute margins, 4-8.5 mm. long, 1.5-3.5 mm. wide below the middle. Spur cylindrical, filiform, tapering at the apex, usually about twice as long as the lip, 1-2.5 cm. long. Column stout, short, 1-2 mm. long.

This species is characterized by the somewhat mammillate, cushion-like callus on the basal part of the lip and the elongated, slender spur which is usually more than twice as long as the lip. It differs from *H. sparsiflora* primarily in these characters as well as in its smaller column. The raceme is usually very long, slender and cylindrical. The lip is characteristically linear and arcuate-recurved below the middle with the small callus in the bend. These characters distinguish it from *H. dilatata* var. *leucostachys*, with which it has sometimes been confused when the habit of the inflorescence approaches that variety.

Habenaria limosa usually grows in boggy soil about springs in gulches and canyons, but it is also rather frequent in mossy ground in open woods, along cold brooks and in open sedge marshes. It commonly occurs between 7,000 and 8,000 feet altitude, but has been found up to 13,000 feet in Guatemala. *Habenaria limosa* flowers from June to September throughout its range.

GEOGRAPHICAL DISTRIBUTION: New Mexico (Socorro County), Nevada (*Clokey 5424*) and Arizona (Cochise and Pima counties) south through Mexico to Guatemala.

PLATE 29.—**Habenaria limosa.** 1, plant, one half natural size. 2, flower, side view, four times natural size. 3, dorsal sepal, four times natural size. 4, petal, four times natural size. 5, lateral sepal, four times natural size. 6, lip, four times natural size. *Drawn by Gordon W. Dillon.*

CULTURAL NOTES: No definite information is available as to the cultivation of this species. It is sometimes found in marshes, but whether sphagnous and acid or salty and alkaline is not recorded. (E. T. W.)

23. **Habenaria nivea** (Nutt.) Spreng., Syst. Veg. 3: 689. 1826. *Orchis nivea* Nutt., Gen. N. Am. Pl. 2:188. 1818. Type locality: "Betwixt St. Mary's and Satilla river, West Florida." (*Gymnadenia nivea* (Nutt.) Lindl.; *Gymnadeniopsis nivea* (Nutt.) Rydb.). PLATES 19 and 30

(The name, *nivea*, is a Latin adjective meaning "snowy," in allusion to the pure snow-white flowers.)

COMMON NAMES: Snowy Orchid, Southern Small White Orchid, Bog Torches, Frog-spear, White Frog-arrow, Savannah Orchid, White Rein-orchid.

Plant erect, slender, rigid, glabrous, 2-9 dm. tall. Roots few, coarse, fibrous, with one or more woody ellipsoid tuberoids which are up to 3 cm. long and 8 mm. in diameter. Leaves two or three, near the base of the stem, rigidly suberect, linear to linear-lanceolate, long-acuminate, conduplicate, strongly keeled, with the lower part sheathing the stem, reduced above to slender acuminate bracts, 7-26 cm. long, about 8 mm. wide near the base. Raceme many-flowered, cylindric, conical at the apex, slender, 3-15 cm. long, 1.3-3 cm. in diameter. Floral bracts mostly longer than the pedicellate ovaries, linear-lanceolate, acuminate, 6-10 mm. long. Flowers snowy-white, rarely tinged with pink, with slender pedicellate ovaries which are about 8 mm. long. Dorsal sepal oval-oblong to suborbicular, obtuse, 2-5 mm. long, 1-4 mm. wide. Lateral sepals, ovate-oblong to oblong-elliptic, auriculate or dilated at the base on the posterior margin, obtuse, 4-6 mm. long, 2-4 mm. wide. Petals linear-oblong to elliptic, obtuse, somewhat falcate, 2-5 mm. long, 1-2 mm. wide. Lip uppermost, linear-oblong to linear-elliptic, often somewhat contracted at the apex, 3-8 mm. long, 1-3 mm. wide. Spur slender, rarely clavellate, almost horizontally extended, curved upward, 1-1.6 cm. long. Capsule cylindrical, strongly ribbed and tuberculate, 8-12 mm. long.

The Snowy Orchid is one of the less common but typical plants found in the dry or moist sandy pine barrens or pine flatwoods which extend brokenly and irregularly from New Jersey and Delaware south to Florida, and along the Gulf Coast to Texas and Arkansas. The slender spike of small, snow-white flowers stands out conspicuously above the grasses and sedges with which it is commonly associated.

The Big Savannah in Pender County, North Carolina, and the extensive savannahs around Brunswick, Georgia, as well as in other southern regions, often contain large colonies of this species which form a blanket of white over the landscape.

For best growth and development, the Snowy Orchid requires a more or less constant supply of water which is acid in reaction. For instance, some of the savannahs in St. Tammany Parish, Louisiana, were ditched and drained just as the flowers of the Snowy Orchid were expanding with the result that all of the orchids, as well as many other savannah and bog plants, were killed.

This is the only *Habenaria* in our region which has the lip uppermost in the flower.

Habenaria nivea is usually found in moist depressions in savannahs, prairies and meadows, in dry or moist pinelands and pine barrens, flatwoods and wet acid bogs, and it also occurs less frequently in hammocks and cypress swamps. Although primarily a Coastal Plain species, it is found up to 1,500 feet altitude in the mountains of northwestern Georgia (Habersham County). The Snowy Orchid flowers from May to September in various parts of its range.

GEOGRAPHICAL DISTRIBUTION: This species is locally distributed from New Jersey (Cape May County) and Delaware (Kent County), south along the Atlantic seaboard to southern Florida, along the Gulf Coast to Texas (Hardin, Harris, Jefferson, Tyler and Taller counties) and Arkansas (Arkansas County); rare inland to Habersham County, Georgia. Erroneously reported from Cuba. (This report, as I pointed out in 1941, was based on a misdetermination of a collection of the Cuban endemic, *Habenaria replicata* A. Rich., a plant which simulates *H. nivea* very closely in habit.)

CULTURAL NOTES: The Snowy Orchid is a native of the southern Coastal Plain, ranging north only to the southern tip of New Jersey where the climate is relatively mild. It grows in the midst of grasses and sedges in moist peaty soil of intensely acid reaction. In the average garden it would be rather difficult to

PLATE 30.—**Habenaria nivea.** Plants, natural size. *Drawn by Blanche Ames.*

maintain the type of habitat to which this orchid is accustomed. Experiments in cultivating it somewhat beyond its native range show that it is not only sensitive to winter cold, but also is highly susceptible to attack by parasitic fungi. (E. T. W.)

24. **Habenaria obtusata** (Banks ex Pursh) Richards. in Franklin, Narr. Journ. to
Polar Sea, Bot., Appen., quarto, ed. 1: 750 (Separate, p. 22). 1823. *Orchis
obtusata* Banks ex Pursh, Fl. Am. Sept. 2: 588. 1814. Type locality and
collection: On Hudson Bay, near Fort Albany, *Hutchinson*. (*Lysiella
obtusata* (Banks ex Pursh) Rydb.; *Habenaria obtusata* var. *collectanea*
Fernald).   PLATE 31

(The name, *obtusata,* is a Latin adjective meaning "blunt," referring to the
more or less rounded appearance of the apex of the solitary leaf in typical plants.)
COMMON NAMES: Northern Small Bog-orchid, One-leaved Rein-orchid.

Plant erect, scapose, small, glabrous throughout, 8-35 cm. tall. Roots fleshy, tapering.
Stem naked or rarely provided with a linear bract at about the middle, 4-angled. Leaf
solitary (rarely two) at the base of the stem, obovate to oblanceolate or linear-oblanceolate
(very rarely suborbicular), broadly rounded to subacute at the apex, usually tapering to the
sheathing base, often oblique, 4-15 cm. long, 1-4.5 cm. wide above the middle. Raceme usually
short, few-flowered, 2.5-17 cm. long, 1.5-2 cm. in diameter. Floral bracts lanceolate, acuminate,
the lowermost often exceeding the flowers, up to 2 cm. long and 5 mm. wide. Flowers greenish
white, with strongly arcuate pedicellate ovaries. Dorsal sepal suborbicular-ovate, rounded at
the apex, concave, 3-nerved, connivent with the petals to form a hood over the column, 3.2-5 mm.
long, 3-4 mm. wide below the middle. Lateral sepals strongly reflexed, elliptic-lanceolate,
subfalcate, somewhat complicate at the obtuse apex, 3-nerved, 4.2-6.5 mm. long, 2-2.5 mm.
wide below the middle. Petals triangular-lanceolate, falcate, acuminate-attenuate, obliquely
dilated and auriculate at the base, 1-nerved, connivent with the dorsal sepal, 4-5.5 mm. long,
1.5-2.2 mm. wide across the dilated base. Lip fleshy, linear to narrowly triangular-lanceolate,
acute, strongly pendent, with a small sulcate callus in the center of the base, usually with
the lateral margins somewhat revolute, 6-10 mm. long, 1-2 mm. wide across the somewhat
dilated base. Spur tapering from a rather broad base, curved, 3-8 mm. long, almost as long as
the lip. Column 2 mm. long and wide, concave. Capsule erect, obliquely ellipsoid, 7-10 mm.
long.

The typically obovate or oblanceolate, solitary basal leaf (rarely two), together
with the tapering lip and subequal spur are characteristics of this species. The
small, few-flowered plants are usually less than 25 cm. tall.

In northern British Columbia, on mossy, grassy slopes of moraines above
timberline, I have seen hundreds of these little orchids standing bravely against the
severest of competition. A little farther south, in virgin spruce forests in sheltered
gorges of the Sikanni Chief River, *H. obtusata* luxuriates in lush mats of mosses.

A superficial variant of *H. obtusata* " . . . with crowded flowers and a yellowish
tone . . . ", described from Newfoundland, has been segregated as var. *collectanea*
Fernald (1926A). This characteristically dwarf plant, with crowded raceme,
occurs in the northernmost portion of the range of the species, and is commonly
found in open moist habitats. In my opinion, this somewhat atypical plant is at
most only a northern form of the species.

This species commonly occurs in damp or wet soil in open or dense coniferous
forest, bogs, muskegs, swamps, turfy barrens and along stream-banks. It is often
found at high elevations on rocky grassy slopes above timberline, and occurs up to
1,200 feet altitude in Newfoundland, 3,000 feet in New Hampshire and Vermont,
5,500 feet in Alberta and British Columbia, 9,000 feet in Utah and 11,500 feet in
Colorado. *Habenaria obtusata* flowers from June to September in various parts
of its range.

GEOGRAPHICAL DISTRIBUTION: Labrador, Newfoundland, throughout eastern and central
Canada to British Columbia, Alaska and the Aleutian Islands, south to Maine, New Hampshire,
Vermont, Massachusetts (Berkshire County), New York (south to Madison and Onondaga
counties), northern Michigan, (?) Illinois (Kane County), Wisconsin (Door and Douglas
counties), northern Minnesota, Montana, Wyoming, Utah (Summit County) and Colorado
(Gilpin and Jefferson counties); also Norway.

CULTURAL NOTES: The One-leaved Rein-orchid is a northerner, ranging across
the continent in Canada and, in the East, extending south only to central New
England and in the West at high altitudes. It grows chiefly in humus-rich soils

in damp, shady woodlands, the soil-reaction being usually subacid. Its soil remains rather cool even in midsummer, being as a rule not exposed to the direct rays of

PLATE 31.—**Habenaria obtusata.** 1, plant, three fourths natural size. 2, flower, front-side view, three times natural size. 3, lip, with spur attached, four times natural size. 4, petal, four times natural size. *Drawn by Blanche Ames.*

the sun for long, and at the same time provided with a permanent supply of evaporating moisture. To be successfully cultivated appreciably south of its native haunts it would be neccessary to have these temperature conditions maintained. Also, slugs would have to be well-controlled, for its fleshy foliage possesses a marked attraction for these pests. Even though the pests do not devour the plant entirely, injuries made by them are soon entered by fungi which complete the destruction. (E. T. W.)

25. **Habenaria orbiculata** (Pursh) Torr., Comp. Fl. North. & Middle States 318. 1826. *Orchis orbiculata* Pursh, Fl. Am. Sept. 2 : 588. 1814. Type locality : In shady beech-woods, on the mountains of Pennsylvania and Virginia. (*Platanthera orbiculata* (Pursh) Lindl.; *Habenaria Menziesii* (Lindl.) Macoun; *H. macrophylla* Goldie; *Lysias orbiculata* (Pursh) Rydb.; *L. macrophylla* (Goldie) House; *L. Menziesii* (Lindl.) Rydb.).   PLATE 32

(The name, *orbiculata,* is a Latin term signifying "round," referring to the shape of the two large basal leaves which are spread on the ground.)

COMMON NAMES: Large Round-leaved Orchid, Moon-set, Heal-all.

Plant erect, scapose, 6-60 cm. tall. Roots fleshy-thickened, fusiform and tapering. Scape stout, glabrous, with a pair of basal leaves and above with one to several lanceolate bracts which are up to 3.5 cm. long. Leaves two, basal, subopposite, orbicular to oblong-elliptic, broadly rounded to sometimes obtuse or rarely abruptly acute at the apex, large, fleshy and smooth, spreading flat on the ground, shining above, silvery beneath, 7-25 cm. long, 4.5-19 cm. wide. Raceme laxly few- to many-flowered, 6-30 cm. long, 4-7 cm. in diameter. Floral bracts linear-oblong to lanceolate, acute to obtuse, shorter than the flowers, 1-1.5 cm. long. Flowers up to twenty or more, greenish white, with slender pedicellate ovaries which are 1.5-2.5 cm. long. Dorsal sepal suborbicular to orbicular, erect, strongly nerved, 3-10 mm. long, up to 8 mm. wide. Lateral sepals ovate to ovate-lanceolate, obtuse, oblique, reflexed, strongly nerved, somewhat cellular-papillose on the inner surface, 6-16 mm. long, 5-9 mm. wide. Petals ovate to ovate-lanceolate, or lanceolate, obtuse to subacuminate, oblique, reflexed, often somewhat cellular-papillose on the inner surface, 5-13 mm. long, 2-4 mm. wide. Lip ligulate or linear-oblong, obtuse, pendent and slightly recurved, 9-24 mm. long, about 3 mm. wide. Spur cylindrical to clavellate, thickened and incurved toward the apex, 1.5-4.5 cm. long, as long as or longer than the pedicellate ovary. Column with a prominent armlike projection on each side, about 6 mm. long. Capsule erect, somewhat curved, obovoid-ellipsoid, 1-1.5 cm. long.

The pair of large, succulent, shining basal leaves spreading upon the ground and the erect, scapose inflorescence characterize this species. The flowers are quite variable in size. The shape of the spur as well as the presence of one or more bracts on the stem readily separate this species from *H. Hookeri* which it superficially resembles.

The plant with exceptionally large leaves and elongated spur, formerly segregated as *H. macrophylla,* is here considered to represent only an extreme condition of the typical form.

Although the Large Round-leaved Orchid is not a common plant, it thrives in its secluded haunts. Perhaps it is the most "timid" of our Habenarias, and when one suddenly comes upon it in a densely forested mountain ravine it affords a pleasant surprise. It is, indeed, a representative of some of our most attractive natural settings.

PURSH, who originally described this plant remarked, "It is known in the mountains by the name of *Heal-all."* I should like to know the reason.

This species usually occurs in dry or moist spots in coniferous, hardwood or mixed forests and rarely in swamps or bogs. It is found up to 2,000 feet altitude in Washington and British Columbia, 3,000 feet in New York, 4,000 feet in Montana and Idaho, and 5,000 feet in North Carolina and Virginia, and flowers from June to September in various parts of its range.

GEOGRAPHICAL DISTRIBUTION: Newfoundland, Miquelon Island, Labrador, Nova Scotia, Prince Edward Island, New Brunswick, Quebec and Ontario, west to British Columbia, Yukon, Alaska and the Aleutian Islands, south through New England, New York, Pennsylvania, West Virginia (Pocahontas County), Maryland (Garrett County) and Virginia (Grayson County), in the mountains to North Carolina (Ashe, Mitchell and Watauga counties), Georgia (*S. B. Buckley*) and (?) South Carolina, through the Lake States, west to Montana (Flathead and

Lake counties), Idaho (Bonner, Boundary, Kootenai and Latah counties), Oregon and Washington (King, Snohomish, Stevens and Whatcom counties).

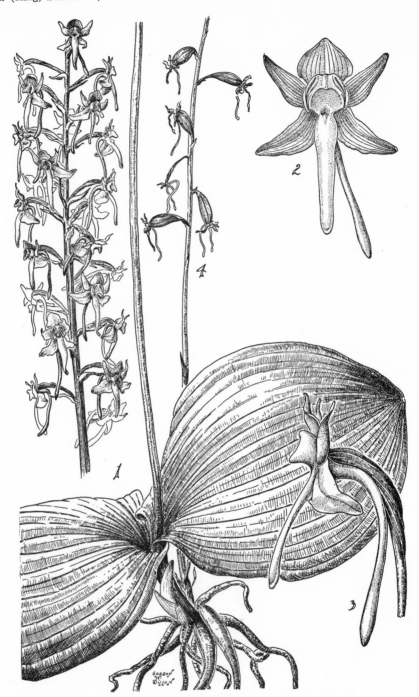

PLATE 32.—**Habenaria orbiculata.** 1, plant, one half natural size. 2, flower, front view, spread out, twice natural size. 3, flower, side view, twice natural size. 4, fruits, one half natural size. *Drawn by Gordon W. Dillon.*

CULTURAL NOTES: While of boreal tendency, the Large Round-leaved Orchid is decidedly more tolerant of summer warming of its soil than is *H. obtusata*. It thrives best in fairly deep woods or swamps in soil of rather intense acidity. The habit of its large fleshy leaves lying prostrate on the surface of the soil often proves its undoing, for fungi soon enter slight crevices in the epidermis caused by contact with coarse particles and the leaves rapidly turn brown and perish. Slugs, snails and small burrowing insects are also very fond of it, so that it rarely persists long under garden conditions. (E. T. W.)

This species was first cultivated in England by Conrad Loddiges & Sons about 1832.

26. **Habenaria peramoena** A. Gray, Am. Journ. Sci. 38: 310. 1840. Type locality: Moist meadows and banks, Pennsylvania, Ohio, and southward. (*Platanthera peramoena* A. Gray; *Blephariglottis peramoena* (A. Gray) Rydb.).

PLATE 33

(The name, *peramoena,* is a Latin adjective meaning "very lovely," a most appropriate designation for the cylindrical raceme of rich phlox-purple flowers.)

COMMON NAMES: Purple Fringeless-orchid, Purple-spire Orchid, Purple Fretlip, Pride-of-the-peak.

Plant stout or occasionally slender, glabrous throughout, 3.5-10.5 dm. tall. Roots fleshy, tuberous, tapering from a thickened base. Leaves linear-elliptic to oblong-elliptic or lanceolate, rather stiffly erect, 7-13 cm. long, 1.2-5 cm. wide. Raceme densely or loosely flowered, cylindrical, 6-17 cm. long, 4-7 cm. in diameter. Floral bracts narrowly lanceolate, 1.5-2.5 cm. long. Flowers rich violet-purple, rose-purple or phlox-purple, showy, with slender pedicellate ovaries which are about 2 cm. long. Dorsal sepal oblong-elliptic .to suborbicular, obtuse, 5-8 mm. long, 4-8 mm. wide. Lateral sepals obliquely ovate to suborbicular, rounded to obtuse at the apex, somewhat reflexed, 6-8 mm. long, 3-6 mm. wide. Petals somewhat obliquely spatulate to oblong-linear, with undulate-crenate margins, broadly rounded to obtuse or rarely subacute at the apex, 4-8 mm. long, 2-5 mm. wide near the apex, rarely with a protuberant tooth on the side near the base. Lip deeply tripartite, 1.1-2 cm. long, 1.5-2.2 cm. wide across the lateral divisions, with the divisions narrowly to broadly cuneate, 4-9 mm. wide across the apex; middle division broadly cuneate to flabellate, deeply notched at the apex. Spur curved, slender-clavate, 2-3 cm. long.

I have seen this species so abundant in a small meadow above the falls at Linville Falls, North Carolina, that the flowers gave to the whole landscape a rich red-purple color. Some of the undisturbed meadows and swamps in the vicinity of Caesar's Head, South Carolina, abound with hundreds of these plants. The unique color of the large flowers, in combination with the comparative rarity of the species, gives to this plant an attractiveness lacking in many of our native orchids.

This species is found in moist woods and meadows, along stream banks, in low alluvial woods, swampy fields and on grassy open banks. It occurs up to 1,000 feet altitude in South Carolina and 2,500 feet in North Carolina, Tennessee and West Virginia, and flowers from June (in Maryland) to the first of October (in Missouri).

GEOGRAPHICAL DISTRIBUTION: Pennsylvania (Chester and Lancaster counties), Delaware (*W. M. Canby*) and Maryland (Cecil, Garrett and Montgomery counties), south to South Carolina (Greenville County), Georgia (*S. B. Buckley*), Alabama (Lauderdale County) and Mississippi (Lafayette and Rankin counties, also Poplar Bluff), through West Virginia (Upshur County), Tennessee (McNairy and Robertson counties) and Kentucky (Calloway County), west to Arkansas (Craighead and Faulkner counties), Missouri (Butler, Dunklin and Ripley counties), Indiana (Clark, Dubois, Greene and Jefferson counties), Illinois (Jackson, Marion, Richland and Union counties), Ohio (Hamilton, Hocking and Ross counties), and western New York.

CULTURAL NOTES: The Purple-spire Orchid is a southern-midland species which ranges from the Gulf States north to western New York. Correspondingly, it is rather tolerant of temperature conditions, both as to summer heat and winter cold. Typically a meadow plant, its roots commonly extend below the humus-rich layer, aerated by grass-root-growth, but just above the impervious clay which usually lies beneath and provides a fairly constant supply of water. The soil-reaction at root-level is normally subacid, but it may vary a little in the direction

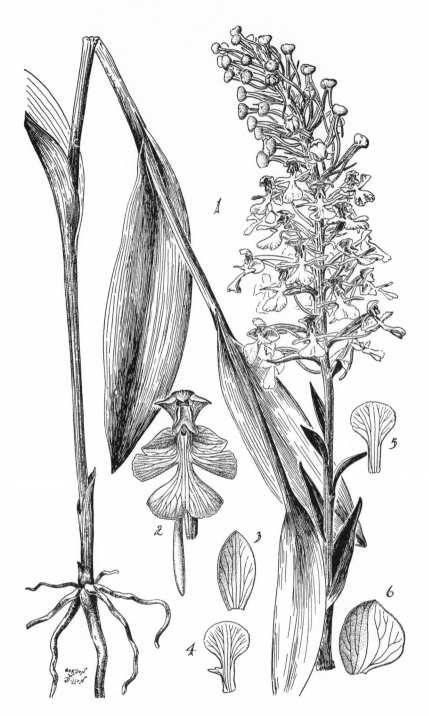

PLATE 33.—**Habenaria peramoena.** 1, plant, one half natural size. 2, flower, partly spread open, one and one half times natural size. 3, dorsal sepal, two and one half times natural size. 4, petal, with a spur on the claw, two and one half times natural size. 5, petal, typical, two and one half times natural size. 6, lateral sepal, two and one half times natural size. *Drawn by Gordon W. Dillon.*

of either more or less acidity. If a garden bed is constructed with soil conditions matching those described in the Introduction, it can be cultivated with some success, although, like most of the genus, it is susceptible to attack by fungi. (E. T. W.)

27. **Habenaria psycodes** (L.) Spreng., Syst. Veg. 3: 693. 1826 (as *psychodes*), as to synonymy and name, excluding description, and Swartz, Adnot. Bot. 45. 1829. *Orchis psycodes* L., Sp. Pl., ed. 1, 2: 943. 1753. Type locality: Canada, *Kalm*. (*Blephariglottis psycodes* (L.) Rydb.; *Habenaria psycodes* var. *ecalcarata* Bryan; *H. psycodes* var. *varians* Bryan).

PLATE 34 and FIGURE 3

(The name, *psycodes,* is a Greek term meaning "butterfly-like," in allusion to the shape and aspect of the numerous small flowers.)

COMMON NAMES: Small Purple Fringed-orchid, Butterfly Orchid, Lesser Purple Fringed-orchid, Fairy-fringe, Flaming Orchid, Lesser Purple Orchid.

Plant glabrous throughout, stout or slender, somewhat succulent, 1.5-9.5 dm. tall. Roots tuberous, fleshy, swollen near the base of the stem, tapering toward the apex. Leaves up to five in number, elliptic-oblong to narrowly lanceolate or often oblong-obovate, sheathing the stem below, 5-22 cm. long, 1.5-7 cm. wide. Raceme densely or laxly flowered, cylindrical, 3-20 cm. long, 2.5-5 cm. in diameter. Floral bracts narrowly lanceolate, 1.5-5 cm. long, 3-5 mm. wide near the base. Flowers lilac-lavender to pinkish purple, rarely almost white, with short pedicellate ovaries which are about 1 cm. long. Dorsal sepal elliptic to oblong-elliptic, concave, obtuse to acute, 5-6.5 mm. long, 2-4 mm. wide. Lateral sepals obliquely ovate, obtuse to acute, 4-7 mm. long, 3-4 mm. wide. Petals orbicular-obovate to narrowly oblong-cuneate or spatulate, coarsely and irregularly dentate along the margins, 4-9 mm. long, 3-7 mm. wide near the apex. Lip deeply tripartite, 7-13 mm. long, 8-15 mm. wide across the lateral divisions, with the divisions coarsely and shallowly toothed along the apical margin (usually cut about one-third of the way to the base); lateral divisions broadly cuneate, 5-6 mm. wide near the apex; middle division broadly cuneate to flabellate, 5-10 mm. wide near the apex. Spur slender, recurved, often clavellate, longer than the pedicellate ovary (often twice as long), 1.2-2 cm. long.

Much confusion has existed in the group of plants comprising the purple fringed-orchids. One factor which has contributed greatly to the confusion is the apparent abundance of the hybrid, × *H. Andrewsii.* Again, the separation of the Small Purple Fringed-orchid from the Large Purple Fringed-orchid proves to be simply an arbitrary procedure based on a difference in the size of the raceme and flowers — a most unsatisfactory criterion. The difficulty of this problem may well be expressed in the words of GIBSON (1905): "In the bother of mentally calculating whether a certain specimen of purple-fringed orchis is a large specimen of *H. psycodes,* or a small one of *H. grandiflora,* one is distracted from an enjoyment of its beauty, and is tempted to feel a trifle of impatience at the naming of names, and to wish one were back in the Garden of Eden, where, according to the little boy's version, 'Adam called the elephant an elephant because it looked like an elephant.' "

Peloric plants have been found in this species, such as that described as var. *ecalcarata* Bryan (1917), where the spur is lacking and the floral segments are essentially regular. Other aberrant forms are sometimes found, such as that described as var. *varians* Bryan (1917), where the lip is broadly cuneate, with the mid-lobe lacking.

This species is commonly found in upland meadows, sedge and grass swamps, in open woods, pastures and wet weedy soil, in sphagnum bogs, cedar or alder swamps and alluvial thickets. It is also found in stream-beds of mountain brooks, in rich grassy humus on the border of dense forests, in wet coniferous forests and swamps, and on sandy beaches (in Maine and Nova Scotia). The Small Purple Fringed-orchid occurs up to 1,500 feet altitude in Vermont, 4,000 feet in Virginia and 6,500 feet in North Carolina and Tennessee, and flowers from early June to August in various parts of its range.

GEOGRAPHICAL DISTRIBUTION: Newfoundland, Miquelon Island, Anticosti, Nova Scotia, Prince Edward Island, New Brunswick, Quebec and Ontario (Elgin County and Temagami), through New England, New York, New Jersey, Pennsylvania, Maryland (Garrett County) and Virginia (Washington County), south in the mountains to North Carolina, Georgia (Union County), Tennessee and Arkansas (*Demaree*), through the Lake States, west to Minnesota (Anoka, Chisago, Itasca and Mille Lacs counties), Iowa and Kentucky (Red River).

PLATE 34.—**Habenaria psycodes.** Plant, natural size. *Drawn by Blanche Ames.*

CULTURAL NOTES: The Lesser Purple Fringed-orchid, preferring a moderately cool climate, evidently survived glaciation in the Appalachians and, after the Pleistocene ice melted, advanced rapidly northward where it eventually reached Newfoundland and Minnesota. It commonly grows in moist clayey soil where the reaction is subacid, minimacid or in some cases neutral because of underlying limestone. If planted in a wild garden in the midst of not too rampant shrubs where its roots can be somewhat protected, it may survive for a reasonable time, provided that it is not found by a rabbit, slug or a tiny fungus. (E. T. W.)

28. **Habenaria psycodes** var. **grandiflora** (Bigel.) A. Gray, Am. Journ. Sci. 38: 310. 1840. *Orchis grandiflora* Bigel., Fl. Bost., ed. 2: 321. 1824. Type locality: Found at Lancaster, Leominster, Deerfield, etc. Abundant in Enfield, New Hampshire. (*Habenaria fimbriata* (Dryander) R. Br.; *Blephariglottis grandiflora* (Bigel.) Rydb.). FIGURE 3

(The name, *grandiflora*, is a Latin adjective signifying "large-flowered" — the chief character in separating this plant from the typical form.)

COMMON NAMES: Large Purple Fringed-orchid, Large Butterfly Orchid, Plume-royal, Greater Purple Fringed-orchid.

There is no noticeable difference to separate *H. psycodes* from its var. *grandiflora* (*H. fimbriata*) except in the size of the racemes and flowers, and even these slight differences tend to break down whenever intergradation occurs. The raceme of var. *grandiflora* may be as much as 25 cm. in length and 8 cm. in diameter. The

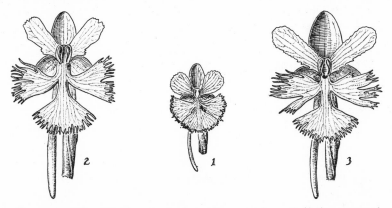

TEXTFIGURE 3.— Flowers, front view, all one and one half times natural size. 1, **Habenaria psycodes.** 2 and 3, **Habenaria psycodes** var. **grandiflora.** *Drawn by Gordon W. Dillon.*

flowers which vary from lilac to white, are fragrant, large and showy. In addition, the petals are more oblong or oblong-obovate than in the typical form. The lip is often as much as 1.8 cm. long and 2.5 cm. wide and the three divisions are sometimes laciniate halfway to the base. However, these differences are merely the result of magnification of the characters found in the typical form of the species. I have arbitrarily considered all those plants to be var. *grandiflora* whose measurements (particularly of the floral segments) exceed those measurements given for *H. psycodes.*

On the whole, the blooming season of var. *grandiflora* precedes that of *H. psycodes,* but, again, in some regions there is an overlapping of the flowering seasons of the two entities.

Forms having pure white flowers, described as *H. fimbriata* forma *albiflora* Rand & Redfield (1894), occur throughout the area of distribution of this variety.

The Large Purple Fringed-orchid is usually found in moist deciduous woods, wet meadows and swampy woods, in rich soil on wooded mountain slopes and in bogs. It occurs up to 2,000 feet altitude in Vermont, 3,200 feet in West Virginia and 6,000 feet in North Carolina, and flowers from early June to August in various parts of its range.

GEOGRAPHICAL DISTRIBUTION: Newfoundland, Miquelon Island, St. Pierre Island, New Brunswick, Nova Scotia, Quebec and Ontario, through New England, New York, New Jersey,

Pennsylvania, West Virginia and Maryland (Glades), south in the mountains to North Carolina (Avery, Buncombe, Haywood, Mitchell and Watauga counties) and Tennessee (Thunderhead Mountain), west to Michigan (Houghton County), Wisconsin (Douglas and Milwaukee counties) and Illinois (Lake County).

CULTURAL NOTES: In geologic history and range var. *grandiflora* is similar to the typical form, but the Greater Purple Fringed-orchid does not tolerate quite as high summer temperatures as the Lesser Purple Fringed-orchid. It also grows in soils which are commonly moister, richer in humus and more acid in reaction. Variety *grandiflora,* which usually blooms earlier than its relative when they grow in the same vicinity, is decidedly the more difficult to cultivate outside of its native haunts. Its soils have to be kept cool and acid and parasitic fungi reduced to a minimum, otherwise it may bloom for but one season and then vanish leaving no trace. (E. T. W.)

According to BROWN (1813), the Large Purple Fringed-orchid was first introduced into England in 1777 by WILLIAM PITCAIRN.

29. **Habenaria quinqueseta** (Michx.) A. Eaton, Man., ed. 5: 253. (Jan. 12) 1829; Sw., Adnot. Bot. 46. (May) 1829. *Orchis quinqueseta* Michx., Fl. Bor.-am. 2: 155. 1803. Type locality: Carolina. (*Habenaria macroceratitis* Willd.; *H. Michauxii* Nutt.; *H. Simpsonii* Small; *H. Habenaria* (L.) Small).   PLATE 35

(The name, *quinqueseta,* is a Latin adjective signifying "five-bristled," probably in allusion to the three narrow, bristle-like segments of the lip together with the additional narrow segment of each petal.)

COMMON NAMES: Long-horned Habenaria, Michaux's Orchid.

Plant slender or stout, erect, leafy (occasionally with the leaves mostly basal), glabrous throughout, 2-9 dm. tall. Roots slender, fibrous, often provided with tuberous swellings (usually with an ovoid tuberoid at the base of the stem). Leaves mainly cauline, thin and chartaceous when dry, rather fleshy when fresh, oblong-elliptic to elliptic-lanceolate or oblong-obovate, broadly rounded to acute or acuminate at the apex, reduced above to clasping ovate acuminate bracts, 6-25 cm. long, 2.5-6 cm. wide. Raceme elongated, laxly few- to many-flowered, 7-25 cm. long, 5-6 cm. in diameter. Floral bracts ovate-lanceolate, acuminate, semitranslucent, as long as or shorter than the pedicellate ovaries, 1.5-2.8 cm. long, 7-15 mm. wide below the middle. Flowers greenish white, with slender pedicellate ovaries which are 2-3 cm. long. Dorsal sepal oblong-elliptic to suborbicular, obtuse to rarely acute, concave, 6-13 mm. long, 5-10 mm. wide at the middle. Lateral sepals ovate-oblong to oblong-lanceolate or oblong-elliptic, obtuse to acute, oblique, 8-16 mm. long, 4-7 mm. wide below the middle. Petals bipartite; posterior division erect, linear-oblong, falcate, obtuse to acute, 6-15 mm. long, about 2 mm. wide; anterior division filiform, almost twice as long as the posterior division, recurved, 1.3-2.5 cm. long. Lip tripartite; lateral divisions filiform, recurved at the apex, 1.5-3 cm. long; middle division linear, with revolute margins, 8-20 mm. long, 2-3 mm. wide. Spur varying from slender to strongly clavellate, recurved, 4-18 cm. long.

A number of segregates from this species have been described, based primarily upon the variable length of the spur and on the shape of the leaves and their arrangement on the stem. I have examined specimens of this species from throughout its area of distribution and I find a graduated series in the length of the spur from 4 to 18 cm. The plant with the extremely long spur was formerly known as *H. macroceratitis.*

It is quite possible that CHARLES WRIGHT collected this species for the first and only time in Texas before 1852.

This species is found mostly in low pinelands and pine or oak flatwoods, but it is also found in hammocks and dry sandy soil or occasionally in swamps, on beaches or on moist grassy banks. In the tropics it grows in sandy pine woods, along wooded streams or in open or shady places on hillsides. It occurs from near sea level in Florida, up to 6,500 feet altitude in Mexico and Central America, and flowers from August to January in various parts of its range.

GEOGRAPHICAL DISTRIBUTION: This species is widely distributed throughout Florida and is local in South Carolina (Beaufort, Berkeley and Charleston counties), Georgia (Chatham

PLATE 35.— **Habenaria quinqueseta.** 1, plant, two thirds natural size. 2, lip and column, front view, twice natural size. 3, petal, twice natural size. 4, lateral sepal, twice natural size. 5, dorsal sepal, twice natural size. *Drawn by Blanche Ames.*

County?), Alabama (Mobile and Tuscaloosa counties), Louisiana (Rapides Parish) and Texas (*C. Wright*); also Mexico and Central and South America, Cuba and Jamaica.

CULTURAL NOTES: This orchid, an inhabitant of damp acid pinelands in the Gulf States, can withstand only moderately cold winter conditions. It is not likely to be amenable to cultivation except in an environment closely matching its native one. (E. T. W.)

PLATE 36.—**Habenaria repens.** 1, plant, natural size. 2, flower, front view, twice natural size. 3, petal, three times natural size. *Redrawn from Blanche Ames by Gordon W. Dillon.*

This species was first introduced into the British Isles from Jamaica by a Dr. DISTAN. It flowered in 1829 in the Glasgow Botanic Garden.

30. **Habenaria repens** Nutt., Gen. N. Am. Pl. 2: 190. 1818. Type locality: On the margins of ponds near Savannah, Georgia, and in Carolina. (*Habenaria Nuttallii* Small). PLATE 36

(The name, *repens,* a Latin adjective meaning "creeping," perhaps refers to the rhizome-like lower part of the stem which is often decumbent and rooting at the nodes, especially when growing in water or in a soft substratum.)

COMMON NAMES: Water-spider Orchid, Creeping Orchid, Floating Orchid.

Plant slender or stout, leafy, glabrous, 1-9 dm. tall. Roots slender, fibrous, often with tuberous swellings. Leaves linear-oblong to linear-lanceolate, acute to acuminate, thin and chartaceous, 3-ribbed, strongly veined, sheathing the stem below, 5-24 cm. long, 3.5-20 mm. wide. Raceme densely many-flowered (rarely consisting of a few scattered flowers), 6-28 cm. long, 2.5-3 cm. in diameter. Floral bracts oblong-lanceolate to lanceolate, acute to acuminate, exceeding the flowers at maturity (rarely shorter than the flowers), 1.5-9 cm. long, about 1 cm. wide near the base. Flowers small, greenish, with slender pedicellate ovaries which are 9-14 mm. long. Dorsal sepal oval to suborbicular-ovate, mucronate, concave, 3-7 mm. long, about 3 mm. wide. Lateral sepals ovate to ovate-oblong, mucronate, 4-7 mm. long, about 3 mm. wide. Petals bipartite; posterior division erect, falcate, oblong-lanceolate to lanceolate, acute, 3-7 mm. long; anterior division filiform, falcate, erect, 4-7.5 mm. long. Lip tripartite to within 2 mm. of the base, strongly reflexed; lateral divisions filiform, 5-11 mm. long; middle division linear to linear-oblong, 4-7 mm. long. Spur slender, about as long as the pedicellate ovary, 9-14 mm. long.

The slender spike of numerous small greenish flowers, which, with their deeply three-parted lip, resemble several filaments drawn closely together with their loose ends dangling, is most inconspicuous standing above the surrounding sedges and rushes with which this species is usually associated.

A striking peculiarity of the Water-spider Orchid is its adaptation to life as an aquatic plant. It is often found on floating mats on the surface of deep water in company with Water Hyacinth (*Eichhornia crassipes*) and other aquatic plants. This species is particularly common on the undulating plains and savannahs of Highlands, Hardee and De Soto counties in south-central Florida, and it may be found in large colonies in and around Highlands Hammock State Park near Sebring. The yellowish green foliage is the most attractive feature of this plant.

This species occurs in ditches, streams, wet meadows, quaking bogs, hammocks, ponds and on lake shores, in miry meadows and fresh-water marshes. It is one of the most widespread species of *Habenaria* in tropical America and is usually found in the lowlands, but rarely grows up to 6,000 feet altitude in the tropics. The Water-spider Orchid flowers from April to December in various parts of its range.

GEOGRAPHICAL DISTRIBUTION: Found along the Atlantic seaboard from southeastern North Carolina (Brunswick and New Hanover counties) to southern Florida, along the Gulf Coast of Texas (Cameron, Gonzales, Guadalupe, Milam and Wood counties); also southern Mexico (Hidalgo), Central and South America, and throughout the West Indies.

CULTURAL NOTES: The Water-spider Orchid grows in very wet places, even at times forming floating islands, usually in the midst of coarse grasses. The water of these ponds and sluggish streams where this orchid thrives varies widely in reaction, from mediacid to calcareous and subalkaline. In the latter case, however, the decomposing litter tends to increase the acidity around the roots of the plant to at least the subacid level. Beyond its native region it may be cultivated with some degree of success in moist peat in a greenhouse, but it does not seem able to attain the luxuriance characteristic of its condition in natural habitats. (E. T. W.)

This species is quite easily transplanted to pools and streams, and may be left out-of-doors during the year in the region where it grows naturally. I have seen the Water-spider Orchid growing in the moat surrounding the Bok Tower, Lake Wales, Florida, where it formed attractive colonies on the surface of the water.

31. **Habenaria saccata** Greene, Erythea 3: 49. 1895. Type locality and collection: Lassen Creek, Modoc County, California, 1894, *Mrs. Austin.* (*Habenaria*

gracilis S. Wats.; *H. stricta* (Lindl.) Rydb.; *H. hyperborea* var. *purpurascens* (Rydb.) Ames; *H. purpurascens* (Rydb.) Tidestrom; *H. neomexicana* Tidestrom; *Limnorchis stricta* (Lindl.) Rydb.; *L. brachypetala* Rydb., in part; *L. gracilis* (S. Wats.) Rydb., in part; *L. purpurascens* Rydb., as to type specimen and description only). PLATE 37

(The name, *saccata,* is a Latin term meaning "saccate" or "bag-shaped," in allusion to the characteristic shape of the spur of the flowers.)

COMMON NAME: Slender Bog-orchid.

Plant strictly erect, slender or stout, glabrous and light green throughout, 1.5-10 dm. tall. Roots tuberous, fusiform, 5-10 mm. in diameter. Stem leafy, provided below with one or more tubular sheaths. Leaves scattered on the stem or occasionally clustered near the base, usually narrowly elliptic to linear-lanceolate or rarely oblanceolate, rounded to subacuminate at the apex, scarcely or not at all sheathing the stem, 4-14 cm. long, 1-4 cm. wide. Raceme spicate, usually much elongated, laxly few- to many-flowered, slender, cylindrical to subsecund, 4-42 cm. long, 0.8-2 cm. in diameter. Floral bracts linear-lanceolate, acuminate, cellular-papillose on the margins, the lowermost up to 6 cm. long and greatly exceeding the flowers. Flowers small, green, commonly tinged or marked with purplish brown, usually scattered along the elongated rachis; sepals rather thin and 3-nerved, the petals and lip fleshy. Dorsal sepal suborbicular to ovate or ovate-elliptic, broadly rounded to obtuse and occasionally minutely cucullate at the apex, erect and connivent with the petals to form a hood over the column, 3-5 mm. long, 3-3.5 mm. wide near the base. Lateral sepals spreading or reflexed, triangular-ovate to elliptic-lanceolate, oblique, obtuse, 4-6 mm. long, 2-3 mm. wide near the base. Petals triangular-lanceolate to elliptic-lanceolate, falcate, obtuse to acute, obliquely dilated and auriculate at the base, usually purplish, 1- to 2-nerved, 3-5 mm. long, 1.5-2.2 mm. wide at the base. Lip linear to occasionally ovate-elliptic, sometimes tapering at the apex, obtuse to acute, usually purplish, 4-7.5 mm. long, 1-2 mm. wide. Spur broadly cylindric-clavate to scrotiform, sometimes slightly didymous, usually broadly rounded at the apex, often purplish, one-third to two-thirds the length of the lip, rarely longer. Column short, thick, about 2 mm. long, sometimes with a rather broad connective. Capsule erect, obliquely ellipsoid, about 1 cm. long.

The inflorescence of *H. saccata* is typically an elongated laxly or remotely flowered, cylindric or subsecund raceme. In this respect, the species strongly resembles some forms of *H. sparsiflora.* While the column is characteristically small, some forms have a large column approaching that of *H. sparsiflora.* The scrotiform or saccate spur of *H. saccata,* however, easily separates such forms from that species. The form possessing a linear-lanceolate or elliptic-lanceolate lip and somewhat denser inflorescence (originally described as *Limnorchis purpurascens*) has been included here. This form doubtless represents an approach to *H. hyperborea,* but its saccate spur is more consonant with *H. saccata* than with that species.

This species is usually found in moist or wet soil in meadows, fields, bogs, thickets, swamps, marshes, canyons, coniferous forests, on open seepage slopes, ledges and in or along streams. It occurs from near sea level in Alaska, up to 3,500 feet altitude in Unalaska, 5,500 feet in Alberta and British Columbia, 6,500 feet in California, 7,500 feet in Idaho, Montana, Nevada and Oregon, 9,500 feet in Arizona, Washington and Wyoming and 12,500 feet in Colorado. The Slender Bog-orchid flowers from May to September in various parts of its range.

GEOGRAPHICAL DISTRIBUTION: New Mexico (San Miguel and Santa Fe counties), Arizona (Apache and Graham counties), Colorado (Clear Creek, El Paso, Jefferson and Larimer counties), Nevada (Elko County), California (Del Norte, Humbolt, Modoc, Siskiyou and Trinity counties), Wyoming (Lincoln and Yellowstone National Park counties), Montana (western part), Idaho (widespread), Oregon (widespread), Washington (mostly northwestern part), Alberta (Waterton Lakes Park), British Columbia, Alaska and the Aleutian Islands.

CULTURAL NOTES: The Slender Bog-orchid is a native of western North America, extending from high altitudes in the mountains of Arizona and Colorado north to sea level in Alaska. It evidently requires a rather cool to cold and decidedly moist climate. Since it prefers rather acid peaty soils, it could perhaps be cultivated if special care is taken to match the conditions of its natural habitat. (E. T. W.)

PLATE 37.—**Habenaria saccata.** 1, plant, one half natural size. 2, flower, side view, five times natural size. 3, dorsal sepal, five times natural size. 4, petal, five times natural size. 5, lateral sepal, five times natural size. 6, lip, with spur attached, side view, five times natural size. 7, lip, five times natural size. *Drawn by Gordon W. Dillon.*

32. Habenaria sparsiflora S. Wats., Proc. Am. Acad. 12: 276. 1877. Type locality: Common in the Sierra Nevada and mountains of northern California. (*Habenaria aggregata* Howell; *H. leucostachys* var. *viridis* Jepson; *Limnorchis ensifolia* Rydb.; *L. sparsiflora* (S. Wats.) Rydb.; *L. aggregata* (Howell) Frye & Rigg). PLATE 38

(The name, *sparsiflora,* is a Latin adjective meaning "with scattered flowers," in allusion to the sparsely flowered inflorescence of typical material.)

COMMON NAME: Sparsely-flowered Bog-orchid.

Plant strictly erect, slender or stout, glabrous and rather light green throughout, 1.5-7.5 dm. tall. Roots fusiform, fleshy-thickened. Stem more or less leafy, provided at the base with tubular sheaths, often several produced from the same rhizome (caespitose). Leaves variable, scattered on the stem or occasionally clustered near the base, oblong-elliptic or oblanceolate-elliptic to linear-lanceolate or rarely linear, broadly rounded to acuminate at the apex, 6.5-30 cm. long, 1-5 cm. wide. Raceme spicate, usually laxly few- to many-flowered, occasionally rather densely flowered, usually much-elongated, 1-4.5 dm. long, 1-3 cm. in diameter. Floral bracts narrowly lanceolate, acuminate, usually about equaling the flowers or the lowermost bracts up to 4 cm. long and greatly exceeding the flowers. Flowers light green, usually scattered in an elongated raceme, the lowermost often remote. Dorsal sepal suborbicular to suborbicular-ovate or ovate-elliptic, broadly rounded to obtuse at the apex, concave, erect and connivent with the petals to form a hood over the column, 3-nerved, 6-7.5 mm. long, 4.5-6 mm. wide near the base. Lateral sepals strongly reflexed, ovate-elliptic to elliptic-lanceolate, obtuse, oblique, 3-nerved, with the margins usually revolute, 6-10 mm. long, up to 4 mm. wide. Petals rather fleshy, triangular-lanceolate to narrowly lanceolate, falcate, obtuse to acuminate, obliquely dilated at the base and somewhat auriculate, often cellular-papillose on the margins, 1- to 2-nerved, connivent with the dorsal sepal, 6-8 mm. long, 3-4.5 mm. wide near the base. Lip fleshy, large for the flower, conspicuously pendent, linear to linear-elliptic or sometimes linear-lanceolate, obtuse to acute, with a more or less fleshy-thickened ridge through the center below the middle, 6-14 mm. long, 1.5-3 mm. wide. Spur cylindric, filiform or only slightly dilated above the middle, usually slightly exceeding the lip (rarely shorter than the lip), up to 1.3 cm. long. Column conspicuous, usually variable in size, large for the flower, with a rather broad connective, usually one-half the length of the dorsal sepal, 2.5-5 mm. long and wide. Capsule obliquely ellipsoid, up to 1.5 cm. long.

This species is represented by two characteristic forms. One form, as exemplified by the type, approaches *H. saccata* in that the rather short, oblong-elliptic, bluntly obtuse leaves are scattered along the stem and the inflorescence has an elongated, lax aspect. Another form (described as *Limnorchis ensifolia*), has linear-lanceolate leaves which are clustered at or near the base of the stem and an inflorescence which is rather short and densely flowered. Intermediate conditions are common. Nevertheless, the essential floral characters are so similar in all of these forms that it seems unwise to attempt their segregation.

Some of the forms of *H. sparsiflora* approach *H. limosa*. Both species are characterized by a fleshy thickening near the base of the lip. In *H. sparsiflora,* however, the thickening extends to about the middle of the lip in contrast to the limited basal callosity of *H. limosa*. The shorter spur and much larger column of *H. sparsiflora* also aid in the separation of this species from *H. limosa*.

The general habit and the typically elongated raceme of *H. sparsiflora* are often quite similar to those of *H. saccata*. However, the large flowers with their large column and slender, elongated spur easily separate this species from *H. saccata*. The lip is usually linear or linear-elliptic but may occasionally be linear-lanceolate.

This species is usually found in moist or wet soil in mountain meadows, marshes, swamps, bogs, open or dense forests, on stream banks and open seepage slopes, and is frequent about springs. It is found from near sea level in California, up to 4,500 feet altitude in Oregon, 8,000 feet in Arizona and New Mexico, 9,500 feet in California, Colorado and Nevada and 11,500 feet in Utah, and flowers from April to September in various parts of its range.

GEOGRAPHICAL DISTRIBUTION: New Mexico (Lincoln County), Arizona (Cochise, Coconino and Navajo counties), Utah (Iron, Piute, Salt Lake and Utah counties), Nevada (Washoe County), California (widespread), Oregon (Curry and Josephine counties), Washington (Skamania County); also Mexico (Baja California).

PLATE 38.—**Habenaria sparsiflora.** 1, plant, one half natural size. 2, flower, side view, three times natural size. 3, petal, three times natural size. 4, lateral sepal, three times natural size. 5, dorsal sepal, three times natural size. 6, lip, three times natural size.

Habenaria sparsiflora var. **brevifolia.** 7, plant, one half natural size. 8, flower, front view, twice natural size. *Drawn by Gordon W. Dillon.*

CULTURAL NOTES: This species is presumably not so tolerant to cold as some of its relatives. So far as known, its habitat requirements and prospects of cultivation are much the same as those of *H. saccata*. (E. T. W.)

33. **Habenaria sparsiflora** var. **brevifolia** (Greene) Correll, Leafl. West. Bot. 3:244. 1943. *Habenaria brevifolia* Greene, Bot. Gaz. 6:218. 1881. Type locality: Dry southward slopes of the Piños Altos Mountains, New Mexico, in open woods of *Pinus ponderosa,* in flower September 14, 1880. (*Limnorchis brevifolia* (Greene) Rydb.). PLATE 38

(The name, *brevifolia,* is a Latin term signifying "short-leaved," in allusion to the abbreviated, bract-like leaves of this variety.)

COMMON NAME: None known.

Variety *brevifolia* is distinguished from the typical form of the species primarily by its abbreviated leaves which are often reduced to clasping sheaths. The reduced leaves are usually more ovate than in the typical form and are rarely as much as 9 cm. long. The flowering habits of both forms are similar, although the raceme of var. *brevifolia* may be somewhat more congested and may extend farther down the stem. Florally, *H. sparsiflora* and var. *brevifolia* are almost identical. However, the sepals of var. *brevifolia* are sometimes more acuminate and the spur, which varies from 1 to 2 cm. in length, always (but usually only slightly) exceeds the lip and is often longer than that of typical *H. sparsiflora.* The column is large, as in the typical form, and is one-half to two-thirds the length of the dorsal sepal.

Variety *brevifolia* also differs from typical *H. sparsiflora* in its habitat requirements. It is a plant of dry open forested slopes, whereas the Sparsely-flowered Bog-orchid nearly always occurs in moist situations. Variety *brevifolia* is commonly found on dry mountain slopes in open pine or spruce forests. It grows between 7,000 and 9,000 feet altitude in New Mexico, and flowers from July to September.

GEOGRAPHICAL DISTRIBUTION: New Mexico (Grant, Lincoln, Socorro and Otero counties); also Mexico (widespread).

CULTURAL NOTES: Variety *brevifolia,* which is endemic to the southernmost Rocky Mountains of New Mexico and the highlands of Mexico, appears to be more tolerant of summer heat than the typical form but less resistant to the cold of winter. No reference to its cultivation has been found. (E. T. W.)

34. **Habenaria sparsiflora** var. **laxiflora** (Rydb.) Correll, Leafl. West. Bot. 3:245. 1943. *Limnorchis laxiflora* Rydb., Bull. Torr. Bot. Club 28:630. 1901, as to type specimen and description only. Type locality and collection: Oregon, Coast Mountains, 1884. *Thomas Howell.* (*Habenaria laxiflora* (Rydb.) S. B. Parish).

(The name, *laxiflora,* is a Latin adjective meaning "loosely-flowered," in allusion to the lax, few-flowered inflorescence of typical material.)

COMMON NAME: Laxly-flowered Bog-orchid.

This is a small-flowered variety. Its small column is less than 2 mm. long (one-third or less the length of the dorsal sepal) and is usually without a broad connective, while the typical form of *H. sparsiflora* has a large column (with a broad connective), which is 2 mm. or more long, and is about one-half as long as the dorsal sepal.

Variety *laxiflora* includes two rather distinctive vegetative types. The form common in the Charleston Mountains of Nevada, characterized by having the linear-elliptic to lanceolate leaves clustered at or near the base of the stem and an elongated, cylindric raceme, is closely allied to *H. limosa* and some forms of *H. hyperborea,* and it might well be regarded as a variety of either of those species. However, the flowers of this plant appear to be more closely allied to *H. sparsiflora.* The form most frequent on the Pacific Coast with elliptic to elliptic-oblong, obtuse leaves scattered on the stem and the remotely spaced flowers, as represented by the type collection of *Limnorchis laxiflora,* superficially resembles a slender-spurred *H. saccata* and it seems to grade imperceptibly into that species.

There is little doubt that most of the species comprising the section *Limnorchis* freely hybridize with one another, thus creating for the taxonomist a most perplexing hybrid population with which to deal.

Variety *laxiflora* is usually found in moist or wet soil in or around springs, in bogs, marshes, ravines, meadows, swamps, woods and along stream-banks. It usually grows at high elevations and occurs up to 11,000 feet altitude in California and Nevada, and flowers from June to August in various parts of its range.

GEOGRAPHICAL DISTRIBUTION: Arizona (Coconino County and Navajo Indian Reservation), Colorado (Rio Blanco and Montrose counties), Utah (Salt Lake and Utah counties), Nevada (Clark, Esmeralda, Mineral and Washoe counties), California (widespread) and Oregon (Klamath County).

CULTURAL NOTES: See this section under the typical form.

35. **Habenaria strictissima** Reichb. f. var. **odontopetala** (Reichb. f.) L. O. Wms., Bot. Mus. Leafl. Harvard Univ. 7:184. 1939. *Habenaria odontopetala* Reichb. f., Linnaea 18:407. 1844. Type locality and collection: Temperate regions of Mexico, *Leibold.* (*Habenaria Garberi* Porter; *Habenella Garberi* (Porter) Small; *H. odontopetala* (Reichb. f.) Small). PLATE 39

(The name, *strictissima,* is a Latin adjective signifying "very straight," in allusion to the appearance of the inflorescence. The name, *odontopetala,* is a classical term meaning "toothed-petal" or "tooth-like petal," referring either to the shape of the petals or to a small tooth at the base of the petals.)

COMMON NAME: None known.

Plant slender or stout, 2.5-8.5 dm. tall. Roots slender, fibrous, bearing tuberoids (an ovoid tuberoid usually occurring at the base of the stem). Stem usually very leafy. Leaves four to nine, scattered alternately along the stem or rarely aggregated near the base of the stem, linear-elliptic to linear-lanceolate, acute to acuminate, 7-17 cm. long, 2-4.5 cm. wide. Raceme open and laxly flowered, 9-40 cm. long, 3-6 cm. in diameter. Floral bracts linear-lanceolate, 8-30 mm. long. Flowers yellowish green, with slender pedicellate ovaries which are about 2 cm. long. Dorsal sepal oblong-elliptic, deeply concave or cucullate, forming a hood over the column, 4-7 mm. long, 4-5 mm. wide when spread out. Lateral sepals ovate-oblong, oblique, obtuse, 5.5-8.5 mm. long, 4-5 mm. wide. Petals oblong-quadrate to linear-oblong, auriculate at the base on the anterior margin, conical-obtuse to sinuately 3-lobed at the apex, 3-5 mm. long, 1-2 mm. wide. Lip slender, linear, pendent, obtuse to rounded at the apex, slightly auricled or lobed on each side at the base, recurved toward the apex, 6-12 mm. long, 3-4 mm. wide at the base, about 2 mm. wide near the middle. Spur slender, as long as or a little longer than the pedicellate ovary, 1.3-2.8 cm. long. Capsule strongly ribbed, curved, 8-12 mm. long.

Habenaria strictissima and its var. *odontopetala* are very similar to one another in habit. Although the shape of the lip is the same in both, that of var. *odontopetala* is usually longer and much more slender than that of *H. strictissima.* The petals of var. *odontopetala* are more oblong-quadrate and the lateral sepals more curved than in the typical form. *Habenaria strictissima* has been found only in Mexico and Guatemala, while var. *odontopetala* has a much wider distribution.

Although collecting plants often becomes a matter of routine, some incidents do occur which might be considered exciting. It might be of interest to relate such an incident which happened to me while I was hunting for this orchid, as well as others, in one of its typical haunts in southern Florida.

I was literally cutting my way through a large water-covered tupelo-cypress swamp. Since the water varied from knee-deep to well over one's head (especially when one had the misfortune to slip into a 'gator hole), every fallen timber and small brush-covered mossy hummock proved a godsend in traveling through the swamp. I had been battling my way through the dense tangled growth all day, and the many swings made with the machete in cutting down brush and small saplings had made me weary and tiresomely careless. It was getting late and my

PLATE 39.— **Habenaria strictissima** var. **odontopetala.** Plant, two thirds natural size. 1, lateral sepal, five times natural size. 2, lip and column, front view, five times natural size. 3 and 4, two types of petals, five times natural size. *Drawn by Blanche Ames.*

thoughts were more and more concerned with returning to my base camp for the night. However, I had just reached the end of a large fallen tree trunk and decided to explore a little farther before returning. Holding my machete across my face with an uplifted arm both to protect my face and to keep the dangerous knife out of the water, I jumped into the brownish palmetta-stained liquid. Instantly, from a hummock surrounding the swollen base of a Tupelo Gum upon which he had been coiled, a large cottonmouth moccasin came hurtling at my face. I instinctively ducked, while carrying through the jump, and simultaneously swung the machete in a wild back-hand stroke. I luckily managed to keep the blade on a horizontal arc and the razor-edged steel accidently caught the reptile in mid-air squarely across its gaping mouth. The sharp blade, meeting the impact of the snake's lightning strike, slit the thick-bodied beast in two and left its gory halves floating on the water. So now I had a snake to my credit, even though the orchid eluded my valiant efforts!

Variety *odontopetala* is commonly found in wet rich soil of deeply shaded woods and hammocks, in mucky soil of cypress swamps and swampy woods, along ditches and on rotton wood, and rarely in scrub hammocks and dry sandy woods. It occurs from near sea level in Florida, up to 5,000 feet altitude in the tropics, blooming sporadically throughout the year, mainly from October to March.

GEOGRAPHICAL DISTRIBUTION: Florida (St. Johns County and southward); also Mexico, through Central America to Panama, Cuba and Puerto Rico.

CULTURAL NOTES: This Caribbean orchid extends well up into peninsular Florida where it is often noticed by northern visitors because it blooms throughout the winter. It grows in damp peaty soils of circumneutral to moderately acid reaction and is cultivated to some extent in wild gardens in Florida. (E. T. W.)

36. **Habenaria unalascensis** (Spreng.) S. Wats., Proc. Am. Acad. 12: 277. 1877, in text. *Spiranthes unalascensis* Spreng., Syst. Veg. 3: 708. 1826. Type locality: Lower Aleutian Islands. (*Habenaria Cooperi* S. Wats.; *Montolivaea unalaschensis* (Spreng.) Rydb.; *Piperia unalaschensis* (Spreng.) Rydb.; *P. Cooperi* (S. Wats.) Rydb.). PLATE 40

(The name, *unalascensis*, is a Latin adjective referring to Unalaska, probably the place of original discovery of this species.)

COMMON NAMES: Alaska Piperia, Slender-spire Orchid, Cooper's Piperia, Lance-leaved Piperia.

Plant scapose, strict, slender or stout, glabrous throughout, occasionally somewhat glaucous, 2.5-9 dm. tall. Roots short, fleshy-fibrous, including a pair of ovoid fleshy tuberoids which are 1-4 cm. long and about 1 cm. in diameter. Stem straw-color or purplish brown, leafy at or near the base, provided above with scale-like bracts. Leaves usually two or four in basal cluster, erect-spreading, oblanceolate to narrowly linear-lanceolate or rarely obovate, obtuse to subacuminate, sheathing the stem below, pale green, usually withering before or during anthesis, 7.5-15 cm. long, 1-3 cm. wide. Raceme spicate, narrowly cylindrical or somewhat subsecund, elongated, densely or laxly many-flowered, 1-3.5 dm. long, 7-15 mm. in diameter. Floral bracts ovate to linear-lanceolate, subobtuse to long-acuminate, concave, prominently 1-nerved, 3-8 mm. long, 2-3 mm. wide near the base, much shorter than the flowers. Flowers small, numerous, in distinct spirals, white, greenish or yellowish green, often marked with purple, the lowermost flowers remote, with strongly arcuate ovaries, fragrant or sometimes malodorous. Sepals rather thin, narrowly elliptic to broadly ovate-elliptic, obtuse to rounded at the apex, more or less concave, 1-nerved, 2-4 mm. long, 0.8-1.5 mm. wide below the middle; lateral sepals oblique, spreading-reflexed, decurrent on the base of the lip. Petals fleshy, sometimes tinged with purple, ovate to elliptic-lanceolate or narrowly triangular-lanceolate, subfalcate, obtuse to subacute, 1-nerved, 1.8-4 mm. long, 0.8-1.5 mm. wide across the more or less dilated base. Lip fleshy, prominently arcuate-recurved, triangular-ovate to linear-elliptic or triangular-lanceolate, usually with a small angle on each side at the base, fleshy-thickened through the center below the middle, 3-nerved, 2.5-4.5 mm. long, 1.2-3 mm. wide across the base. Spur cylindric, slender or slightly clavellate, curved, 3-4.5 mm long, usually about equal to the lip. Capsule suberect, obliquely ellipsoid, 6-10 mm. long.

This species varies considerably in habit. The leaves, when present, vary in shape from linear-lanceolate to oblanceolate or rarely obovate. The inflorescence sometimes consists of only a few scattered flowers and sometimes is a rather densely

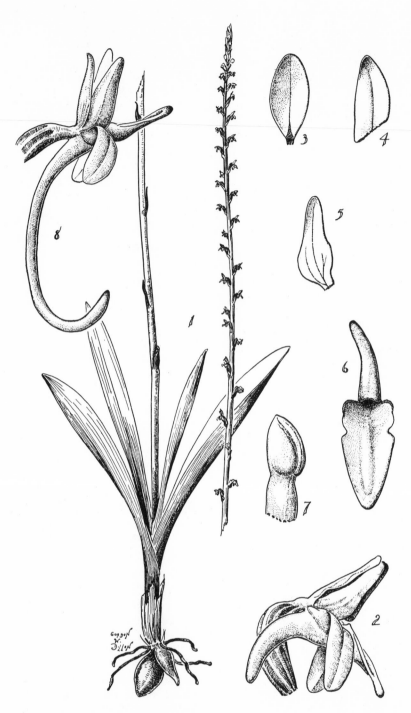

PLATE 40.— **Habenaria unalascensis.** 1, plant, one half natural size. 2, flower, side view, five times natural size. 3, dorsal sepal, five times natural size. 4, lateral sepal, five times natural size. 5, petal, five times natural size. 6, lip and column, front view, spread out, five times natural size. 7, column, side view, ten times natural size.

Habenaria unalascensis var. **elata.** 8, flower, side view, five times natural size. *Drawn by Gordon W. Dillon.*

flowered cylindric raceme. Except for minor variations, however, the flowers are similar in all of the forms examined. Since they are usually twisted sideways they appear to have their floral segments asymmetrically arranged—a condition which does not seem actually to be the case.

This typically far-western species is remarkable in that it occurs in a few isolated, if not disjunct, stations far to the eastward. Within its range, this species is almost ubiquitous, being found under various ecological conditions. It usually grows in dry or moist soil on grassy open slopes, in forests, chaparral, brush-lands, meadows, sandy or gravelly soil along rivers and streams and in leaf mold of coniferous or mixed coniferous-hardwood forests. Although usually found at low elevations, it occurs from near sea level in California, up to 4,500 feet altitude in Alberta and Washington, 5,000 feet in Oregon, 7,000 feet in Idaho, Montana and Wyoming, 8,000 feet in Colorado, California and Nevada and 10,200 feet in Utah. *Habenaria unalascensis* flowers from April to August in various parts of its range.

GEOGRAPHICAL DISTRIBUTION: Anticosti, Quebec, Ontario (Bruce and Manitoulin counties), west to Alberta and British Columbia, northward to Alaska and the Aleutian Islands, south and west to Montana (Flathead and Missoula counties), South Dakota (Lawrence County), Colorado (S. Boulder Peak), Utah (Summit and Weber counties), Nevada (Elko County and E. Humbolt Mountains), California (common and widespread), Oregon (mostly in the Cascade Mountains) and Washington (Cascade and Olympic Mountains) ; also Mexico (Baja California).

CULTURAL NOTES: Primarily a western species, the Slender-spire Orchid occurs at rather high elevations from northwestern Mexico northward, descending to sea level in Alaska and the St. Lawrence Valley. Included under one species are several entities which are difficult to distinguish but which vary to some extent in their environmental preferences. Those studied by the contributor of these notes have been seen growing in open woods in the western mountains where winter temperatures are very low and the soil does not warm up much even in midsummer. The soil-reaction proved to be subacid on the average, but was circumneutral near limestone outcrops. Some attempts have been made to cultivate one or more members of this complex species in eastern wild gardens, but without success, as the pungent fragrance attracts slugs from afar and the plants are soon destroyed. (E. T. W.)

37. **Habenaria unalascensis** var. **elata** (Jepson) Correll, Leafl. West. Bot. 3: 246. 1943. *Habenaria elegans* var. *elata* Jepson, Fl. Calif. 1, pt. 6: 330. 1921. Type locality and collection: California, Solano County, Gates Cañon, Vaca Mountains, June 20, 1892, *W. L. Jepson 21286.* (*Habenaria elegans* (Lindl.) Bolander; *H. Michaelii* Greene; *H. multiflora* (Rydb.) Blankenship; *H. longispicata* S. B. Parish; *H. elegans* var. *multiflora* (Rydb.) Peck; *Piperia elegans* (Lindl.) Rydb.; *P. elongata* Rydb.; *P. lancifolia* Rydb.; *P. leptopetala* Rydb.; *P. multiflora* Rydb.; *P. longispica* Rydb.; *P. Michaelii* (Greene) Rydb.; *Montolivaea elegans* (Lindl.) Rydb.). PLATE 40

(The name, *elata,* is a Latin adjective meaning "tall," referring to the usually tall, strict plants.)

COMMON NAMES: Elegant Piperia, Narrow-petaled Piperia, Wood Rein-orchid, Many-flowered Piperia, Purple-flowered Piperia, Long-spiked Piperia.

Variety *elata* is florally identical to the typical form except for its elongated spur. However, the floral segments are often slightly larger and the spur, which is 8 to 18 mm. long, is about twice as long as the lip, or longer. The plant is usually stouter and taller than the typical form and the leaves larger, being characteristically oblong-elliptic. Also, the raceme, which may be as much as 6 dm. long, is usually more densely flowered than in the typical form.

This variety usually grows in dry woods, but it is also found in dry or moist soil in canyons, brushlands, open slopes, barrens, sandhills and on rocky ridges. It usually occurs at low elevations and is found from near sea level in California and

Oregon, up to 2,000 feet altitude in British Columbia and Washington, 6,000 feet in Idaho and Montana and 8,000 feet in California, and flowers from April (rarely) and May to September in various parts of its range.

GEOGRAPHICAL DISTRIBUTION: California (common and widespread), Oregon (mostly in the Cascade Mountains), Washington (widespread), Idaho (mostly the northern part), Montana (Flathead County) and British Columbia (southwestern part).

CULTURAL NOTES: See this section under the typical form.

38. **Habenaria unalascensis** var. **maritima** (Greene) Correll, Leafl. West. Bot. 3: 247. 1943. *Habenaria maritima* Greene, Pittonia 2: 298. 1892. Type locality: On dry hills near the sea at Point Lobos, near San Francisco, flowering from August to October. (*Piperia maritima* (Greene) Rydb.; *Habenaria elegans* var. *maritima* (Greene) Ames; *H. Greenei* Jepson).

(The name, *maritima,* is a Latin adjective signifying "by the sea," referring to the habitat where this variety was first found.)

COMMON NAME: Coast Piperia.

Variety *maritima* is apparently a robust form of var. *elata.* However, I have maintained it as a distinct variety of *H. unalascensis.* This form is a short, stout plant with large, broad leaves and a conspicuously congested, often pyramidal, raceme. The flowers are more nearly white than in the typical form and are said to be quite fragrant.

This variety is usually found in sandy soil of slopes, fields, pastures, bluffs, cliffs and terraces facing the sea, near or at sea level along the coast. It flowers from July to September.

GEOGRAPHICAL DISTRIBUTION: This variety is found only under the influence of salt air in the littoral regions of California (Del Norte, Marin, Mendocino, Monterey, San Francisco and San Mateo counties) and Oregon (Coos, Curry, Lincoln and Tillamook counties).

CULTURAL NOTES: See this section under the typical form.

39. **Habenaria viridis** (L.) R. Br. var. **bracteata** (Muhl. ex Willd.) A. Gray, Man. Bot. North. U. S., ed. 5: 500. 1867. *Orchis bracteata* Muhl. ex Willd., Sp. Pl. 4: 34. 1805. Type locality: Pennsylvania. (*Habenaria bracteata* (Muhl. ex Willd.) R. Br.; *H. viridis* var. *interjecta* Fernald; *H. virescens* (Muhl. ex Willd.) Spreng.; *H. flava* var. *virescens* (Muhl. ex Willd.) Fernald, as to name, not as to plant; *Coeloglossum bracteatum* (Muhl. ex Willd.) Parl.). PLATE 41 and FIGURE 4

(The name, *viridis,* is a Latin adjective meaning "green," in reference to the color of the flowers. The name, *bracteata,* is a Latin term meaning "bracted," in allusion to the long floral bracts characteristic of this variety.)

COMMON NAMES: Long-bracted Habenaria, Long-bracted Orchid, Satyr Orchid, Frog Orchid, American Frog-orchid.

Plant stout, occasionally slender, glabrous throughout, 0.6-6 dm. tall. Roots fleshy, palmate, from a thickened and swollen rootstock. Stem leafy. Leaves variable, the lower blades obovate to oblanceolate, the upper blades oblong to lanceolate, obtuse to acute, 4-15 cm. long, 1-6.5 cm. wide. Raceme densely or laxly flowered, up to 20 cm. long. Floral bracts linear-lanceolate, acuminate, 1.5-5.5 cm. or more long, usually two to four times the length of the flower (according to the age of the plant). Flowers green, with stout pedicellate ovaries which are 5-10 mm. long. Dorsal sepal ovate-orbicular to oblong-elliptic, concave, 3-6 mm. long, 2-3.5 mm. wide. Lateral sepals obliquely ovate-oblong, obtuse, 4-6 mm. long, 2-4 mm. wide below the middle. Petals linear-lanceolate to linear-oblong, acute to subobtuse, 3-5 mm. long. Lip narrowly oblong-spatulate or narrowly cuneate, 2- to 3-toothed at the apex (the middle tooth short and often obscure), 5-10 mm. long, 2-4 mm. wide near the apex, with a small thickened keel along the center below the middle, occasionally tinged with reddish brown, two to three times longer than the abbreviated saccate whitish spur. Spur scrotiform. Capsule ellipsoid, 7-10 mm. long.

The rather large, pendent lip which is unequally tridentate at the apex, and the scrotiform spur are characteristics of this variety. The lowermost floral bracts always greatly exceed the flowers.

PLATE 41.—**Habenaria viridis** var. **bracteata.** Plant, two thirds natural size. *Drawn by Blanche Ames.*

I have compared the North American variant with numerous specimens of *H. viridis,* from Eurasia, and I find much variation in the plants of both regions. Although long-bracted forms are often found among those from Eurasia, the plants of North America are more constantly long-bracted. An extreme northern variant, described as var. *interjecta* Fernald (1926A), is only a dwarf form whose inflorescence is considered to be intermediate between that of the typical form and var. *bracteata* (hence the varietal name). I do not consider this proposed segregate worthy of separation from the var. *bracteata*. A collection of VAN SCHAACK (No. 756) from Attu Island in the Aleutians contained a plant only 6 cm. tall with about eight flowers and only two leaves. Superficially, it resembled *H. behringiana*.

Variety *bracteata* is commonly found in moist or wet soil in dense hardwood or mixed coniferous-hardwood forests, in meadows, prairies, thickets, bogs and swamps, on open grassy slopes, turfy barrens and beach-meadows. It occurs up to 1,500 feet altitude in Alaska, 1,900 feet in New Hampshire, 2,500 feet in Quebec, New York, Vermont and Virginia, 4,500 feet in British Columbia, Nebraska and North Carolina, 5,500 feet in Alberta, 6,000 feet in Montana and Wyoming and 9,000 feet in Colorado and New Mexico. It flowers from March (in Michigan) and May to August in various parts of its range.

TEXTFIGURE 4.— Habenaria viridis var. bracteata, lip and spur, front-side view, five times natural size. *Drawn by Gordon W. Dillon.*

GEOGRAPHICAL DISTRIBUTION: Newfoundland, Nova Scotia, New Brunswick, Quebec and Ontario, west to British Columbia, Alaska and the Aleutian Islands, through New England, New York, New Jersey, Pennsylvania and Maryland (Frederick County), south in the mountains to Virginia (Bath and Smyth counties) and North Carolina (Buncombe and Mitchell counties), through the Lake States to Minnesota, Iowa (Johnson County) and Nebraska (Cass, Dawes and Otoe counties), west and southwest to Colorado (Gilpin, Jefferson, Larimer and Ouray counties), New Mexico (San Miguel and Sierra counties), Utah (Iron County), Wyoming (Sheridan County), Montana (Gallatin, Lake and Wheatland counties) and Washington (rare in the Cascade Mountains); also Iceland, Japan and China.

CULTURAL NOTES: Circumboreal in distribution, the American Frog-orchid ranges south at moderate elevations into North Carolina and the Rocky Mountains, evidently surviving glaciation in the latter regions. It grows chiefly in subacid soil in damp open woods, being tolerant of a fairly wide range of temperature. Little success has rewarded attempts to cultivate it in wild flower gardens, however, partly because of the difficulty of keeping the soil sufficiently acid and partly owing to its susceptibility of attack by parasitic fungi. (E. T. W.)

According to BROWN (1813), this variety was first introduced into England in 1805 by Messrs. Napier and Chandler.

* * * * *

Habenaria conopsea (L.) Benth., Journ. Linn. Soc. 18: 354. 1881.

In 1913, BRITTON and BROWN (page 553) included this species (as *Gymnadenia conopsea* (L.) R. Br.) in their Flora with the following note: ". . . otherwise known only from the Old World, [it] has been collected at Litchfield, Connecticut. The flower has a broad 3-lobed lip and a slender spur much longer than the ovary."

This Eurasian orchid doubtless occurred as a non-persistent waif in Connecticut for, since the above report, it apparently has not been found again in this country.

> *Bigelow thinks it [Habenaria psycodes var. grandiflora] the most beautiful of all the orchises. . . . It is fairest seen rising from amid brakes and hellebore, its lower part, or rather naked stem, concealed. Where the most beautiful wild flowers grow, there man's spirit is fed and poets grow. . . . Nature has taken no pains to exhibit it, and few that bloom are ever seen by mortal eyes.* (THOREAU: "Summer", 1884).

4. Listera R. Br.

Listera R. Br. in Ait., Hort. Kew., ed. 2, 5 : 201. 1813, conserved name.

(The name, *Listera,* is in honor of Dr. MARTIN LISTER (1638-1712), an English naturalist.)

Small inconspicuous terrestrial herbs with fibrous roots and slender stems which are more or less glandular-pubescent above. Leaves two, opposite or subopposite, sessile, inserted at about the middle of the stem. Inflorescence a terminal raceme composed of small greenish or purplish flowers. Sepals and petals free, similar and subequal. Lip longer than the sepals and petals, rounded and apiculate to deeply bilobed at the apex, variously toothed, auricled, lobed or sometimes entire on each side at the base. Column wingless; stigmas with a rounded beak; anther borne on the back of the column near the apex; pollinia two, powdery. Capsule small, slender, pedicellate.

This is a small genus of about twenty-five species which are widely distributed in boreal and temperate regions of the Northern Hemisphere. They are found primarily in thickets, wooded ravines, in humus of low woods, sphagnum bogs, pine barrens and mossy evergreen swamps in usually strongly acid soils.

Although several of the species are widely distributed, most of them (except *L. cordata*) appear to be more or less rare and of local occurrence.

KEY FOR THE IDENTIFICATION OF THE SPECIES OF LISTERA

1. Lip linear-oblong, cleft halfway (or more) to the base into linear-filiform to linear-lanceolate lobes, not flaring at the apex; column 0.5 mm. or less long..............................2
  2. Lip with prominent curved basal lateral teeth; lamina less than 6 mm. long; stem green...
  ....*L. cordata* (p. 126)
  2. Lip slightly auriculate at the base but without lateral teeth; lamina more than 6 mm. long; stem purplish...*L. australis* (p. 119)
1. Lip oblong to narrowly cuneate or obovate, cleft (sometimes not cleft) less than halfway to the base into oblong or broadly rounded lobes, flaring or only slightly dilated at the apex; column 1.5-4 mm. long...3
  3. Lip essentially oblong, auriculate, usually broadest at the base, without lateral teeth, with a fleshy ridge in the center near the base.......................................4
    4. Auricles small, clasping the column; sepals and petals 4 mm. or less long; distribution entirely eastern...*L. auriculata* (p. 117)
    4. Auricles rather large, divergent; sepals and petals usually more than 4.5 mm. long; distribution Rocky Mountains and Mingan Islands (Quebec) ....*L. borealis* (p. 121)
  3. Lip cuneate to obovate, not auriculate, broadest at the apex, provided with obsolescent or prominent lateral teeth, without a fleshy ridge.....................................5
    5. Lip with a short slender claw, provided with an obsolescent triangular tooth on each side at the base; column slender, 2.5-3 mm. long............*L. convallarioides* (p. 124)
    5. Lip sessile, with a prominent tooth on each side at the base; column short, stout, 1.5-2 mm. long 6
      6. Leaves suborbicular-ovate to elliptic-ovate, usually obtuse; pedicels glandular; lip rounded to lightly retuse at the apex, less than 5 mm. wide; lateral teeth of lip with a dark swelling at the base; distribution northwestern............*L. caurina* (p. 123)
      6. Leaves ovate-reniform, acute or mucronate; pedicels glabrous; lip deeply cleft with the large lobes divergent, 5 mm. or more wide; lateral teeth of lip without a swelling at the base; distribution eastern.................................*L. Smallii* (p. 127)

1. **Listera auriculata** Wiegand, Bull. Torr. Bot. Club 26 : 166, pl. 356, fig. 2. 1899.
    Type locality: Cedar swamps and mossy banks, Quebec, New Hampshire and Maine. (*Ophrys auriculata* (Wiegand) House).   PLATE 42

(The name, *auriculata*, is a Latin adjective signifying "auriculate" or "with ears," in allusion to the small auricles found at the base of the lip.)

COMMON NAME: Auricled Twayblade.

Plant 6.5-24 cm. tall. Stem slender, pale green, 3.5-18 cm. long, glabrous below, densely glandular-puberulent above, rarely with a linear bract below the raceme. Leaves two, sub-

PLATE 42.— **Listera auriculata.** 1, plant, two thirds natural size. 2, flower, spread out, four times natural size. 3, column, side view, ten times natural size.
   Listera borealis. 4, plant, two thirds natural size. 5, flower, spread out, four times natural size. *Drawn by Gordon W. Dillon.*

opposite, inserted above the middle of the stem or just below the raceme, suborbicular to suborbicular-ovate or elliptic-ovate, subobtuse to rounded at the apex, thin, glabrous, pale green, 2.5-6 cm. long, 1.5-4.2 cm. wide. Raceme laxly flowered, 2-10 cm. long, about 2 cm. in diameter; rachis pubescent. Floral bracts broadly elliptic to oblong-lanceolate, obtuse, glabrous,

2-7 mm. long, 1-2 mm. wide when spread out. Flowers usually numerous, pale whitish green, usually tinged with purple, on rather stout glabrous or sparsely pubescent pedicels which are 2-4 mm. long, with the sepals and petals strongly reflexed. Dorsal sepal elliptic-obovate, rounded to subobtuse at the apex, 1-nerved, 3-3.5 mm. long, about 1.5 mm. wide. Lateral sepals very oblique, semiorbicular-elliptic to broadly ovate-lanceolate, subobtuse to acute, 1-nerved, 3-4 mm. long, 1.3-1.5 mm. wide. Petals linear-oblong to linear, obtuse, falcate, 1-nerved, 3-3.5 mm. long, about 0.8 mm. wide. Lip oblong, somewhat narrowed at about the middle, ciliate on the margins, 6-12.5 mm. long, about 2.5 mm. wide across the middle, cleft at the somewhat dilated apex into a pair of oblong obtuse lobes which are up to 4 mm. long, with or without an apicule in the sinus, slightly dilated and auriculate at the base; auricles rather small and narrow, incurved and clasping the column, acutely angled on the inner margin at the apex; disc 3-nerved with the lateral nerves branched and with a ridge in the center at the base, somewhat thickened along the center. Column arcuate, 2.5-3 mm. long. Capsule obliquely ovoid, about 8 mm. long.

This species is extremely close to *L. borealis*. However, in typical material, the Auricled Twayblade has broader and usually thinner leaves than *L. borealis*. The apical lobes of the lip are also usually narrower and not conspicuously divergent as in *L. borealis,* and the auricles are narrower, incurved and clasping the column instead of being broad and divergent as in the Northern Twayblade. The pedicel and ovary of the Auricled Twayblade is usually glabrous while those of *L. borealis* are provided with long whitish glandular hairs. The lip of *L. auriculata* is also much narrower than that of *L. borealis*.

Listera auriculata is commonly found in alluvial soils in low woods, swamps, thickets, and in moist mossy soil along wooded river-banks. It is found at low elevations, and flowers from June to August.

GEOGRAPHICAL DISTRIBUTION: Newfoundland (Beachan Junction), Quebec (Bonaventure, S. Gaspé and Matane counties), New Brunswick, Ontario, Maine (Aroostook, Hancock, Oxford, Penobscot, Piscataquis and Somerset counties), New Hampshire (Coös County) and Michigan (Keweenaw County).

CULTURAL NOTES: This orchid of cool climates presumably survived glaciation in bogs around the margin of the ice sheets, and when the ice melted, migrated into the barren area and perished in its more southern stations. Not only does it require a soil which remains cool throughout the summer, but it also thrives best in soils of a high degree of acidity, such as are developed in sphagnum bogs. Only where special efforts are made to maintain these conditions could its cultivation be successful. (E. T. W.)

2. **Listera australis** Lindl., Gen. and Sp. Orch. Pl. 456. 1840. Type citations: Carolina, *Elliott, Drummond*. (*Ophrys australis* (Lindl.) House).

PLATE 43

(The name, *australis,* is a Latin term meaning "southern," designating the region where this species was originally discovered.)

COMMON NAMES: Southern Twayblade, Apiculate Cleft-lip, Shining Twayblade.

Plant slender, 8-29 cm. tall; roots often matted, fibrous. Stem purplish, succulent, glabrous below, sparsely glandular-pubescent above, occasionally growing in clusters of as many as ten together. Leaves two, opposite, inserted at or above the middle of the stem, ovate to ovate-oblong or elliptic, obtuse to apiculate, often subcordate at the base, deep green, 1.3-4 cm. long, 0.5-2.1 cm. wide near the base. Raceme open, few- to many-flowered, 4.5-11 cm. long, 1.5-3 cm. in diameter. Floral bracts minute, suborbicular-ovate, obtuse (rarely abnormally leaf-like, becoming ovate-lanceolate and as much as 18 mm. long and 8 mm. wide). Flowers small, reddish purple, on filiform pedicels which are 4-6 mm. long. Dorsal sepal ovate-elliptic, obtuse, less than 1.5 mm. long, about 1 mm. wide. Lateral sepals ovate, obtuse, less than 2 mm. long and 1 mm. wide. Petals oblong-quadrate, recurved, less than 1.5 mm. long, about 1 mm. wide. Lip sessile, linear, cleft one-third to three-fourths of the way to the base, 6-12 mm. long, about 2 mm. wide near the middle, with a small incurved auricle on each side at the base, with a slight ridge in the center near the base; apical lobes linear-attenuated, acuminate, separated by a minute tooth in the sinus. Column thick, about 0.5 mm. long.

The occurrence of this typically southern plant in several isolated stations in Canada is most interesting. It is the only species in the genus extending from Florida to Canada, and is probably the rarest orchid to be found in the eastern half of the Dominion.

PLATE 43.—**Listera australis.** 1, plant, natural size. 2, flower, front view, five times natural size. 3, flower, front-side view, five times natural size. 4, petal, six times natural size. *Drawn by Gordon W. Dillon.*

According to MOUSLEY (1940), the Southern Twayblade was found for the first time in Canada in the large bog, Mer Bleue, about fifteen miles east of Ottawa, by Prof. FLETCHER on June 21, 1893.

The Southern Twayblade is commonly found in rich humus of low moist woods, ravines, in low pine barrens, marshes, sphagnum bogs and thickets. It often grows on the thick rhizome of Cinnamon Fern (*Osmunda cinnamomea*) and Royal Fern (*O. regalis* var. *spectabilis*). It is found at low elevations, and flowers from February (in the South) to July (in the North).

GEOGRAPHICAL DISTRIBUTION: Found locally in Quebec (Laval County), Ontario (Carleton County), (?) Maine (Aroostook County), Vermont (Lamoille County), New York (Cayuga, Oneida, Onondaga, Oswego, Suffolk and Wayne counties) and New Jersey, through the Atlantic States to central Florida (south to Manatee and Polk counties), along the Gulf Coast to Texas (Hardin, Harris and Jefferson counties).

CULTURAL NOTES: In contrast to *L. auriculata,* this species is relatively indifferent to climatic conditions. Ranging as it does from the Gulf Coast to the Great Lakes, it is evidently able to withstand extremes of both summer heat and winter cold. It seems to require fairly acid soils, growing toward the northern part of its range in thickets where sphagnum moss is abundant, and southward occupying moist pinelands and hardwood forests. There is no record of its successful cultivation for any length of time, for even when its soil requirements are satisfied, it is soon attacked by garden pests, especially slugs, and one bite is likely to injure fatally the plant's delicate stem. (E. T. W.)

3. **Listera borealis** Morong, Bull. Torr. Bot. Club 20: 31. 1893. Type locality and collection: Fort Smith, Slave River, Hudson Bay Territory, June 28, 1892, *Miss E. Taylor.* (*Ophrys borealis* (Morong) Rydb.). PLATE 42

(The name, *borealis,* is a Latin adjective meaning "northern," designating the region where this species was originally discovered and where it is most frequent.)

COMMON NAME: Northern Twayblade.

Plant usually small, 6-27 cm. tall. Stem rather stout, somewhat 4-angled, greenish white, glabrous below, sparsely glandular-puberulent above, 5-18 cm. long. Leaves subopposite, inserted above the middle of the stem, usually narrowly elliptic to ovate-elliptic, rarely suborbicular-ovate, obtuse to rounded at the apex, rather thick and fleshy, glabrous, pale green, 1.3-6 cm. long, 0.7-3 cm. wide. Raceme few-flowered, open, 2-9 cm. long, about 3 cm. in diameter; rachis glandular-puberulent. Floral bracts minute, ovate to oblong, obtuse, 1-2 mm. long. Flowers pale green or yellowish green, with the nerves of the strongly reflexed sepals and petals darker green, on filiform pedicels which are 3.5-7 mm. long; ovary and pedicels often provided with long whitish glandular hairs. Dorsal sepal elliptic-lanceolate to linear-elliptic, obtuse to rounded at the apex, 1-nerved, 4-6 mm. long, 1.5-2.2 mm. wide. Lateral sepals linear-elliptic to oblong-lanceolate, obtuse to rounded (sometimes nearly retuse) at the apex, falcate, 1-nerved, 4.5-7 mm. long, 1.4-2.3 mm. wide. Petals linear to linear-oblong, obtuse, 1-nerved, 4-5.5 mm. long, 0.7-1.5 mm. wide. Lip broadly oblong, somewhat narrowed at the middle, ciliate on the margins, 7-12 mm. long, 4.2-6.5 mm. wide above the middle, cleft at the somewhat dilated apex into a pair of oblong or semiorbicular lobes which are up to 3 mm. long and wide, with a large apicule in the sinus, prominently dilated at the base and with conspicuous auricles; auricles broadly rounded and bluntly angled, divergent, at least 1.5 mm. long and 1.3 mm. wide; disc 3-nerved, the lateral nerves being much branched and purplish, with a ridge in the center at the darker green base, thickened along the center. Column rather stout, arcuate, 3-4 mm. long.

This little plant occurs in some of the most attractive surroundings imaginable. The following observation was made in 1943 along the Alaskan Highway in the mountains just north of Summit Lake in northern British Columbia.

Having made my way down a narrow dry gulch I eventually came to a river-forest where the mosses and lichens had accumulated to form a deep, spongy forest-floor. In this mossy cushion grew two little orchids—the Northern Twayblade and the Northern Coral-root (*Corallorhiza trifida*). The latter, a straw-colored saprophyte, was not only represented by typical plants having brownish purple-spotted flowers but also by those which had greenish flowers with white markings. The mauve-colored lips of the twayblades, already well past their prime, hung limply along their threadlike rachis. I turned upstream and entered a dense spruce forest which supported a luxuriant undergrowth of willows, alders and several

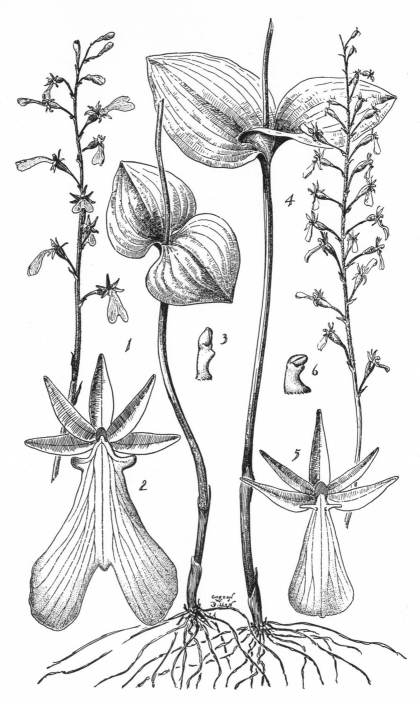

PLATE 44.—**Listera Smallii.** 1, plant, natural size. 2, flower, with the column removed, front view, spread open, five times natural size. 3, column, side view, five times natural size.

Listera caurina. 4, plant, natural size. 5, flower, with column removed, front view, spread open, five times natural size. 6, column, side view, five times natural size. *Drawn by Gordon W. Dillon.*

species of currants, the latter bearing clusters of small yellowish green flowers which hung from the tips of leafy twigs. Growing beneath them were glistening plants of the Northern Twayblade, intermingled with the startlingly white flowers of the One-flowered Wintergreen which were held rigidly erect like fairy umbrellas in the deep green mosses.

The Northern Twayblade is found commonly in rich moist mossy coniferous or coniferous-hardwood forests, swamps, in ravines along rivers and streams, and on subalpine slopes and bluffs. It usually grows at high elevations, and occurs up to 6,000 feet altitude in Idaho, Alberta and British Columbia and 10,000 feet in Colorado and Utah. This species blooms from March (in Alberta) to July.

GEOGRAPHICAL DISTRIBUTION: Hudson Bay, Mackenzie, Alberta (Banff, Cypress Hills, Ponoka), British Columbia, the Yukon, Alaska (Fairbanks, *fide Porsild*), Colorado (Chaffee County), Montana, Wyoming (Sublette County), Idaho (Bonneville, Custer and Fremont counties) and Utah (Salt Lake and Summit counties); also Mingan Islands (Gulf of St. Lawrence).

CULTURAL NOTES: This species apparently survived glaciation at high elevations in the Rocky Mountains, then after the melting of the ice, the orchid migrated far north to Alaska and the Hudson Bay region. It evidently requires an especially cold soil, and its growth in sphagnum bogs indicates high acidity preference. (E. T. W.)

4. **Listera caurina** Piper, Erythea 6: 32. 1898. Type citations: Common in the Cascade Mountains, at about 3,000 feet altitude, in coniferous woods, *Henderson, Piper;* Olympic Mountains, *Lamb;* Cedar Mountains, Latah County, Idaho, *Piper.* (*Ophrys caurina* (Piper) Rydb.). PLATE 44

(The name, *caurina,* is a Latin adjective signifying "of the northwest wind," apparently in allusion to the Northwest where this species occurs.)

COMMON NAME: Northwest Twayblade.

Plant erect, glabrous below, densely glandular-puberulent above, 1-3 dm. tall. Stem slender, rarely with one or two bracts below the raceme, 8-17 cm. long. Leaves two, nearly opposite, inserted above the middle of the stem, suborbicular to suborbicular-ovate to elliptic-ovate, rounded to obtuse or subacute at the apex, 2.5-7 cm. long, 1.8-4.5 cm. wide. Raceme few- to many-flowered, open, 5-13 cm. long, 2-3 cm. in diameter; rachis puberulent. Floral bracts rhombic-ovate to lanceolate, acute to acuminate, glabrous or slightly glandular (the lower bracts occasionally bifurcating and subtending two flowers), 2-10 mm. long. Flowers small, greenish or dull yellow, on filiform glandular-puberulent pedicels which are 4-12 mm. long. Sepals linear-lanceolate to lanceolate, acute to acuminate or attenuate, 1-nerved, spreading, 3-4 mm. long, about 1 mm. or less wide; lateral sepals falcate. Petals linear-lanceolate to lanceolate, acute to acuminate, spreading, 1-nerved, 2.8-3.5 mm. long, 0.5-0.8 mm. wide. Lip sessile, cuneate to obovate, rounded to retuse at the apex, apiculate or (if retuse) with a mucro in the sinus, slightly erose or crenulate on the apical margin, several-nerved with the nerves branched, 4.5-6 mm. long, 2-4.5 mm. wide near the apex, provided with a short filiform tooth on each side at the base, with a dark swelling at the base of each tooth, the teeth nerveless and less than 1 mm. long. Column short, 1.5-2 mm. long. Capsule ovoid, glabrous, about 5 mm. long.

Although this is a most distinct species, it is often confused with *L. convallarioides.* The Northwest Twayblade is the only *Listera* in our region whose lip is entire (or merely retuse) at the apex. All the other species have their lip prominently cleft at the apex.

The Northwest Twayblade is commonly found in dense moist coniferous forests and on boggy wooded slopes, especially in the mountains. In Alaska, it has been collected in alluvial soil of moist hardwood forests. It occurs up to 300 feet altitude in Alaska, 5,500 feet in California and 7,000 feet in Idaho and Washington, and flowers from the first of June to September (in Alaska).

GEOGRAPHICAL DISTRIBUTION: Montana (Flathead, Gallatin and Teton counties), Idaho (Bonner and Teton counties), Washington (Jefferson, Kittitas, Lewis, Pierce, Skamania, Snohomish and Whatcom counties), Oregon (Curry, Hood River and Klamath counties), California (Del Norte and Humboldt counties), Alberta (Carbondale River Region), British

Columbia (Vancouver Island, Selkirk Mountains) and Alaska (Sitka, Glacier Bay and Funter Bay).

CULTURAL NOTES: This tiny twayblade has been studied in the western mountains where it is locally abundant in the litter of needles in coniferous forests. When tested, the reaction of the soil around its roots proved to be subacid and the temperature to be rather low. It may possibly be cultivated in the garden in situations similar to those described. (E. T. W.)

5. **Listera convallarioides** (Sw.) Nutt., Gen. North. Am. Pl. 2:191. 1818, *nomen,* and Torr., Comp. Fl. North. and Middle States 320. 1826. *Epipactis convallarioides* Sw., Kongl. Svens. Vetens. Acad. Nya Handl. 21: 232. 1800. Type locality: North America. (*Ophrys convallarioides* (Sw.) W. F. Wight). PLATE 45

(The name, *convallarioides,* is a classic term meaning "like the Lily of the Valley," referring to the superficial resemblance of the plants of this species to those of *Convallaria.*)

COMMON NAMES: Broad-leaved Twayblade, Broad-lipped Twayblade.

Plants slender or occasionally stout, stoloniferous, glabrous below, densely and minutely whitish glandular-pubescent above, 6-37 cm. tall. Leaves two, opposite or occasionally sub-opposite, mostly above the middle of the stem, broadly ovate to elliptic, oval or suborbicular, obtuse or rarely acute to apiculate, glabrous, 2-7 cm. long, 1.5-5.8 cm. wide. Raceme loose, laxly many-flowered, 2-12 cm. long, 2.5-4 cm. in diameter. Floral bracts rhombic-ovate, acute to acuminate, semitranslucent, 3-5 mm. long. Flowers yellowish green, on slender pedicels which are 4-7 mm. long. Dorsal sepal ovate-lanceolate, narrowly obtuse to acute, 4.5-5 mm. long, about 1.8-2 mm. wide. Lateral sepals lanceolate, strongly falcate-recurved, acute to subacute, 1-nerved, 4.5-5.5 mm. long, 1.5-1.8 mm. wide below the middle. Petals linear-falcate, obtuse, 1-nerved, 4-5 mm. long, 0.8-1 mm. wide. Lip with a short slender claw, narrowly cuneate, shallowly notched at the apex, with the lateral lobules obtusely rounded, minutely toothed in the sinus, with a short triangular tooth on each side near the base, minutely bristly-ciliate along the margins, 8-13 mm. long, 5-7 mm. wide near the apex. Column slender, slightly recurved, 2.5-3 mm. long. Capsule nearly glabrous.

Although this species is now clearly defined it was confused by some authors with *L. cordata* and *L. australis* until the time of WIEGAND's revision of the genus in 1899.

The occurrence of this widespread Canadian and Northwestern species in the mountains of North Carolina is extremely interesting. It is another example of the exceptionally rich flora of the Southern Appalachian Mountains, particularly in relation to relic species which still exist on the higher peaks in that region.

The Broad-leaved Twayblade occurs in leaf mold in damp mossy coniferous or mixed coniferous-hardwood forests, bogs, meadows, various types of evergreen swamps, wet thickets in forests and in peaty barrens. It usually grows at high elevations, being found up to 400 feet altitude in Newfoundland, 1,500 feet in New York, 5,000 feet in Oregon and Washington and 8,500 feet in Arizona, California and Nevada. The Broad-leaved Twayblade flowers from June to September in various parts of its range.

GEOGRAPHICAL DISTRIBUTION: Newfoundland and Ontario, west to British Columbia, Alaska and the Aleutian Islands (rare), Wyoming (Medicine Bow Mountains), Idaho (Boundary, Latah and Teton counties), Utah (Juab County), Nevada (Douglas, Elko and Ormsby counties), Arizona (Pima County), California (south to Fresno County), Oregon and Washington; south to Vermont (Caledonia, Lamoille and Orange counties), New York (Essex County) and Michigan (Cheboygan, Keweenaw, Mackinac, Marquette and Schoolcraft counties); also mountains of "Carolina" and Tennessee, and Asia (Commander Islands, *fide* Hultén).

CULTURAL NOTES: The Broad-leaved Twayblade is a widespread plant, extending from Newfoundland and Central New England to the mountains of California, and north to Alaska. As would be expected, it prefers a cool soil. Otherwise, it is rather adaptable, growing in rich humus in open woods where the soil may be

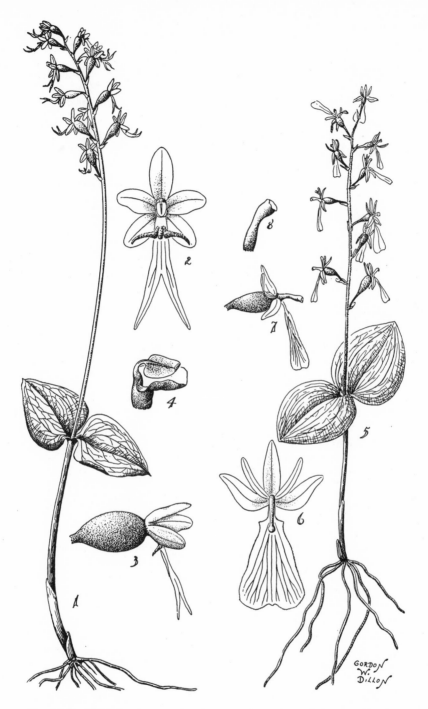

PLATE 45.—**Listera cordata.** 1, plant, natural size. 2, flower, front view, spread open, five times natural size. 3, flower, side view, five times natural size. 4, column, side view, fifteen times natural size.

Listera convallarioides. 5, plant, natural size. 6, flower, front view, spread open, three times natural size. 7, flower, side view, twice natural size. 8, column, side view, five times natural size. *Drawn by Gordon W. Dillon.*

circumneutral or at most only mildly acid in reaction. In attempting to cultivate it, more attention must therefore be given to temperature than to the composition of the soil. It is, however, extraordinarily susceptible to attack by parasitic fungi, so unless these can be controlled its successful cultivation seems unlikely. (E. T. W.)

6. **Listera cordata** (L.) R. Br. in Ait., Hort. Kew., ed. 2, 5: 201. 1813. *Ophrys cordata* L., Sp. Pl., ed. 1, 2: 946. 1753. Type locality: Moist cold forests of Europe. (*Listera nephrophylla* Rydb.; *Ophrys nephrophylla* Rydb.).

PLATE 45

(The name, *cordata,* is a Latin adjective meaning "heart-shaped," referring to the shape of the leaves.)

COMMON NAME: Heart-leaved Twayblade.

Plant slender, delicate, glabrous throughout (except for a small glandular-pubescent area just above the leaves), 6.5-25 cm. tall; roots often somewhat matted. Leaves two, opposite, about midway up the stem, broadly to narrowly ovate-cordate or deltoid, mucronate, 0.9-4 cm. long, 0.7-3.8 cm. wide. Raceme densely or loosely flowered, slender, 2-10 cm long, 8-15 mm. in diameter. Floral bracts small, purplish to yellowish green, on slender pedicels which are 1-4 mm. long. Dorsal sepal ovate-oblong to oblong-elliptic, obtuse, 2-3 mm. long, about 1 mm. wide. Lateral sepals ovate-oblong to elliptic or oblong-linear, obtuse, somewhat oblique, 2-3 mm. long, 0.5-1.5 mm. wide. Petals elliptic to oblong-linear, obtuse or occasionally truncate, 1.5-2.5 mm. long, 0.5-1 mm. wide. Lip linear-oblong, cleft one-half to two-thirds of the distance to the base into two linear-lanceolate lobes, with a subulate transverse tooth on each side near the base, the lamina being 3-6 mm. long and 1-1.5 mm. wide near the middle. Column short, about 0.5 mm. long.

As HULTÉN points out, two color types exist in this species, especially in Alaska, the Canadian Rocky Mountains and the Selkirk Range. One type has greenish flowers (segregated as var. *nephrophylla* (Rydb.) Hult.) while the other (the typical form) has dark purple or purplish black flowers. Although the two forms usually grow intermingled in the same localities, very few intermediates occur.

In the mountainous country south of Lake Muncho in northern British Columbia I observed large colonies of this little orchid growing in a most picturesque setting. At the time, our party was encamped in a high mountain pass along the Alaskan Highway. The rich spruce-balsam forest which sloped precipitously eastward from our camp lay quiet and cool. Sheltered beneath its low branches were numerous "shy" Heart-leaved Twayblades. These frail delicate plants threaded their long slender stems through a thick carpet of moss to lift their weak rachis of mauve-colored flowers above the spongy forest-floor. Saw-toothed leaves of alder shrubs cast jagged shadows about the tiny orchids as narrow sharp rays of sunlight cut their way through chance openings in the needle-studded canopy above.

The Heart-leaved Twayblade is found usually in mountainous regions in mossy damp coniferous or mixed coniferous-hardwood forests, sphagnum bogs, various kinds of evergreen swamps and in subalpine forests and thickets. In the Aleutian Islands it occurs commonly on mossy heath-slopes of hills and in meadows. This species is found near sea level in Oregon, up to 1,000 feet altitude in Newfoundland, 3,000 feet in New Hampshire, 4,500 feet in British Columbia and Washington, 6,500 feet in Idaho, 9,000 feet in New Mexico and 11,500 feet in Colorado. It flowers from April to September in various parts of its range.

GEOGRAPHICAL DISTRIBUTION: Greenland (Trollfjordeidet and Godhavn), Miquelon Island, Newfoundland, Labrador, Anticosti, Nova Scotia, Prince Edward Island, New Brunswick, Quebec and Ontario, west to British Columbia, Alaska and the Aleutian Islands (common), through northern New England, New York and New Jersey, south in the mountains to North Carolina, west to Wyoming, Montana (Flathead County), Idaho (Boise and Custer counties), Colorado (Boulder, Huerfano and Larimer counties), Utah (Summit County), New Mexico (Pecos River National Forest), California (Humboldt County), Oregon (Boulder, Clackamas, Lane and Polk counties) and Washington; also Iceland, Europe and Japan.

CULTURAL NOTES: One of the most widely distributed Listeras, the Heart-leaved Twayblade does not appear to be very particular as to its environment.

While chiefly northern in distribution—occurring from the Atlantic to the Pacific— it extends far south in the Appalachian Mountains, so it apparently can stand fairly high summer temperatures. It is often found in wet thickets where sphagnum moss creates a strongly acid environment, but it also occurs in subacid humus in moist woodlands. It may be cultivated in bog gardens, provided parasites are not too abundant. (E. T. W.)

7. **Listera Smallii** Wiegand, Bull. Torr. Bot. Club 26: 169, t. 357, fig. 7. 1899.
   Listera reniformis Small, Bull. Torr. Bot. Club 24: 334. 1897, not *L. reniformis* D. Don (1825). Type locality: Damp thickets on the mountains of Maryland, Virginia and North Carolina, ranging from about 1000 to 1750 meters altitude. (*Ophrys Smallii* (Wiegand) House). PLATE 44

(The name, *Smallii,* is in honor of JOHN KUNKEL SMALL (1869-1938), distinguished American botanist who worked and published primarily on the flora of the southeastern United States.)

COMMON NAMES: Appalachian Twayblade, Kidney-leaf Twayblade.

Plant slender, 6-35 cm. tall; roots somewhat matted. Stem glabrous below, glandular-pubescent above with several alternate bracts. Leaves two, opposite, inserted about midway up the stem or a little below the middle, ovate-reniform, acute, mucronate or apiculate to short-acuminate, dark green, 2-4 cm. long, 1.5-3.5 cm. wide. Raceme laxly few-flowered, 4-10 cm. long. Floral bracts small, ovate, acute, 3-4 mm. long. Flowers yellowish or whitish green, on slender pedicels which are 6-7 mm. long. Sepals lanceolate or linear-lanceolate, 3-4 mm. long. Petals linear-lanceolate, acute, reflexed. Lip sessile, broadly obovate to cuneate, dilated and deeply cleft at the apex into a pair of divergent broadly rounded lobes, shallowly toothed in the sinus, with a short recurved tooth on each side near the base; lamina 6-10 mm. long, 5-7 mm. wide above. Column short, thick, 1.5-2 mm. long.

This species, which was originally confused with *L. convallarioides,* differs in its more slender habit, reniform leaves which are apiculate or shortly acuminate at the apex and cordate or subcordate at the base, and the lip which is sharply cleft (often nearly to the middle) and forms a V-shaped sinus.

The earliest collection I have seen of this species in our region is that of a specimen in the Elliott Herbarium in the Charleston (South Carolina) Museum which was found at "Three Rivers," South Carolina in 1825.

In the virgin hemlock forest (known as "Ravenel's Forest") near Highlands in the mountains of North Carolina, this species grows abundantly in the decayed needles which have accumulated to a depth of several feet. One of its favorite haunts is in rich humus beneath tangled growths of Rhododendron.

The Appalachian Twayblade is usually found on moist wooded mountain slopes, in moist humus in deep woods, in damp shaded thickets, and sometimes in wooded sphagnum bogs. It occurs up to 4,000 feet altitude in the mountains of North Carolina and Tennessee, and flowers during June and July.

GEOGRAPHICAL DISTRIBUTION: Pennsylvania ("Mts. Penn.", *Porter;* Center County, *fide Wherry*), Maryland, West Virginia (Pocahontas County) and Virginia (Augusta County), south in the mountains to South Carolina (Three Rivers), Georgia (Union County) and Tennessee (Johnson County); also Asia. (There is a sheet of this species in the University of Michigan Herbarium said to have been collected by a Mr. SHOOP at Rock Harbor, Isle Royale, Michigan. This is a questionable record and must remain so until verified.)

CULTURAL NOTES: The Appalachian Twayblade ranges from northernmost South Carolina to Center County, Pennsylvania, at moderate to high elevations. It can thus tolerate both severe winter and fairly high summer temperatures. Toward the northern part of its range, it is found chiefly in sphagnous thickets, but southward it often occupies the accumulations of leaf-litter under Rhododendron thickets. In both cases, the soil-reaction is decidedly acid. Because of not requiring extreme conditions, it is perhaps the easiest of the genus to cultivate, but if the Rhododendron leaves in the garden also harbor slugs, the plant does not survive long. (E. T. W.)

5. Epipactis Sw.

Epipactis Sw., Kongl. Svens. Vetens. Acad. Nya Handl. 21: 231. 1800, in part; emend. L. C. Rich., De Orch. Europ. Annot. 29. 1817 (in Mém. Mus. Hist. Nat. Par. 4: 51. 1818), conserved name.

(The name, *Epipactis,* is a classical name used by THEOPHRASTUS. The plant was supposed to be used to curdle milk.)

Plant terrestrial, consisting of a simple leafy stem arising from a short creeping rhizome; roots fibrous. Leaves variable, plicate-venose, orbicular to linear-lanceolate. Inflorescence a few- to many-flowered prominently bracted and more or less secund raceme. Floral bracts foliaceous, conspicuously exceeding the flowers. Flowers small or medium-sized, greenish to purplish or variously colored. Sepals free, subequal, spreading or loosely connivent. Petals similar to the sepals but smaller. Lip sessile on the base of the column, fleshy, saccate at the base, expanded above into a flat lamina, constricted or distinctly 3-lobed above, with the lateral lobes erect and forming a sac. Column short, broadened above; anther sessile, behind the broad truncate stigma on a slender-jointed base; pollinia four, mealy-granulose, becoming attached to the gland capping the small rounded beak of the stigma. Capsule obovoid to ellipsoid, pendent to spreading.

This is a genus of about twenty species mainly in temperate and mountainous regions of Europe and Asia, with two species in North America. They are found primarily in meadows, woodlands, ravines, swamps and on seepage slopes in acid to calcareous soils.

KEY FOR THE IDENTIFICATION OF THE SPECIES OF EPIPACTIS

1. Lip distinctly 3-lobed; lateral lobes erect and forming a gibbous sac; sac papillose at the base within; mid-lobe usually linear-oblanceolate, adorned with two fleshy wing-like keels on the lower half ....*E. gigantea* (p. 128)
1. Lip not 3-lobed, somewhat constricted about the middle; sac not papillose within; apical half of lip usually broadly triangular-ovate, adorned with two fleshy calli at the base......
....*E. Helleborine* (p. 130)

1. **Epipactis gigantea** Dougl. ex Hook., Fl. Bor.-am. 2: 202, pl. 202. 1839. Type citations: Northwest America. On the subalpine regions of the Blue and Rocky Mountains, *Douglas.* Columbia River, about Fort Vancouver, *Dr. Scouler.* (*Epipactis americana* Lindl.; *Peramium giganteum* (Dougl. ex Hook.) Coulter; *Serapias gigantea* (Dougl. ex Hook.) A. A. Eaton; *Helleborine gigantea* (Dougl. ex Hook.) Druce; *Amesia gigantea* (Dougl. ex Hook.) A. Nels. & Macbr.).   PLATE 46

(The name, *gigantea,* is a Latin adjective signifying "gigantic," probably in allusion to the typically large, robust plants of this species.)

COMMON NAMES: Giant Helleborine, Stream Orchid, Chatterbox, Giant Orchid, False Lady's-slipper.

Plant large, erect, nearly glabrous, 3-14 dm. tall. Stem usually stout, leafy, often tinged with purple at the base. Leaves variable, clasping the stem or with a short tubular petiole, plicate, erect-spreading, broadest on the lower part of the stem, ovate to ovate-elliptic or narrowly lanceolate, broadly obtuse to acuminate, 5.5-20 cm. long, 2-7 cm. wide, reduced below to closely appressed obtuse scarious sheaths, gradually narrowed and reduced on the upper part of the stem and finally becoming floral bracts in the elongated raceme, somewhat scarious on the veins beneath. Raceme two- to twelve- (or more) flowered, elongated, lax, glabrous to minutely pubescent. Floral bracts foliaceous, lanceolate, acuminate, exceeding the flowers, the lower ones up to 15 cm. long and 2 cm. wide, gradually reduced up to the the apex of the raceme. Flowers distant, rather showy, with rather stout arcuate puberulent pedicellate ovaries which are up to 1.5 cm. long. Sepals greenish to rose-color with purple or dull red nerves, deeply concave, nervose, dorsally carinate along the midnerve, hispid on the outer surface, recurved at the apex; dorsal sepal erect, elliptic-lanceolate, shortly acuminate or tapering to an acute apex, 1.5-2 cm. long, 7-8 mm. wide; lateral sepals spreading, ovate to ovate-lanceolate, subacute to acuminate at the apex, very oblique, occasionally falcate, 1.6-2.4 cm. long, 8-9 mm. wide near the base. Petals pale pink to rose-color with red or

PLATE 46.— **Epipactis gigantea.** 1, plant, three fourths natural size. 2, lip, spread open, front view, natural size. 3, lateral sepal, three fourths natural size. 4, petal, three fourths natural size. 5, column and ovary, side view, natural size. *Drawn by Blanche Ames.*

purple nerves, erect, broadly ovate to ovate-elliptic or ovate-lanceolate, obtuse to acute, oblique, 1.3-1.7 cm. long, 6-8 mm. wide below the middle. Lip strongly veined and marked with red or purple, sessile on the base of the column, complex, deeply and unequally 3-lobed; lateral lobes obliquely subquadrate to triangular-ovate or suborbicular, obtuse to broadly rounded at the apex, often dilated on the posterior margin, strongly nervose with the nerves carinate on the inner surface, 8-9 mm. long, 7-8 mm. wide, porrect to form (with the fleshy-thickened papillose disc) a gibbous sac; mid-lobe much smaller than the lateral lobes, erect-arcuate in natural position, linear-oblanceolate to narrowly spatulate-oblanceolate, rounded and with the margins somewhat involute at the apex, often yellowish, 8-11 mm. long, about 4 mm. wide above the middle, 3-nerved, adorned with an erect wing-like corrugated-fleshy callus on the lateral nerves below the middle, lamellate-thickened along the center nerve nearly to the apex. Column short, erect, stout, provided with bluish lateral horns just beneath the clinandrium, 8-10 mm. long. Capsule ellipsoid, pendent, 2-2.5 cm. long.

This species occurs in the West in habitats similar to those of *Cypripedium californicum*. In limestone regions where springs break through the porous substratum from underground streams, this species may be expected. Such a phenomenon exists in Frio Canyon on the Prade Ranch in Real County, Texas. Here, about the numerous springs which spurt from a limestone bluff to form the Frio River, are hundreds of this plant luxuriating among a rank growth of Southern Shield Fern (*Dryopteris normalis*).

The Indians of Mendocino County, California, are said to drink a decoction of the roots of the Giant Helleborine to combat mania and the most severe cases of illness, especially when the patient is unable to walk or move about.

The Giant Helleborine is usually found in swamps, marshy places and moist shady soil along rivers and streams, in wet prairies, meadows and savannahs, on seepage slopes, limestone bluffs and ledges, and is occasionally semiepiphytic in swamps and on decayed floating logs in water. It is sometimes found about hot springs, salt springs and in alkaline meadows. The Giant Helleborine occurs from near sea level in California, up to 2,000 feet altitude in British Columbia, 6,000 feet in Arizona and New Mexico, 7,500 feet in California and Nevada and 9,000 feet in Colorado, and flowers from March to August in various parts of its range

GEOGRAPHICAL DISTRIBUTION: This species is scattered from South Dakota (Fall River County), Wyoming (Shell Creek), Montana (Flathead and Lake counties), Colorado (Chaffee, Mesa and Montrose counties), New Mexico (Eddy, Grant and Socorro counties), Arizona (Coconino, Mohave, Navajo, Pima and Santa Cruz counties), Nevada (Clark, Douglas, Esmeralda, Nye and Ormsby counties), Utah (San Juan and Utah counties), Oklahoma (Murray County) and Texas (widespread); west to British Columbia (Ainsworth and Cowser Lake), Washington (Clallam, Grant and Kittitas counties), Oregon and California (widespread); also Mexico (Baja California and Hidalgo).

CULTURAL NOTES: Extending from Mexico to British Columbia and inland to Texas and South Dakota, this orchid is evidently essentially indifferent to temperature conditions. Observations as to its soil requirements have been made from the Pacific beaches to Dakotan ravines, and the reaction has been circumneutral throughout. It has been cultivated in western wild gardens with some degree of success. (E. T. W.)

This species has been cultivated in England since before 1900, and is quite hardy at the Royal Botanic Gardens, Kew, where I observed it in 1945.

2. **Epipactis Helleborine** (L.) Crantz, Stirp. Austr., ed. 2, fasc. 6: 467. fig. 6. 1769. *Serapias Helleborine* L., Sp. Pl., ed. 1, 2: 949. 1753. Type locality: Not given. (*Serapias Helleborine a. latifolia* L.; *S. latifolia* (L.) Huds.; *Epipactis latifolia* (L.) All.; *Amesia latifolia* (L.) A. Nels. & Macbr.).

PLATE 47 and FIGURE 5

(The name, *Helleborine,* is a Latin term signifying "like a Hellebore," apparently so-called because of the resemblance of this plant to some species in the ranunculaceous genus *Helleborus*.)

COMMON NAMES: Helleborine, Broad-leaved Helleborine, Bastard Hellebore.

Plant erect, small or large, 2-12.5 dm. tall. Stem usually slender, leafy, glabrous below, puberulent above, up to 1 cm. in diameter. Leaves variable, clasping the stem or with short channeled petioles, orbicular, suborbicular-ovate, elliptic, elliptic-lanceolate or narrowly lanceolate, broadly rounded and apiculate to long-acuminate at the apex, plicate, erect-spreading, broadest at about the middle of the stem, 4-18 cm. long, 1.5-8.5 cm. wide, reduced above and finally becoming floral bracts in the elongated raceme, glabrous or slightly puberulent. Raceme laxly or densely few- to many-flowered, commonly secund, up to 4 dm. long, tapering toward the apex, 3-6 cm. in diameter; rachis puberulent. Floral bracts foliaceous, erect-spreading to subhorizontal, elliptic-lanceolate to linear-lanceolate, acuminate, glabrous, usually much longer than the flowers, the lower ones up to 5 cm. or more long and 1.8 cm. wide. Flowers small, broadly campanulate, greenish, tinged with purple or rose-red, with stout

PLATE 47.— **Epipactis Helleborine.** Plant, two thirds natural size. *Drawn by Blanche Ames.*

arcuate puberulent pedicellate ovaries which are about 1 cm. long. Sepals more or less campanulate-connivent or spreading, ovate to ovate-lanceolate, obtuse to acuminate, deeply concave, 3- to 5-nerved with some of the nerves branched, hispid-puberulent or glabrous on the outer surface, dorsally carinate especially below the middle along the central nerve, 1-1.3 cm. long, 4.5-6 mm. wide below the middle; lateral sepals oblique, with the dorsal keel often excurrent at the recurved apex. Petals obliquely ovate-elliptic, obtuse to subacuminate, glabrous, 3- to 5-nerved with the outer nerves branched, usually dorsally carinate along the central nerve below the middle, minutely crenulate on the margin, 9-11 mm. long, 4.2-5.5 mm. wide below the middle. Lip greenish and purplish, dark purple on the lower half, sessile on the base of the column, porrect, somewhat constricted about the middle, 8-11 mm. long when spread out, 3-nerved with the lateral nerves branched, glabrous; lower half fleshy, semiglobose-saccate, somewhat tuberculate on the inner surface near the point of attachment to the column, 4-6 mm. long, 4-5.5 mm. wide, 2.5-3 mm. deep; apical half thin, broadly triangular-ovate to suborbicular-reniform or somewhat cordate, rounded or obtuse to acute or apiculate at the strongly recurved apex, with the margin crisped-undulate, 4-6 mm. long, 5-7.5 mm. wide, adorned with a fleshy suborbicular callus on each side at the base and often with a slender raised callus in the middle. Column short, fleshy, 3-6 mm. long. Capsule pendent, obovoid-ellipsoid, about 1 cm. long.

It is not clear why most botanical workers have ignored LINNAEUS' *Serapias Helleborine* and have taken up his *a. latifolia* as the typical plant found in Europe and the United States. CRANTZ's description and figure of the flower of his *E. Helleborine* is very good and represents the plant found in North America. It is my opinion that CRANTZ typified this species, and his name is adopted in this work.

This Old World plant was apparently first discovered in the United States in August 1879 in the vicinity of Syracuse, New York by a Mrs. M. O. RUST of the Syracuse Botanical Club. The following comment accompanied her report of this find in the Bulletin of the Torrey Botanical Club for that year: "I should judge that there could be no doubt as to the plant's being indigenous. Its home is right in the woods, the nearest habitation being a small farm-house. It does not grow over any great territory; I should think not more than a hundred feet square. It is on a hill under beeches, elms, maples and a few pines. In the valley near it I found, for the first time, *Pogonia pendula* [*Triphora trianthophora*] . . ."

TEXTFIGURE 5.— **Epipactis Helleborine**, lip, from above, two and one half times natural size. *Drawn by Gordon W. Dillon.*

The gallant editor's quaint response concerning this find was: "No plants are so eagerly sought for as orchids. Yet Epipactis, all these centuries, has shut itself up, waiting for the sharp eyes of the ladies of the Syracuse Botanical Club. What new discoveries are to be expected from their penetrating glances." And this was written in 1879!

Apparently the earliest collection in Canada was made at Lambton Mills, near Toronto, Ontario in July 1890 by W. and O. WHITE.

Since its first discovery in our region the Helleborine has spread rapidly and, in every area where it has gained a foothold, it has tenaciously established itself. How it came to be introduced no one seems to know. Notwithstanding, it now extends from Quebec and northern New England to Missouri—a most remarkable example of the aggressiveness of a weed, orchid or otherwise, once it gains entry into fertile ground. In Ethan Allen Park, a natural area north of Burlington, Vermont, I have seen hundreds of plants vying with other herbaceous species for a place on the boulder strewn forested slopes. In central New York State the Helleborine is quite common, and in some counties it has become one of the herbaceous plants which are characteristic of the woodlands.

This is the only European orchidaceous weed that has apparently been introduced and become thoroughly naturalized in this Hemisphere. In European folk lore, this plant is valued as a remedy for gout.

The Helleborine usually occurs in moist or dry rocky woods and thickets, on steep gravelly slopes, along wooded roadsides and waste places, and occasionally in grassy fields. It is found at rather low elevations in North America, but in India it occurs up to 10,000 feet or more altitude in the Himalaya Mountains. The Helleborine flowers from June to September in various parts of its range.

GEOGRAPHICAL DISTRIBUTION: Quebec (Hochelaga, Montmagny and Philipsburg counties), Ontario (Welland and York counties), New Hampshire (Sullivan County), Vermont (Addison, Chittenden and Windsor counties), Massachusetts (Barnstable and Berkshire counties), Connecticut (Hartford and Litchfield counties), New York (widespread), Pennsylvania (Bradford, Bucks and Warren counties), west to Michigan (Ingham County), Indiana (La Porte County), Missouri (Jasper County) and Montana (Lewis and Clark County—probably cultivated here) ; also Eurasia.

CULTURAL NOTES: The Helleborine has been introduced into America chiefly in the eastern Great Lakes region, though for some years there was a flourishing colony on the grounds of the Soldiers Home in the District of Columbia. It seems to prefer rather cool, shady places where the soil is circumneutral and rich in nitrogen, even invading refuse dumps where the latter element is likely to be abundant. (E. T. W.)

6. Cephalanthera L. C. Rich.

Cephalanthera L. C. Rich., De Orch. Europ. Annot. 29. 1817 (in Mém. Mus. Hist. Nat. Par. 4: 51. 1818).

(The name, *Cephalanthera,* is a Greek designation meaning "head" and "anther," so-called because of the position of the anther in relation to the column.)

Terrestrial saprophytic (in ours) or non-saprophytic plants with branched creeping rhizomes, whitish throughout (in ours) or green. Leaves normal or reduced to scarious sheaths. Inflorescence a loosely flowered terminal raceme. Flowers subsessile, subtended by scarious bracts. Dorsal sepal and petals erect, free, connivent. Lateral sepals spreading, free, dorsally carinate. Petals a little smaller than the sepals. Lip sessile, free, with a gibbous-saccate base, 3-lobed above the middle; lateral lobes erect and clasping the column; mid-lobe concave, spreading, adorned with fleshy-thickened nerves. Column semiterete, wingless; clinandrium toothed on each side; anther terminal, incumbent, erect, stipitate, 2-celled; pollinia granular-mealy, 2-parted in each anther-cell. Capsule erect, obovoid-ellipsoid.

This is a small genus of about fifteen species which are widely scattered in temperate and boreal regions of Eurasia, Africa and North America.

1. Cephalanthera Austinae (A. Gray) Heller, Cat. North Am. Pl., ed. 2: 4. 1900.

Chloraea Austinae A. Gray, Proc. Am. Acad. 12: 83. 1876. Type locality and collection: Banks of a wooded ravine in the Sierra Nevada Mountains, near Quincy, Plumas County, California, *Mrs. R. M. Austin.* (*Cephalanthera oregana* Reichb. f.; *Eburophyton Austinae* (A. Gray) Heller; *Serapias Austinae* (A. Gray) A. A. Eaton). PLATE 48

(The name, *Austinae,* is in honor of REBECCA MERRITT AUSTIN (1832-1919), a student and collector of California plants, known for her observations upon the habits of *Darlingtonia.*)

COMMON NAMES: Phantom Orchid, Snow Orchid.

Plant slender, erect or somewhat flexuous, glabrous, essentially white throughout, 1.9-6.5 dm. tall, from a slender rhizome which produces fibrous fusiform-thickened roots. Stem provided with three or four tubular obtuse scarious sheaths below and several clasping lanceolate acuminate scarious sheaths above. Leaves reduced to scarious sheaths. Raceme loosely five- to twenty-flowered, 4-20 cm. long, up to 3 cm. in diameter. Floral bracts usually small, triangular-lanceolate, acuminate, scarious, the lowermost bracts foliaceous. Flowers whitish, subsessile, arcuate, fleshy, tubular-urceolate. Sepals narrowly elliptic-lanceolate, obtuse to subacute, usually 3-nerved, 1.2-2 cm. long, 4-6.5 mm. wide; lateral sepals somewhat sigmoid, dorsally carinate along the mid-nerve. Petals elliptic-oblong to oblanceolate, broadly obtuse to rounded at the apex, 3-nerved, 1.1-1.7 cm. long, 3-6 mm. wide above the middle. Lip sessile, free, suberect and recurved in natural position, saccate below with the central nerve of the saccate portion thickened, constricted about the middle to form three lobes, 8-12 mm. long, 9-14 mm. wide across the lateral lobes when spread out; lateral lobes obliquely triangular-ovate, obtuse to rounded at the apex, erect and clasping the column in natural position, 3-4 mm. long and wide, producing a sac at the base; mid-lobe large, concave in natural position, suborbicular-ovate when spread out, bluntly obtuse to rounded at the recurved apex, with the four or five central nerves fleshy-thickened and wavy, cellular-papillose on the upper surface above the middle, 5-7 mm. long, 6-8 mm. wide. Column semiterete, 8-10 mm. long; clinandrium with a short triangular tooth on each side. Capsule erect, obovoid-ellipsoid, about 1.5 cm. long.

The Phantom Orchid is unique in the genus in being a saprophyte. Although it is florally inseparable from the species comprising the genus *Cephalanthera,* some authors have proposed its segregation as a monotypic genus on the basis of its saprophytic habit and geographic isolation. These characters, however, do not appear to me to be sufficiently strong to sustain a separate genus.

Although it has been suggested that this species is without chlorophyll, HOLM (1904) states that this ". . . is not correct, since we have observed the presence

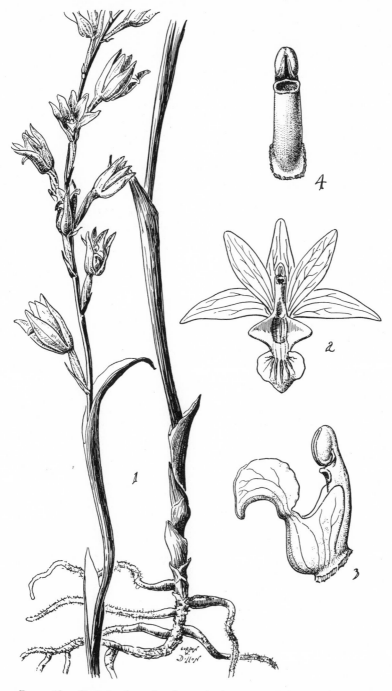

PLATE 48.— **Cephalanthera Austinae.** 1, plant, natural size. 2, flower, front view, spread open, twice natural size. 3, lip and column, side view, in natural position, four times natural size. 4, column, front view, four times natural size. *Drawn by Gordon W. Dillon.*

of chorophyll grains in the ovary; the guard-cells of the stomata as well as the adjoining epidermis-cells are well supplied with chlorophyll."

From my limited experience, I seriously doubt whether any of the Orchidaceae are wholly lacking in chlorophyll. It is true that this species, as well as most of those in *Hexalectris* and *Corallorhiza* in our region, apparently lack it. However, this is doubtless a case of suppression, where the green pigments are entirely obscured by other pigments or they are in such small amounts that they do not appear to be present.

This species is commonly found in dense moist coniferous forests, especially in the mountains. It usually occurs on the lower slopes of mountains, and is found up to 6,500 feet altitude in California and Oregon. The Phantom Orchid flowers from June to September.

GEOGRAPHICAL DISTRIBUTION: Idaho (Kootenai County), Washington (Klickitat and Walla Walla counties), Oregon (Benton, Curry, Douglas, Josephine, Multnomah and Polk counties) and California (widespread).

CULTURAL NOTES: This saprophytic orchid is endemic in the western mountains. As seen in the field, it is just about as snowy white as a plant can be. Wholly lacking (to the eye) in pigments, it is probably unable to carry on much photosynthesis, obtaining practically all its nourishment from the acid coniferous humus through which its roots ramify. As with most saprophytes, its equilibrium with the environment is so delicate that cultivation is out of the question. (E. T. W.)

7. Triphora Nutt.

Triphora Nutt., Gen. N. Am. Pl. *2*: 192. 1818.

(The name, *Triphora,* is a classic term meaning "three-bearing," probably in allusion to this usual number of flowers borne by the various species or to the number of crests on the lip.)

Inconspicuous terrestrial herbs which are stoloniferous and bear fleshy tubers. Stem slender, with several small clasping alternate leaves. Inflorescence composed of several small nodding or erect-spreading flowers borne in the axils of the uppermost leaves, racemose or corymbose. Flowers small, inconspicuous, with the perianth parts distinct. Lip 3-crested. Column free, entire at the apex; anther erect or subincumbent, rigidly attached to the top of the column; pollen-masses two, with the grains cohering in tetrads, the extine pitted or reticulate. Capsule erect or pendent, ellipsoid to ellipsoid-obovoid.

This is a small New World genus of about ten species, several of which are rather difficult to differentiate. They are widely distributed in temperate and tropical America where they occur primarily in rich soil or on rotted wood in shaded forests in slightly acid to neutral soils. This genus was formerly included in *Pogonia.*

KEY FOR THE IDENTIFICATION OF THE SPECIES OF TRIPHORA

1. Perianth parts less than 1.1 cm. long; lip oblanceolate; petals linear; column less than 8 mm. long; inflorescence usually corymbose.........................*T. cubensis* (p. 137)
1. Perianth parts more than 1.2 cm. long; lip obovate; petals oblong to spatulate; column more than 9 mm. long; inflorescence racemose.........................*T. trianthophora* (p. 139)

1. **Triphora cubensis** (Reichb. f.) Ames, Sched. Orch., No. 7: 35. 1924. *Pogonia cubensis* Reichb. f., Nederl. Kruidk. Arch. 4: 322. 1858 (by typographical error as *rubensis*). Type citations: Cuba, among coffee trees, a plant regarded as injurious, June 1823, *Lemonal;* Cuba, in plantations of coffee in places abounding in clay, *Poeppig.*   PLATE 49

(The name, *cubensis,* designates Cuba as the place where this species was first discovered.)

COMMON NAMES: Cuban Triphora, Cuban Pogonia.

Plants glabrous, slender or stout, reddish brown, often branched above, 9-26 cm. tall, produced from elongated cylindrical tubers; tubers up to 6 cm. long; roots coarse, slender, whitish. Leaves ovate, acute or apiculate, sheathing or appressed to the stem, scattered alternately along the stem, 1-1.5 cm. long. Inflorescence corymbose, composed of three to ten (rarely more) flowers which are borne in the axils of the uppermost leaves on slender pedicels (the pedicels of the lower flowers are elongated to form a corymb). Flowers magenta, nodding, very slender, with the floral segments subparallel. Sepals subequal, linear-lanceolate, 6-11 mm. long, about 2 mm. wide. Petals linear to filiform, 8-10 mm. long, about 1 mm. wide. Lip oblanceolate, 3-lobed, subacute, 8-10 mm. long, about 3 mm. wide across the lateral lobes; lateral lobes triangular, obtuse, with the free portion projecting about 1 mm.; mid-lobe suborbicular, about 2 mm. long and wide. Column about 7 mm. long. Capsule ellipsoid-obovoid, 1.2-1.5 cm. long.

This rare species was discovered for the first time in the United States by CHARLES T. SIMPSON at Little River, Dade County, Florida, in 1919. It was apparently not collected again until 1938 when it was found again in Dade County.

This species grows in pinelands and clearings near sea level in southern peninsular Florida, but occurs up to 4,500 feet altitude in Central America, and flowers in July (in Florida).

GEOGRAPHICAL DISTRIBUTION: Florida (Dade County); also Mexico, Guatemala, Panama and the West Indies.

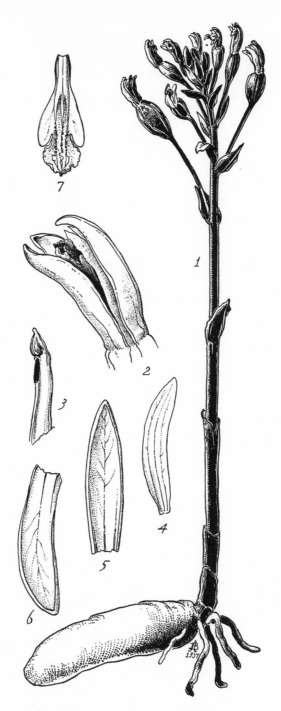

PLATE 49.—**Triphora cubensis.** 1, plant, natural size. 2, flower, side view, four times natural size. 3, column, side view, four times natural size. 4, petal, four times natural size. 5, dorsal sepal, four times natural size. 6, lateral sepal, four times natural size. 7, lip, front view, spread open, four times natural size. *Drawn by Blanche Ames.*

CULTURAL NOTES: This species is said to grow in marly soils in Florida and the West Indies. There are no records of its cultivation, but it might be grown in sub-tropical wild gardens. (E. T. W.)

2. **Triphora trianthophora** (Sw.) Rydb. in Britton, Man. Fl. North. States & Can., ed. 1: 298. 1901. *Arethusa trianthophoros* Sw., Kongl. Svens. Vetens. Acad. Nya Handl. 21: 230. 1800. Type locality: North America (*Triphora pendula* (Muhl. ex Willd.) Nutt.; *Pogonia pendula* (Muhl. ex Willd.) Lindl.; *Pogonia trianthophora* (Sw.) BSP.). PLATES 50 and 51

(The name, *trianthophora*, is a classic term meaning "bearing three blossoms," referring to the number of flowers usually borne by this species.)

COMMON NAMES: Three Birds Orchid, Nodding Pogonia, Nodding-crest, Nodding-cap, Nodding-ettercap, Pendulous Pogonia.

Plant glabrous, 8-30 cm. tall, stoloniferous, producing at the end of the stolons waxy ovoid tubers; tubers up to 3 cm. long, giving rise to new plants; roots slender, whitish. Stem slender or stout, succulent, usually tinged with maroon, translucent in drying. Leaves small, broadly ovate, obtuse to shortly acute, concave, clasping and partly sheathing the stem, scattered alternately along the stem, usually tinged and veined with maroon, 8-20 mm. long, 5-13 mm. wide. Inflorescence composed of one to six (usually three) flowers borne in the axils of the upper leaves. Flowers pale pink to almost white, veined or suffused with purple and green, nodding, fugacious (lasting about a day), with the floral segments ringent. Dorsal sepal oblong-lanceolate, obtuse to acute, 1.4-1.5 cm. long, about 5 mm. wide. Lateral sepals oblong-lanceolate, falcate, obtuse to acute, 1.3-1.4 cm. long, about 4 mm. wide. Petals elliptic to oblong-spatulate, falcate, obtuse to acute, obscurely crenulate at the apex, 1.3-1.5 cm. long, about 4 mm. wide. Lip 3-lobed, obovate in outline, narrowed to a slender claw, 1.3-1.6 cm. long, about 1 cm. wide when spread out, 3-keeled or crested on the median line of the disc with the keels broken into teeth or tubercles above; lateral lobes ovate-triangular, obtuse; mid-lobe dilated, elliptic to suborbicular, sinuate on the margin. Column semiterete at the base, laterally dilated near the middle, about 1 cm. long. Capsule ellipsoid, pendent, 1.5-2 cm. long.

Variety *Schaffneri* Camp (1940), named in honor of JOHN HENRY SCHAFFNER (1866-1939), a noted American botanist, differs from the typical form solely on the basis of its erect, elongated peduncles and erect fruits. It was originly described from Ohio and has also been found in Indiana, Illinois, Kentucky, Missouri and Arkansas.

The Three Birds Orchid, like all of its allies, has the peculiar habit of being common in a locality in one year and exceedingly rare the next. As AMES (1947) has noted, the tendency of these species is apparently subterranean and the vegetative system would appear to explain their periodical scarcity and recurrent appearance. The superficial stem, leaves and flowers seem to be but a brief stage in the developmental history of this plant.

On forested slopes overlooking the "pink beds," a mountain basin filled with Rhododendron near Brevard, North Carolina, I have seen this little orchid growing profusely in rich humus and on rotten wood in company with *Tipularia discolor*. Its pale nodding flowers are markedly contrasted with the dimness of its usually densely shaded haunts.

The Three Birds Orchid is found on rotten logs and in rich humus and leaf mold of low hammocks and hardwood or coniferous forests, in rich woods along streams and on the edge of swamps, in floodplain woods and on steep mountain slopes. It occurs from near sea level in Florida, up to 2,300 feet altitude in South Carolina, 3,500 feet in Tennessee, 6,000 feet in North Carolina and 10,000 feet in Guatemala, and flowers from July to the middle of October.

GEOGRAPHICAL DISTRIBUTION: Widespread but not common from Canada (old record), through New England and the Atlantic States, south to central Florida (south to Highlands and Hillsborough counties), along the Gulf Coast to Texas (Anderson and Jefferson counties), west through the Central and Lake States to Michigan (Cass and Kalamazoo counties), Wisconsin (Green County), Iowa (Clayton, Fayette and Washington counties), Missouri (Dunklin, Jackson and St. Louis counties) and Arkansas (Hempstead and Pulaski counties): also Mexico, Guatemala and Panama.

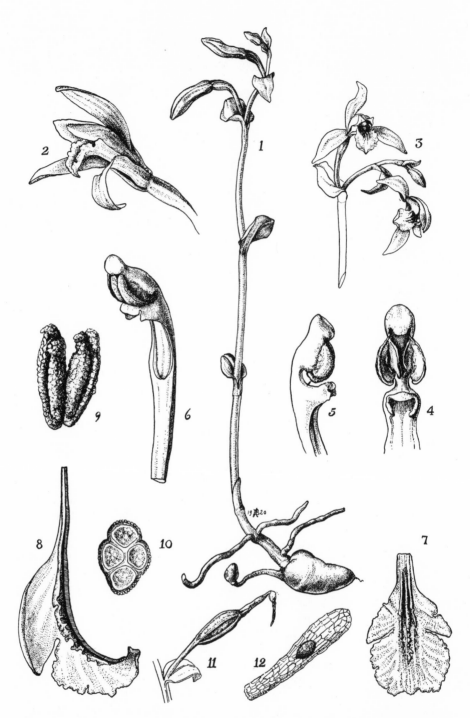

PLATE 50.— **Triphora trianthophora.** 1, plant, in bud, natural size. 2, flower, side view, twice natural size. 3, flowers, natural size. 4, upper part of column, with the pollinia removed, eight and one half times natural size. 5, upper part of column, side view, eight and one half times natural size. 6, column, side-front view, six and one half times natural size. 7, lip, spread out, three times natural size. 8, longitudinal section through center of lip, five times natural size. 9, pollinia, fourteen times natural size. 10, pollen tetrad, median section to show pitted extine, highly magnified. 11, capsule, natural size. 12, seed, highly magnified. *Drawn by Blanche Ames.*

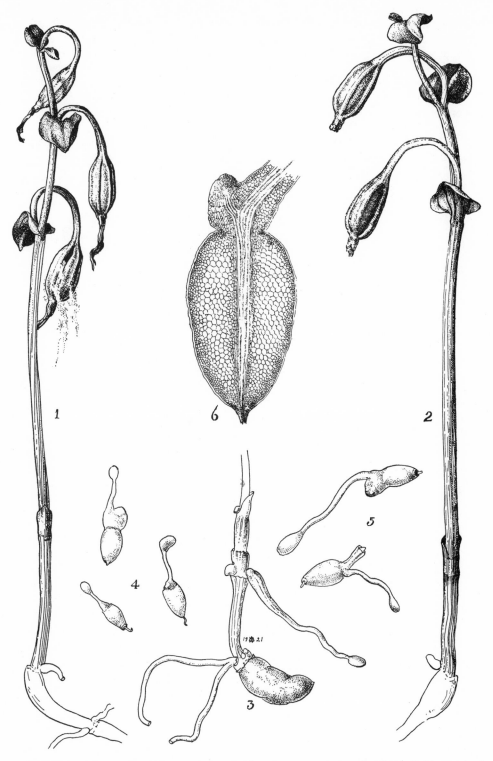

PLATE 51.— **Triphora trianthophora.** 1 and 2, fruiting plants, natural size. 3, tuber and stolons, natural size. 4, young tubers, showing original point of attachment to a stolon, at the basal end, and illustrating the development of a stolon and minute tuber (lower left), and the formation of a bud from which a stem is about to arise (upper center), twice natural size. 5, tubers, a later stage of development than shown in figure 4, the stolon has elongated and the tuber has become enlarged, twice natural size. 6, longitudinal section through the middle of the uppermost tuber shown in figure 5 (semidiagrammatic). *Drawn by Blanche Ames.*

CULTURAL NOTES: Theoretically, the Three Birds Orchid should be the easiest of the crested orchid group to cultivate, because it is the one member which grows naturally in rich loamy soil, such as is present in the average garden. It is adapted also to a wide range of climatic conditions, being found throughout the eastern United States. But it is a plant with a long resting period, its tubers remaining dormant under ground for several years, so that its blooming is erratic. Meanwhile, rodents and other animals feed upon these succulent stems, and in a garden where pests become abundant because of protection from their natural enemies, few of the plants escape destruction. (E. T. W.)

This species was first introduced into England, supposedly from Canada, by DAVID DOUGLAS sometime before 1824, during which year it flowered in the open at Chiswick.

8. **Isotria** Raf.

Isotria Raf., Med. Repos. N. Y., Hex. 2, 5: 357. 1808.

(The name, *Isotria,* is a Greek term signifying "equal" and "three," referring to the number of sepals which are of the same shape and approximate length and are arranged symmetrically in the perianth.)

Terrestrial herbs with long slender hairy roots and five or six verticillate leaves inserted at the top of the stem. Inflorescence composed of one (rarely two) flowers just above the leaves. Flowers inconspicuous, with the perianth parts distinct. Lip tuberculate-crested. Column free, toothed at the apex; anther terminal, incumbent, stalked, operculate; pollen-masses two, with the grains compound and cohering in tetrads. Capsule erect, cylindrical or ellipsoid.

This genus is closely allied to *Pogonia,* to which genus it is sometimes referred. It is composed of two species, both of which are apparently confined to the United States. They are found primarily in woodlands, along streams and in moist situations, usually in strongly acid soils.

Key for the identification of the species of Isotria

1. Flowers essentially sessile; sepals less than 2.8 cm. long, light green.. *I. medeoloides* (p. 143)
1. Flowers on a pedicel at least 1.5 cm. long; sepals more than 3 cm. long, brownish purple... ....*I. verticillata* (p. 145)

1. **Isotria medeoloides** (Pursh) Raf., Fl. Tell. 4: 47. 1838. *Arethusa medeoloides* Pursh, Fl. Am. Sept. 2: 591. 1814. Type locality: In shady woods on the Blue Mountains, Pennsylvania or New Jersey. (*Pogonia affinis* Austin ex A. Gray; *Isotria affinis* (Austin ex A. Gray) Rydb.). PLATE 52

(The name, *medeoloides,* is a Greek adjective meaning "like a Medeola," doubtless in allusion to the vegetative similarity of this species to the common liliaceous Indian Cucumber-root, *Medeola virginiana.*)

COMMON NAMES: Smaller Whorled Pogonia, Small Whorled Crest-lip, Green Five-leaved Orchid.

Plant slender, glabrous, 9.5-25 cm. tall; roots slender, fibrous, hairy. Stem hollow, greenish or purplish tinged. Leaves five or six in a whorl at the top of the stem, pale dusty green and glaucous, elliptic to elliptic-obovate, broadly rounded and apiculate to shortly acuminate at the apex, drooping, 2-8.5 cm. long, 1.1-4 cm. wide. Flowers one or two terminating the stem, yellowish green, ringent, subsessile or with a short pedicel (after fertilization). Sepals linear-oblanceolate to narrowly spatulate, somewhat narrowed at the base, up to 2.5 cm. long, about 3 mm. wide near the middle; lateral sepals slightly oblique, shorter than the dorsal sepal. Petals oblanceolate to oblong-elliptic, rounded to obtuse at the apex, up to 1.7 cm. long, about 3 mm. wide. Lip almost white, crested with pale green, obovate-cuneate to oblong-oval, 3-lobed, 1.3-1.5 cm. long, with a bicarinate callus extending from the base to about the middle of the disc and produced above into blunt elongated wart-like processes that stand erect on the middle nerves; lateral lobes triangular at the apex, involute, irregularly tuberculate along the veins; mid-lobe cuneate-flabellate, with the upper half free from calli. Capsule erect, ellipsoid-cylindrical, 1.7-3 cm. long, on a short pedicel which is up to 1.5 cm. long.

The smaller subsessile flowers and subequal sepals and petals readily separate this species from *I. verticillata.* Both species of *Isotria* superficially resemble young plants of *Medeola virginiana,* with which they are commonly associated. However, when not in flower, the hollow stout stem of *Isotria* will conveniently separate this genus from *Medeola* with its solid and more slender stem.

For many years this plant has been known as *Pogonia affinis* or *Isotria affinis.* Recently, however, FERNALD (1947) has correctly pointed out that PURSH's earlier

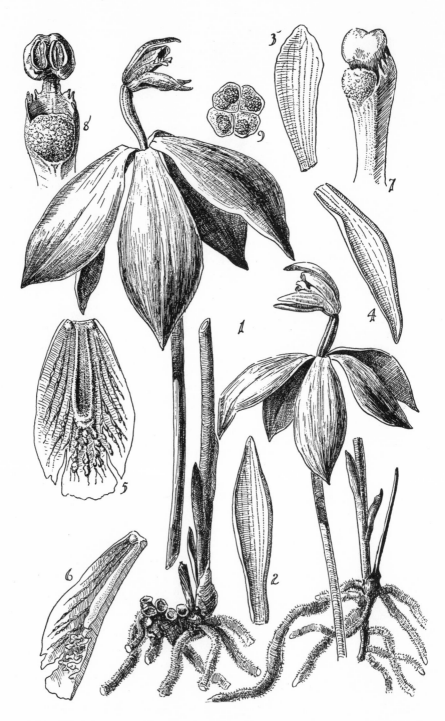

PLATE 52.—**Isotria medeoloides.** 1, plant, natural size. 2, dorsal sepal, three and one fourth times natural size. 3, petal, three and one fourth times natural size. 4, lateral sepal, three and one fourth times natural size. 5, lip, front view, spread open, three and one third times natural size. 6, lip, side view, longitudinally dissected to show calli, three and one third times natural size. 7, column, with anther in normal position, front-side view, enlarged. 8, summit of column showing stigma, anther turned back, pollen removed, enlarged. 9, pollen tetrad, highly magnified. *Redrawn from Blanche Ames by Gordon W. Dillon.*

and clearly described *Arethusa medeoloides* is identical with this plant. Therefore, the epithet *medeoloides* must replace *affinis*.

This species grows in mixed hardwood forests or under hemlocks in moist or dry leaf mold, in rather dry flat open woods, on rocky wooded slopes along streams, mostly in acid soils, but sometimes on limestone hills (in Missouri). It occurs up to 1,000 feet in Surry County, North Carolina, and flowers from May to early June.

GEOGRAPHICAL DISTRIBUTION: Found locally in New England, New York, Pennsylvania and New Jersey (Bergen County), south to Virginia (James City County) and North Carolina (Cumberland (?) and Surry counties); also Missouri (Bollinger County).

CULTURAL NOTES: The Green Five-leaved Orchid has been collected at only a few localities, from North Carolina to Maine. It has one of the longest resting periods of any of our eastern orchids, during which time it remains dormant underground and sends up no leaves or flowers—at least ten and possibly twenty years elapsing from one blooming season to another. Tests of its soil-reaction have indicated preference for subacid soils, in deciduous woodlands. There is no record of its successful cultivation, apparently because the slightest injury to its roots—which form a radiating group around the crown—permits the entrance of destructive fungi. (E. T. W.)

2. **Isotria verticillata** (Muhl. ex Willd.) Raf., Med. Repos. N. Y., Hex. 2, 5: 357. 1808. *Arethusa verticillata* Muhl. ex Willd., Sp. Pl. 4: 81. 1805. Type locality: Pennsylvania and Maryland. (*Pogonia verticillata* (Muhl. ex Willd.) Nutt.). PLATES 53 and 54

(The name, *verticillata,* is a Latin adjective signifying "whorled," referring to the position and disposition of the leaves at the summit of the stem.)

COMMON NAMES: Whorled Pogonia, Five-leaved Orchid, Green Adderling, Large Whorled Crest-lip, Purple Five-leaved Orchid, Whorl-crest.

Plant erect, glabrous, 9-35 cm. tall, propagating by means of root-shoots, last year's fruiting stalk often persisting; roots very long, fibrous, slender, densely hairy. Stem purplish or reddish brown, glaucous, hollow. Leaves five or six in a whorl at the top of the stem, oblong-lanceolate to broadly obovate or elliptic, obtuse to acute or rarely shortly acuminate at the apex, projecting at right angles to the stem, greenish above, somewhat glaucous beneath, 3-9.5 cm. long, 2.5-5.2 cm. wide. expanding noticeably as the capsule matures. Flowers one or rarely two terminating the stem, pale yellowish green and purple, ringent, on long pedicels; pedicels 2.5-5 cm. long. Sepals subequal, madder-purple, narrowly lanceolate, acuminate, conduplicate, 3.4-6 cm. long, about 3 mm. wide. Petals yellowish green, elliptic-obovate to elliptic-lanceolate, obtuse to acute, 2-2.5 cm. long, about 5 mm. wide. Lip yellowish green, streaked with purple, oblong-cuneate, 3-lobed near the apex, 1.5-2.5 cm. long, about 1 cm. wide when expanded, crested with a broad fleshy ridge (somewhat papillose above) along the middle of the disc; lateral lobes obtuse to subacute, involute and forming a shallow groove in natural position; mid-lobe transversely oblong-elliptic, truncate to retuse at the apex. Column about 1 cm. long. Capsule erect, ellipsoid, 2-3.5 cm. long.

The slender fibrous roots of this species extend for a phenomenal distance from the plant. They run just beneath the surface of the ground and may reach several feet in length. An interesting developmental phase is the continuous and simultaneous growth of the leaves with the flowers and fruit. Almost as soon as the young leaves expand the flower-bud bursts into blossom, and by the time the fruit has matured the leaves have increased four or five times in size.

A two-flowered plant of this species in which fasciation had occurred was found near North Easton, Massachusetts. The pedicels of the flowers and the basal portion of the ovaries had become united.

This species is found in dry or moist sandy pine woods, low rich damp hardwoods along streams and in floodplain areas, tamarack swamps, shady ravines, boggy situations in upland woods or on mixed hardwood slopes. It occurs from near sea level in Florida, up to 3,000 feet altitude in North Carolina, Tennessee and

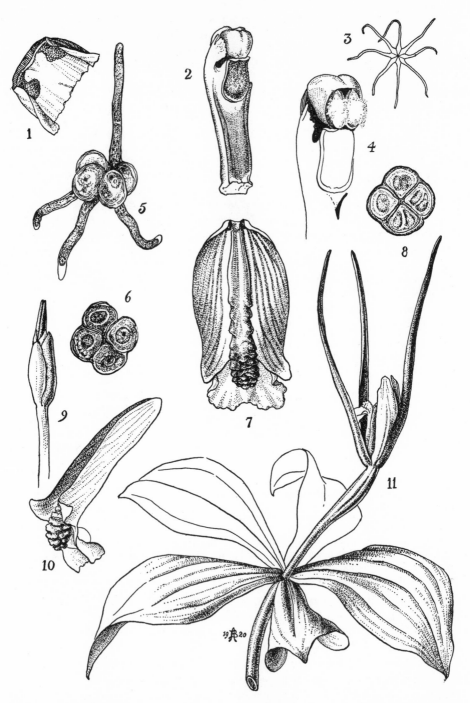

PLATE 53.— **Isotria verticillata.** 1, base of lip, to show gland on each side, eight times natural size. 2, column, to show papillose stigma and the anther in normal position, four times natural size. 3, a stellate trichome, usually abundant on the lip in fresh specimens but easily deciduous, highly magnified. 4, upper part of column with the anther turned back and the mealy pollen exposed, five and one half times natural size. 5, pollen tetrad, found germinating *in situ,* highly magnified. 6 and 8, pollen tetrad, before germination, highly magnified. 7, lip, spread out, two and one half times natural size. 9, flower bud invested by the verticil of leaves, natural size. 10, lip, side view, two and one half times natural size. 11, flower and leaves, natural size. *Drawn by Blanche Ames.*

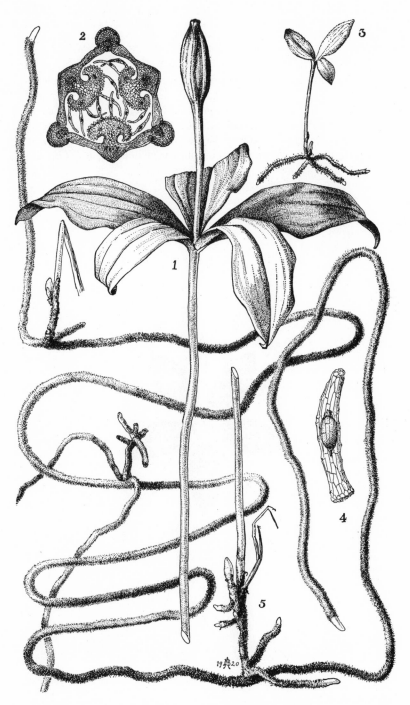

PLATE 54.— **Isotria verticillata.** 1, upper part of fruiting specimen, natural size. 2, cross-section of capsule, four times natural size. 3, seedling, natural size. 4, seed, highly magnified. 5, lower part of stem, natural size. *Drawn by Blanche Ames.*

Virginia, and flowers from April to the middle of August in various parts of its range.

GEOGRAPHICAL DISTRIBUTION: The Whorled Pogonia is found throughout New England and the Atlantic States where is is rather frequent, south to northern Florida (Gadsden County), along the Gulf Coast to Texas (Nacogdoches County), west through the Central and Lake States to Michigan (Eaton, Gratiot and Kent counties), Missouri and Arkansas (Howard and Pulaski counties).

CULTURAL NOTES: Unlike its relative, *I. medeoloides,* the Purple Five-leaved Orchid is a rather frequent species, ranging from the Gulf to the Great Lakes. It appears to differ also by spreading into colonies through the means of root-shoots, and in preferring mediacid soil under pine or oak trees. Attempts to cultivate it, however, are rarely successful, owing to the difficulty of keeping the garden soil sufficiently acid, and of preventing fungi from overwhelming it. (E. T. W.)

9. Pogonia Juss.

Pogonia Juss., Gen. Pl. 65. 1789, excluding synonymy in part.

(The name, *Pogonia,* is derived from the Greek word meaning a "beard," referring to the bearded or fringed crest of the lip.)

Terrestrial herbs with slender fibrous roots, erect, with a solitary leaf inserted about halfway up the stem. Inflorescence composed of one to three flowers terminating the stem; perianth parts distinct. Lip bearded. Column free, coarsely toothed at the apex; anther terminal, incumbent, stalked, operculate; pollen-masses two, with the grains simple and not cohering in tetrads. Capsule erect, ellipsoid.

This is a small genus of less than ten species which are widely dispersed in both hemispheres. They are found primarily in meadows, swamps, pine and oak barrens, savannahs, damp forests and sphagnum bogs in usually rather strongly acid soils.

1. **Pogonia ophioglossoides** (L.) Ker-Gawl., Bot. Reg. 2: t. 148. 1816. *Arethusa ophioglossoides* L., Sp. Pl., ed. 1, 2: 951. 1753. Type locality: Virginia and Canada. (*Pogonia ophioglossoides* var. *brachypogon* Fernald). PLATE 55

(The name, *ophioglossoides,* is a classical term meaning "like the Adder's Tongue fern," in allusion to the shape and position of the solitary leaf which superficially resembles that of many species of *Ophioglossum.*)

COMMON NAMES: Rose Pogonia, Adder's-tongue-leaved Pogonia, Beard Flower, Crested-ettercap, Ettercap, Rose Crest-lip, Rose Crested-orchid, Snake Mouth, Sweet Crest-orchid, Adder's Mouth.

Plant slender, glabrous, propagating by means of rootshoots, 0.8-7 dm. tall. Stem green or brownish green. Leaf solitary, about halfway up the stem (occasionally with one or two long-petiolate leaves arising from the base of the stem), ovate to elliptic or broadly ovate-lanceolate, obtuse to subacute, 2-12 cm. long, 1-3 cm. wide, rarely smaller. Floral bract foliaceous, oblong-elliptic to oblong-lanceolate, 1-3 cm. long, 3-8 mm. wide. Flowers one to three (usually one) terminating the stem, rose to white, of several days' duration, fragrant. Dorsal sepal oblong-elliptic to linear-oblong, subobtuse, 1.5-2.3 cm. long, 3-6 mm. wide. Lateral sepals narrowly elliptic to linear-oblong or linear-lanceolate, acute to rarely obtuse, 1.5-2.7 cm. long, 3-6 mm. wide. Petals oblong-elliptic to elliptic-obovate, broadly rounded at the apex, 1.3-2.5 cm. long, 5-11 mm. wide. Lip narrowly oblong-spatulate, narrowed at the base, lacerate-toothed along the apical margin, prominently bearded along the three central veins of the disc with short fleshy yellow-white bristles, 1.5-2.5 cm. long, 8-10 mm. wide near the apex. Column about 1 cm. long, toothed at the apex. Capsule ellipsoid, 2-3 cm. long.

Wherever open sphagnous bogs occur in the range of this species there nearly always occur some plants of the Rose Pogonia. When once established in this type of habitat, the species often forms large colonies because of the ease with which it spreads by means of stolons or rootshoots. It is one of the most abundant bog-orchids of eastern North America. Those plants found in the southeastern states commonly have two or three flowers instead of the usual one-flowered inflorescence typical of the northern plants.

A variant, described from Nova Scotia as var. *brachypogon* Fernald (1921), is a caespitose plant which has the beard of the lip obsolescent (only represented by short knobs) and the segments of the perianth scarcely spreading. In my opinion, this plant represents only a northern form of the species.

White-flowered forms, originally described from Maine as forma *albiflora* Rand & Redfield (1894), occur throughout the range of the species.

Pogonia, through its representative *P. ophioglossoides,* exemplifies one of those peculiar cases of the geographical distribution of plants emphasized long ago by

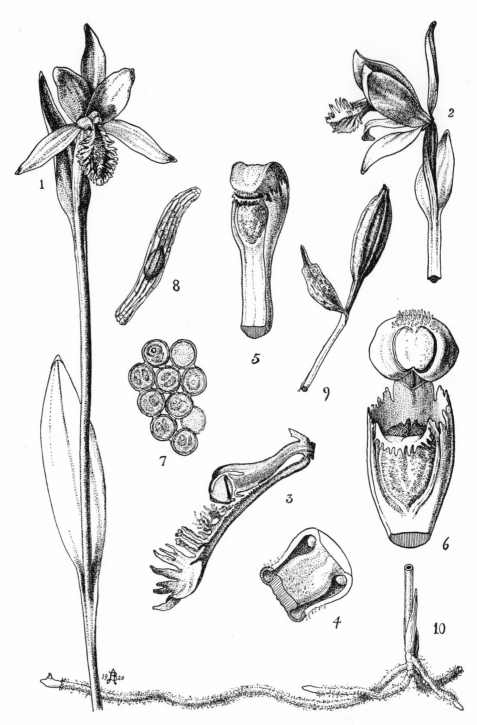

PLATE 55.— **Pogonia ophioglossoides.** 1, upper part of plant, natural size. 2, flower, side view, natural size. 3, longitudinal section through center of lip and column, to show the structure of the median keel of the lip and the position of the anther in relation to the clinandrium, three times natural size. 4, base of lip, to show gland on each side, six and one half times natural size. 5, column, with anther in normal position, four and one half times natural size. 6, upper part of column, anther turned back, nine times natural size. 7, ten pollen grains, highly magnified. 8, seed, highly magnified. 9, capsule, natural size. 10, base of stem, natural size. *Drawn by Blanche Ames.*

Asa Gray. Gray clearly demonstrated that certain elements of the flora of China and Japan, have representatives in the eastern United States and Canada rather than on the West Coast of America where one would expect to find them. The Rose Pogonia has a counterpart in China and Japan. On the other hand, it is of interest to note that *Cephalanthera Austinae* is isolated on the West Coast from the rest of the genus which occurs chiefly in Europe and Africa.

The Rose Pogonia is commonly found in meadows, swamps, low moist grassy pine barrens, boggy savannahs and prairies, pocosins, damp flatwoods, on the edge of cypress swamps and sandy-gravelly beaches of lakes, in low wet open woods along streams, on high seepage slopes in sphagnum and mud, or in sphagnum bogs associated with grasses and sedges. It occurs from near sea level on the Atlantic Coastal Plain and Gulf Coast, up to 450 feet altitude in Vermont and 2,500 feet in North Carolina, and flowers from March (in the deep South) to August (in the far North).

Geographical distribution: Newfoundland, Nova Scotia, New Brunswick, Prince Edward Island, Quebec and Ontario (Bruce and Lambton counties, Sault St. Marie and Temagami districts, Wellington), through New England and the Atlantic States, south to southern Florida, along the Gulf Coast to East-central Texas, west through the Central and Lake States to Minnesota (northwest to Cass and Hubbard counties), Illinois (Lake and Lee counties), Missouri (Reynolds County, *fide Steyermark*) and Tennessee (Fentress and Polk counties).

Cultural notes: The Sweet Crest-orchid occurs in practically every extensive sphagnum bog and acid meadow in the eastern United States and Canada. Thus it evidently requires a mediacid soil but is indifferent to temperature conditions. While some writers on wild-flower cultivation claim it to be easily grown in gardens, this is not the case. Attempts to grow it are futile unless one has or can construct a bed of sandy humus of acid nature, with a constant supply of water free from lime. (E. T. W.)

This species was first introduced into English gardens about 1815 by Thomas Nuttall.

The adder's tongue arethusa [Pogonia ophioglossoides] smells exactly like a snake. How singular that in Nature, too, beauty and offensiveness should be thus combined. In flowers as well as persons we demand a beauty pure and fragrant which perfumes the air. The flower which is showy but has no odor, or an offensive one, expresses the character of too many mortals. (Thoreau: "Summer", 1884).

10. Cleistes L. C. Rich.

Cleistes L. C. Rich., Mém. Mus. Hist. Nat. Par. 4: 31. 1818.

(The name, *Cleistes,* is a Greek term meaning "closed," in allusion to the narrowly funnel-shaped corolla.)

Terrestrial herbs with slender fibrous roots, erect, with a solitary leaf (in ours) inserted above the middle of the stem. Inflorescence composed of one to three flowers terminating the stem; perianth parts distinct. Lip crested. Column free, with a somewhat eroded apical margin; anther terminal, incumbent, stalked, operculate; pollen-masses two, with the grains compound and cohering in tetrads. Capsule erect, cylindrical.

This is a genus of about twenty-five species which were formerly included in *Pogonia.* They are confined to the Western Hemisphere, mainly in South America. They occur primarily in wet soil along rivers, in wet forests, bogs, depressions in prairies and savannahs in usually strongly acid soils.

1. **Cleistes divaricata** (L.) Ames, Orch., fasc. 7: 21, pl. 108, 1922. *Arethusa divaricata* L., Sp. Pl., ed. 1, 2: 951. 1753. Type locality: Swamps of North America. (*Pogonia divaricata* (L.) R. Br.; *Cleistes divaricata* var. *bifaria* Fernald). PLATE 56

(The name, *divaricata,* is a Latin adjective signifying "spreading widely," probably in reference to the position of the sepals.)

COMMON NAMES: Rosebud Orchid, Spreading Pogonia, Funnel-crest, Ladies' Ettercap, Spreading Crest-lip, Lily-leaved Pogonia.

Plant erect, glabrous, up to 7.5 dm. tall; roots slender, fibrous. Leaf solitary, inserted above the middle of the stem, oblong-lanceolate to elliptic-oblong, subobtuse to acuminate, glaucous, with a thin translucent margin, 3-20 cm. long, 1-2 cm. wide. Floral bract foliaceous, narrowly lanceolate, acuminate, 4-10 cm. long, 5-12 mm. wide. Flowers one to rarely three terminating the stem, magenta-pink to white and brown or veined with brown, showy. Sepals similar, ascending, linear-lanceolate, acuminate, brownish or purple, 3-6.5 cm. long, about 5 mm. wide. Petals and lip connivent and forming a cylindrical tube. Petals magenta-pink to white, spatulate-oblanceolate, acute, 2-4.5 cm. long, 1-1.4 cm. wide at or near the apex. Lip broadly oblong-cuneate, strongly veined, indistinctly 3-lobed, crenulate along the margins, with a linear-grooved somewhat fleshy papillose crest extending through the median line of the disc, 3.5-4.5 cm. long, about 2 cm. wide above the middle when expanded; lateral lobes broadly rounded at the apex, involute and forming a trough; apical lobe ovate-triangular, somewhat revolute and recurved in natural position, projecting about 1 cm. beyond the lateral lobes. Column slender, 2-2.5 cm. long. Capsule narrowly cylindrical, about 3 cm. long.

The delicate coloration of the flowers makes this plant one of our most attractive orchids. It is of rather local and rare occurrence, but when once established in a congenial habitat it soon becomes quite abundant. Although the Rosebud Orchid is usually found in moist soil, I have collected it in quite dry fields of Broomsedge (*Andropogon* spp.) in eastern North Carolina and on open dry mountain slopes in northwestern South Carolina.

Recently, FERNALD (1946A) segregated as var. *bifaria* (meaning "from two areas of development") a plant which he states is generally smaller in all of its parts than in typical material. He considered this plant to be the biological type of the species, since it is supposed to be the only form found on the ancient Blue Ridge Mountains and Cumberland Plateau and Mountains. The somewhat larger-flowered plant, FERNALD's so-called nomenclatural type of the species, was supposed to have developed on the Coastal Plain when the Cretaceous and Tertiary seas moved east and south.

It is my opinion that *C. divaricata* is not susceptible of division.

This species is found in low moist grassy pine barrens, savannahs, prairies, flat-woods, swamps, bogs, along stream banks and in meadows, on the edge of pocosins

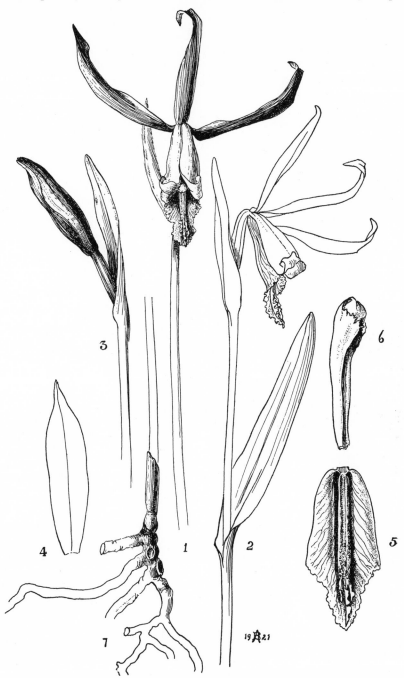

PLATE 56.—**Cleistes divaricata.** 1 and 2, plant, natural size. 3, flower bud, natural size. 4, petal, natural size. 5, lip, spread out, natural size. 6, column, twice natural size. 7, rhizome and roots, natural size. *Drawn by Blanche Ames.*

and rarely on open dry grassy slopes and mountain tops. It occurs from near sea level on the Atlantic Coastal Plain and Gulf Coast, up to 4,000 feet altitude in the mountains of North Carolina and Tennessee, and flowers from the middle of April to July in various parts of its range.

GEOGRAPHICAL DISTRIBUTION: Rare and of local distribution from New Jersey (Quaker Bridge), Delaware (Sussex County) and Virginia, south to central Florida (south to Lake County), along the Gulf Coast to Louisiana (St. Tammany Parish) and eastern Texas (*E. J. Palmer*), west to Tennessee (west to Franklin County) and Kentucky.

CULTURAL NOTES: More essentially southern in range than its relative, *Pogonia ophioglossoides,* the Rosebud Orchid also occupies rather different habitats. In the Coastal Plain it grows in grasslands and in shrub thickets which, while they may be inundated after heavy rains, are rather dry much of the year. Its colonies in the mountains are often on gravelly slopes where drainage is good. In all cases, however, the soil of its habitat is intensely acid. It can be cultivated, therefore, in a bed of humus-rich sand which is maintained at a high degree of acidity. If protected by litter, its roots can withstand moderately cold winter conditions, but it is exceedingly sensitive to fungi, and if its roots are damaged in transplanting, it soon succumbs to these parasites. (E. T. W.)

According to BROWN (1813), the Rosebud Orchid was first introduced into England in 1787 by JOHN FRASER.

11. Vanilla Sw.

Vanilla Sw., Nov. Act. Soc. Sci. Upsal. 6: 66. 1799.

(The name, *Vanilla,* is from the Spanish *vainilla,* the diminutive of *vaina* (pod), in allusion to the slender bean-like fruits.)

Stout or slender climbing herbs, more or less branching. Stems leafy or sometimes aphyllous or only bracteate, emitting adventitious roots. Leaves (when present) leathery, chartaceous or membranaceous. Racemes few- to many-flowered, axillary, usually short. Flowers large, often fleshy. Sepals free, subequal, spreading. Petals similar to the sepals. Lip adnate to the column and often enclosing the column or its base, simple or 3-lobed. Column long, without a foot; anther solitary, attached to the margin of the clinandrium, incumbent; pollen powdery or granular. Capsule long, cylindrical or fusiform, often clavellate, fleshy, usually indehiscent.

This is a complex genus of fifty or more species found in the tropics and subtropics throughout the world. Several species are cultivated for their aromatic properties. Unfortunately our knowledge of the genus is still imperfect. The flowers are not only ephemeral but are also quite unsatisfactory to press, so that the botanical specimens brought in by collectors are usually sterile or so poorly preserved that the floral characters are difficult to interpret. Throughout the literature devoted to the genus, this situation has been emphasized. It is hoped, therefore, that in the future efforts will be made to preserve flowers of *Vanilla* in alcohol; identification of the species will be greatly facilitated thereby.

CULTURAL NOTES: This is one of the most interesting genera of the orchids occurring in collections, if for no other reason than that one of its species, *V. planifolia,* produces most of the vanilla of commerce. Terrestrial in nature, plants may be grown in a fibrous, well-aerated porous leaf mold. At least half-shade is best and the supporting member for these rampant tropical vines can be a lath house post, a lawn tree or a cypress board in a greenhouse. An abundance of water at the roots and over the tops when growth begins should be alternated with a partial withholding of moisture during the winter or the post-flowering dormant period. *Vanilla* will grow in osmundine and will, in fact, thrive and establish itself even if the stem should become severed near the ground. Thus, the plants may become epiphytes. (J. V. W.)

KEY FOR THE IDENTIFICATION OF THE SPECIES OF VANILLA

1. Leaves with distinct blades more than 9 cm. long, 2.5 cm. or more wide, not noticeably recurved at the apex...2
  2. Flowers more than 6.5 cm. long; capsule thick....................*V. phaeantha* (p. 159)
  2. Flowers less than 6 cm. long; capsule slender.......................*V. planifolia* (p. 159)
1. Leaves abortive, bract-like or scale-like, usually much less than 9 cm. long, less than 2 cm. wide, strongly recurved at the apex...3
  3. Lip less than 4 cm. long, deeply 3-lobed at the truncated apex, with the sinuses prominent ....*V. barbellata* (p. 155)
  3. Lip more than 4 cm. long, broadly rounded above with a projecting apical lobe, without distinct sinuses..*V. Dilloniana* (p. 157)

1. **Vanilla barbellata** Reichb. f., Flora 48: 274. 1865. Type locality and collection: Cuba, near Monte Verde, *C. Wright 3352.* (*Vanilla articulata* Northrop).   PLATE 57

(The name, *barbellata,* is a Latin adjective meaning "with a little beard," doubtless in allusion to the retrorse tuft of short stiff straight hairs on the disc of the lip.)

COMMON NAMES: Link-vine, Worm-vine, Wormwood.

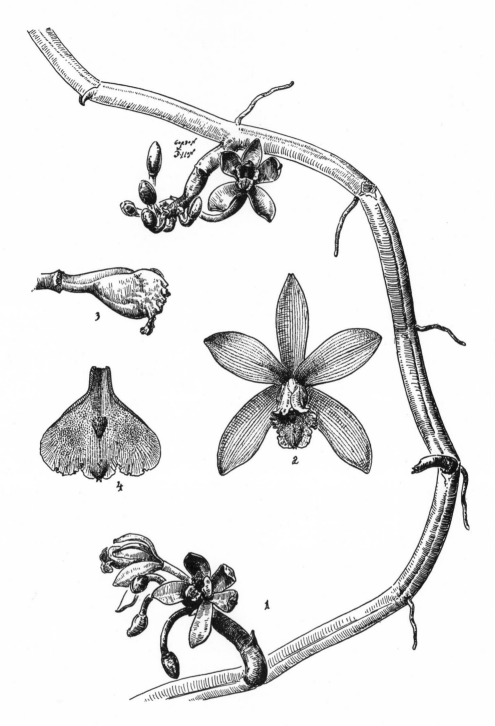

PLATE 57.— **Vanilla barbellata.** 1, upper part of plant, one half natural size. 2, flower, front view, lip in natural position, sepals and petals spread open, natural size. 3, lip, attached to column, in natural position, side view, natural size. 4, lip, detached from column, spread open, natural size. *Drawn by Gordon W. Dillon.*

Plant climbing. Stem jointed, succulent, producing at the nodes bracts or abortive leaves and aerial roots; internodes smooth and somewhat angular, up to 3 dm. long. Leaves abortive, linear-lanceolate, acute, conduplicate and recurved, up to about 4 cm. long and 8 mm. wide; bracts of stem ovate, acute, up to 1.5 cm. long. Flowers twelve or less, produced in short axillary racemes, fleshy. Floral bracts broadly ovate to triangular, obtuse, about 5 mm. long. Sepals and petals green. Dorsal sepal oblong-elliptic, obtuse, longitudinally concave, 3-4 cm. long, 9-10 mm. wide. Lateral sepals slightly oblique, oblong-elliptic to elliptic-oblanceolate, obtuse, 3-4 cm. long, 1.1-1.2 cm. wide Petals elliptic-oblanceolate, broadly obtuse, prominently keeled on the back, 2.9-3.9 cm. long, 1.1-1.4 cm. wide above the middle. Lip greenish below, deep red above shading to white on the edge, attached to the lower two-thirds of the column, in natural position involute with the mid-lobe strongly reflexed, 3-3.8 cm. long, 3.2-3.5 cm. wide when spread out; lamina broadly cuneate-flabellate, pleated and distinctly 3-lobed at the broadly truncated apex; disc with a retrorse tuft of hairs in the middle of the center and one or more lines of minute excrescences from the tuft of hairs to the thickened apex of the mid-lobe. Column arcuate, glabrous, 2.3-3.3 cm. long. Capsule elongated, somewhat compressed, about 8 cm. long.

Although species of *Vanilla* have been known to occur in southern Florida for more than sixty years, it is not possible to say just when the genus was first discovered there, and, as is the case of many orchids of southern Florida, it is impossible to determine how long the genus has been present in Florida. It was not until the beginning of this century, when J. K. SMALL, A. A. EATON and others began an intensive exploration of subtropical Florida, that it was possible to obtain a check on the flora of that region. Moreover, it is of interest that few orchid species have been added to the flora of subtropical Florida since these explorations by EATON and SMALL before 1910.

This species has been collected on limestone rocks, in serpentine soils and on river banks. It occurs from near sea level in Florida, up to 450 feet altitude in the West Indies, and flowers from May to July.

GEOGRAPHICAL DISTRIBUTION: I have seen specimens of the Link-vine from southern peninsular Florida (Dade and Monroe counties), Cuba and the Bahama Islands. It doubtless occurs elsewhere in the West Indies.

CULTURAL NOTES: See this section under the generic discussion.

2. **Vanilla Dilloniana** Correll, Am. Orch. Soc. Bull. 15: 331, pl. 1946. Type locality and collection: Florida, Dade County, Brickell Hammock, *Ralph H. Humes*. (*Vanilla Eggersii* of authors, not *V. Eggersii* Rolfe, *nomen confusum*). PLATE 58

(The name, *Dilloniana,* is in honor of GORDON WINSTON DILLON (1912-   ), Editor of the American Orchid Society *Bulletin* and delineator of many species in the orchid family.)

COMMON NAME: Leafless Vanilla.

Plant climbing, branching. Stem terete, about 1.3 cm. in diameter, provided below with abortive leaves which gradually become scale-like bracts above; nodes slightly constricted, each provided with one adventitious root; internodes 5-14 cm. long. Leaves abortive, fleshy, triangular-lanceolate to oblong-lanceolate, acuminate, up to 9 cm. long and 1.2 cm. wide; bracts fleshy, 1-1.5 cm. long, ovate, acute, conduplicate and recurved. Flowers about eight, in a short axillary raceme. Sepals and petals greenish. Dorsal sepal oblong-oblanceolate, obtuse, about 5.5 cm. long and 1.2 cm. wide. Lateral sepals obliquely oblong-oblanceolate, obtuse, 4.5-5.5 cm. long, 1.2-1.3 cm. wide Petals obliquely oblong-oblanceolate, obtuse, strongly keeled on the back, 4.6-5.5 cm. long, about 1.3 cm. wide. Lip white and purplish, attached to the lower two-thirds of the column, tubular below and reflexed and dilated above in natural position, about 4.5 cm. long, 4-4.5 cm. wide. when spread out; lamina (when expanded) flabellate, broadly 3-lobed, pleated and broadly rounded above with an obtuse lobe at the apex; disc with a retrorse tuft of hairs at about the middle, with several lines of small excrescences extending from the tuft of hair to the fleshy tip of the apical lobe, minutely papillose on the sides below. Column about 3.3 cm. long, arcuate near the apex, glabrous. Capsule clavellate, somewhat compressed, 6-10 cm. long.

Judging from the number of available botanical collections, this is perhaps the most frequent and widespread species of *Vanilla* in Florida. This species and

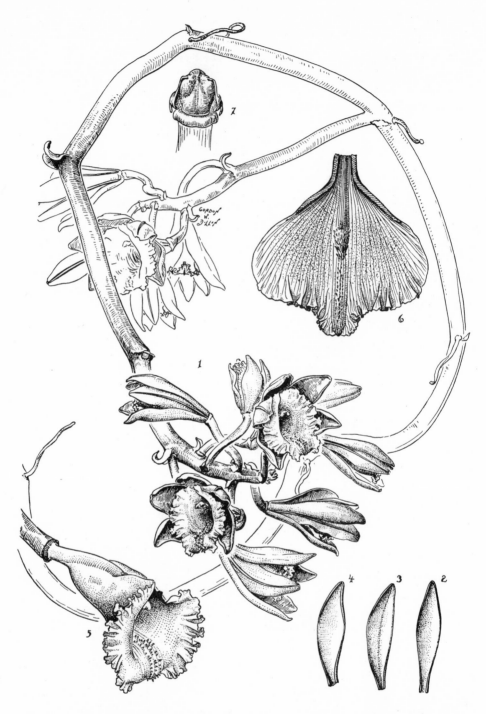

PLATE 58.— **Vanilla Dilloniana.** 1, upper part of plant, one half natural size. 2, dorsal sepal, one half natural size. 3, petal, one half natural size. 4, lateral sepal, one half natural size. 5, lip, attached to column, in natural position, front-side view, natural size. 6, lip, detached from column, spread open, natural size. 7, column, apex, front view, two and one half times natural size. *Drawn by Gordon W. Dillon.*

V. barbellata are two of the three so-called "leafless" Vanillas known to occur in the Western Hemisphere.

This species has been collected in rather dry hammocks, on limestone rocks and other calcareous places at low elevations. Its flowering period is from March to June.

GEOGRAPHICAL DISTRIBUTION: I have seen specimens from southern Florida (Dade and Monroe counties), Cuba and Santo Domingo. It doubtless occurs elsewhere in the West Indies.

CULTURAL NOTES: See this section under the generic discussion.

3. Vanilla phaeantha Reichb. f., Flora 48: 274. 1865. Type locality: Not given.
PLATE 59

(The name, *phaeantha,* is a Greek term meaning "dusky flower," referring to the typically gray-green color of the flowers.)
COMMON NAMES: Leafy Vanilla, Oblong-leaved Vanilla.

Plant climbing. Stem about 1.2 cm. in diameter, with internodes up to 17 cm. long, producing an adventitious root at each node. Leaves sessile, oblong-elliptic, tapering above to the acute apex, fleshy, somewhat shorter than the internodes, up to 14 cm. long, 2.5-4.3 cm. wide. Flowers about twelve, in short axillary racemes, greenish, fleshy. Floral bracts ovate, acute, up to 1.4 cm. long and 8 mm. wide. Sepals fleshy, narrowly oblanceolate, obtuse to acute, 7.5-9 cm. long, 1.3-1.8 cm. wide above the middle; lateral sepals oblique. Petals obliquely linear-oblanceolate, acute to subacuminate, thin, strongly keeled on the back, 8-8.7 cm. long, 1-1.4 cm. wide above the middle. Lip attached to the column almost to its apex and forming a tube, upcurved in natural position with the apex flaring, 7.5-8.3 cm. long, about 4.5 cm. wide near the apex when spread out; lamina obovate-cuneate, retuse at the broadly rounded and undulate-crenulate apex, keeled on the back with the keel ending in a prominent mucro just below the apex; disc prominently veined, thin, smooth, adorned with a retrorse tuft of fimbriated scales at about the middle and with several obscure lines of excrescences extending from the tuft of scales nearly to the apex. Column recurved above the middle, bearded on the ventral surface, 6.5 cm. long, about 5 mm. wide at the apex. Capsule cylindrical, somewhat compressed, about 8 cm. long.

The Leafy Vanilla is closely allied to *V. Pompona* Schiede, of tropical America, but differs from that species in the smaller leaves and more acute or acuminate sepals and petals. In addition, the lip is shorter than the sepals instead of being longer as in *V. Pompona.* This species is an inhabitant of the Big Cypress Swamp in Collier County, Florida.

This species occurs in low hammocks and cypress swamps of southern peninsular Florida. In the tropics it grows on rocks in open forests at low elevations. It flowers from April to June.

GEOGRAPHICAL DISTRIBUTION: Florida (Collier County); also the Bahama Islands and the West Indies.

CULTURAL NOTES: See this section under the generic discussion.

4. Vanilla planifolia Andrews, Bot. Repos. 8: t. 538. 1808. Type locality: West Indies. (*Vanilla Vanilla* (L.) Britton; *V. fragrans* (Salisb.) Ames).
PLATE 60

(The name, *planifolia,* is a Latin term meaning "flat-leaved," in allusion to the broad flat leaves.)
COMMON NAMES: Vanilla, Vanilla Vine.

Plant climbing, branching, leafy. Stem terete, about 1 cm. in diameter. Leaves subsessile, oblong-elliptic to narrowly lanceolate, acute to shortly acuminate, fleshy-succulent, up to 23 cm. long and 8 cm. wide, but usually smaller. Racemes axillary, up to 8 cm. long, with twenty or more flowers. Floral bracts ovate-oblong, obtuse to subacute, 5-10 mm. long. Flowers greenish yellow, with pedicellate ovaries which are about 2.5 cm. long. Sepals and petals sublinear to oblong-oblanceolate, obtuse to subacute. Sepals 4-5.5 (rarely 7) cm. long, 1-1.5 cm. wide above the middle. Petals somewhat shorter and narrower than the sepals. Lip attached to the column almost to its apex and forming a tube, dilated and reflexed at the apex, when spread out 4-5 cm. long and 1.5-3 cm. wide at the widest point; lamina cuneate-obovate in outline, obscurely 3-lobed, retuse and irregularly fringed on the revolute margins; disc with a retrorse tuft of hairs near the center and several verrucose lines extending from

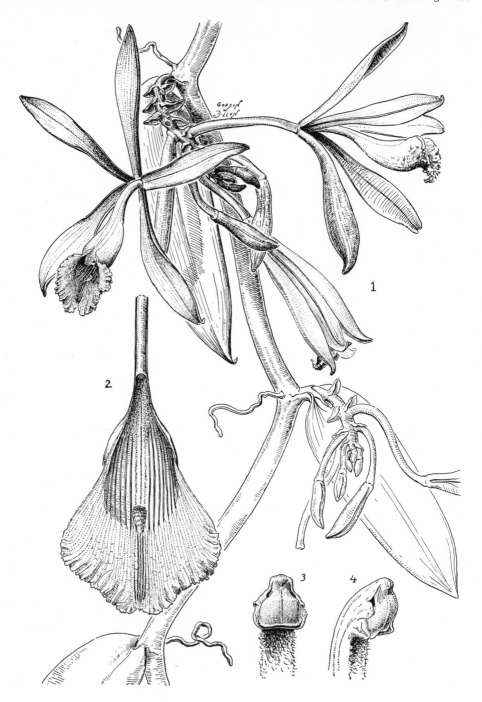

PLATE 59.— **Vanilla phaeantha.** 1, plant, one half natural size. 2, lip, detached from column, spread open, natural size. 3, column, apex, front view, three times natural size. 4, column, apex, front-side view, three times natural size. *Drawn by Gordon W. Dillon.*

the tuft of hairs to the thickened apex of the lip. Column arcuate, bearded on the ventral surface, about 3 cm. long. Capsule narrowly cylindrical, fragrant, up to 25 cm. long and 8 mm. in diameter.

This species provides the best vanilla of commerce and is grown for commercial purpose in many parts of the tropics and subtropics in both hemispheres. Since this plant, together with several other species of *Vanilla,* is the only orchid of extensive commercial value, other than those whose flowers are sold in the floral industry, it may be of interest to discuss in some detail its history and uses. The following information is extracted from one of my papers, published in 1944.

The history of vanilla is replete with adventure and romance. BERNAL DIAZ, a Spanish officer under CORTEZ, was perhaps the first white man to take note of this spice when he observed MONTEZUMA, the intrepid Aztec emperor, drink "Chocolatl." This drink, prepared from the pulverized seeds of the cacao tree, was flavored with ground vanilla fruits or "beans," which the Aztecs called "tlilxochitl," derived from *tlilli,* meaning "black" and *xochitl,* here interpreted as meaning "pod." Vanilla beans were considered to be among the rarer tributes paid to the Aztec emperor by his subject tribes. CORTEZ was subsequently introduced by MONTEZUMA to his first cup of chocolate, served according to legend in golden goblets, with spoons of the same metal; but the Aztecs jealously guarded their secret — the flavoring principle of the drink. After the vanilla ingredient was finally discovered, the Spaniards imported vanilla beans about 1510 into Spain, where factories were established as early as the second half of the sixteenth century for the manufacture of chocolate, flavored with vanilla. Thus, vanilla may be considered a by-product of the Spanish Conquistadors' search for the hidden wealth of the Americas; a by-product which is today one of the most important of the minor extractive industries in Mexico.

BERNARDINO DE SAHAGUN, a Franciscan friar, who arrived in Mexico in 1529, was perhaps the first to write about vanilla when he stated that the Aztecs used "tlilxochitl" in cacao, sweetened with honey, and that they sold vanilla spice in their markets. His work, "Historia General de las Cosas de Nueva España," originally written in the Aztec language, was not published until 1829-30, in Mexico —three hundred years after SAHAGUN's arrival in that country.

The first observation of botanical interest was made by CAROLUS CLUSIUS, in 1605, in his "Exoticorum Libri Decem," where he described and gave the name *Lobus oblongus aromaticus* to some dried vanilla beans which he had received, in 1602, from HUGH MORGAN, apothecary to Queen ELIZABETH. These beans were considered to be the fruits of *V. planifolia,* the true Mexican vanilla, although nothing seems to have been known of their native country or uses. This same MORGAN was the first European to suggest vanilla as a flavoring in its own right, a fact already known to the Aztecs.

When first introduced into Europe, vanilla was used primarily as a flavoring for chocolate or as a tobacco perfume. Early explorers of tropical America, however, extolled its supposed medicinal virtues and vanilla soon became an important drug, its reputation as an aphrodisiac being widespread. Belief in the medicinal properties of vanilla was strong during the sixteenth century; as early as the beginning of the seventeenth century it was given a place in the German Pharmacopoeia, and in 1721 it had a place in the London Pharmacopoeia. The use of vanilla as a medicine waned during the latter part of the eighteenth century, and by the end of the nineteenth century, for all practical purposes, it was discarded as a drug. It is still used to some extent, however, in medicines mainly to flavor otherwise distasteful elixirs. In Europe, vanilla was at one time used as a cure for hysteria, low fevers, impotency and rheumatism, and it was thought to prevent sleep and to "increase the energy of the muscular system." It was used by Spanish physicians in America to cure various maladies, being considered a strong stimulant and stomachic, and as an antidote to poison and to the bite of venomous animals.

Vanilla is by far the most popular flavor at the present time in the ice cream, baking and chocolate industries of the United States. It is used chiefly as a flavoring for chocolate, beverages, confections, cakes, custards, puddings, ices, ice cream, and in the manufacture of soaps, tobaccos, perfumes, glues and sachet powders.   When added to the heavy oriental varieties of perfume, vanilla extract makes the odor more delicate.   Vanilla is ordinarily used in the form of an extract

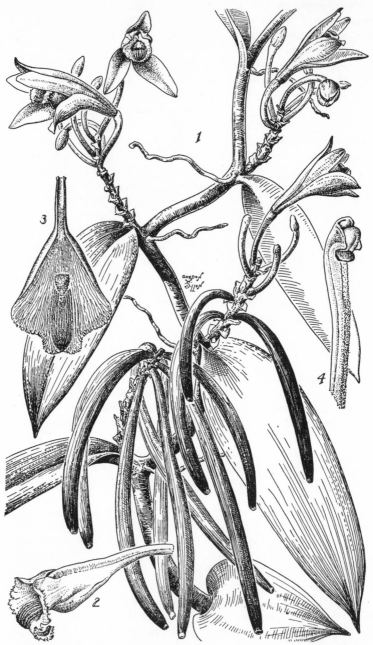

PLATE 60.—**Vanilla planifolia.** 1, plant, one half natural size. 2, lip, front-side view, in natural position, natural size. 3, lip, spread open, natural size. 4, column, front-side view, twice natural size. *Drawn by Gordon W. Dillon.*

from the beans. In the manufacture of chocolate, however, the beans are usually ground finely with sugar and included with the chocolate. Some chefs still insist on using the bean, itself, in the food to be flavored instead of using the extract. Since the vanilla essence is known to be more volatile at high temperatures, there is perhaps some justification for this rather expensive practice.

Although science has devised substitutes for this popular flavoring material, vanilla, like so many other natural products which have been synthesized, should survive these encroachments. The delicate, ephemeral essence of the natural product, which leaves no unpleasant aftertaste, has not been completely captured by the test tube.

This species occurs in hammocks of southern peninsular Florida. In the tropics, it is found in soil and climbing on trees in swamps, wet thickets and mixed forests in the lowlands. Although usually found at low elevations, it occurs up to 2,000 feet altitude in Mexico and Central America. It flowers sporadically throughout the year in accordance with the region where it is growing.

GEOGRAPHICAL DISTRIBUTION: Florida (Dade County); also Mexico, Central and South America and the West Indies; cultivated in both hemispheres where it occurs as an escape.

CULTURAL NOTES: See this section under the generic discussion; also see COR-RELL (1944).

Attempts were made to cultivate this species outside its native region in England before 1733. However, in its native habitat, it was doubtless long under cultivation in Mexico by the Aztecs before the arrival of Europeans.

> *"If we admit that fully twenty thousand distinct species, distributed among six hundred genera, constitute the magnificent aggregation of plants known to botanists as the Orchidaceae, it is indeed remarkable that the only species of economic importance was singled out by the American Indians, captured, as it were, from the vast flora of Middle America, and then utilized as a precious spice through the ages."*
>
> OAKES AMES, Vanilla, American
> Orchid Society Bulletin, 1945.

12. **Arethusa** [Gron.] L.

Arethusa [Gron.] L., Sp. Pl., ed. 1, 2: 950. 1753.

(The name, *Arethusa,* is that of the mythical and classical river nymph, perhaps so applied because of the beauty of the flowers and the typically moist habitat of this species.)

Low terrestrial scapose herbs which are produced from bulbous corms. Leaf solitary, linear, developing after the flower opens. Inflorescence composed of one or rarely two showy ringent flowers terminating the scape. Sepals and petals subequal. Lip crested. Column adherent to the lip, dilated above, petaloid; anther 2-celled, operculate; pollen-masses two in each cell of the anther. Capsule erect, ovoid.

This genus is composed of two species, one native to Japan and the one under consideration confined to North America.

1. **Arethusa bulbosa** L., Sp. Pl., ed. 1, 2: 950. 1753. Type locality: Virginia and Canada. PLATE 61

(The name, *bulbosa,* is a Latin adjective signifying "with a bulb," in reference to the thickened corm which comprises the rootstock.)

COMMON NAMES: Arethusa, Wild Pink, Dragon's-mouth, Bog-rose.

Plant scapose, glabrous, with the past season's fruiting stalk often persisting, 6-39 cm. tall. Rootstock a bulbous corm giving rise to one or rarely two flower-shoots, 0.5-1.5 cm. in diameter. Scape slender, erect. Leaf solitary, developing as the capsule matures, grass-like, linear-lanceolate, acute or rarely obtuse, 5-23 cm. long, 3-12 mm. wide. Floral bract minute, subulate to broadly ovate, 3-4 mm. long. Flowers one or rarely two terminating the scape, rose-purple, with short pedicellate ovaries. Dorsal sepal linear-oblong to linear-elliptic, obtuse or rarely acute, 3-4.8 cm. long, 5-10 mm. wide, connivent with the petals and forming a hood over the column. Lateral sepals broadly oblong-lanceolate, falcate, acute, 2.3-4.6 cm. long, 6-9 mm. wide at about the middle. Petals linear-oblong to linear-lanceolate, obtuse to acute, recurved, with a slender claw, 2.7-4.2 cm. long, 5-10 mm. wide at the widest point. Lip with a short claw, oblong, often shallowly 3-lobed, arcuate-recurved, notched or somewhat 3-lobulate at the apex, shallowly crenulate-denticulate or erose along the margins, 1.9-3.5 cm. long, 1-1.7 cm. wide, strongly veined throughout; disc with the central vein crested with glandular capillary-fringed fleshy tissue having a yellow base and purple tip. Column much compressed, narrowly linear-spatulate in outline, abruptly cuneate and shallowly erose or dentate on the apical margin, 2.6-3.5 cm. long, 7-11 mm. wide at the apex. Capsule ovoid, 1.5-2.5 cm. long.

Arethusa is a true bog plant. Its typical habitat is in deep sphagnum moss in company with ericaceous shrubs. Its beautifully colored flower is held primly erect by the rigid scape, and strangely enough it has the appearance of a fanciful little beast, with ears distended and lolling tongue, straining to recognize the intruder of its peaceful haunts.

Two color forms, originally found in Maine, have been segregated from this species by RAND & REDFIELD (1894). These are forma *albiflora* with pure white flowers, and forma *subcaerulea* with the flowers bluish or lavender.

As in the case of *Pogonia ophioglossoides,* where this matter is discussed, *Arethusa,* through *A. bulbosa,* demonstrates the close affinity of the flora of eastern North America with that of eastern Asia where, in Japan, is to be found a counterpart of *A. bulbosa.*

Arethusa is said to have been used at one time as a remedy for toothache.

I have seen a single plant of this species mounted on an herbarium sheet with *Pogonia ophioglossoides* and labeled as having been collected in Louisiana. Until verified, this record should be considered as the result of a probable error in the

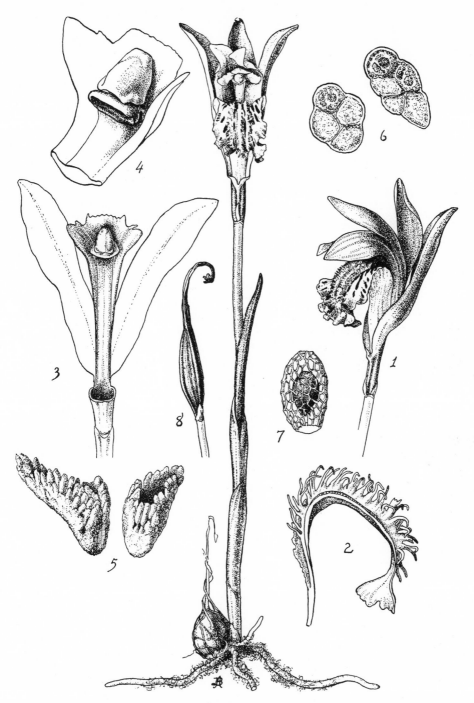

PLATE 61.— **Arethusa bulbosa.** Plant, natural size. 1, flower, side-front view, natural size. 2, longitudinal section through lip, to show the crest, side view, two and one third times natural size. 3, column and petals, front view, one and two thirds times natural size. 4, upper part of column, to show anther and stigma, front-side view, six times natural size. 5, pollen masses, highly magnified. 6, pollen tetrads, highly magnified. 7, seed, highly magnified. 8, capsule, showing persistent remains of column, natural size. *Drawn by Blanche Ames.*

mounting of the specimens. If this northern plant should occur in central Louisiana (Rapides Parish) it would be most extraordinary. However, its presence on the Piedmont Plateau of North Carolina (Forsyth County) is almost as unusual as would be its occurrence in Louisiana.

Arethusa grows in sphagnum bogs, wet turfy meadows, various types of swamps, open swales and on river flats. It occurs up to 350 feet altitude in Vermont and 3,500 feet in the mountains of North Carolina, and flowers from early May (in the South) to early August (in the far North).

GEOGRAPHICAL DISTRIBUTION: Newfoundland, Nova Scotia, Anticosti, New Brunswick, Quebec and Ontario (Huron and Wellington counties), through New England, New York, New Jersey and Pennsylvania, south to the mountains and Piedmont Plateau of North Carolina (Forsyth, Henderson and Transylvania counties) and (?) South Carolina, through the Central and Lake States to Wisconsin (Barron and Jefferson counties) and Minnesota (Chisago County); also (?) Louisiana (Rapides Parish).

CULTURAL NOTES: During the advances of the ice in the Glacial Period, this species survived in the Carolina mountains, but after the last ice melted the orchid soon invaded the newly developing bogs, and reached northern Ontario and Newfoundland. Its root-system consists of a solitary corm, requiring for its growth a surrounding bed of intensely acid sphagnum moss. Even if this is provided, the orchid is likely to vanish from the garden through the activities of rodents. One cultivator records that the only way he could keep this orchid alive was to plant it in moss supported on pieces of wood entirely surrounded by water. (E. T. W.)

This species was first introduced into the British Isles from Canada in 1819 by ROBERT GRAHAM, Professor of Botany in the University of Edinburgh, where it flowered in the Botanic Garden the following year.

13. Calopogon R. Br.

Calopogon R. Br. in Ait., Hort. Kew., ed. 2, 5: 204. 1813, conserved name.

(The name, *Calopogon,* is from two Greek words meaning "beautiful" and "beard," in allusion to the colorful beard or crest adorning the lip.)

Terrestrial scapose herbs arising from globose or ellipsoid corms, with one (rarely more) grass-like leaf sheathing the stem near the base. Inflorescence a subdense or lax few- to several-flowered terminal raceme. Flowers non-resupinate, showy, varying in color from white to deep crimson or magenta. Sepals and petals free, spreading. Lip forming the uppermost segment of the perianth, with a minute lateral lobe on each side near the base, strongly dilated and bearded above with numerous clavellate hairs in the center and papillae at the apex. Column free, slender and somewhat incurved, winged on each side at the apex; anther terminal, operculate; pollinia four, two in each cell, with the grains connected by filaments. Capsule erect, cylindrical or ellipsoid.

This is a small New World genus of four species, chiefly occurring in the southeastern United States with one species widespread in eastern Canada and the United States. They are found primarily in sphagnum bogs, depressions in prairies and savannahs, acid meadows and low pinelands, grassy swamps, and on sandy pine and oak ridges in moderate to intensely acid soils.

This genus amply demonstrates the complexity which often occurs in the Orchidaceae. Indeed, it is rather surprising to find how so few species can create such confusion as has existed in the past and give rise to so much perplexity. In 1933, SMALL recognized six species of *Calopogon* based on minor variations which are difficult to interpret. The present treatment is more conservative in recognizing only four species.

KEY FOR THE IDENTIFICATION OF THE SPECIES OF CALOPOGON

1. Flowers opening successively up the raceme; column usually 8 mm. or more long..........2
  2. The pair of column-wings (when spread out) forming together a suborbicular lamina that tapers gradually at the base; flowers pink to rose-purple............*C. pulchellus* (p. 173)
  2. The pair of column-wings (when spread out) forming together a semioval lamina which is more or less truncate at the base; flowers white to light rose-pink or white tinged with pink ....*C. pallidus* (p. 171)
1. Flowers opening almost simultaneously or (in *C. barbatus*) opening in rapid succession; column usually 8 mm. or less long...3
  3. Petals widest below the middle; floral bracts 2-5 mm. long............*C. barbatus* (p. 167)
  3. Petals widest above the middle; floral bracts 5-10 mm. long........*C. multiflorus* (p. 169)

1. **Calopogon barbatus** (Walt.) Ames, Orch., fasc. 2: 272. 1908. *Ophrys barbata* Walt., Fl. Carol. 221. 1788. Type locality: Not given; probably eastern Carolina. (*Calopogon parviflorus* Lindl.; *C. pulchellus* var. *graminifolius* Ell.; *C. graminifolius* Ell. ex Weatherby & Griscom; *Limodorum parviflorum* (Lindl.) Nash; *L. graminifolium* (Ell.) Small). PLATE 62

(The name, *barbatus,* is a Latin adjective meaning "bearded," in allusion to the beard-like crest of the lip.)

COMMON NAMES: Bearded Grass-pink, Bearded Calopogon.

Plant scapose, slender, erect, somewhat rigid, glabrous, 1.5-4.5 dm. tall. Rootstock a bulbous corm, having a tuft of roots at the proximal end and usually the remains of the old stalks at the distal end. Stem light green or tinged with reddish brown (occasionally two stems are produced from the same corm). Leaves (when present) one or two, basal, narrowly linear and grass-like, long-acuminate, strongly ribbed, 5-18 cm. long, about 2 mm. wide. Raceme short, often somewhat capitate, three- to five- (or rarely more-) flowered. Floral bracts subulate to shortly lanceolate, 2-4 mm. long. Flowers rose-pink, rarely white, mostly opening simultaneously, with the slender pedicellate ovaries 6-10 mm. long. Dorsal sepal

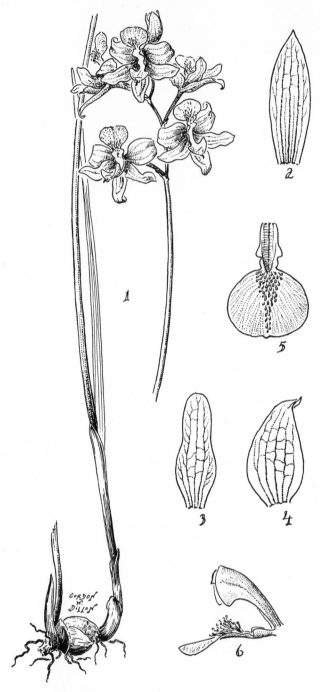

PLATE 62.— **Calopogon barbatus.** 1, plant, natural size. 2, dorsal sepal, two and one half times natural size. 3, petal, two and one half times natural size. 4, lateral sepal, two and one half times natural size. 5, lip, spread out, two and one half times natural size. 6, lip and column, side view, two and one half times natural size. *Drawn by Gordon W. Dillon.*

narrowly oblong-elliptic to linear-oblong, acute to apiculate, 1.3-1.7 cm. long, 4-6 mm. wide. Lateral sepals arising from a broad base, obliquely ovate-deltoid, somewhat keeled at the apex, abruptly acute or apiculate, about 1.3 cm. long, 5-7 mm. wide. Petals with a short claw, varying in shape from narrowly oblong-pandurate to ovate-lanceolate or oblong-elliptic with a distinct constriction near the middle, or with an ovate-orbicular base and gradually tapering to oblong above, elongated, obtuse or abruptly acute, widest below the middle, 1.2-1.5 cm. long, 3-5 mm. wide. Lip obscurely 3-lobed, 1-1.3 cm. long; lateral lobes near the base, inconspicuous, with a triangular apex, involute, separated from the large mid-lobe by a gradually dilated isthmus; mid-lobe broadly obovate to suborbicular, broadly rounded (sometimes retuse) at the apex, with broadly rounded lateral margins, 7-10 mm. wide; disc bearded on the central portion with clavellate hairs, the basal and central hairs being deep rust-red and the anterior hairs (usually extending to the apical margin) being gradually reduced to pale lavender papillae. Column broadly winged on each side near the apex, 7-8 mm. long, 4.5-7.5 mm. wide across the wings, with the pair of wings (when spread out) forming a semiorbicular lamina which is either subtruncate at the base or tapering down the sides of the column.

This species is sometimes confused with *C. pallidus.* However, the flowers of the Bearded Grass-pink usually expand almost simultaneously and last but a short time, while those of *C. pallidus* are produced in slow succession during a prolonged flowering season. The latter condition results in bud, flowers and fruits usually being found together in the same raceme. Furthermore, the pedicellate ovary of *C. barbatus* is longer than that of *C. pallidus.*

The unique contrivance whereby insect-pollination is brought about is the same for all the Calopogons. The lip, which is uppermost in the perianth, acts as a flexible elevator when an insect lights upon it. The insect, clinging to the glandular-hairy surface of the lip, is lowered down against the column to deposit on the stigma any pollinia it may be carrying. At the same time new pollinia are attached to the insect to be carried to the next flower visited. In this manner cross-pollination is effected.

The Bearded Grass-pink is usually found in peaty depressions in savannahs, in acid meadows and low pinelands, grassy swamps, in moist sandy soil on the edge of cypress swamps, hammocks, and pocosins, and rarely in oak woods and on sandy pine ridges. It often occurs in company with other orchids, pitcher plants (*Sarracenia* spp.), butterworts (*Pinguicula* spp.), broom-sedges (*Andropogon* spp.) and other plants. It is confined to the Atlantic Coastal Plain and Gulf Coast, and flowers from early February to the last of May.

GEOGRAPHICAL DISTRIBUTION: North Carolina (Coastal Plain), along the Atlantic seaboard to Florida (south to Lee and Palm Beach counties), west along the Gulf Coast to Louisiana (St. Tammany Parish).

CULTURAL NOTES: The Bearded Grass-pink grows in damp acid soil in pine- and grass-lands in the lowlands of the Coastal Plain. It may be cultivated in gardens where the soil can be maintained in the requisite condition and where the winter temperatures are not too severe. (E. T. W.)

2. **Calopogon multiflorus** Lindl., Gen. and Sp. Orch. Pl. 425. 1840. Type locality and collection: Florida, *F. Cozzens.* (*Limodorum multiflorum* (Lindl.) Mohr; *L. pinetorum* Small; *Calopogon barbatus* var. *multiflorus* (Lindl.) Correll). PLATE 63

(The name, *multiflorus,* is a Latin adjective meaning "many-flowered," in allusion to the several flowers of the raceme.)

COMMON NAMES: Many-flowered Grass-pink, Many-flowered Calopogon.

Plant scapose, erect, rigid, glabrous, 1.5-4.5 dm. tall. Rootstock a horizontal elongated (rarely bulbous) corm which is often 4 cm. long and 5 mm. in diameter, with a tuft of roots at the proximal end and the remains of the old stalk at the distal end. Stem green below, dark madder-purple above, usually geniculate at the base (two stems occasionally produced from the same corm), with several scarious imbricating sheaths at the base. Leaves (when present) one or two, basal, narrowly linear, long-acuminate, firm and rigid, strongly ribbed, conduplicate, 4-19 cm. long, mostly less than 5 mm. wide. Raceme densely or laxly six- to ten-flowered, elongated, with the flowers opening in rapid succession, 3.5-15 cm. long, 3-3.5 cm.

in diameter. Floral bracts ovate-lanceolate to lanceolate, long-acuminate, 5-10 mm. long. Flowers vividly magenta-purple to crimson, showy, with the slender pedicellate ovaries 6-10 mm. long. Dorsal sepal narrowly oblong, somewhat concave, acute to apiculate, 1.2-1.5 cm. long,

PLATE 63.— **Calopogon multiflorus.** Plants, natural size. 1, lip, spread out, twice natural size. 2, lateral sepal, twice natural size. 3, dorsal sepal, twice natural size. 4, petal, twice natural size. *Drawn by Blanche Ames.*

4-6 mm. wide. Lateral sepals rising from a broad base, ovate-elliptic to broadly lanceolate, falcate, abruptly acute to acuminate, often long-acuminate, sometimes keeled at the apex, 1.1-1.3 cm. long, 5-7 mm. wide. Petals with a rather prominent claw, broadly oblong-elliptic, pandurate to obovate, rarely cuneate, rounded to obtuse or acute, widest above the middle, with the upper margin often irregularly crenulate, 1-1.3 (averaging 1.1) cm. long, 4-6 mm. wide above the middle. Lip obscurely 3-lobed, 8-9.5 mm. long; lateral lobes basal, broadly rounded, separated from the mid-lobe by a short isthmus with parallel sides; mid-lobe tri-angular-deltoid or broadly cuneate, the wide apex being either slightly rounded to truncate or retuse (sometimes apiculate), with essentially straight (not rounded) lateral margins, 8-10 mm. wide; disc bearded on the central portion with clavellate (often bifurcate) hairs, the long hairs near the base being bright yellow, the shorter central hairs orange and the anterior hairs (not reaching the apical margin) gradually reduced to purple papillae. Column 5.5-7 mm. long, broadly winged on each side near the apex, 4.5-6 mm. wide across the wings; with the pair of wings (when spread out) forming a semiorbicular lamina which is subtruncate at the base.

This species is closely allied to *C. barbatus* and I formerly regarded it as only varietally different from that species. With further study of these plants, however, several differences have been noted which seem to be sufficiently strong to maintain it as a separate entity. Although some intergradations occur, this species has more flowers in the raceme and petals which are constantly widest above the middle (in contrast to the petals of *C. barbatus* which are constantly widest below the middle). The floral bracts of *C. multiflorus* are 5-10 mm. long, whereas those of *C. barbatus* are 2-5 mm. long, and the flowers which open in rapid succession are always deeper and more richly colored. Its flowering period also extends into the summer, while that of *C. barbatus* usually ends in May.

From an ecological standpoint, this species is of interest in that it is able to survive surface fires. In burned-over flat pinelands this little orchid is often the only evident herbaceous plant as it sends its trim spike of beautiful flowers up through the fire-blackened earth with vigor and freshness.

This species is found in damp sandy pinelands, in flatwoods, pine barrens, among Saw Palmetto, on the edge of hammocks and in swampy fields and savannahs. It is confined to the Atlantic Coastal Plain and Gulf Coast, and flowers from early March (rarely February) to July.

GEOGRAPHICAL DISTRIBUTION: Florida (widespread), Georgia (Camden and Charlton counties), Alabama (Mobile County) and Mississippi (Jackson County).

CULTURAL NOTES: See this section under *C. barbatus*.

3. Calopogon pallidus Chapm., Fl. South. U. S., ed. 1: 457. 1860. Type locality: Wet pine barrens, west Florida, near the coast, to North Carolina. (*Limodorum pallidum* (Chapm.) Mohr). PLATE 64

(The name, *pallidus,* is a Latin adjective signifying "pale," in allusion to the whitish or pale rose or pink flowers.)

COMMON NAME: Pale Grass-pink.

Plant scapose, essentially erect, slender, glabrous, 2.2-6.5 dm. tall. Rootstock a small bulbous or ellipsoid corm having a tuft of slender whitish roots at the proximal end. Leaves one or rarely two, basal, narrowly linear and grass-like, long-acuminate, strongly ribbed and conduplicate, 6-31 cm. long, 2-6 mm. wide. Raceme laxly few- to many-flowered, flexuous, 5-23 cm. long, with the flowers approximate and opening successively up the raceme (the flowering period extending over several weeks). Floral bracts subulate to shortly lanceolate, 3-5 mm. long. Flowers rose-pink to white, tinged with pink, sometimes pure white, with the slender pedicellate ovaries 4-7 mm. long. Dorsal sepal linear to oblong-lanceolate, rarely oblanceolate, keeled at the acute apex, 1.3-1.8 cm. long, 3-5 mm. wide at about the middle. Lateral sepals rising from a broad base, obliquely elliptic, slightly keeled at the abruptly acute apex, 9-12 mm. long, 5-6 mm. wide. Petals linear to linear-oblong or rarely narrowly oblanceolate, obtuse to acute, often with slightly sinuate margins, 1.2-1.5 cm. long, 2-4 mm. wide. Lip obscurely 3-lobed, 8-12 mm. long; lateral lobes shallow, inconspicuous, separated from the mid-lobe by a short isthmus with almost parallel sides; mid-lobe obovate to obcordate or narrowly flabellate, truncate to slightly rounded at the apex, apiculate or occasionally retuse with an apicule in the sinus, 5-9 mm. wide; disc bearded on the lower central portion to about the middle of the mid-lobe with clavellate (often bifurcate) hairs, the long hairs near the base being somewhat united and deep purple, the shorter central hairs distinct and orange-yellow and the anterior hairs gradually reduced to flesh-colored papillae. Column 8-10 (averaging 9) mm. long, broadly and abruptly winged on each side near the apex, 6-8 mm. wide across

PLATE 64.— **Calopogon pallidus.** 1, plants, one and one fourth times natural size. 2, lip and column, side view, three times natural size. 3, lip, spread out, three times natural size. 4, petal, three times natural size. 5, dorsal sepal, three times natural size. 6, lateral sepal, three times natural size. *Redrawn in part from Blanche Ames by Gordon W. Dillon.*

the wings; the pair of wings (when spread out) forming a semielliptic lamina which is distinctly truncate at the base with the basal margins forming a right angle with the column.

The short pedicellate ovaries of *C. pallidus*, which are only 4-7 mm. long, cause the prominently spreading-reflexed lateral sepals to curve about the rachis, thus giving to the raceme a more strict appearance than in any of the other species. Besides the above characteristic, the pale flowers and long blooming period (often of several weeks duration) readily separate the Pale Grass-pink from closely allied species.

This species is nearly always found in wet situations in savannahs, low pinelands, along creeks and rivers, in sphagnum bogs on the edge of cypress swamps, pocosins, hammocks, swamps and in wet coastal prairies. It is confined to the Atlantic Coastal Plain and Gulf Coast, and flowers from February to July in various parts of its range.

GEOGRAPHICAL DISTRIBUTION: Virginia (Isle of Wight and Nansemond counties) and North Carolina (Coastal Plain), along the Atlantic seaboard to southern Florida, along the Gulf Coast to Louisiana (St. Tammany Parish).

CULTURAL NOTES: The Pale Grass-pink, like its relatives, is an occupant of moist to wet acid soils, mostly in openings in pinelands. Since it extends northward into Virginia, it is evidently more resistant to frost in winter than its nearest relative, *C. barbatus*. To cultivate it successfully high acidity must be maintained. (E. T. W.)

4. Calopogon pulchellus (Salisb.) R. Br. in Ait., Hort. Kew., ed. 2, 5: 204. 1813.

Limodorum pulchellum Salisb., Prodr. Hort. Chap. All. 8. 1796. Type locality: Not given. (*Calopogon tuberosus* BSP. and *Cathea tuberosa* Morong, not *Limodorum tuberosum* Linnaeus).   PLATES 65 and 66

(The name, *pulchellus*, is a Latin adjective signifying "little beauty," an appropriate designation because of this plant's most attractive flowers.)

COMMON NAMES: Grass-pink, Pretty Calopogon, Tuberous-rooted Calopogon.

Plant scapose, erect, slender to somewhat stout, glabrous, 1-13.5 dm. tall. Rootstock a rather small corm having a tuft of slender whitish roots at the proximal end. Leaves one or rarely two, basal, linear to linear-lanceolate, occasionally semiterete or linear-setaceous and bristly, strongly ribbed, flat or keeled, up to 5 dm. or more long and 5 cm. wide. Raceme laxly flowered, elongated, 8-46 cm. long, composed of four to twenty showy flowers. Floral bracts ovate to ovate-lanceolate, acuminate, 3-9 mm. long. Flowers opening successively up the raceme, pink to rose-purple or magenta-crimson, rarely pure white. Dorsal sepal narrowly oblong to oblong-elliptic, acute to apiculate, 2-2.7 cm. long, 5.5-10 mm. wide. Lateral sepals ovate to ovate-lanceolate or oblong-elliptic, oblique, abruptly acute, often somewhat keeled and apiculate at the apex, 1.2-2.3 cm. long, 9-13 mm. wide. Petals with a short claw, narrowly pandurate, oblong-pandurate, ovate-lanceolate or oblong-elliptic, usually somewhat constricted above the middle, widest near the base, broadly rounded to obtuse or rarely acute at the apex, 1.3-2.4 cm. long, 4-9 mm. wide below the middle. Lip obsolescently 3-lobed, 1-2 cm. long; lateral lobes minute, separated from the mid-lobe by an elongated linear isthmus; mid-lobe broadly cuneate-flabellate to obreniform or transversely elliptic-oblong, retuse to broadly rounded and apiculate at the apex (occasionally retuse with an apicule in the sinus), 6-18 mm. wide; disc bearded on the three central veins with clavellate hairs, the filaments of the basal hairs being united and deep purple and the shorter central hairs distinct and gradually becoming cream-colored with orange-colored tips, the anterior hairs being gradually shortened and deep rust-red becoming flesh-colored papillae near the apex. Column strongly incurved, 1-2 cm. long, broadly winged on each side at the apex, 6-9 mm. across the wings; the pair of wings (when spread out) forming a suborbicular to rhombic or broadly obovate lamina. Capsule ellipsoid, three-angled, prominently 6-ribbed, 1.2-2.3 cm. long, 5-10 mm. in diameter.

Two variants have been segregated from this highly variable species representing extreme conditions found at the northern and southern limits of the species. The northern plant, var. *latifolius* (St. John) Fernald (1946A) — originally described from Nova Scotia — usually has paired short leaves which are broadly oblong-lanceolate to narrowly oblong-ovate and conspicuously exceeding the scape. Moreover, it has a large corm which is 2 cm. in diameter and is heavily dark-coated.

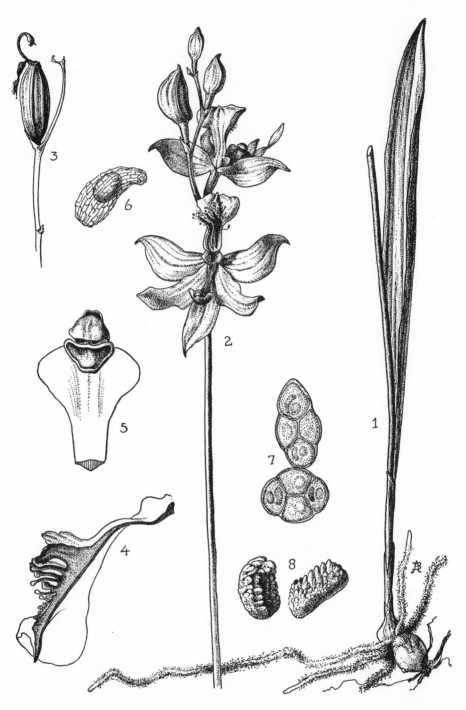

PLATE 65.— **Calopogon pulchellus.** 1, basal part of plant, natural size. 2, inflorescence, natural size. 3, mature capsule, to show the persistent column, natural size. 4, longitudinal section through center of lip, to show the papillae, four times natural size. 5, upper part of column, four times natural size. 6, seed, highly magnified. 7, two pollen tetrads, highly magnified. 8, pollen masses, highly magnified. *Drawn by Blanche Ames.*

PLATE 66.— **Calopogon pulchellus.** Flowers, natural size. *Drawn by Blanche Ames.*

The southern variant, var. *Simpsonii* (Small) Ames (1904) — originally described as *Limodorum Simpsonii* Small from Florida — is a coarse robust plant of the southern Coastal Plain (often more than 10 dm. tall) with leaves commonly semi-terete or linear-setaceous and bristly, and the mid-lobe of the lip more transversely elliptic than that of more northern plants. Occasionally plants with pure white flowers, known as forma *albiflorus* (Britton) Fernald (1921)—originally described from New Jersey — occur throughout the range of the species.

It is my opinion that *C. pulchellus* should be considered as a highly variable species which is represented at its northern and southern limits by the above described extreme forms.

The Grass-pink is nearly always found in wet situations in acid bogs and meadows, in sphagnum swamps, marshes and low pinelands, in depressions of savannahs and prairies, on the edge of dense swamps, cypress ponds and along stream banks. It often grows in damp oak and pine barrens, flatwoods, cranberry bogs and in wet dune-hollows along the coast. It is found from near sea level along the Atlantic Coastal Plain and Gulf Coast, up to 450 feet altitude in Vermont, 2,000 feet in Tennessee and 3,000 feet in North Carolina. It flowers sporadically throughout the year in Florida and the West Indies, but primarily from March to August within its range.

GEOGRAPHICAL DISTRIBUTION: Widespread and rather frequent from Newfoundland, Nova Scotia, New Brunswick, Prince Edward Island, Quebec and Ontario (Lambton and Wellington counties), through New England and the Atlantic States, south to southern Florida, along the Gulf Coast to Texas (west to Lamar and Leon counties), west through the Central and Lake States to Minnesota (Anoka, Cass, Chisago, Clearwater, Hubbard and Ramsey counties), Iowa (Fayette and Johnson counties), Missouri, Arkansas (Arkansas, Drew and Lonoke counties) and Oklahoma (Le Flore County); also Cuba and the Bahama Islands.

CULTURAL NOTES: Since the Grass-pink occurs throughout the eastern half of the United States and Canada, it is tolerant of a wide range of temperature conditions. Its fleshy corm lies imbedded in moist peat sand of moderately to intensely acid reaction, and it is fairly easy to cultivate if soil of this type is available. While this plant has been successfully grown in a small number of gardens, it does not persist in the neighborhood of mice and chipmunks since the corms form one of their favorite foods.

Variety *Simpsonii* is wholly different from the typical form in its soil preference, growing in the Everglades of southern Florida in marl soil (of circumneutral reaction) which is sterile from the standpoint of availability of nitrogen and other plant foods. (E. T. W.)

According to BROWN (1813), the Grass-pink was cultivated in England before 1771 by WILLIAM MALCOLM. As early as 1740 it was being cultivated in Holland.

14. **Prescottia** Lindl.

Prescottia Lindl. in Hook., Exot. Fl. 2: t. 115. 1824.

(The name, *Prescottia,* is in honor of JOHN D. PRESCOTT, noted British botanist of the early nineteenth century (died in 1837) who traveled extensively in Siberia.)

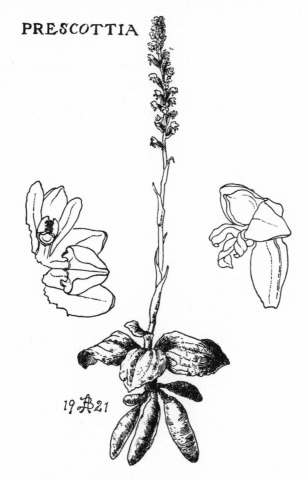

TEXTFIGURE 6. — **Prescottia oligantha.** Plant, natural size, Flowers, spread out and side view, much enlarged. *Drawn by Blanche Ames.*

Terrestrial large or inconspicuous herbs with fasciculate fibrous or fleshy roots from a short rhizome. Leaves basal (or essentially so), sessile or with long petioles, membranaceous. Inflorescence a slender or thick spike of few or numerous small non-resupinate flowers. Sepals thin, membranaceous, connate at the base and forming a short cup or tube, spreading or revolute at the apex. Petals narrow, adnate to the sepaline cup. Lip on the upper side of the flower, with the claw adnate to the sepaline cup, entire, auriculate at the base, arched, deeply concave or galeate, often enclosing the column. Column very short, adnate to the sepaline cup; anther erect on the margin of the clinandrium; pollinia four, granular or powdery. Capsule small, suberect, ovoid to ellipsoid.

This genus consists of about thirty-five species which are natives of tropical and subtropical America from Florida, Mexico and the West Indies to Brazil, Ecuador and Peru.

1. **Prescottia oligantha** (Sw.) Lindl., Gen. and Sp. Orch. Pl. 454. 1840. *Cranichis oligantha* Sw., Prodr. Veg. Ind. Occ. 120. 1788. Type locality: Jamaica.

PLATE 67 and FIGURE 6

(The name, *oligantha,* is a Greek adjective meaning "few-flowered," characterizing the inflorescence of this species.)

COMMON NAME: Small Prescottia.

Plant scapose, glabrous, small, 1.3-3.4 dm. tall. Roots short, thick, fleshy, fasciculate, partly covered by a thick tomentum, 4-6 mm. in diameter. Stem slender, purplish. Leaves radical, petioled, 1.5-7 cm. long (including the petiole), reduced above to sheathing lanceolate bracts; blades ovate-oblong to obovate, suborbicular or elliptic, obtuse to acute, rarely apiculate, 3-4 cm. long, 1-3 cm. wide. Spike densely flowered, slender, 2.5-8 cm. long, 5-7 mm. in diameter. Floral bracts narrowly lanceolate, translucent, 3-5 mm. long. Flowers minute, white, green or pink, less than 2.5 mm. long; perianth parts cohering at the base. Dorsal sepal ovate, obtuse to rarely acute, 1-2 mm. long, about 1 mm. wide. Lateral sepals arising from a broad connate base, triangular or deltoid, somewhat concave near the apex, obtuse to subacute, 1-2.2 mm. long, a little more than 1 mm. wide at the base. Petals linear to narrowly obovate-spatulate, retuse or truncate to obtuse at the apex, 1-1.5 mm. long, about 0.5 mm. wide. Lip uppermost in the flower, suborbicular, concave-saccate, apiculate, with lateral auricles at the base, 1-1.5 mm. long, about 2 mm. wide when spread out. Column laterally winged near the apex. Capsule ellipsoid, shallowly 6-keeled, less than 5 mm. long.

This species was first collected in the United States in hammocks near Homestead, Dade County, Florida, by ALVAH AUGUSTUS EATON in 1903. EATON found it again in 1905 in the same vicinity. Since then, as far as I know, it has not been collected again in our region. This is not unusual, for the Small Prescottia is a diminutive plant, and even where abundant it is most elusive.

The Small Prescottia occurs in hammocks of southern peninsular Florida where it flowers in winter (February). In the tropics, it grows on mossy logs and rocks on the edge of dense rain forests, on brushy rocky banks and in clayey soil. In the Bahama Islands, it is found on stone walls. It grows at near sea level in Florida, up to 2,000 feet altitude in Puerto Rico and Dominica, 4,500 feet in Guatemala, Costa Rica and Panama, 5,000 feet in Jamaica and 7,500 feet in Venezuela, and flowers from December to March in various parts of its range.

GEOGRAPHICAL DISTRIBUTION: Florida (Dade County); also Mexico, through Central America to Panama, the West Indies, Colombia and Venezuela.

CULTURAL NOTES: Found in the United States only in circumneutral soil in hammocks of subtropical Florida, this orchid cannot be expected to succeed in cultivation elsewhere. (E. T. W.)

15. Cranichis Sw.

Cranichis Sw., Prodr. Veg. Ind. Occ. 8, 120. 1788.

(The name, *Cranichis*, is from the Greek words meaning "having a helmet," doubtless referring to the concave lip which is uppermost and usually projects out over the column to form a "helmet.")

Terrestrial (rarely epiphytic) scapose herbs with fasciculate fleshy roots. Leaves basal or radical, sometimes with reduced cauline leaves. Scape slender, simple, provided with tubular dilated or clasping sheaths. Inflorescence a slender spicate terminal raceme of small non-resupinate flowers. Sepals free, subequal or with the lateral pair somewhat broader than the dorsal sepal, more or less connivent. Petals free or somewhat adnate to the base of the column, spreading, smaller than the sepals. Lip on the upper part of the flower, adnate to the base or middle of the column, concave or saccate, usually embracing the column. Column short; anther solitary, 2-celled; pollinia four, granular-powdery. Capsule suberect, ovoid or ellipsoid.

This genus consists of about thirty species which are natives of tropical and subtropical America. The pattern of the veins of the lip in some of the species forms a reliable diagnostic character.

1. Cranichis muscosa Sw., Prodr. Veg. Ind. Occ. 120. 1788. Type locality: Jamaica.
PLATE 67

(The name, *muscosa*, is a Latin adjective meaning "mossy," perhaps in allusion to the habitat where this species was first found. SWARTZ later stated that the species grew in damp shaded woods.)

COMMON NAME: None known.

Plant scapose, 9-44 cm. tall. Roots fleshy, coarsely fibrous, fasciculate. Scape slender, tinged with madder-purple. Leaves four to six, radical, petioled, reduced above to sheathing ovate to lanceolate leaf-like bracts, blades subcordate or broadly ovate to elliptic, obtuse to acute, 2.5-9.5 cm. long, 1.5-4 cm. wide; petiole winged, 1-4 cm. long. Raceme few- to many-flowered, 1.5-13 cm. long, 1.5-2.3 cm. in diameter Floral bracts ovate-lanceolate, acute to acuminate, 3-5 mm. long. Flowers white. Sepals ovate to ovate-oblong or oblong-elliptic, obtuse to abruptly acute, 2-3 mm. long, 1-2 mm. wide at about the middle; lateral sepals oblique. Petals linear-oblong to oblong-spatulate, obtuse, 2-3 mm. long, 0.5-1 mm. wide. Lip white, spotted with green, uppermost in the flower, sessile, suborbicular or oblong-quadrate, concave, rarely mucronate, with entire undulate margins, tuberculose or slightly crested along the three median veins of the disc within, 2-3 mm. long, 1.5-2 mm. wide. Column slightly winged, about 1 mm. long. Capsule essentially sessile, 7-10 mm. long, ovoid.

This species was first collected in the United States in Lee County, Florida, by J. E. LAYNE in May 1903. In December of the same year A. A. EATON found it in moss and humus about lime-sinks in a hammock in Dade County, Florida. Since then, as far as I know, it has not been collected again in the United States.

Cranichis muscosa occurs on stumps and cypress knees and in moss around the edges of lime-sinks and pot-holes in hammocks and cypress swamps of southern peninsular Florida. In the tropics, it grows on moist rocks in streams and on banks in wet mountain forests. It occurs from near sea level in Florida, up to 2,000 feet altitude in Cuba, 3,000 feet in Mexico and Guatemala and 5,000 feet in Costa Rica, and flowers from December to March in various parts of its range.

GEOGRAPHICAL DISTRIBUTION: Florida (Dade and Lee counties); also Mexico, Guatemala, Costa Rica, Panama, the Bahama Islands, the West Indies, Trinidad and Venezuela.

CULTURAL NOTES: Found in the United States only in circumneutral soil in hammocks of subtropical Florida, this orchid cannot be expected to succeed in cultivation elsewhere. (E. T. W.)

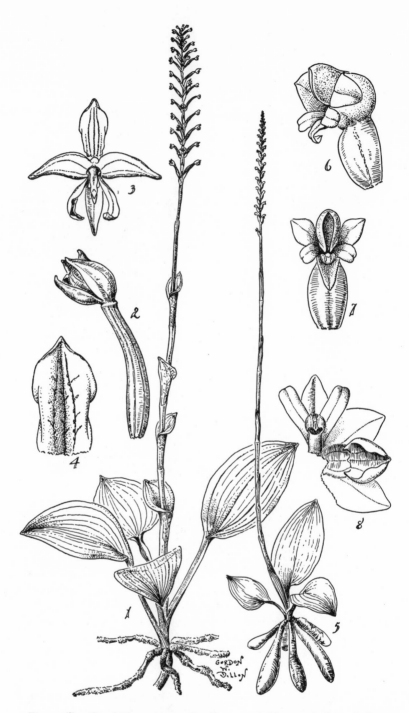

PLATE 67.— **Cranichis muscosa.** 1, plant, one half natural size. 2, flower, side view, five times natural size. 3, flower, front view, partly spread open, five times natural size. 4, lip, ten times natural size.

Prescottia oligantha. 5, plant, one half natural size. 6, flower, side view, with a lateral sepal and petal turned back, ten times natural size. 7, flower, front view, ten times natural size. 8, flower, spread open, ten times natural size. *Drawn by Gordon W. Dillon.*

16. Ponthieva R. Br.

Ponthieva R. Br. in Ait., Hort. Kew., ed. 2, 5: 199. 1813.

(The name, *Ponthieva,* is in honor of HENRI DE PONTHIEU, French botanist, who collected in the Caribbean region and sent plants to Sir JOSEPH BANKS in 1778.)

Terrestrial (rarely epiphytic) scapose herbs with fleshy or somewhat fibrous roots and radical leaves which are subsessile to long-petioled. Inflorescence a lax terminal raceme of small non-resupinate flowers. Sepals free or with the lateral sepals slightly united at the base, spreading. Petals grown to the column above its base, oblique, often adherent to the dorsal sepal at the apex. Lip on the upper part of the flower, with its claw grown to the column above its base, abruptly dilated and ascending. Column short, semiterete, somewhat longitudinally winged on each side; anther solitary, 2-celled, erect behind the rostellum; pollinia four, joined in pairs, powdery-granular. Capsule suberect, ellipsoid to obovoid-ellipsoid.

In this genus there are about twenty-five species which are found in the warmer regions of the Western Hemisphere from southeastern Virginia to Chile, including Mexico, Central America, the West Indies and South America.

1. **Ponthieva racemosa** (Walt.) Mohr, Contrib. U. S. Nat. Herb. (Plant Life of Alabama) 6: 460. 1901 and Blake, Rhodora 17: 136. 1915. *Arethusa racemosa* Walt., Fl. Carol. 222. 1778. Type locality: Not given. Probably eastern Carolina. (*Ponthieva glandulosa* (Sims) R. Br.; *P. Brittonae* Ames). PLATE 68

(The name, *racemosa,* is a Latin adjective meaning "like a raceme," referring to the kind of inflorescence found in this species.)

COMMON NAMES: Shadow-witch, Many-flowered Ponthieva, Glandular Ponthieva, Glandular Neottia.

Plant erect, scapose, glandular-pubescent throughout (except the leaves), 1.3-6 dm. tall. Roots thick, fleshy, fasciculate, often lanuginose. Stem reddish brown to purplish or greenish. Leaves mostly in a basal rosette, oblong-elliptic to obovate or oblanceolate, obtuse to subacute, subsessile to long-petioled, 2-17 cm. long (including the broad petiole), 1-5.5 cm. wide, glaucous beneath, succulent when fresh, thin and papery when dry, reduced above to sheathing bracts. Raceme lax, consisting of few to many wide-spreading flowers, 5-24 cm. long, 1.5-5 cm. in diameter. Floral bracts ovate-lanceolate to narrowly lanceolate, long-acuminate, 5-9 mm. long. Flowers whitish green, with the rather stout ascending pedicellate ovaries 1-2.2 cm. long. Dorsal sepal oblong-elliptic to broadly elliptic-lanceolate, obtuse to subacute, 3.8-8.5 mm. long, 2-3 mm. wide. Lateral sepals broadly and obliquely ovate to ovate-oblong, obtuse to acute, 4.3-8 mm. long, 2.5-4 mm. wide. Petals clawed; lamina obliquely triangular to semicordate, incurved, dilated on the outer margin at the base, constricted near the apex, obtuse to subacute, mostly ciliate, 4-8 mm. long, 1.5-5 mm. wide near the base; claw adnate to the column for about 1 mm. above the base, free part slender. Lip uppermost in the flower, with a short claw, suborbicular, concave-saccate, terminated by a linear obtuse to acute apical lobule, with an obscure linear median crest on the disc, 4-7.5 mm. long, 2.5-6 mm. wide when spread out; claw 1-2 mm. long. Column 2-4.5 mm. long, curved. Capsule ellipsoid, 8-13 mm. long, about 5 mm. in diameter.

This species often occurs in exceedingly picturesque localities. It is quite abundant in the "Devil's Millhopper" near Gainesville, Florida, a large limestone sink-hole filled with a subtropical growth, and at the "Devil's Slide" near Dayton, Texas. The latter place consists of a series of ravines along the lower Trinity River whose seepage banks are luxuriantly covered with the Southern Shield Fern (*Dryopteris normalis*), Southern Magnolia (*Magnolia grandiflora*) and pines. At both stations the Shadow-witch spreads its sleek leaves over the rims of eroded banks and ledges of marly earth.

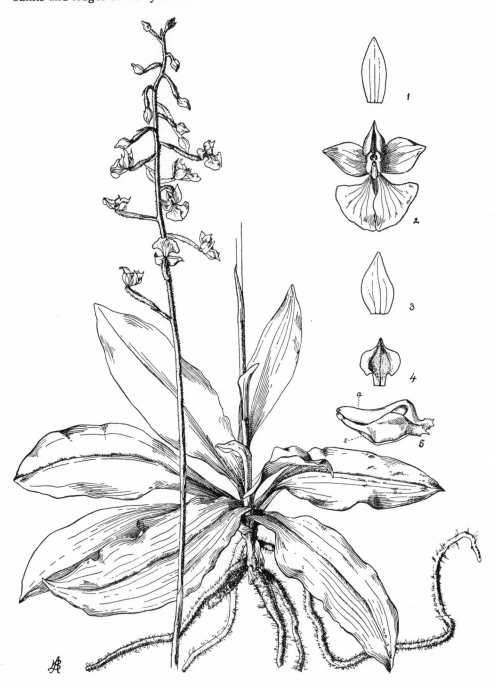

PLATE 68.— **Ponthieva racemosa.** Plant, two thirds natural size. 1, dorsal sepal, twice natural size. 2, flower, partly spread out, twice natural size. 3, lateral sepal, twice natural size. 4, lip, spread open, twice natural size. 5, column (*a,* anther; *s,* stigma), side view, eight times natural size. *Drawn by Blanche Ames.*

While botanizing in West Florida with some friends we located a region where this species occurs quite frequently. We had been exploring the eastern slopes of some heavily forested hills when we abruptly came out onto the open summit of a bluff. From this high promontory on the crown of what later proved to be Alum Bluff, we could look out over the valley of the Apalachicola River. The floodplain and upland forests stretched westward as far as we could see. It was a fascinating and inviting land — a country just as wild and alluring now as when Asa Gray wandered, intrigued, through its valleys and ravines more than a century ago. It presented a level peaceful appearance which concealed its true nature, for the limestone strata beneath were honeycombed and pitted from eternal erosion, and deep narrow fissures (from which dripped a fine spray of water) scarred its misshapen and irregular face. Gracefully draped from the damp cavernous walls of these cuts were countless slender fronds of Venus' Maidenhair Fern (*Adiantum Capillus-Veneris*), while on the drier ledges near the ferns were scattered silvery plants of the Shadow-witch, and just below the ferns, interlacing and spreading its flat dichotomous "branches" over the wet face of the rock, grew large mats of the acridly pungent liverwort, *Conocephalum*. The endemic Stinking-cedar (*Tumion taxifolium*) bordered the edges of the crevices and lifted its lax needle-studded branches to cast feathery shadows into the cavernous depths.

Although it is primarily a Coastal Plain species in our region, I have found the Shadow-witch well up on the Piedmont Plateau in the vicinity of limerocks in Morgan County, Alabama.

The earliest collection I have seen of this species in our region is that obtained by a Dr. Denny from Suggsville, Clarke County, Alabama, on October 28, 1852.

According to Paul C. Standley, this species is known in Costa Rica as "Ipecacuanha," its roots being used as a substitute for ipecac.

This species is usually found in the vicinity of limestone or in calcareous soils in hammocks, on limestone ledges and (in Florida) on the edge of limerock sinkholes, in damp woods along streams or on the rim of eroded stream banks in wooded ravines and on the edge of muddy sloughs and ponds. In the tropics, it grows in damp tropical forests and barrancas, on damp cliffs and open brushy banks, wooded hillsides and in damp sunny places. In Costa Rica it has been observed to be an epiphyte. It occurs at near sea level in Florida and Panama, up to 700 feet altitude in Alabama, 2,500 feet in Jamaica, 6,500 feet in Mexico and Guatemala and 12,000 feet in Panama. The Shadow-witch flowers sporadically throughout the year, especially from September to April in the United States.

GEOGRAPHICAL DISTRIBUTION: On the Atlantic Coastal Plain from southeastern Virginia (Gloucester, Isle of Wight, James City, Southampton and Surry counties) to southern Florida, through Alabama (Clark, Morgan and Talladega counties) to Louisiana (Natchitoches and West Feliciana parishes) and Texas (Jasper and Liberty counties); also Mexico, Central America, the Bahama Islands, the West Indies and South America.

CULTURAL NOTES: The Shadow-witch ranges from Florida north to the warmer parts of Virginia, growing in circumneutral soil in moist woodlands. It can be cultivated in wild gardens where the winter is mild. It has been grown successfully farther north in cool greenhouses. (E. T. W.)

According to Brown (1813), the Shadow-witch was first introduced into England in 1800 by E. I. A. Woodford, Esq.

17. Spiranthes L. C. Rich.

Spiranthes L. C. Rich., De Orch. Europ. Annot. 28. 1817 (in Mém. Mus. Hist. Nat. Par. 4: 50. 1818), conserved name.   PLATE 69

(The name, *Spiranthes,* is a combination of two Greek words meaning "coil" and "flower," in allusion to the typically spiraled arrangement of the flowers in the spicate inflorescence of many of the species, especially in the section Euspiranthes (true *Spiranthes*).)

Coarse or delicate terrestrial herbs with clustered tuberous or rarely fibrous roots. Leaves various, mostly basal, broadly ovate, elliptic, narrowly linear or semiterete, persistent, marcescent or fugacious, reduced above to persistent sheathing bracts. Flowers variously colored, usually white and variously tinged with green, yellow, cinnabar-red, brown or lavender, sometimes brick-red, deep crimson, yellowish orange or yellowish scarlet, in a more or less spirally twisted showy or inconspicuous terminal spike. Sepals free; dorsal sepal and petals adherent; lateral sepals usually somewhat decurrent on the ovary and often gibbous at the base or extended to form a mentum. Lip sessile or with a short claw, concave and embracing the column, spreading or arcuate-recurved at the apex, crisped, wavy, toothed or 3-lobed, with a minute or conspicuous callosity on each side at the base or sometimes ecallose. Column short or elongated, terete to clavate, essentially footless or extended into a long foot at the base; anther erect on the back of the column, 2-celled; pollinia two, powdery-granular, narrowly obovoid, with their filaments coherent to the narrow viscid gland which is set in the thin beak (rostellum) terminating the column; after the removal of the gland the beak is left as a 2-toothed or forked tip. Capsule erect, ellipsoid to ovoid or obovoid, often 3-keeled.

This is a polymorphic genus of about three hundred species which are widely dispersed throughout the temperate zone of both hemispheres. It occurs in tropical Asia through Oceania to Australia, Tasmania and New Zealand, and in America extends south to Chile. The species are found primarily in fields, savannahs, meadows, forests, swamps, dry open waste places, thickets, rocky barrens and sandy places in intensely acid to calcareous soils.

Spiranthes is a highly technical genus composed of a complex and variable group of plants. In the past, the genus has been divided into a number of segregates both generic and specific. Since most of these concepts are desperately difficult to define I have followed the conservative course in upholding but one polymorphic genus. Although *Spiranthes* is not the largest genus in our area it is one of the most difficult from a taxonomic standpoint.

Several points of interest relative to this genus in Texas have been called to my attention by H. B. PARKS. He writes, "From the history of this genus as I know it, it appears to me that it depends upon rain in place of time of year for its blooming period." He also writes, "There is one thing I wish you would notice and some time comment upon and that is the right- or left-handedness of the spirals of this genus."

There is little doubt that in those regions of Texas where semiarid conditions exist, the flowering period of such species as *S. michuacana* and *S. cinnabarina* is directly influenced by rainfall. This is true of a number of orchids, as well as other plants, found in the western and southwestern states where the annual rainfall is low and more or less periodic. The fact that the blooming period of some of the species usually coincides with the period directly following the rainy season or period of heaviest rainfall would seem to substantiate this assumption.

As to the right- or left-handedness in the spiraling of single-ranked inflorescences, no statistics as to the frequency of either are available. I have collected and observed numerous plants of *S. gracilis* and *S. Grayi,* as well as others, which exhibited mostly a right-handed spiraling of the single row of flowers.

THE SPIRIT OF SPIRANTHES

PLATE 69.— **Spiranthes,** one of the few orchid genera with around-the-world distribution, occurring in North and South America, the British Isles, Europe, Asia, the East Indies, Japan, Australia, Tasmania and New Zealand. *Drawn by Blanche Ames.*

KEY FOR THE IDENTIFICATION OF THE SPECIES OF SPIRANTHES

1. Flowers forming a dense cylindrical spike, apparently in several spiral ranks; basal leaves (when present) with linear, lanceolate, oblong-elliptic or oblanceolate blades, never with a distinct petiole, having the lower part sheathing the stem.............................2
   2. Plant usually small, slender; spike 1.5 cm. or less in diameter; lip 5.5 mm. or less long (somewhat longer in *S. Romanzoffiana* var. *porrifolia*)................................3
      3. Distribution far western; lip essentially ovate-lanceolate in outline...................
         ....*S. Romanzoffiana* var. *porrifolia* (p. 222)
      3. Distribution eastern and southwestward 4
         4. Lip quadrate to oblong-quadrate, yellow; distribution mainly northeastern; flowering season June and July..*S. lucida* (p. 208)
         4. Lip rhombic-ovate to ovate-oblong, white; distribution mainly southern and southwestward; flowering season August to November..................*S. ovalis* (p. 212)
   2. Plant usually large, stout; spike commonly much more than 1.5 cm. in diameter; lip more than 6 mm. long..5
      5. Spike large, showy, 3-6 cm. in diameter; flowers highly colored, varying from greenish white to yellow-scarlet or deep crimson; lateral sepals long-decurrent on the ovary; column-foot elongated and about as long as the column; rostellum a long awl-shaped bristle-like point 6
         6. Leaves basal, appearing only after anthesis; flowers typically brick-red throughout....
            ....*S. orchioides* (p. 212)
         6. Leaves on the lower part of the stem, present during anthesis; flowers typically yellow-scarlet or yellow-orange......................................*S. cinnabarina* (p. 191)
      5. Spike comparatively slender, mostly inconspicuous, 3 cm. or less in diameter; flowers usually white, rarely orange-yellow; lateral sepals only shortly decurrent on the ovary; column-foot short or indistinct; rostellum not awl-shaped..........................7
         7. Lamina of lip ecallose; flowers varying in color from nearly white to greenish white or orange-yellow, suffused or striped with bluish green........*S. michuacana* (p. 210)
         7. Lamina of lip with a prominent or small callosity on each side at the base; flowers white, sometimes tinged or marked with yellow.........................8 (a, b, c)
            8a. Lip thin, panduriform or essentially ovate-lanceolate in outline, deeply constricted or abruptly tapering at about the middle (when tapering only slightly dilated at the apex), with the orbicular or oblong-quadrate basal portion deeply concave; calli small; flowers ascending and ringent....................................9
               9. Lip panduriform, orbicular at the base, strongly dilated and usually lacerate at the apex; calli minute or obsolescent...............*S. Romanzoffiana* (p. 220)
               9. Lip essentially ovate-lanceolate in outline, usually oblong-quadrate at the base, slightly dilated and only cellular-papillose on the margins at the apex; calli rather prominent...........................*S. Romanzoffiana* var. *porrifolia* (p. 222)
            8b. Lip fleshy-thickened, only slightly or not at all constricted at about the middle, ovate-oblong to rhombic-ovate; calli large, prominent; flowers nodding perceptibly 10
               10. Lip ovate-oblong, usually slightly constricted at about the middle and then somewhat dilated at the apex, mostly less than 1 cm. long; leaves basal or only on the lower part of the stem.............................*S. cernua* (p. 187)
               10. Lip broadly rhombic-ovate, with the basal half dilated, tapering to the obtuse or subacute apex, often as much as 1.4 cm. long; leaves often extending up the stem......................................*S. cernua* var. *odorata* (p. 190)
            8c. Flowers and floral segments more or less intermediate between those of *S. Romanzoffiana* and *S. cernua* ....× *S. Steigeri* (p. 224)
1. Flowers forming a loose or dense (usually spiral) single rank, often secund; basal leaves (when present) with ovate, oblong-elliptic, lanceolate or semiterete blades, with a distinct petiole or with the lower part sheathing the stem.....................................11
   11. Lip ovate-lanceolate to lanceolate...12
      12. Callosities obsolescent; distribution Florida...................*S. polyantha* (p. 216)
      12. Callosities rather prominent; distribution far western.............................
         ....*S. Romanzoffiana* var. *porrifolia* (p. 222)
   11. Lip not lanceolate, variously shaped; callosities prominent, minute or sometimes wanting 13
      13. Lip obscurely 3-lobed or panduriform, with a narrow isthmus or constriction separating the basal portion from the more or less expanded apical lobe or lobule..........14
         14. Basal half of lip oblong-quadrate, adorned in the center with a pair of spongy cinnabar-red blotches......................................*S. parasitica* (p. 214)
         14. Basal half of lip orbicular, concave, not provided with a spongy cinnabar-red tissue 15

15. Lip with a pair of prominent basal callosities, less than 7.5 mm. long; claw without a tuft of hairs...16

  16. Apical lobe of lip obliquely quadrate, narrower than the basal part of the lamina...*S. cranichoides* (p. 191)

  16. Apical lobe of lip mostly transversely elliptic, about as wide as the basal part of the lamina and separated from it by a narrow isthmus...*S. elata* (p. 195)

15. Lip ecallose, more than 10 mm. long; claw with a tuft of hairs in the center....
....*S. durangensis* (p. 193)

13. Lip neither 3-lobed nor prominently panduriform, ovate to oval or oblong, essentially simple and entire, at most fringed, erose or crenulate..........................17

17. Lip oval (5-5.5 mm. long); petals oval to obovate or suborbicular, with the anterior margin more or less erose; leaves absent at time of flowering...*S. Parksii* (p. 216)

17. Lip ovate to oblong, if oval more than 5.5 mm. long; petals linear to elliptic-oblong or oblanceolate; leaves absent or present at time of flowering..................18

  18. Basal leaves widely spreading, with the relatively short and broad blades having a distinct petiole, rather broad, ovate to narrowly oblong-elliptic, either persistent or fugacious (marcescent)......................................19

    19. Lip quadrate to oblong-quadrate when expanded, white, less than 4 mm. long; root consisting of one tuberoid.....................*S. Grayi* (p. 202)

    19. Lip ovate, oblong-quadrate or oblong, white marked with green or yellow, 4.6 mm. long (rarely 3.5 mm. long in *S. gracilis* var. *brevilabris*); roots usually consisting of several fasciculate tuberoids.......................20

      20. Plant essentially glabrous throughout..............................21

        21. Lip with a broad green stripe on the central portion of the disc; leaves fugacious or marcescent; usually flowering in the fall..............
....*S. gracilis* (p. 197)

        21. Lip with a broad yellow stripe on the central portion of the disc, often flecked with green; leaves mostly persistent; usually flowering in the spring ....*S. gracilis* var. *floridana* (p. 199)

      20. Plant with a densely pubescent spike; lip deeply fringed and with a prominent tuft of hairs on the disc near the apex; leaves usually persistent; flowering in the spring........*S. gracilis* var. *brevilabris* (p. 199)

  18. Basal leaves erect, ascending, narrow, linear, narrowly lanceolate or oblong-elliptic, without a petiole, the lower portion sheathing the stem, either persistent or fugacious..22

    22. Flowers secund (rarely slightly spiraled); lip from a broad base tapering to the obtuse apex, 6-9.5 mm. long; basal leaves fugacious.*S. longilabris* (p. 206)

    22. Flowers strongly spiraled; lip ovate, orbicular-quadrate, oblong or oblong-quadrate; basal leaves persistent or fugacious.........................23

      23. Plant usually small, slender; lip 6 mm. or less long, ovate to orbicular-quadrate or oblong-quadrate......................................24

        24. Leaves oblong-elliptic to elliptic-lanceolate, fleshy, shining; lip quadrate to oblong-quadrate, yellow with green stripes on the central portion of the disc; mainly northeastern in distribution (west to Missouri and Kansas).....................................*S. lucida* (p. 208)

        24. Leaves filiform-terete to narrowly linear, thin, dull; lip ovate to orbicular-quadrate, with a broad green stripe on the central portion of the disc; southeastern in distribution..................*S. tortilis* (p. 225)

      23. Plant usually large, stout; lip usually more than 6 mm. long, ovate to oblong or oblong-elliptic......................................25

        25. Lip oblong-elliptic to oblong, with parallel lateral margins or often broadest at the distal end, membranaceous, usually veined with green; spike subglabrous or very sparsely pubescent with capitate hairs....
....*S. praecox* (p. 218)

        25. Lip ovate to ovate-oblong or ovate-elliptic, broadest at or near the base, usually fleshy-thickened; spike more or less pubescent with capitate or sharp-pointed hairs......................................26

          26. Spike densely pubescent; ovaries usually covered by a thick mat of reddish brown sharp-pointed hairs; lip ovate to ovate-elliptic.....
....*S. vernalis* (p. 225)

          26. Spike more or less pubescent with capitate hairs; lip ovate-oblong, often from a suborbicular base, conspicuously laciniate along the apical margins............................*S. laciniata* (p. 204)

1. **Spiranthes cernua** (L.) L. C. Rich., De Orchid. Europ. Annot. 37. 1817 (in Mém. Mus. Hist. Nat. Par. 4: 59. 1818). *Ophrys cernua* L., Sp. Pl., ed. 1,

2:946. 1753. Type locality: Virginia and Canada. (*Gyrostachys cernua* (L.) O. Ktze.; *G. triloba* Small; *G. constricta* Small; *Spiranthes constricta* (Small) K. Schum.; *S. triloba* (Small) K. Schum.; *S. montana* Raf.; *Ibidium cernuum* (L.) House; *I. trilobum* Small). PLATES 70 and 83

(The name, *cernua,* is a Latin adjective meaning "nodding," in allusion to the characteristic position of the flowers in the raceme.)

COMMON NAMES: Nodding Ladies' Tresses, Autumn Tresses, Nodding Tresses.

Plant erect, glabrous below, downy-pubescent above, occasionally stoloniferous, 1-5.5 dm. tall; roots slender, fleshy. Leaves mostly basal or fugacious, linear to linear-lanceolate, acute to acuminate, 4.5-25 cm. long, 6-20 mm. wide. Spike densely flowered, compact, consisting of rather small nodding flowers in two to four (rarely one) spiral or nearly vertical ranks, 3-17 cm. long, 2-3 cm. in diameter. Floral bracts ovate to oblong-lanceolate, long-acuminate, 8-15 mm. long. Flowers white, usually fragrant; perianth parts somewhat downy-pubescent on the outer surface. Dorsal sepal oblong-lanceolate, obtuse to subacute, 6-11 mm. long, 1.5-3 mm. wide near the base. Lateral sepals free, lanceolate, subacute to acute, somewhat spreading and recurved above the middle, 6-11.5 mm. long, 1.5-2.5 mm. wide near the base. Petals adherent to the dorsal sepal, linear to linear-lanceolate, subacute, 6-11 mm. long, 1-3 mm. wide. Lip ovate-oblong, arcuate-recurved, usually constricted at about the middle and dilated at the apex or from an ovate-suborbicular base becoming abruptly oblong-elongated, with crisped or erose margins, 6-10 mm. long, 3-6 mm. wide at the widest point; basal callosities prominent, pubescent. Column stout, 3-5 mm. long.

In the eastern part of the continent, the Nodding Ladies' Tresses is our most widespread *Spiranthes*. It is exceedingly variable and is here treated as an extremely polymorphic species. Although the flowers are characteristically in two or more ranks, plants with flowers in a single rank have been found. These forms resemble some specimens of *S. vernalis*.

Peloric specimens are rather common in the Southwest, especially in Missouri, Arkansas, Louisiana, Oklahoma and Texas. These plants have flowers with the irregularity of the lip suppressed so that it is similar to the sepals and petals.

This species commonly occurs in bogs, meadows, swamps, marshes, wet woods, on the edge of lakes and streams, in peaty and gravelly soil in open barrens and on seepage slopes, in hammocks and wet pine barrens and flatwoods, in wet fields and prairies, on beach sand dunes, and on limestone and sandstone ledges — rarely on floating logs and rotten wood in water. The Nodding Ladies' Tresses occurs at near sea level on the Atlantic and Gulf coasts, up to 600 feet altitude in Vermont, 2,500 feet in Arkansas and 6,000 feet in North Carolina, and flowers from July to December in various parts of its range.

GEOGRAPHICAL DISTRIBUTION: Widespread and rather common from Nova Scotia, Quebec and Ontario (Elgin, Middlesex and Sudbury counties), through New England and the Atlantic States, south to southern Florida, along the Gulf Coast to Texas (west to Kendall County), west through the Central and Lake States to Minnesota (Anoka, Crow Wing, Hennepin and Traverse counties), North Dakota (Richland County), South Dakota (Brookings County), Nebraska (Kearney and Thomas counties), central Kansas (west to Cloud, Reno and Sedgewick counties), Oklahoma (Ellis and Payne counties) and New Mexico (Rio Arriba County); also Utah (Salt Lake County, *Jones 1908*).

CULTURAL NOTES: This widespread hardy species comprises several variants that differ in number of rows of flowers in the raceme, in the intensity of fragrance, and in minor morphological characters. These also differ in their physiological requirements, some growing in dry barren circumneutral soils, others in wet intensely acid sphagnum peat. Thus far, no one has worked out the correlation between their morphology and soil-reaction preference, and no general directions, therefore, can be given for the individual cultural needs. When transplanting any one of its variants, the features of the habitat should be noted and reproduced as nearly as possible or practicable in the garden. Even so, it rarely survives in gardens more than a year or two, being all too susceptible to destruction by parasitic fungi and other pests. (E. T. W.)

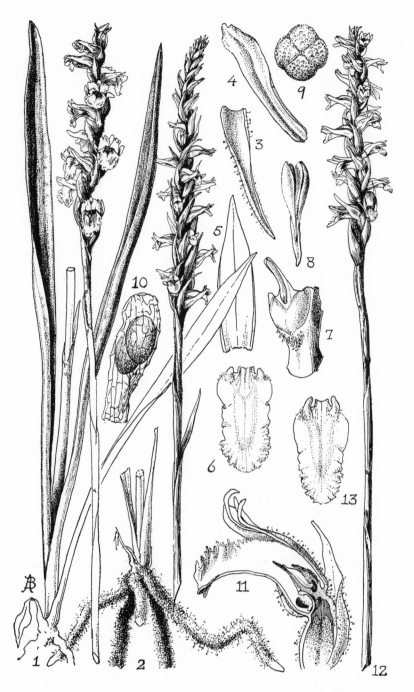

PLATE 70.— **Spiranthes cernua.** 1 and 2, general habit, natural size. 3, lateral sepal, four times natural size. 4, petal, four times natural size. 5, dorsal sepal, four times natural size. 6, lip, spread out, three times natural size. 7, column, front-side view, eight times natural size, the heart-shaped area represents the stigmatic surface. 8, pollinia, ten times natural size. 9, pollen tetrad, highly magnified. 10, seed, much enlarged, showing polyembryony. 11, section through perianth, column and ovary, four times natural size, to show position of anther, pollinia and honey gland.

Spiranthes cernua var. **ochroleuca.** 12, general habit, leaves and roots removed, natural size. 13, lip, spread out, three times natural size. *Drawn by Blanche Ames.*

According to BROWN (1813), this species was first introduced into England in 1796 by WILLIAM HAMILTON, Esq.

2. **Spiranthes cernua** var. **odorata** (Nutt.) Correll, Bot. Mus. Leafl. Harvard Univ. 8: 79. 1940. *Neottia odorata* Nutt., Journ. Acad. Nat. Sci. Phila. 7: 98. 1834. Type locality: " . . . along the borders of the Neuse River, at Newbern, North Carolina, on the wet and muddy shores . . . " (*Spiranthes odorata* (Nutt.) Lindl.; *Gyrostachys odorata* (Nutt.) O. Ktze.; *Ibidium odoratum* (Nutt.) House). PLATE 83

(The name, *odorata*, is a Latin adjective meaning "fragrant," referring to the typically vanilla-scented flowers.)

COMMON NAMES: Fragrant Ladies' Tresses, Fragrant Tresses, Swamp Tresses, Sweet Ladies' Tresses, Tidal Tresses.

Similar in habit to the typical form. Plant erect, stout or slender, often quite succulent, glabrous below, downy-pubescent above, usually stoloniferous (especially so in swampy areas), 1.8-9.5 dm. tall; roots long, fleshy, coarse. Leaves mostly basal, often extending up the stem, linear to lanceolate, subacute to acuminate, 5-40 cm. long, 5-20 mm. wide. Spike densely flowered, compact, consisting of tubular ringent flowers in several spiral or vertical ranks, 4.5-18 cm. long, 1-3 cm. in diameter. Floral bracts lanceolate, acuminate-attenuate, mostly longer than the flowers, 8-15 mm. long. Flowers white, marked with green or tinged with cream-color, very fragrant with the odor of vanilla. Sepals oblong-lanceolate to lanceolate, acute to acuminate, 6-13.5 mm. long; lateral sepals free. Petals adherent to the dorsal sepal, linear, obtuse to acute, 6-13.5 mm. long, 1-2 mm. wide. Lip with the basal half dilated, rhombic, tapering to the obtuse to subacute apex, broadly ovate to broadly obcuneate, 6-14 mm. long, 3.5-8 mm. wide near the base; basal callosities prominent, recurved, pubescent. Column about 5 mm. long.

The typically ovate or rhombic-ovate lip, stoloniferous and more leafy habits, and its preference for a more swampy environment are the characteristics which most readily separate this plant from the typical form. The odor emitted by the flowers is a strong mixture of vanilla, cumarin and jasmine.

In many tupelo-cypress swamps of the southeastern states, I have seen large colonies of these plants standing in water and supporting above their leafy stems large spikes of creamy white flowers. The conspicuous floral spikes are a striking contrast to the somber background of the swamp against which they are projected.

Another variant of this species, segregated as var. *ochroleuca* Ames (1905), is separated primarily on the basis of having normal seeds instead of the polembryonic seeds characteristic of typical *S. cernua*. However, for all practical purposes to the average individual such ultratechnical characters are not readily usable. In order to be absolutely certain of one's ground in using this embryo character, it is necessary to have the use of a compound microscope. It is of interest, nevertheless, that this anatomical difference does exist, and doubtless future cytological and genetical studies on the Orchidaceae will reveal much pertinent information now hidden from the naked eye. In addition, var. *ochroleuca* (*cf.* PL. 70) is said to be an upland form with yellowish tinged flowers and longer floral bracts.

Variety *odorata* is largely confined to the coastal region in wet swampy situations in low marshes, swamps, hammocks, low woods, wet pinelands or mucky soil on the edge of dense swamps, rivers and lakes. It often grows in the water or on rotten stumps and wood in flooded tupelo-cypress swamps where it occurs in dense clumps because of its stoloniferous habit. In Illinois, it has been found in beach sand dune pockets. It occurs up to 5,000 feet altitude in the mountains of North Carolina and Tennessee where it grows in dry sandy soils on open hillsides and wooded ridges or in grassy places and in well-drained partly shaded and grassy sandy loam. It blooms from September to January in various parts of its range, and rarely from May to July in Florida.

GEOGRAPHICAL DISTRIBUTION: This variety occurs rather frequently in the southern part of the range of the species and sparsely in the North.

CULTURAL NOTES: This well-marked variety grows in moist soil—sometimes even in tidal marshes—especially in the lower Coastal Plain from Texas to Virginia. It is tolerant of both summer heat and winter cold, even surviving moderate freezing, and also seems fairly resistant to fungus attack. Spreading into clumps by reason of its stoloniferous rootstocks, and exhaling a delightful cumarin fragrance, it is well worthy of cultivation, both in the swamp garden and in a cool greenhouse. (E. T. W.)

3. **Spiranthes cinnabarina** (La Llave & Lex.) Hemsl. in Godm. & Salvin, Biol. Centr.-Am., Bot. 3: 300. 1884 (as *S. cinnabarinus*). *Neottia cinnabarina* La Llave & Lex., Nov. Veg. Descr., fasc. 2, Orch. Opusc. 3. 1825. Type locality: Mexico, "prope Irapaeum, S. Michael del Monte." (*Stenorrhynchus cinnabarinus* (La Llave & Lex.) Lindl.; *Gyrostachys cinnabarina* (La Llave & Lex.) O. Ktze.). PLATE 71

(The name, *cinnabarina,* is from a Greek word meaning "scarlet-colored," in allusion to the typical color of the flowers.)

COMMON NAME: Scarlet Ladies' Tresses.

Plant stout, glabrous below, pubescent above with brown or whitish articulated hairs, 2-9.5 dm. tall. Leaves on the lower part of the stem, distichous, conduplicate, oblanceolate to linear-lanceolate, subobtuse to shortly acuminate, 11-23 cm. long, 1.5-3.2 cm. wide. Spike usually short, congested, many-flowered, 4-17 cm. long, 3-6 cm. in diameter. Floral bracts narrowly ovate to lanceolate, acuminate, 1.2-2.5 cm. long, about 7 mm. wide Flowers tubular, yellowish orange to yellow-scarlet, with the floral segments conspicuously recurved and flaring near the apex. Sepals and petals minutely papillose, with the sepals sparingly pubescent on the outer surface. Dorsal sepal lanceolate, acuminate, 1.2-2.2 cm. long, about 3 mm. wide. Lateral sepals somewhat obliquely lanceolate, acute to shortly acuminate, 1.2-2.5 cm. long, 2.2-3.2 mm. wide. Petals linear-lanceolate, acute, falcate, 1.2-2.2 cm. long, about 2.5 mm. wide. Lip sessile, obovate-lanceolate to elliptic-lanceolate, narrowly long-acuminate above the middle, 1.2-2.5 cm. long, 3-6 mm. wide at the widest point, expanded and shallowly concave below the middle, thickened at the apex; disc puberulent on the lower part, with a longitudinal flat callus on each side at the base. Column thick, papillose on the ventral surface, 6-10 mm. long; rostellum flat, slender, 2 mm. or more long.

The Scarlet Ladies' Tresses and *S. orchioides* are the largest flowered and most attractive *Spiranthes* found in our region. Both often occur in extremely dry situations, and are intrusions from the tropics and subtropics.

Apparently the first collection of this species in the United States is that from the foothills of the Chisos Mountains in Brewster County, Texas, by VALERY HAVARD in August 1883.

This species is found on rocky mountain slopes, grassy hills and in canyons and meadows, often on limestone hills, up to 7,000 feet altitude in the mountains of Texas and 7,500 feet in Mexico and Guatemala. It flowers from July to October.

GEOGRAPHICAL DISTRIBUTION: Texas (Brewster County); also Mexico and northwest Guatemala.

CULTURAL NOTES: The Scarlet Ladies' Tresses is said to grow in calcareous soil. There is no record of its successful cultivation. (E. T. W.)

4. **Spiranthes cranichoides** (Griseb.) Cogn. in Urban, Symb. Antill. 6: 338. 1909. *Pelexia cranichoides* Griseb., Cat. Pl. Cub. 269. 1866. Type locality and collection: Western Cuba, *C. Wright 3293.* (*Spiranthes Storeri* Chapm.; *Sauroglossum cranichoides* (Griseb.) Ames; *Cyclopogon cranichoides* (Griseb.) Schltr.; *Beadlea cranichoides* (Griseb.) Small; *B. Storeri* (Chapm.) Small). PLATE 72

(The name, *cranichoides,* is a Greek term meaning "like a Cranichis," in allusion to the habit of this species which superficially resembles some species of *Cranichis.*)

COMMON NAME: None known.

Plant scapose, slender, glabrous below, pubescent above, 1.4-4.8 dm. tall. Roots tuberous, coarse, fasciculate, about 3.5 cm. long and 1 cm. in diameter. Stem greenish, yellowish or purplish, provided with loose inflated white-spotted sheaths. Leaves in a basal rosette, with

PLATE 71.— **Spiranthes cinnabarina.** 1, plant, one half natural size. 2, flower, spread open, two and one half times natural size. 3, flower, side view, two and one half times natural size. *Drawn by Gordon W. Dillon.*

short petioles; petiole 1-4.5 cm. long; lamina obliquely ovate to ovate-elliptic, acute to acuminate, often purplish beneath or variegated, 2.5-7 cm. long, 1.5-4 cm. wide. Spike loosely flowered, 2-11 cm. long, 1.5-2.3 cm. in diameter. Floral bracts lanceolate, acuminate, maculate, semitranslucent, 8-13 mm. long. Flowers small. Sepals greenish, tinged with madder-purple, often flecked with white; dorsal sepal narrowly ovate-lanceolate to oblong-elliptic, obtuse to acute, 4-5 mm. long, about 2 mm. wide; lateral sepals lanceolate, acute, 5-5.5 mm. long, 1-2 mm. wide. Petals adherent to the dorsal sepal, linear-spatulate, subobtuse to acute or somewhat apiculate, 4-5 mm. long, about 1.5 mm. wide near the apex, greenish at the base and along the margins, otherwise white. Lip white, 3-lobed above the middle, cuneate-oblong in outline when expanded, 5-6 mm. long, 2-3 mm. wide near the middle; lateral lobes broad, upcurved and clasping the column, rounded at the apex; mid-lobe orbicular-quadrate, subtruncate, sometimes apiculate, 1-2 mm. long; basal callosities erect, glabrous, somewhat thickened. Column 3-4 mm. long. Capsule obliquely obovoid-ellipsoid, 6-9 mm. long.

Spiranthes cranichoides may be distinguished from allied species, especially *S. elata,* by the narrow subquadrate apical lobe of the lip which is not expanded at the apex as in *S. elata.*

Apparently the first collection of this species in the United States is that from Holly Hill, Volusia County, Florida, by ALICE EASTWOOD in April 1890. The second collection was also obtained from Volusia County, near Enterprise, by F. A. STORER about 1897, when A. W. CHAPMAN, thinking it to be a new species, named the orchid *Spiranthes Storeri,* in honor of its collector. JOHN K. SMALL later based his genus *Beadlea* on a duplicate specimen of this collection. The type specimen of *Spiranthes Storeri* was deposited with CHAPMAN's herbarium in the Biltmore Herbarium, situated on a tributary of the French Broad River in Biltmore, North Carolina. In July 1916, the Biltmore Herbarium, which was the repository of an excellent representation of the flora of the southeastern United States, was irreparably damaged by an unprecedented flash flood. The remnants were given to the National Herbarium in Washington. The destruction of more than three-fourths of the Biltmore Herbarium and the total destruction by fire, on January 18, 1934, of the A. Gattinger Herbarium in the University of Tennessee deprived the South of two of its historically notable herbaria.

Spiranthes cranichoides occurs in rich soil, decaying leaves and vegetable matter or on rotten wood in hammocks and moist woodlands of southern peninsular Florida. In the tropics, it grows in leaf mold, humus and on rotten logs in dense forests at low elevations; flowering from December to May in various parts of its range.

GEOGRAPHICAL DISTRIBUTION: Rather frequent in Florida (Alachua, Collier, Dade, Highlands, Monroe, Pasco and Volusia counties); uncommon in Guatemala, British Honduras and the West Indies.

CULTURAL NOTES: This species is accustomed to moist circumneutral soils in peninsular Florida. It can perhaps be cultivated in wild gardens in regions having a mild climate. (E. T. W.)

5. **Spiranthes durangensis** Ames & C. Schweinf., Bot. Mus. Leafl. Harvard Univ. 3: 128. 1935. *Spiranthes saltensis* Ames, Orch., fasc. 2: 258. 1908 and Orch., fasc. 3: 72, pl. 51. 1909 (not Griseb., 1879). Type locality and collection: Near El Salto, State of Durango, Mexico, July 12, 1898, *E. W. Nelson 4545.* (*Schiedeella saltensis* (Ames) Schltr.).   PLATE 73

(The name, *durangensis,* is a Latin adjective designating the State of Durango, Mexico, as the place where this species was first found.)

COMMON NAME: None known.

Plant scapose, erect, 2.4-5 dm. tall; roots large, fleshy, tuberous, fasciculate, up to 12 cm. or more long and 1 cm. in diameter. Stem slender, glabrous below, glandular-pubescent above, often tinged with reddish brown, provided with tubular sheaths at the nodes; sheaths somewhat dilated, scarious, acuminate, up to 4.5 cm. long, often striate-nervose. Leaves usually absent at anthesis, when present in a basal cluster, obliquely lanceolate, acuminate, glabrous, up to 1.5 dm. or more long and 2 cm. wide. Spike three- or more-flowered, secund, glandular-pubescent, 6-18 cm. long, about 2 cm. in diameter. Floral bracts ovate-lanceolate, acuminate, usually striate-nervose, 1-2.5 cm. long. Flowers spirally arranged, arcuate-nodding, with the odor of violet or rose, the stout pedicellate ovaries being about 1 cm. long. Sepals and petals dull brownish pink to purplish, often with green nerves. Sepals glandular-pubescent

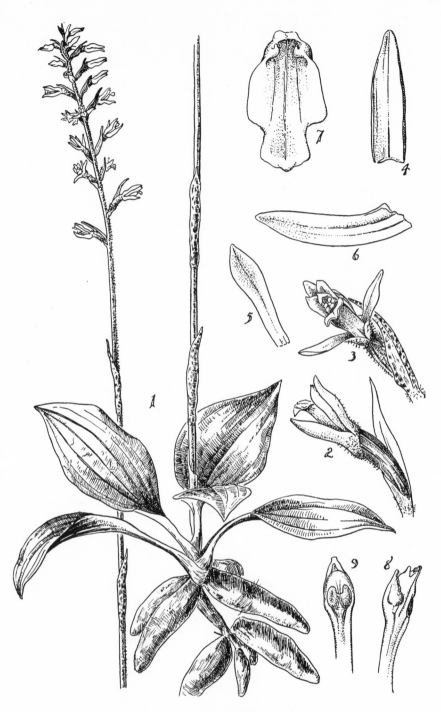

PLATE 72.— **Spiranthes cranichoides.** 1, plant, natural size. 2, flower and floral bract, side view, four times natural size. 3, flower and floral bract, front view, four times natural size. 4, dorsal sepal, seven times natural size. 5, petal, seven times natural size. 6, lateral sepal, seven times natural size. 7, lip, front view, spread open, seven times natural size. 8, column, side view, ten times natural size. 9, column, front-ventral view, ten times natural size. *Redrawn from Blanche Ames by Gordon W. Dillon.*

on the outer surface, recurved near the apex, 3-nerved with the lateral nerves often branched; dorsal sepal elliptic-obovate, abruptly tapering to an obtuse or acute apex, concave, often slightly constricted near the base and forming a small sac, 1.2-1.9 cm. long, 4.2-5.2 mm. wide; lateral sepals obliquely linear-lanceolate, somewhat sigmoid, acute, 1.2-1.7 cm. long, 2-3.5 mm. wide. Petals adherent to the dorsal sepal, linear-oblanceolate, sigmoid, narrowly obtuse to acute, 3- to 5-nerved, 1.1-1.7 cm. long, 2-3.5 mm. wide. Lip whitish pink with green nerves, with a short arcuate claw, 1.3-2 cm. long (including the claw), panduriform, deeply constricted at about the middle, ecallose, 3- to 5-nerved with the outer nerves much-branched; basal half orbicular, concave, pubescent on the lower part, 7-10 mm. wide; upper half suborbicular-ovate to ovate-elliptic, obtuse to rounded and sometimes apiculate at the apex, with crenulate or erose margins, 5-6 mm. wide; claw fleshy, sulcate, adorned with a tuft of hairs in the center. Column stout, clavate, with a slender sharp rostellum, about 1 cm. long.

This species was first discovered in the United States on June 22, 1931 by J. A. MOORE and J. A. STEYERMARK in the Chisos Mountains of Texas. It is an exceedingly rare plant.

Spiranthes durangensis grows in grassy soil pockets of rim rocks, in loamy soil on rocky bluffs and seepage slopes, at 8,000 feet altitude in the mountains of Texas. It flowers from May to July.

GEOGRAPHICAL DISTRIBUTION: Texas (Brewster County); also Mexico.

CULTURAL NOTES: There is no record of this species ever having been cultivated.

6. **Spiranthes elata** (Sw.) L. C. Rich., Orch. Europ. Annot. 37. 1817 (in Mém. Mus. Hist. Nat. Par. 4: 59. 1818). *Satyrium elatum* Sw., Prodr. Veg. Ind. Occ. 119. 1788. Type locality: Jamaica and Hispaniola. PLATE 74

(The name, *elata,* is a Latin adjective meaning "tall," referring to the relatively tall erect peduncle and spicate inflorescence.)

COMMON NAME: Tall Neottia.

Plant erect, scapose, variable, stout or slender, glabrous below, pubescent above, 8.5-60 cm. tall. Roots fleshy, coarse, fasciculate. Stem yellowish purple, purplish or greenish, provided with closely appressed acuminate sheaths. Leaves basal, with rather long petioles; petiole sulcate, dilated and clasping the stem at the base, 1-10 cm. long; lamina oblong-elliptic to ovate-lanceolate or narrowly lanceolate, acute to acuminate, 3-15 cm. long, 1-6 cm. wide. Spike loosely flowered, spirally twisted or secund, 3-22 cm. long, 1-2.5 cm. in diameter. Floral bracts oblong-lanceolate, acuminate, maculate, 7-20 mm. long. Flowers nodding, green or brownish green. Dorsal sepal oblong to ovate-lanceolate, obtuse to subacute, 4-6.5 mm. long, 1.3-1.7 mm. wide. Lateral sepals linear-oblong to linear-lanceolate, obtuse to acute, somewhat falcate, 5-7.5 mm. long, 1.3-2 mm. wide near the base. Petals adhering to the dorsal sepal, linear-spatulate to oblanceolate, obtuse to rounded at the apex, 4-6 mm. long, about 0.5 mm. wide. Lip 4-8 mm. long, with the lower half oblong-quadrate with rounded corners, abruptly contracted above into a narrow isthmus and then expanded into a suborbicular to flabellate or transversely elliptic apical lobe; basal portion of the lip somewhat concave-saccate, with the margins incurved and the pair of submarginal mammillate calli white; apical lobe 2-5.3 mm. wide, as wide as or wider than the lower part of the lip, somewhat tricrenate at the apex or minutely crisped and crenulate on the margins. Column 1.5-3 mm. long. Capsule 7-12 mm. long.

This species was found apparently for the first and only time in the United States "on rocky hummocks" in Hernando County, Florida, by ALLEN HIRAM CURTISS in April 1881. Throughout tropical America, however, it is a rather common and extremely variable species. *Cyclopogon elatus* (Sw.) Schltr. belongs here.

The Tall Neottia is found near sea level in rocky hammocks of southern peninsular Florida. In the tropics, it grows in leaf mold and loamy soil in forests and dense thickets, from near sea level, up to 6,500 feet altitude in Central and South America. It has been found in flower in April in Florida but in various parts of its range it flowers sporadically throughout the year.

GEOGRAPHICAL DISTRIBUTION: Florida (Hernando County); also Mexico, Central America, the West Indies, Trinidad and South America.

CULTURAL NOTES: This tropical and subtropical species grows in hammocks in Florida in damp humus-rich circumneutral soil. It may perhaps be cultivated in gardens where these conditions are found. (E. T. W.)

PLATE 73.—**Spiranthes durangensis.** 1, plant, one half natural size. 2, dorsal sepal, twice natural size. 3, lateral sepal, twice natural size. 4, petal, twice natural size. 5, lip, spread out, twice natural size. 6, lip, side view, twice natural size. *Drawn by Gordon W. Dillon.*

According to BROWN (1813), this species was first introduced into England in 1790 by JOHN FAIRBAIRN.

7. Spiranthes gracilis (Bigel.) Beck, Bot. North. & Midl. States, ed. 1: 343. 1833. *Neottia gracilis* Bigel., Fl. Bost., ed. 2: 322. 1824. Type locality: Massachusetts, vicinity of Boston, in dry hilly woods, July. (*Gyrostachys gracilis* (Bigel.) O. Ktze.; *Ibidium gracile* (Bigel.) House; *Spiranthes lacera* (Raf.) Raf.). PLATE 75

(The name, *gracilis,* is a Latin adjective meaning "slender," referring to the wand-like stem and inflorescence.)

COMMON NAMES: Slender Ladies' Tresses, Green Pearl-twist, Green-lip Ladies' Tresses, Green Spiral-orchid, Long Tresses.

Plant slender, essentially glabrous throughout, rarely sparsely pubescent above, 1.8-7.5 dm. tall, occasionally two or three plants produced from the same rootstock; roots fasciculate, stout, short, fleshy. Leaves basal, fugacious, broadly ovate to elliptic or ovate-lanceolate, short-petioled; lamina 1.5-6.5 cm. long, 1-2.3 cm. wide. Spike slender, densely or loosely flowered, strongly spiraled or sometimes secund, very rarely bifurcate, 3-26 cm. long. Floral bracts ovate to ovate-lanceolate, acute to long-acuminate, 5-10 mm. long. Flowers small, in a single rank, white with a green stripe in the center of the lip; perianth 4-6 mm. long. Sepals and petals about equal in length, 4-5.5 mm. long; dorsal sepal elliptic-oblong to oblong-lanceolate, obtuse to acute; lateral sepals lanceolate, acute to somewhat acuminate; petals adherent to the dorsal sepal, linear, obtuse to subacute. Lip oblong-quadrate to elliptic-oblong, 4-6 mm. long, about 2.5 mm. wide, with the apical margins crenulate to somewhat fringed-erose, the slightly grooved central portion being conspicuously green; basal callosities short, erect. Column 2-3 mm. long.

Two quite distinctive varieties of this species are recognizable—var. *brevilabris* and var. *floridana.* FERNALD (1946), however, has recently advocated a further division of this species into a northern and southern species. He adopted RAFINESQUE's *S. lacera* for those plants which have a typically secund, not spirally twisted, inflorescence, and which he states are relatively more northern in distribution, usually have their leaves present at the time of flowering and have flowers which are rather distant in the spike. Those plants with a more southern distribution, designated by FERNALD as typical *S. gracilis,* were supposed to have strongly spiraled racemes with the flowers approximate and the basal leaves rarely present at the time of flowering. Although the above forms may be more prevalent in the regions to which FERNALD assigns them, in my opinion their geographic separation is not justifiable since both forms occur too frequently throughout the range of the species.

This species is found in sandy hardwoods, in gravelly-sandy soil, on thinly wooded slopes and grassy hills, in grassy pinelands and flatwoods, dry fields and beaches along the coast. It is less frequent in moist rich woods, meadows and moist grassy soil along streams. The Slender Ladies' Tresses occurs from near sea level along the Atlantic and Gulf coasts, up to 1,600 feet altitude in Vermont, 2,000 feet in Georgia and South Carolina and 3,500 feet in North Carolina and Tennessee. It flowers mainly from June to September or October in various parts of its range, and sometimes in April and May in the deep South.

GEOGRAPHICAL DISTRIBUTION: Rather frequent from Nova Scotia, New Brunswick, Prince Edward Island, Quebec, Ontario and (?) Manitoba, through New England and the Atlantic States, south to south-central Florida, along the Gulf Coast to east-central Texas, west through the Central and Lake States to Minnesota (Cass, Clearwater, Itasca and Saint Louis counties), Iowa (Decatur County), Missouri (St. Louis County) and Oklahoma (Creek County).

CULTURAL NOTES: While similar to *S. cernua* in being a common and widespread orchid, the Green-lip Ladies' Tresses differs from that species in being essentially constant in its characters over much of the eastern United States and southeastern Canada. Its favorite habitat is grassland on soils of moderate acidity. The winter rosette stage is best adapted for transplanting, but the species may also be grown from seed sown in turf, its blooming state being reached in three to five years. Fairly resistant to attack by fungi, it is one of the easier species to cultivate. (E. T. W.)

PLATE 74.—**Spiranthes elata.** 1, plant, one half natural size. 2, flower, side view, five times natural size. 3, lip, front view, spread out, five times natural size. 4, column, side view, five times natural size. *Drawn by Gordon W. Dillon.*

8. **Spiranthes gracilis** var. **brevilabris** (Lindl.) Correll, Bot. Mus. Leafl. Harvard Univ. 8: 74. 1940. *Spiranthes brevilabris* Lindl., Gen. and Sp. Orch. Pl. 471. 1840. Type citations: Texas, *Drummond, Andrieux.* PLATE 76

(The name, *brevilabris,* is a combination of Latin words meaning "short" and "lip," in allusion to the characteristically short lip of the variety.)

COMMON NAME: Texas Ladies' Tresses.

Similar to the typical form except for the densely pubescent spike and persistent leaves. Rachis with whitish pubescence; ovaries more or less covered with a dense mat of reddish brown hairs (rarely sparsely pubescent); perianth parts somewhat pubescent on the outer surface. Plant 1-3.5 dm. tall. Leaves similar to those of the typical form, usually persistent. Spike 2-15 cm. long, slender. Floral bracts usually much longer than in the typical form, 5-14 mm. long, subulate at the apex. Flowers apparently white or cream-colored (no fresh material seen). Petals usually irregularly erose near the apex. Lip with longer and more deeply and finely lacerate fringes on the apical margins than in the typical form, often fringed along the margin to the base, strongly arcuate-recurved, often conspicuously constricted at about the middle, usually provided with a dense tuft of hairs on the disc near the apex; basal callosities thick, stout, prominent.

LINDLEY, in describing *S. brevilabris,* wrote: "This seems distinct from *S. gracilis,* to which it is the most nearly allied, in its spike being very dense and covered with coarse short hairs; the lip too has quite a distinct form. Flowers are stated by Andrieux to be purple."

The Texas specimens of this variety are so robust and densely pubescent that, if they were aphyllous or if they had linear instead of ovate-oblong leaves, they could immediately be referred to *S. vernalis.* Besides having a densely pubescent spike, var. *brevilabris* is characterized by the lip having very deeply fringed and finely lacerate-fringed margins and usually a dense tuft of hairs on the disc near the apex.

This variety occurs in dry prairies and pine flatwoods or in open sandy soil and wet pinelands. It grows at low elevations and flowers from February to May.

GEOGRAPHICAL DISTRIBUTION: Florida (Hillsborough, Lee and Polk counties), Georgia (Thomas County and Wrightsboro), Louisiana (Orleans Parish) and Texas (Galveston and Harris counties).

CULTURAL NOTES: There is no record of this plant ever having been cultivated and its cultivation probably has never been attempted.

9. **Spiranthes gracilis** var. **floridana** (Wherry) Correll, Bot. Mus. Leafl. Harvard Univ. 8: 76. 1940. *Ibidium floridanum* Wherry, Journ. Wash. Acad. Sci. 21: 49, fig. 1. 1931. Type locality and collection: Near Loretto, Duval County, Florida, April 14, 1930, *Edgar T. Wherry.* (*Spiranthes floridana* (Wherry) Cory). PLATE 76

(The name, *floridana,* is a Latin adjective designating Florida as the state where this plant was collected.)

COMMON NAME: Florida Ladies' Tresses.

Similar to the typical form except for the lip having a yellow (instead of green) center and the leaves being persistent and much narrower and elongated. This variety also differs markedly from the typical form in having the spike usually secund or rarely spiraled. Plant glabrous or occasionally sparsely pubescent above, 1.4-5.4 dm. tall. Stem and leaves light green or yellowish green. Lateral sepals narrowly lanceolate, acuminate, projecting horizontally and noticeably beyond the arcuate-recurved lip. Petals often irregularly erose near the apex. Lip ovate to ovate-oblong, truncate and rarely retuse at the apex; median portion of the disc yellow, rarely with an obsolescent tuft of hairs on the disc near the apex; basal callosities stout or slender.

This plant is a rather distinctive geographical variant, and is the most attractive phase of this variable species. Its rosette of persistent leaves which are usually longer and narrower than in typical *S. gracilis,* and the elongated secund spike of yellow-tinged flowers make a pleasing contrast to the usually leafless *S. gracilis.*

Variety *floridana* is found in wet sandy open pine barrens and flatwoods, mucky or boggy soil in low pinelands, in savannahs and coastal prairies, palmetto-scrub

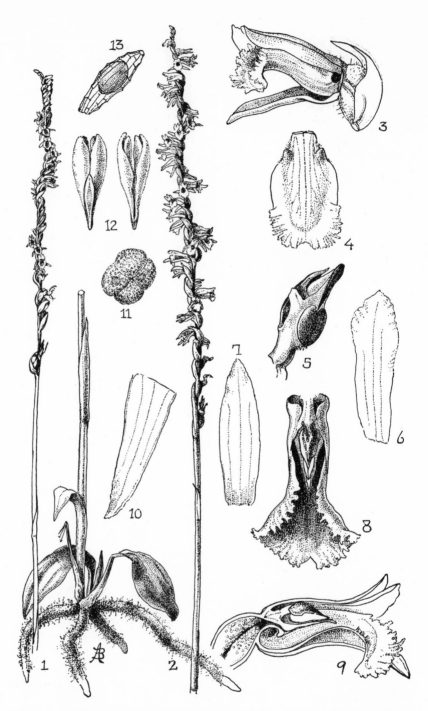

PLATE 75.— **Spiranthes gracilis.** 1 and 2, plant, natural size. 3, flower, side view, with one lateral sepal removed, six times natural size. 4, lip, spread out, six times natural size. 5, column, eleven times natural size. 6, petal, eleven times natural size. 7, dorsal sepal, eleven times natural size. 8, lip and column, in natural position, front view, eleven times natural size. 9, longitudinal section through center of perianth and ovary, eight times natural size. 10, lateral sepal, eight times natural size. 11, pollen tetrad, highly magnified. 12, pollinia, from below (at left), from above (at right), twenty times natural size. 13, seed, highly magnified. *Drawn by Blanche Ames.*

PLATE 76.—**Spiranthes gracilis var. floridana.** 1, plant, natural size. 2, flower, side view, five times natural size. 3, lip, spread out, five times natural size.

Spiranthes gracilis var. brevilabris. 4, inflorescence, natural size. 5, flower, side view, five times natural size. 6, lip, spread out, five times natural size. *Drawn by Gordon W. Dillon.*

pinelands or oak woods, or on the edge of swamps and pocosins. It is a plant of the Coastal Plain and Gulf Coast, flowering from January to June and rarely in November and December in Florida. It is of interest to note that both var. *floridana* and var. *brevilabris* bloom in the spring, whereas typical *S. gracilis* usually blooms in summer and fall.

GEOGRAPHICAL DISTRIBUTION: Variety *floridana* is of local occurrence and rare from eastern North Carolina (Pender County), south in the Coastal Plain to southern Florida, along the Gulf Coast to Texas (Hardin and Harris counties).

CULTURAL NOTES: Since this plant occurs in rather strongly acid peaty habitats, this type of soil should be supplied if its cultivation is attempted. (E. T. W.)

10. **Spiranthes Grayi** Ames, Rhodora 6: 44. 1904. *Spiranthes simplex* A. Gray, Man. Bot. North. U. S., ed. 5: 506. 1867, not Grisebach (1864). Type locality: Massachusetts, New Jersey and Delaware. (*Spiranthes Beckii* of authors; *S. tuberosa* Raf. apud Fernald; *S. tuberosa* var. *Grayi* (Ames) Fernald; *Gyrostachys simplex* (A. Gray) O. Ktze.; *G. Grayi* (Ames) Britton; *G. Beckii* of authors; *Ibidium Beckii* of authors). PLATE 77

(The name, *Grayi,* is in honor of ASA GRAY (1810-1888), famous American botanist.)

COMMON NAMES: Little Ladies' Tresses, Beck's Tresses, Little Pearl-twist, White Spiral-orchid.

Plant very slender, scapose, glabrous throughout, 8-60 cm. tall (occasionally two or three plants produced from the same rootstock); root solitary or very rarely more than one, slender or tuberous, tapering, up to 10 cm. long (last season's root often persisting). Leaves basal, fugacious, ovate to narrowly oblong-elliptic, obtuse to acute, short-petioled, 2.5-6.5 cm. long, 6-15 mm. wide, reduced above to sheathing acuminate bracts. Spike slender, loosely or densely flowered, secund to strongly spiraled, 1-15 cm. long, 5-10 mm. in diameter. Floral bracts ovate to ovate-lanceolate, gradually or abruptly acute to long-acuminate. Flowers small, white, in a single rank; perianth 2-4 mm. long. Sepals and petals about equal in length, 2-3.5 mm. long, narrow; dorsal sepal oblong-elliptic to oblong-lanceolate, obtuse; lateral sepals lanceolate, acute, somewhat sinuate and recurved. Petals adherent to the dorsal sepal, linear-oblong to linear-spatulate, rounded to obtuse at the apex. Lip white, ovate to suborbicular-quadrate or oblong-quadrate, recurved and somewhat dilated and crisped-erose at the apex, occasionally slightly constricted at about the middle, 2.3-4 mm. long, 1.5-2 mm. wide; basal callosities small. Column about 1.5 mm. long. Capsule obliquely ovoid, about 4 mm. long.

After much deliberation and weighing of the evidence, I have concluded that the most acceptable name for this much bandied about orchid is *S. Grayi* Ames. This name is not only appropriate, being in honor of the outstanding American botanist, but it is based upon extant material which was the basis for GRAY's correctly and adequately described *S. simplex*.

As FERNALD pointed out recently (1946), the name *S. Beckii* Lindl. was born in confusion, not only as to the description but also as to the synonymy cited by LINDLEY. Also, according to OAKES AMES, the type sheet of *S. Beckii* in the Lindley Herbarium contains five plants, all of which are referable to *S. gracilis*. It seems best to me to consider the name *S. Beckii* Lindl. to be in the status of *nomen confusum.*

Recently FERNALD (1946) has adopted the name *S. tuberosa* Raf. for the plant in question. The only character occurring in RAFINESQUE's brief description of *S. tuberosa* which can be interpreted as being distinctive of *S. Grayi* is that his plant possessed a solitary tuberous root. It is not uncommon for collectors to fail to obtain more than one of the fasciculate thickened roots of *S. gracilis,* a closely allied species, when that species occurs in rocky or hard soil. RAFINESQUE described the lip of his plant as being cuneate and acute — a condition I have never observed in *S. Grayi*. It seems to me that to reject the thoroughly sound name *S. Grayi* for the dubious *S. tuberosa* Raf. is not in the best interests of accuracy.

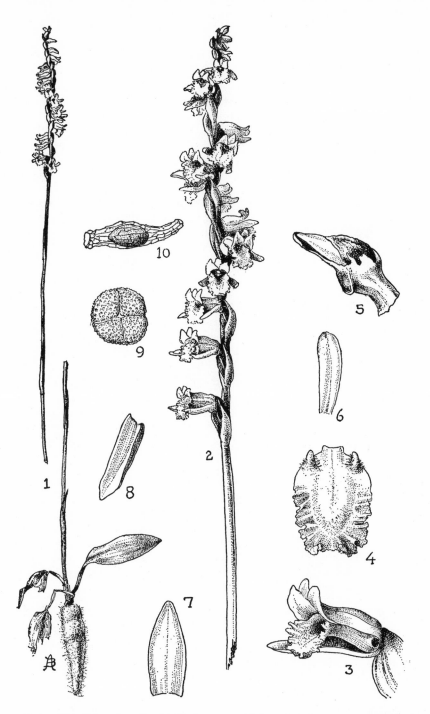

PLATE 77.— **Spiranthes Grayi.** 1, plant, natural size. 2, inflorescence, three times natural size. 3, flower, front-side view, with one lateral sepal removed, eight times natural size. 4, lip, eight times natural size. 5, column, twenty times natural size. 6, petal, eight times natural size. 7, dorsal sepal, eight times natural size. 8, lateral sepal, eight times natural size. 9, pollen tetrad, highly magnified. 10, seed, highly magnified. *Drawn by Blanche Ames.*

I am therefore considering the name *S. tuberosa* Raf. as being in the category *nomen dubium*.

This little plant, like other species in the genus, is variable in habit and general aspect, and the various forms are susceptible of segregation. For example, after adopting *S. tuberosa* Raf. for the southern phase, FERNALD (1946) proposes *S. tuberosa* var. *Grayi* for the plant which he states is confined to north of South Carolina and " . . . has a relatively close spike with closely spiralling and often crowded and overlapping flowers." The typical form, according to FERNALD is limited to New Jersey and southward and has a spike strongly secund, without or with but few spiral twists in the raceme, and with the relatively few flowers distant and not overlapping. The tuberous root was also considered to be more slender than that of the northern phase.

After examining hundreds of plants in the field and numerous collections in the herbarium, it is my opinion that, although the above forms are more prevalent in the regions to which they have been assigned, their geographic separation is not practicable since both forms occur too frequently throughout the range of the species. If aspect alone is to be used as a basis for segregation, it would be just as appropriate to give names to those plants exhibiting a left- or right-handed twisting of the rachis. Such forms would certainly be more satisfactorily distinguished from one another.

This species most often occurs on rather dry rocky well-drained sparsely wooded pine-hardwood slopes, in pine or oak barrens and flatwoods, dry fields, among palmettos, on grassy slopes and in thickets and sandy dry savannahs and coastal prairies. It rarely grows in damp woods and moist grassy ravines and hollows, and occurs at near sea level along the Atlantic and Gulf coasts and up to 4,000 feet altitude in the mountains of North Carolina and Tennessee. The species flowers from March to October in various parts of its range, but mainly from July to September.

GEOGRAPHICAL DISTRIBUTION: The Little Ladies' Tresses is found in eastern Massachusetts, Rhode Island (every county) and Connecticut (Fairfield, Hartford, New Haven and New London counties), through the Atlantic States, south to south-central Florida, west to eastern Texas, Arkansas (Pulaski and Sevier counties) and Kentucky (Union County); also Michigan (Cheboygan County).

CULTURAL NOTES: Surviving Tertiary geological changes in the Appalachian region, this species invaded the emerging Coastal Plain where it spread widely. It requires a higher degree of acidity than is usually supplied in a garden and is therefore not readily cultivated. If moved in early spring, before the winter rosettes of tiny leaves have vanished, and planted in a sandy soil rich in mediacid humus, it can be brought to bloom the following summer. Its fleshy root is esteemed by pine mice, however, so these rodents must be excluded if the plant is to survive long. (E. T. W.)

11. **Spiranthes laciniata** (Small) Ames, Orch., fasc. 1: 120. 1905. *Gyrostachys laciniata* Small, Fl. Southeast. U. S., ed. 1: 318. 1903. Type locality: In sand, Eustis, Florida. (*Ibidium laciniatum* (Small) House). PLATE 78

(The name, *laciniatum,* is a Latin adjective meaning "slashed," referring to the irregularly fringed margin of the lip.)

COMMON NAME: Lace-lip Spiral-orchid.

Plant coarse, 7-9.5 dm. tall, glabrous below, varying from subglabrous to densely and copiously pubescent above. Leaves basal and cauline, linear-lanceolate to narrowly oblanceolate, obtuse to acuminate, with the lower part usually somewhat inflated and sheathing the stem, 9-30 cm. long, 3-19 mm. wide, reduced above to sheathing bracts. Spike varying from strongly spiraled to secund, 5-25 cm. long; rachis and ovaries subglabrous to densely pubescent with articulated ball-tipped hairs. Floral bracts ovate-lanceolate, long-acuminate, 7-13 mm. long. Flowers white, often fragrant, with the parts of the perianth more or less pubescent on the outer surface. Sepals similar, linear-oblong to lanceolate, obtuse to subacute, 7-10.5 mm.

long. Petals oblong, falcate, obtuse and often somewhat crenulate at the apex, 7-9.5 mm.
long. Lip ovate-oblong, often from a suborbicular base and rather abruptly contracted above
to form an oblong lamina, truncate to broadly rounded at the apex, mostly denticulate-laciniate

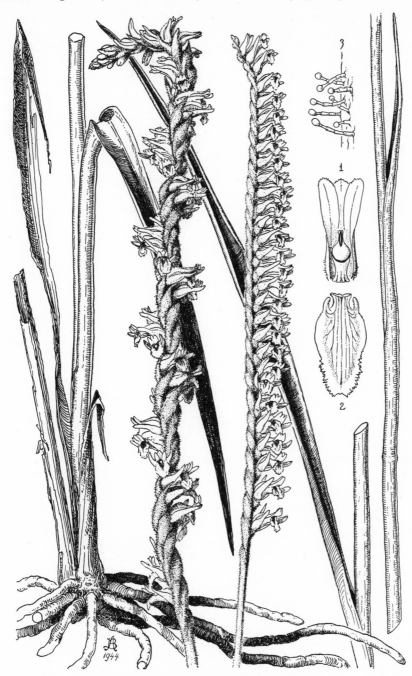

PLATE 78.— **Spiranthes laciniata.** Plant, showing two types of inflorescence,
natural size. 1, dorsal sepal, petals and column, front-ventral view, twice natural
size. 2, lip, spread out, three and one half times natural size. 3, capitate glandular
hairs of the inflorescence, highly magnified. *Drawn by Blanche Ames.*

along the margins of the apical portion, sometimes veined or marked with green, 5.5-9 mm.
long, strongly arcuate-recurved at the apex in natural position; basal callosities slender or
stout.

At one time I thought this plant to be a hybrid of *S. praecox* $\times$ *S. vernalis,* and in 1940 I reported it as such. However, with further study, I am now convinced that, although it is closely allied to *S. praecox,* it should be maintained as a separate entity. In *S. laciniata,* as in *S. praecox,* the glandular, articulated hairs of the inflorescence are capitate or ball-tipped and serve to distinguish it from *S. vernalis* which has sharp or blunt hairs. Its predilection for swampy places in standing water is another characteristic of this plant. I have collected it in eastern Georgia and Florida where its robust stems often rise to well above the waist.

The Lace-lip Spiral-orchid is usually found in wet ground or in shallow water of cypress swamps, marshes and ponds where it is commonly associated with Lizard's-tail (*Saururus cernuus*), arrow heads (*Sagittaria* spp.), saw-grasses (*Mariscus* spp.), spatter-docks (*Nymphaea* spp.), etc. It is also found in river swamps, low wet pinelands, boggy depressions in savannahs, in pocosins and in clayey mud of dried-up ponds. It is confined to the Atlantic Coastal Plain and Gulf Coast, and flowers from May to August in various parts of its range.

GEOGRAPHICAL DISTRIBUTION: Found sparingly along the Atlantic seaboard from New Jersey (Cape May and Ocean counties, and Quaker Bridge) to southern Florida, and along the Gulf Coast to Texas (Hardin, Harris and Matagorda counties).

CULTURAL NOTES: This orchid commonly grows in places which are inundated at least part of the year. This type of habitat is usually rich in humus and fairly acid in reaction. Where the above condition exists in southern wild gardens, it should be possible to cultivate this species.

12. **Spiranthes longilabris** Lindl., Gen. and Sp. Orch. Pl. 467. 1840. Type locality and collection: Louisiana, *Drummond.* (*Spiranthes brevifolia* Chapm.; *Gyrostachys brevifolia* (Chapm.) O. Ktze.; *G. longilabris* (Lindl.) O. Ktze.; *Ibidium longilabris* (Lindl.) House). PLATE 79

(The name, *longilabris,* is a combination of Latin words meaning "long lip," in allusion to the somewhat elongated lip of this species.)

COMMON NAME: Giant Spiral-orchid.

Plant erect, slender, flexuous, essentially glabrous throughout, occasionally pubescent above, 1.2-6 dm. tall. Roots fleshy, numerous, fasciculate. Leaves (when present) basal, linear to narrowly lanceolate, acute, 3-10 cm. long, mostly less than 5 mm. wide, reduced above to sheathing bracts. Spike slender, secund or at most only slightly spiraled, 5-14 cm. long. Floral bracts broadly ovate to ovate-lanceolate, long-acuminate, 5-12 mm. long. Flowers white or white tinged with cream-color, conspicuously ringent, tubular, projecting almost horizontally from the rachis. Sepals 6-10 mm. long, 2-3 mm. wide; dorsal sepal oblong-elliptic to oblong-lanceolate, subacute to acute; lateral sepals linear-lanceolate, spreading and curved upward. Petals linear, obtuse to subacute, 6.5-9.5 mm. long, about 1 mm. wide. Lip yellow-white, narrowly ovate to ovate-oblong, from a broadened base, tapering to the obtuse or subacute apex, usually somewhat dentate or crenate along the apical margin, 6-10 mm. long, 3-5.5 mm. wide near the base, strongly arcuate-recurved in natural position, callosities rather slender. Column about 4 mm. long.

The conspicuously secund or scarcely spiraled spike of comparatively large flowers and the late fall and winter blooming season are characteristics of this species. Its secund spike and elongated type of lip are quite similar to those of *S. laciniata,* but its essentially glabrous inflorescence immediately separates it from that species.

The Giant Spiral-orchid is commonly found in wet grassy pine barrens and flatwoods, swamps, marshes, wet savannahs and coastal prairies, sandy bogs and moist grassy meadows. It also occurs in hammocks, dry shady oak woods and in palmetto thickets in low open fields. It is a species of the Atlantic Coastal Plain and Gulf Coast, flowering from October to December, rarely May in Florida.

GEOGRAPHICAL DISTRIBUTION: Florida (widespread) and Georgia (Camden County), along the Atlantic seaboard to North Carolina (Pender County) and Virginia (Norfolk County), west along the Gulf Coast to Louisiana (Livingston, Orleans, St. Helena and St. Tammany parishes) and Texas (Newton County).

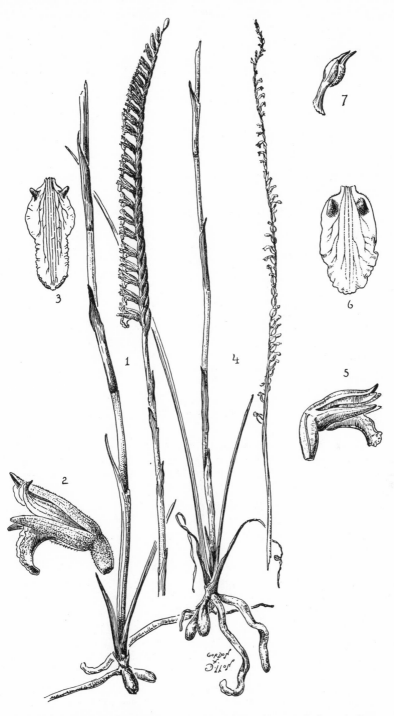

PLATE 79.—**Spiranthes longilabris.** 1, plant, one half natural size. 2, flower, side view, three times natural size. 3, lip, spread out, three times natural size.

Spiranthes tortilis. 4, plant, one half natural size. 5, flower, side view, five times natural size. 6, lip, spread out, five times natural size. *Drawn by Gordon W. Dillon.*

CULTURAL NOTES: This large-flowered species is a native of moist open pine-lands along the Gulf Coast, its soil preference being correspondingly mediacid. While it can stand moderately cold winter conditions, it seems highly susceptible to attack by fungi and so is difficult to cultivate successfully. (E. T. W.)

13. **Spiranthes lucida** (H. H. Eaton) Ames, Orch., fasc. 2: 258. 1908. *Neottia lucida* H. H. Eaton, Transylvania Journ. Med. and Assoc. Sci. 5: 107. 1832. Type locality: "Grows in Troy and other parts of New York." (*Spiranthes plantaginea* Rafinesque (1833) and Torrey (1843), not Sprengel (1826) nor Lindley (1840); *S. latifolia* Torr.; *Gyrostachys latifolia* (Torr.) O. Ktze.; *G. plantaginea* (Raf.) Britton & Brown; *Ibidium plantagineum* (Raf.) House). PLATE 80

(The name, *lucida,* is a Latin adjective meaning "shining," in reference to the glossy sheen of the leaves.)

COMMON NAMES: Wide-leaved Ladies' Tresses.

Plant usually small, slender, glabrous below, nearly glabrous to sparsely pubescent above, 6.5-37 cm. tall. Roots fleshy, fasciculate, tapering from a much-thickened base. Stem scapose, terete or slightly angular above, provided with one to several scarious remote bracts. Leaves several, in a basal cluster or on the lower part of the stem, oblong-elliptic to elliptic-lanceolate, bluntly obtuse to subacuminate, glabrous, sheathing the stem below, fleshy and shining, 2.5-12.5 cm. long, 5-18 mm. wide. Spike slender, cylindrical, up to 11 cm. long and 1-1.5 cm. in diameter, often slightly pubescent, with the few- to many-flowers in one rank or apparently arranged in two or more ranks and spirally twisted. Floral bracts lanceolate, acute to acuminate, scarious, up to 1.5 cm. long, exceeding the ovary. Flowers white, tubular, arcuate-nodding. Dorsal sepal linear-oblong to linear-lanceolate, obtuse, connivent with the petals to form a hood over the column, 1- to 3-nerved, 4.5-5.2 mm. long, 1.1-1.8 mm. wide. Lateral sepals free, scarcely or not at all spreading, linear, obtuse, slightly oblique, 1- to 3-nerved, 5-6 mm. long, 1-1.5 mm. wide. Petals linear to oblanceolate, obtuse, slightly oblique, 1-nerved, 5-6 mm. long, 0.8-1.2 mm. wide Lip conduplicate, arcuate and clasping the column in natural position; lamina when spread out subquadrate to oblong-quadrate, truncate to broadly rounded at the somewhat flaring apex, the margins being undulate-crenulate above the middle, 3-nerved with the lateral nerves branched, adorned with a small callosity on each side at the base and with a broad central stripe of yellow and fine green lines, 5-5.5 mm. long, 2-2.8 mm. wide. Column about 3 mm. long.

This little plant forms a most interesting distributional pattern. For, although several questionable stations lie far from its center of distribution in the northeastern United States and Canada, there are still other reliable stations — such as those in Missouri and Kansas — which appear to represent disjunct areas.

In the sandy soil of woods and on open gravelly slopes near the mouth of the Winooski River in Chittenden County, Vermont, I have seen large colonies of this species. There it was growing in one of its most usual habitats — on shingly-gravelly river banks.

The Wide-leaved Ladies' Tresses is commonly found on gravelly river banks and sand-gravel bars, and on stony shores of lakes, in wet meadows, bogs and swales, and on moist sparsely wooded slopes, often in calcareous areas. It occurs near sea level in Delaware, up to 500 feet altitude in Vermont and 2,500 feet in Virginia, blooming from May (in Missouri) to August (in Quebec).

GEOGRAPHICAL DISTRIBUTION: New Brunswick, Quebec, Ontario (Bruce, Huron and Lambton counties), throughout New England, south through New York, New Jersey (Sussex County), Pennsylvania, Delaware (New Castle Bay) to "southwest Virginia" and (?) Tennessee, west through Ohio (Cuyahoga and Medina counties), Indiana (Jennings and St. Joseph counties), Kentucky (Wayne County), Michigan and Wisconsin; also Missouri (Shannon County), Kansas (Cloud County) and (?) Oregon (Trinchora Creek, *Horner*).

CULTURAL NOTES: One of the more northern members of the genus, the Wide-leaved Ladies' Tresses survived glaciation in the southern Appalachian and Piedmont Plateau regions and with the melting of the ice, this little orchid migrated well up into Ontario and Quebec. It seems to prefer circumneutral soil, though it is also found in subacid peat. Although relatively indifferent to temperature con-

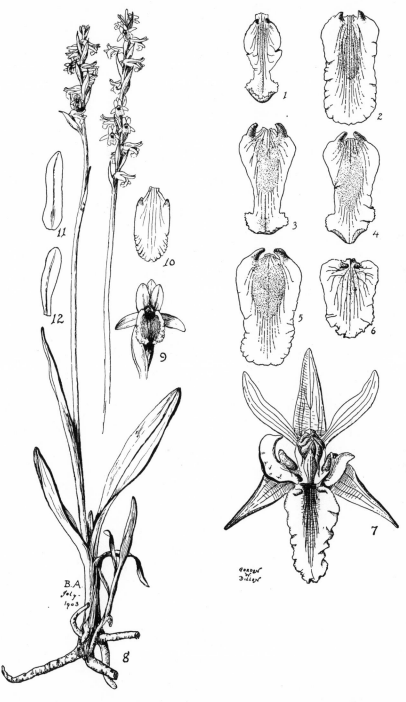

PLATE 80.— × **Spiranthes Steigeri**, and lips of putative parents. 1, lip of *S. Romanzoffiana*, three times natural size. 2, lip of *S. cernua*, three times natural size. 3-6, lips of × *S. Steigeri*, three times natural size. 7, abnormal flower of × *S. Steigeri*. *Drawn by Gordon W. Dillon.*

Spiranthes lucida. 8, plant, natural size. 9, flower, front view, four times natural size. 10, lip, front view, spread out, four times natural size. 11, lateral sepal, four times natural size. 12, petal, four times natural size. *Drawn by Blanche Ames.*

ditions, it is rather difficult to cultivate. In the garden it usually soon falls prey to fungi and slugs, which are especially fond of it. (E. T. W.)

14. **Spiranthes michuacana** (La Llave & Lex.) Hemsl. in Godm. & Salvin, Biol. Centr.-Am., Bot. 3: 301. 1884 (as *mechoacana*). *Neottia michuacana* La Llave & Lex., Nov. Veg. Descr., fasc. 2, Orch. Opusc. 3. 1825. Type locality: Mexico, State of Michoacán, near Vallisoleto, especially toward Jesus-del-monte. (*Stenorrhynchus michuacanus* (La Llave & Lex.) Lindl.).

PLATE 81

(The name, *michuacana,* designates the State of Michoacán, Mexico, where this species was first collected.)

COMMON NAME: None known.

Plant erect, 1.6-8 dm. tall. Roots fleshy, clavate to cylindrical, fasciculate, up to 10 cm. long and 5 mm. in diameter. Stem rather stout, glabrous below, pubescent above, light colored, nearly concealed by large tubular sheaths; sheaths pale brown or whitish, striate, scarious, more or less inflated, glabrous, acute to acuminate. Leaves (when present) several, basal or on the lower part of the stem, linear-lanceolate to ensiform, acuminate, 1-5 dm. long (including the sheathing base), 1-3 cm. wide, the more or less purplish sheaths clasping the stem. Spike densely few- to many-flowered, cylindrical, often tapering at the apex, 5-19 cm. long, 1.5-3 cm. in diameter; rachis more or less covered by a whitish tomentum. Floral bracts large, broadly ovate to ovate-lanceolate, acuminate, prominently nervose, glandular-pilose on the outer surface, often ciliate on the hyaline margins, 2-3.5 cm. long, about equaling or exceeding the flowers, up to 1.5 cm. wide near the base Flowers tubular-urceolate, the perianth segments connivent below and ringent above, variously colored, usually orange-yellow, green-white or whitish, suffused or striped with bluish green or dark nerves, fragrant, with the stout pilose pedicellate ovaries about 7 mm. long. Sepals with a prominent central nerve, densely glandular-pilose on the outer surface, spreading at the apex; dorsal sepal linear-oblong to narrowly triangular-oblong, obtuse, sometimes apiculate, 1.5-1.9 cm. long, 3-6 mm. wide below the middle; lateral sepals linear to narrowly lanceolate-oblong, somewhat falcate to sigmoid, obtuse, decurrent on the ovary but not forming a mentum, 1.7-2 cm. long, 3.5-5 mm. wide below the middle. Petals shortly clawed, narrowly lanceolate-linear, obtuse, with a prominent central nerve, about 1.7 cm. long and 4-5 mm. wide below the middle. Lip with a short slender claw, somewhat conduplicate and arcuate in natural position: lamina when expanded usually triangular-ovate below and tapering above the middle, also panduriform or rhombic-lanceolate, rounded to broadly obtuse at the apex, truncate to broadly cuneate at the base, pubescent in the center just in front of the claw, 1-1.5 cm. long, 6.5-9 mm. wide at or near the base; claw sulcate, pubescent, about 3 mm. long and 1.5 mm. wide, with the fleshy-thickened margins terminating as minute mammillate calli at the base. Column stout, fleshy, stipitate, about 1 cm. long; rostellum cuspidate.

This rare species was doubtless collected for the first time in the United States in the Chinati Mountains of Presidio County, Texas, by VALERY HAVARD in 1880. The following year it was collected in the Chiricahua Mountains of Cochise County, Arizona, by JOHN GILL LEMMON "and wife." Apparently the occurrence of this species in the United States was not reported until 1944 when it was included in the Orchidaceae for the Flora of Texas—sixty-four years after its original discovery in this country. It is of interest that in 1947 I collected this species at the type locality near Jesus del Monte, a few miles southeast of Morelia, Michoacán State, Mexico, more than 122 years after its original discovery. There were many plants which grew on eroded grassy slopes.

This plant is fragrant with the odor of musk and honey, and it has been known to maintain its fragrance after being dried for more than twenty-five years.

Spiranthes michuacana occurs in clayey soil of scrub forests, barrancas, in openings in pine forests, on grassy slopes, and in fields. This species usually grows at high elevations, and is found up to 7,200 feet altitude in Arizona and 8,500 feet in Mexico. It flowers from September to February in various parts of its range.

GEOGRAPHICAL DISTRIBUTION: Texas (Presidio County) and Arizona (Cochise and Pima counties); also Mexico (rather widespread).

CULTURAL NOTES: There is no record of this species ever having been cultivated.

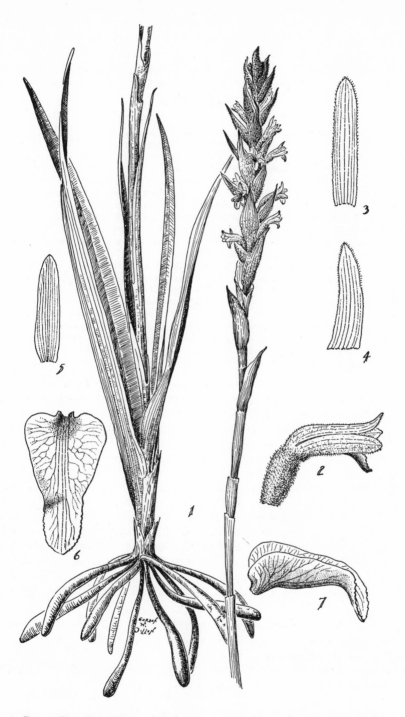

PLATE 81.—**Spiranthes michuacana.** 1, plant, one half natural size. 2, flower, side view, one and one half times natural size. 3, dorsal sepal, one and one half times natural size. 4, lateral sepal, one and one half times natural size. 5, petal, one and one half times natural size. 6, lip, spread out, two and one half times natural size. 7, lip, side view, two and one half times natural size. *Drawn by Gordon W. Dillon.*

15. **Spiranthes orchioides** (Sw.) A. Rich., La Sagra Fl. Cub. Fanerog. 11: 252. 1850. *Satyrium orchioides* Sw., Prodr. Veg. Ind. Occ. 118. 1788. Type locality: Jamaica. (*Stenorrhynchus orchioides* (Sw.) L. C. Rich.; *S. jaliscanus* (S. Wats.) Nash; *Spiranthes jaliscana* S. Wats.; *Gyrostachys orchioides* (Sw.) O. Ktze.). PLATE 82

(The name, *orchioides,* is a Greek adjective meaning "like an orchis," in allusion to the superficial similarity of this species to some of the species in the genus *Orchis.*)

COMMON NAME: Leafless Beaked Orchid, Frost-flowered Neottia.

Plant scapose, slender or stout, erect, somewhat scurfy with white papillose scales, glandular-pubescent except for the leaves and rarely the lower part of the scape, 3.5-6.5 (rarely 9) dm. tall. Roots tuberous, fleshy, coarse, fasciculate, mostly clavate. Leaves basal, appearing after anthesis, narrowly oblong to oblong-elliptic or oblong-lanceolate, occasionally oblong-oblanceolate, obtuse to acute, glabrous and somewhat marginate, 1-4 dm. long, 2.5-5 cm. wide, reduced above to sheathing membranaceous bracts; bracts oblong-lanceolate to lanceolate, attenuate-cuspidate, with hyaline margins, 2-4 cm. long. Spike loosely or densely flowered, conspicuous, 6-17 cm. long, 4-6 cm. in diameter. Floral bracts narrowly lanceolate, long-acuminate, usually punctate with bright red resinous dots, 1.5-2.5 cm. long. Flowers showy, suberect, grading from almost white to brick-red or deep crimson. Dorsal sepal erect, broadly to narrowly lanceolate, acuminate, 1.4-2.2 cm. long, about 7 mm. wide near the base. Lateral sepals produced at the base into a short mentum, narrowly lanceolate above, acuminate, erect, 1.5-3 cm. long from the base of the mentum, the free portion being 3.5-5 mm. wide. Petals adherent to the dorsal sepal, lanceolate, falcate, acute to acuminate, 1.3-2 cm. long, about 6 mm. wide at about the middle. Lip sessile, entire, narrowly ovate-lanceolate to lanceolate or elliptic-lanceolate, 1.5-2.5 cm. long, 5-10 mm. wide at about the middle, saccate in natural position, acuminate and with slightly revolute margins near the apex, linear and convolute below the middle, with a pair of linear submarginal calli; disc pubescent below the middle and on the margins. Column about 1 cm. long; rostellum cuspidate, rigid and bristle-like, about 5 mm. long. Capsule ellipsoid, 1-1.5 cm. long.

Spiranthes orchioides is a highly variable species, particularly in the size and color of the flowers. In the tropics, the plants appear quite suddenly after the beginning of the rainy season and then quickly fade, leaving little evidence of their presence. It is rather widespread and frequent in central peninsular Florida.

Probably the first collection of this species from the United States is that from Orange Bend, Lake County, Florida, by GEORGE V. NASH in April (16-30), about 1894.

The Leafless Beaked Orchid is usually found in dry waste places or along roadsides and in high pinelands. It also grows in high or rarely low hammocks, in open boggy ground and in damp sandy soil. In the tropics, it is found in dry or damp open grassy hills, in fields and savannahs, in xerophytic forests and damp soil in pinelands. It occurs near sea level in Florida and Panama, up to 8,500 feet altitude in Mexico, and flowers from March to August in various parts of its range.

GEOGRAPHICAL DISTRIBUTION: Florida (Alachua, Baker, Lake, Lee, Orange, Pasco and Polk counties); also Mexico, Central and South America, Bahama Islands and the West Indies.

CULTURAL NOTES: This rather showy subtropical and tropical member of the genus grows in humus-rich soil of circumneutral reaction, and could perhaps be cultivated in local wild gardens. (E. T. W.)

According to BROWN (1813), this species was first introduced into England from Jamaica about 1806 by E. I. A. WOODFORD, Esq.

16. **Spiranthes ovalis** Lindl., Gen. and Sp. Orch. Pl. 466. 1840. Type locality and collection: Texas, *Drummond.* (*Spiranthes cernua* var. *parviflora* Chapm.; *S. parviflora* (Chapm.) Ames; *Gyrostachys ovalis* (Lindl.) O. Ktze.; *G. parviflora* (Chapm.) Small; *Ibidium ovale* (Lindl.) House). PLATE 83

(The name, *ovalis,* is a Latin adjective meaning "oval," probably in allusion to the outline of the inflorescence which commonly tapers at both ends.)

PLATE 82.— **Spiranthes orchioides.** 1, inflorescence, three fourths natural size. 2, basal part of plant showing leaves and roots, three fourths natural size. 3, flower, longitudinally dissected to show the column, twice natural size. *Drawn by Blanche Ames.*

Plant erect, glabrous below, more or less pubescent above, 1.4-4.5 dm. tall. Roots fasciculate, fleshy, slender. Leaves two to four at the base of the plant, gradually reduced above to sheathing bracts, oblong-elliptic to oblanceolate or linear-lanceolate, obtuse to subacute (rarely acute to acuminate), usually narrowed below the middle, 5-15 cm. long, 6-15 mm. wide. Spike slender, somewhat congested, spiraled, composed of several ranks of small flowers, elongate-ovoid to cylindrical and pyramidal at the apex, 2-10 cm long, 1-1.3 cm. in diameter. Floral bracts ovate-lanceolate to narrowly lanceolate, long-acuminate, 4-10 mm. long. Flowers white, less than 5 mm. long. Sepals similar, lanceolate, subacute to acute, 4-5 mm. long, 1-2 mm. wide. Petals adherent to the dorsal sepal, linear to linear-lanceolate, 4-5 mm. long, about 1 mm. wide. Lip rhombic-ovate to ovate-oblong, broadly rounded at the base, often constricted above the middle, narrowed or rarely dilated at the apex, 4-5.3 mm. long, 2.4-4 mm. wide near the base, arcuate-recurved in natural position; callosities slender, rarely stout, strongly incurved. Column about 2 mm. long.

The Oval Ladies' Tresses is typically a woodland orchid. On the Piedmont Plateau of North Carolina I have found it in the brushy bed of an abandoned logging road which traversed a well-drained slope in a heavily wooded extensive hardwood forest, and in Louisiana I have seen it growing in dense alluvial pine-hardwood forests. Although it occurs throughout a large part of the eastern United States, the Oval Ladies' Tresses is a rare plant and its occurrence within its area of distribution is exceedingly sporadic.

FERNALD (1946) has recently adopted the name *S. montana* Raf. for this species. However, I consider that name to be more applicable to *S. cernua* than to this species.

This species is usually found in moist shady woods and on the edge of thickets, on wooded hills, in hammocks and wet grassy soil on the edge of dense swamps, in palmetto swamplands, on dry pine-hardwood slopes along streams, and rarely in floodplain woods. It usually occurs at low elevations but is found up to 2,500 feet altitude in southwest Virginia, and flowers from the last of August to November in various parts of its range.

GEOGRAPHICAL DISTRIBUTION: Rare from West Virginia (Cabell County) and Virginia (Dinwiddie, Greenville, Henrico, Smyth, Southampton and Sussex counties), south to north-central Florida (Alachua, Gadsden and Levy counties), along the Gulf Coast to Texas (Brazos and Dallas counties), west through the Central and Lake States to Indiana (Crawford and Spencer counties, *fide Deam*), Missouri (Jackson and St. Louis counties), Arkansas (Hempstead County) and Oklahoma.

CULTURAL NOTES: Surviving the geological changes in the midland plateaus from Arkansas to Kentucky, this diminutive late-blooming species has spread rather widely, though seemingly never becoming very abundant. Its favorite habitat is a moist open woodland where the soil is fairly rich in humus and slightly to moderately acid in reaction. Attempts to cultivate it have not been very successful for, although it is tolerant of a wide range of temperature and there is no difficulty in furnishing suitable soil, it is soon eliminated from the garden by slugs or other pests. (E. T. W.)

17. **Spiranthes parasitica** A. Rich. & Gal., Ann. Sci. Nat. ser. 3, 3: 32. 1845. Type locality: Mexico. PLATE 86

(The name, *parasitica*, is a Greek word meaning "deriving nourishment from some other organism (the host)," doubtless so-named because of the apparent lack of green in this plant which led to the assumption that it depended upon other organisms for its livelihood.)

COMMON NAME: None known.

Plant slender, erect, glabrous below, glandular-pubescent above, 1-3.4 dm. tall. Roots short, fleshy, fasciculate, 2-4 cm. long. Stem and sheaths brownish red or light brown. Leaves fugacious, when present basal, with a slender petiole; lamina apparently elliptic. Spike very slender, remotely few-flowered, 3.5-7 cm. long. Floral bracts broadly ovate to elliptic-lanceolate, acuminate, concave, usually concealing the ovary, scarious, white or pinkish, with conspicuously hyaline margins, 3-nerved, 9-15 mm. long. Flowers small, ascending; sepals and petals pink; lip white with three green stripes extending almost to the apex, with spongy cinnabar-red tissue on the basal portion. Dorsal sepal elliptic-oblong to lanceolate, obtuse to acute, 5-7 mm. long, 1.5-2.5 mm. wide. Lateral sepals somewhat obliquely lanceolate, obtuse to acute, 6-8 mm. long, 1.5-2 mm. wide. Petals obliquely oblanceolate, broadly rounded to sub-acute at the apex, irregularly crenulate above the middle, 5-6.5 mm. long, about 1.5 mm wide.

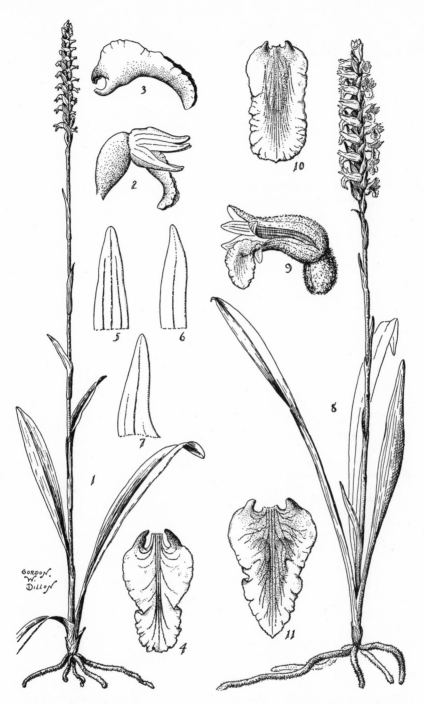

PLATE 83.— **Spiranthes ovalis.** 1, plant, one half natural size. 2, flower, side view, three and one half times natural size. 3, lip, side view, six times natural size. 4, lip, spread out, six times natural size. 5, dorsal sepal, six times natural size. 6, petal, six times natural size. 7, lateral sepal, six times natural size.

Spiranthes cernua. 8, plant, one half natural size. 9, flower, front-side view, three times natural size. 10, lip, spread out, three times natural size.

Spiranthes cernua var. odorata. 11, lip, spread out, three times natural size. *Drawn by Gordon W. Dillon.*

Lip in natural position concave below and strongly recurved at the apex, constricted just above the middle and forming a suborbicular lobule whose margins are undulate-lacerate; lamina when spread out oblong in outline, with the basal portion oblong-quadrate, 6-9 mm. long, 3-5 mm. wide; disc pubescent below on the spongy cinnabar-red blotch and on the apical lobule. Column about 4 mm. long. Capsule ovoid, strongly ribbed, about 7 mm. long.

The persistent cinnabar-red blotch on the lower part of the lip distinguishes this species from its close allies in our region. From outward appearances, this plant seems to be lacking in chlorophyll.

This species was apparently collected for the first time in the United States in the Santa Catalina Mountains of Pima County, Arizona, by JOHN JAMES THORNBER in 1906. In 1926, it was found by E. J. PALMER in Jeff Davis County, Texas, while he was on a botanical expedition in the Davis Mountains.

Spiranthes parasitica usually occurs on dry slopes, in coniferous and mixed coniferous-hardwood forests, in cloud-forests, meadows and moist shaded soil along streams, and rarely epiphytic. This species usually grows at high elevations, and occurs up to 8,500 feet altitude in Arizona and 10,000 feet in Mexico and Central America. It flowers during June and July.

GEOGRAPHICAL DISTRIBUTION: Texas (Jeff Davis County) and Arizona (Pima County); also Mexico and Central America.

CULTURAL NOTES: There is no record of this species ever having been cultivated.

18. **Spiranthes Parksii** Correll, Am. Orch. Soc. Bull. 16: 400, pl. 1947. Type locality and collection: Texas, Brazos Co., Democrat Bridge, Navasota River, October 19, 1945, *H. B. Parks.*   PLATE 84

(The name, *Parksii,* is in honor of HALIBURTON BRALEY PARKS (1879-), Texas botanist and botanical collector.)

COMMON NAME: None known.

Plant erect, 2-3.3 dm. tall; roots fasciculate, fleshy. Stem slender, glabrous below, glandular-pubescent above, provided with several tubular acuminate sheaths. Leaves basal, absent at time of flowering. Spike short, few-flowered, glandular-pubescent, up to 5 cm. long and 1 cm. in diameter. Floral bracts ovate-lanceolate, acuminate, concave, 8-10 mm. long. Flowers in a single spiral rank, ascending. Sepals pubescent on the outer surface, 3-nerved. Dorsal sepal ovate-elliptic to broadly ovate-lanceolate, abruptly recurved at the acute-apiculate apex, deeply concave, about 6 mm. long and 2.8 mm. wide below the middle. Lateral sepals narrowly triangular-lanceolate, acuminate, oblique, with involute margins, about 7 mm. long and 2-2.5 mm. wide below the middle. Petals adherent to the dorsal sepal, oval to obovate or suborbicular, rounded and sometimes irregularly notched at the apex, with the anterior margin more or less erose, 5-nerved, scarcely oblique, about 5 mm. long and 2.5-3.5 mm. wide. Lip oval, broadly rounded or emarginate at the apex, minutely erose-laciniate on the upcurved margins, 5-5.5 mm. long, 3.8-4 mm. wide at about the middle; basal callosities stout, pubescent. Column short, stout, about 3.5 mm. long.

Although discovered in Texas in 1945, this species was only recently examined and described. No notes of flower-color accompanied the collection, but in the dried specimens the flowers appear to have been white. The leaves which are not present in the material I have examined appear to have been entirely basal.

This species has no close allies in our flora. Its affinity seems to be with several Mexican and Central American species. It apparently occurs in a moist habitat, and blooms in October.

GEOGRAPHICAL DISTRIBUTION: Texas (Brazos County).

CULTURAL NOTES: This species has doubtless never been cultivated.

19. **Spiranthes polyantha** Reichb. f., Linnaea 18: 408. 1844. Type locality and collection: Mexico, Chapultepec, *Leibold.* (*Ibidium lucayanum* Britton; *Mesadenus lucayanus* (Britton) Schltr.).   PLATE 85

(The name, *polyantha,* is a Greek adjective meaning "many-flowered," in allusion to the numerous flowers in the elongated inflorescence.)

COMMON NAME: Green Ladies' Tresses.

Plant scapose, very slender, erect to flexuous or weakly ascending, glabrous below, sparsely pubescent above, 1.5-5.8 dm. tall. Roots fasciculate, tuberous, fleshy. Stem purplish.

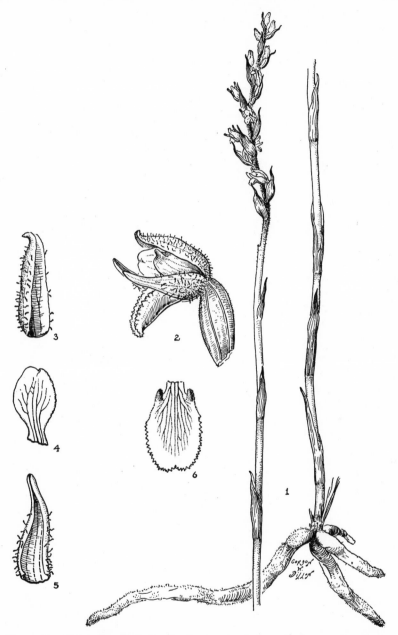

PLATE 84.—**Spiranthes Parksii.** 1, plant, natural size. 2, flower, side view, four times natural size. 3, dorsal sepal, four times natural size. 4, petal, four times natural size. 5, lateral sepal, four times natural size. 6, lip, spread out, four times natural size. *Drawn by Gordon W. Dillon.*

Leaves clustered at the base of the plant, spreading from slender petioles, elliptic to oblanceolate or linear-lanceolate, obtuse to acuminate, conspicuously reticulate-veined (when dry), 5-28 cm. long, 1.5-5 cm. wide, reduced above to somewhat inflated sheathing acuminate-attenuate bracts. Spike loosely or densely many-flowered, slender, flexuous, 5-35 cm. long, 1-1.5 cm. in diameter. Floral bracts ovate-lanceolate, acuminate, 4-11 mm. long. Flowers greenish to grayish green or greenish purple, strongly ringent and spreading. Sepals linear to linear-lanceolate, subacute to acute, 3.2-7 mm. long, about 1 mm. wide near the base; dorsal sepal strongly recurved above the middle; lateral sepals falcate, upcurved. Petals adherent to the dorsal sepal, linear, somewhat falcate, strongly upcurved above the middle, 3-5.5 mm. long, less than 1 mm. wide. Lip elliptic-lanceolate to narrowly lanceolate, subacute to acuminate, usually narrowed and strongly arcuate-recurved at about the middle, 3.5-6.5 mm. long, 1.5-2.5 mm. wide at the widest point; basal callosities minute. Column about 2.5 mm. long. Capsule sessile, ellipsoid, blunt, 4.5-6 mm. long.

This species was apparently first discovered in the United States on the lower part of Elliott's Key in Dade County, Florida, by J. K. SMALL and C. A. MOSIER in March 1915. As far as I know, it has not been collected in our region since that time.

Spiranthes polyantha is found in hammocks of southern peninsular Florida, where it flowers in March. In the tropics, this species grows on and among rocks on hills and in lava fields, on springy bluffs and ledges and in leaf mold in coniferous or hardwood forests. It occurs from near sea level in Florida and the West Indies, up to 8,500 feet altitude in Mexico, and blooms from January to October in various parts of its range.

GEOGRAPHICAL DISTRIBUTION: Florida (Dade County); also Mexico, Guatemala, Bahama Islands, Puerto Rico and Santo Domingo.

CULTURAL NOTES: There is no record of this species ever having been cultivated.

20. **Spiranthes praecox** (Walt.) S. Wats. in A. Gray, Man. Bot. North. U. S., ed. 6: 503. 1890, as to synonymy. *Limodorum praecox* Walt., Fl. Carol. 221. 1788. Type locality: Not given. Probably eastern Carolina. (*Gyrostachys praecox* (Walt.) O. Ktze.; *Ibidium praecox* (Walt.) House). PLATE 86

(The name, *praecox,* is a Latin word meaning "early maturing," so-called because of the time of year when this species blooms in the southern part of its range.)

COMMON NAMES: Grass-leaved Ladies' Tresses, Giant Ladies' Tresses, Grass-leaf Spiral-orchid, Water-tresses.

Plant usually slender, often essentially glabrous, sparsely pubescent above, 2-7.5 dm. tall. Roots fasciculate, rather slender, elongated. Leaves (when present) as many as seven, mostly basal, narrowly linear to filiform, 10-25 cm. long, 1-5 mm. wide. Spike loosely to densely flowered, spirally twisted or often nearly secund, sparsely pubescent with articulated capitate or ball-tipped hairs, 3-15 cm. long, about 1.5 cm. in diameter. Floral bracts ovate-lanceolate, long-acuminate, often with strongly hyaline margins, 4-15 mm. long. Flowers white or white veined and marked with green. Sepals usually puberulent on the outer surface, 5.5-10 mm. long, 2-3 mm. wide; dorsal sepal oblong-elliptic to lanceolate, subacute, often slightly constricted near the apex; lateral sepals lanceolate, acute. Petals adherent to the dorsal sepal, linear, obtuse to subacute or rarely acute, 5.5-10 mm. long, 1-2 mm. wide. Lip thin, with a short claw, oblong to broadly elliptic, often dilated and broadest at the distal end, prominently veined with green or with green on the central portion of the disc, mostly wavy and slightly crenulate or toothed on the apical margin, 5.5-11 mm. long, 2-6 mm. wide; basal callosities slender or sometimes stout, straight. Column 2.5-5 mm. long.

The Grass-leaved Ladies' Tresses is a rather common species in the coastal regions of the southeastern states. It appears to be closely allied to *S. laciniata* and to *S. longilabris,* but the divergent emerald green veins of the lip which are usually present readily distinguish it from those species. In *S. praecox,* as in *S. laciniata,* the glandular articulated hairs of the inflorescence are capitate or ball-tipped and aid in separating it from their common ally, *S. vernalis.*

This species usually occurs in low wet grassy pine barrens and flatwoods, in wet soil in coastal prairies, savannahs, pastures and meadows, in swamps, grassy bogs, low woods and floodplain areas, in upland pine forests, on the edge of cypress swamps, pocosins and marshes, and also in dry oak woods, gravelly sandy soil, coastal salt marshes and moist soil among saw-palmettos. The Grass-leaved Ladies' Tresses is a plant of the Atlantic Coastal Plain and Gulf Coast, and flowers mainly from March to June (rarely November and December) in the deep South and July to September in the northern part of its range.

PLATE 85.— **Spiranthes polyantha.** 1, plant, one half natural size. 2, flower, side view, four times natural size. 3, flower, front view, spread open, three times natural size. 4, column, side view, five times natural size. 5, column, front-ventral view, five times natural size. *Drawn by Gordon W. Dillon.*

GEOGRAPHICAL DISTRIBUTION: Local and rare in New Jersey (Cape May County), south along the Atlantic seaboard to southern Florida and west along the Gulf Coast to east-central Texas and Arkansas; also Rhode Island (*W. W. Bailey,* August 1876).

CULTURAL NOTES: Where this species survived Tertiary geological changes is a mystery, for it is at present known only in the recently emergent Gulf and Atlantic Coastal Plain with a few isolated stations as far north as Rhode Island. It grows there in moist sandy mediacid soil, usually among sedges and grasses. Cultivation is unsatisfactory, not only because of the difficulty of supplying sufficiently acid soil, but also because of extreme susceptibility to attack by parasites. (E. T. W.)

21. **Spiranthes Romanzoffiana** Cham., Linnaea 3: 32. 1828. Type locality: In grassy depressions everywhere, in the lowermost valleys of Unalaska. (*Ibidium strictum* House; *I. Romanzoffianum* (Cham.) House; *Spiranthes stricta* (House) A. Nelson).   PLATE 87

(The name, *Romanzoffiana,* is in honor of NICHOLAS ROMANZOF (1754-1826), Russian minister of state and patron of learning.)

COMMON NAMES: Hooded Ladies' Tresses, Romanzof's Ladies' Tresses.

Plant erect, glabrous below, somewhat glandular-pubescent above, 8-55 cm. tall. Roots fasciculate, long, fleshy. Leaves mostly basal, linear to oblanceolate or oblong-lanceolate, 5-26 cm. long, 6-13 mm. wide. Spike densely flowered, cylindrical, composed of three spiral ranks of flowers, 3-12 cm. long, 1.5-3 cm. in diameter. Floral bracts ovate to ovate-lanceolate, acuminate, semitranslucent, nervose, 1.2-2.5 cm. long. Flowers white or creamy white, tubular, dilated and ringent above the middle. Sepals and petals connivent and forming a hood over the column. Sepals 6.5-13 mm. long, 3-4 mm. wide near the base; dorsal sepal oblong-elliptic to oblong-lanceolate, obtuse to acute; lateral sepals oblong-lanceolate to lanceolate, somewhat falcate, obtuse to acute. Petals linear, obtuse, 6.5-12 mm, long, 1-2 mm. wide. Lip pandurate, with the thin suborbicular base strongly concave and prominently veined, conspicuously constricted above the middle, somewhat dilated above the constriction, 7-11 mm. long, 5 mm. wide across the lower half, strongly arcuate-recurved near the apex in natural position; basal callosities minute. Column 2-3 mm. long.

This species and *S. cernua* are our two most widely distributed species of *Spiranthes*. I have seen a single plant of this species mounted on an herbarium sheet together with a plant of *S. cernua* var. *odorata* supposedly having been collected in South Carolina. This is a most dubious record for the probability of this typically northern species occurring in South Carolina is extremely remote since its nearest northern station is in New York.

The following observations, based on notes in my Alaskan Highway journal of 1943, describes one of the typical areas where this species grows in the Northwest. The region is along the Liard River near Watson Lake in southern Yukon.

I carefully made my way down a dry slope covered with Lodgepole Pines which scarcely sheltered the tall grasses and shrubs growing waist-high among its trunks. The day was hot and the dryish grasses crackled like burning straw beneath my feet, and, with every step, disturbed dust and pine pollen rose in faint puffs from the sheaths and spikelets of the tawny-colored grasses. The scent of pungent pine needles and crushed sweet grass lay heavy in the sultry atmosphere. Weak gusts of air pulsated from the deeply forested country below, bringing with it the sound of the busy waters of the Liard as they overcame rocky obstacles in their rush to the Arctic Ocean. Suddenly, through the wide-spaced trees came the glazed reflection of quiescent waters as small ponds began to take form on a terraced plain at the base of the slope. Here was something unexpected — perhaps an unforeseen obstacle in my way to the Liard.

From where I stood a series of open terraces dropped from the edge of the pine forest to a lush somber spruce forest beyond. Each terrace formed a broad alkaline meadow in which needle-leaved Tamaracks and crowded tussocks of sedges and grasses formed small islands in the shallow covering of scummy water. Thread-like plants of Arrow Grass (*Triglochin* spp.) stood like pieces of wire in the saline water and the rigid spikes of ghostly white flowers of Romanzof's Ladies' Tresses ascended stiffly above the lax clumps of grasses on the scattered islets. Tiny plants

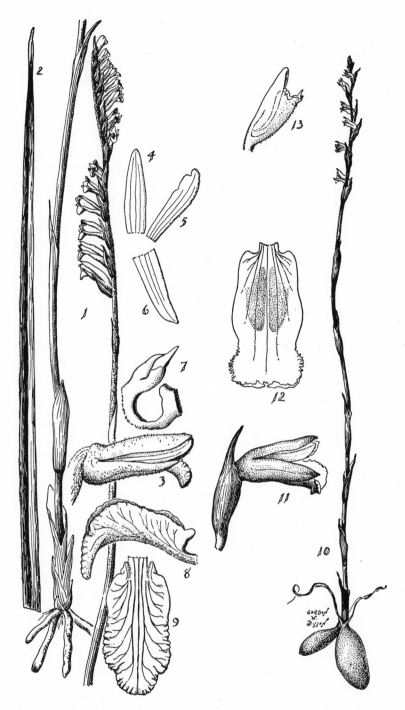

PLATE 86.— **Spiranthes praecox.** 1, plant, natural size. 2, leaf, natural size. 3, flower, side view, three times natural size. 4, dorsal sepal, two and one half times natural size. 5, petal, two and one half times natural size. 6, lateral sepal, two and one half times natural size. 7, column and base of lip, side view, five times natural size. 8, lip, side view, five times natural size. 9, lip, spread out, five times natural size.
Spiranthes parasitica. 10, plant, one half natural size. 11, flower, side view, three times natural size. 12, lip, spread out, five times natural size. 13, column, side view, five times natural size. *Drawn by Gordon W. Dillon.*

of pondweeds grew beneath the water and spread their awl-shaped leaves over the silty bottom.

This little wilderness "hanging" garden was so engrossing that I lost track of time. But, a pale rosy haze was now settling over the flats and the shadowy spruce forest seemed to fade into a solid serrated dark gray wall against the sky as the sun slipped below the horizon. As I turned to look back over the quiet scene a dull hollow sound reverberated from the river forest. It was the plaintive *Oh-ah-oh-ah,* call of the bull moose.

Spiranthes Romanzoffiana is found in moist or wet situations in bogs, marshes, meadows, slat flats, muskegs, thickets, on sandy-gravelly beaches and occasionally in dry woods and on dry open hillsides. The Hooded Ladies' Tresses often grows with lichens and mosses in low open woods, and occurs at high elevations, being found up to 1,600 feet altitude in New York and Vermont, 3,000 feet in British Columbia and the Yukon, 4,500 feet in Alberta, Montana and Utah, 9,000 feet in Idaho and 10,000 feet in Arizona, California, Nevada and Colorado. It flowers from July to October in various parts of its range.

GEOGRAPHICAL DISTRIBUTION: Newfoundland, Labrador, Nova Scotia, Anticosti, Prince Edward Island and New Brunswick, through northern and (?) western New England to New York (south to Tompkins County), west to the Yukon, Alaska and the Aleutian Islands, British Columbia, Washington, Oregon and California, southwest through Iowa (Emmett County), South Dakota (Pennington County), Nebraska and Colorado (Costilla, Grand, Lake, Larimer and Summit counties) to Nevada (Washoe County), Arizona (Apache, Coconino and Graham counties) and New Mexico (Sandoval County); also (?) South Carolina (*M. A. Curtis*) and Ireland.

CULTURAL NOTES: Most northern member of the genus, the Hooded Ladies' Tresses evidently survived glaciation close to the southern margin of the ice sheet, and with the melting of the ice, the species spread all the way across Canada and northward to the Arctic Circle. It prefers moist circumneutral soil, reports of its occurrence in sphagnum bogs apparently representing merely superficial development of acidity at levels well above its actual root system. Its attractive cumarin scent would make it a desirable plant for cultivation, but it cannot withstand the warm summer temperatures of regions much south of its natural range. Moreover, it has great interest for slugs, to say nothing of being highly susceptible to southern fungi. (E. T. W.)

22. **Spiranthes Romanzoffiana** var. **porrifolia** (Lindl.) Ames & Correll, Bot. Mus. Leafl. Harvard Univ. 11: 1. 1943. *Spiranthes porrifolia* Lindl., Gen. and Sp. Orch. Pl. 467. 1840. Type locality and collection: Western North America, *Douglas.* (*Gyrostachys porrifolia* (Lindl.) O. Ktze.; *Ibidium porrifolium* (Lindl.) Rydb.). PLATE 87

(The name, *porrifolia,* is a combination of Latin words meaning "leek-green" and "leaves," in allusion to the succulent yellowish green leaves.)

COMMON NAME: Western Ladies' Tresses.

Plant erect, essentially glabrous throughout, 1.5-6 dm. tall. Roots fasciculate, fleshy, tapering from a much-thickened base. Stem slender, terete, provided with two or more remote scarious acuminate bracts. Leaves usually fugacious at anthesis, when present several, basal or on the lower part of the stem, linear to elliptic-lanceolate or oblanceolate, broadly obtuse to acute, sheathing the stem below, 4-20 cm. long, 7-25 mm. wide. Spike cylindrical or sometimes secund, densely flowered, with the flowers arranged in one or several spiral ranks, 4-20 cm. long, 1-2 cm. in diameter. Floral bracts broadly ovate-lanceolate to narrowly lanceolate-triangular, long-acuminate, 7-20 mm. long. Flowers small, greenish white or cream-colored. Sepals and petals recurved at the apex, often somewhat constricted just below the apex. Sepals narrowly triangular-lanceolate to linear-lanceolate, obtuse to acute, 1- to 3-nerved, 7.5-10.5 mm. long, 2-2.5 mm. wide near the base; dorsal sepal connivent with the petals and forming a hood over the column; lateral sepals somewhat oblique. Petals linear-lanceolate, obtuse, subfalcate to nearly sigmoid, 1-nerved, 8-10 mm. long, 1.5-2 mm. wide near the base. Lip strongly arcuate, conduplicate and clasping the column in natural position, when spread out broadly ovate-lanceolate in outline, ovate to subquadrate and concave below, gradually or rather abruptly constricted at about the middle and then tapering above or only slightly dilated at the apex, 7-8.5 mm. long, 3-3.5 mm. wide across the lower half, provided with **a**

PLATE 87.—**Spiranthes Romanzoffiana var. porrifolia.** 1, plant, one half natural size. 2, flower, side view, twice natural size. 3, lip, five times natural size.
Spiranthes Romanzoffiana. 4, plant, one half natural size. 5, flower, side view, twice natural size. 6, lip, five times natural size. *Drawn by Gordon W. Dillon.*

rather prominent mammillate callosity on each side at the base, densely cellular-papillose **and** puberulent at the apex. Column 3-4 mm. long. Capsule ovoid, about 8 mm. long.

I consider the localized western plant to be a geographic variety of the widespread and fairly common *S. Romanzoffiana.* The characters commonly used to separate them may be summed up as follows: 1) *S. Romanzoffiana,* calli of the lip minute; lip panduriform, suborbicular below the constriction, strongly dilated at the apex and usually lacerate on the apical margin. 2) Variety *porrifolia,* calli rather prominent; lip essentially ovate-lanceolate in outline, usually oblong-quadrate below the constriction, scarcely (if at all) dilated at the apex and usually only cellular-papillose on the apical margin.

Intergrading forms between these two entities occur. Often a lip, in other respects like that of typical *S. Romanzòffiana,* has large fleshy calli comparable to those which occur normally in var. *porrifolia.* Conversely, a lip like that of var. *porrifolia* shows the characteristic minute or almost obsolescent calli which characterize *S. Romanzoffiana.* The inflorescence of typical var. *porrifolia* is composed of several ranks of flowers and is characteristically more slender than that of *S. Romanzoffiana.* Several collections of var. *porrifolia* have been seen with flowers disposed in a single secund row or spiral rank. However, this occurrence is rare.

The Western Ladies' Tresses grows in wet soil of bogs, marshes, meadows, swamps and on wet grassy hillsides. It occurs from near sea level up to 8,000 feet altitude in California, and flowers from May to August in various parts of its range.

GEOGRAPHICAL DISTRIBUTION: Utah (Weber County), Nevada (*Miller 2113*), Washington (Klickitat County), Oregon (Josephine (?) and Marion counties) and California (widespread, south to San Bernardino County).

CULTURAL NOTES: This Pacific Coast member of the genus grows in bogs and moist grasslands in soils of moderately acid reaction. While it is occasionally offered by dealers, there is no record of its successful cultivation in gardens outside of its native region. (E. T. W.)

23. × **Spiranthes Steigeri** Correll, Am. Orch. Soc. Bull. 9: 241, t. 9. 1941. Type locality and collection: New Hampshire, dense marshy grassland, Warner, Merrimack County, September 22, 1940, *Theodore L. Steiger.* PLATE 80

(The name, *Steigeri,* is in honor of THEODORE LINDSAY STEIGER (1893-   ), Swiss-American botanist, who first discovered this putative hybrid.)

COMMON NAME: Steiger's Ladies' Tresses.

The type collection of this putative natural hybrid of *S. cernua* × *S. Romanzoffiana* shows a more or less intermediate condition between these two species, and has flowers which are extremely variable in size and in the shape of the lip. As shown by the illustration, the plant which typifies the hybrid is most unusual. The flowers of the spike present the characteristic ascending appearance of the flowers of *S. Romanzoffiana.* When the lips of three flowers of this plant were examined, one was found to approach the lip of *S. cernua* (FIG. 2) while another approached that of *S. Romanzoffiana* (FIG. 1). The third flower examined was found to be asymmetrical. The general outline of the lip in FIGURE 3 resembles that of *S. Romanzoffiana* (FIG. 1), whereas the general outline of the lip in FIGURE 5 resembles essentially that of *S. cernua* (FIG. 2). The lip illustrated in FIGURE 4 is most striking in that it has a bilaterally asymmetrical lamina, of which one half resembles FIGURE 3 and the other half simulates FIGURE 5. The large callosities at the base of all three lips (FIGS. 3, 4 and 5) approach most closely those of *S. cernua* (FIG. 2).

The largest plant in the hybrid collection is a teratological form, a rather common occurrence in a hybrid population. The flowers (FIG. 7) have lips with the basal callosities abnormally developed. There are two additional, laterally placed, abortive lips which consist partly of fertile tissue (pollinia) and partly of sterile tissue. The flowers have eight pollinia instead of the normal two. In general appearance this large specimen resembles plants of *S. cernua* var. *ochroleuca* (Rydb.) Ames (PL. 70, FIGS. 12-13). However, since it is a monster and was found growing with the hybrid, it should perhaps be referred to × *S. Steigeri.*

This putative hybrid occurs in dense marshy grasslands and sandy clearings. It blooms in September and October.

GEOGRAPHICAL DISTRIBUTION: New Hampshire (Merrimack County) and Nova Scotia (Yarmouth County).

CULTURAL NOTES: This plant has doubtless never been cultivated.

24. **Spiranthes tortilis** (Sw.) L. C. Rich., Orch. Europ. Annot. 37. 1817 (in Mém. Mus. Hist. Nat. Par. 4: 59. 1818, exclude synonym *Neottia quadridentata*). *Neottia tortilis* Sw., Kongl. Svens. Vetens. Acad. Nya Handl. 21: 226. 1800. Type locality: West Indies. (*Ibidium tortile* (Sw.) House). PLATE 79

(The name, *tortilis*, is a Latin adjective meaning "twisted," referring to the strongly spiraled inflorescence.)

COMMON NAMES: Southern Ladies' Tresses, Rush-leaf Spiral-orchid.

Plant slender, glabrous below, subglabrous to somewhat pubescent above, up to 7 dm. tall. Roots fasciculate, long, slender. Leaves (when present) basal, filiform-terete to narrowly linear or sometimes semiterete, 8-30 cm. long. Spike slender, spiraled, composed of a single row of flowers, subglabrous or sparsely pubescent with blunt or ball-tipped hairs, 3-22 cm. long. Floral bracts ovate to ovate-lanceolate, acuminate, mostly with hyaline margins, 3-7 mm. long. Flowers white, marked with green, often fragrant. Sepals 3.5-6.5 mm. long, 1-2 mm. wide; dorsal sepal oblong-elliptic to oblong-lanceolate, subacute to acute; lateral sepals lanceolate, acute to acuminate. Petals adherent to the dorsal sepal, linear to linear-spatulate, obtuse to subacute, 3.5-5.5 mm. long, about 1 mm. wide. Lip ovate to oblong-quadrate or orbicular-quadrate, often conspicuously constricted just above the middle, green or yellowish green on the central portion of the disc, with the apical margin crenulate-undulate and whitish, strongly recurved in natural position, 3-6 mm. long, 1.5-3 mm. wide; callosities slender or stout, mammillate.

The Southern Ladies' Tresses is a perfectly distinct species when its leaves or remnants of leaves are present, but is easily confused with *S. gracilis* when its linear or filiform leaves are absent. The flowers strongly resemble those of *S. gracilis* in the shape of the lip and in color. In habit, it approaches some forms of *S. vernalis,* especially the plant described as *Gyrostachys linearis* Rydb. However, the essentially glabrous inflorescence separates *S. tortilis* from *S. vernalis:* and, when the inflorescence is sparsely pubescent, the hairs are blunt or ball-tipped instead of being sharp-pointed as in *S. vernalis.* The green-centered lip also serves to separate this species from *S. vernalis.*

Spiranthes tortilis was probably first collected in the United States in Orleans Parish, Louisiana, by THOMAS DRUMMOND in 1832.

This species is commonly found in dry rocky pinelands or open grasslands, and often grows rooted in shallow rock crevices. In the tropics it also occurs on open or brushy mountain slopes and in brackish areas. The Southern Ladies' Tresses grows near sea level in Florida, up to 3,500 feet altitude in Cuba and 5,000 feet in Jamaica, and blooms from November to July in various parts of its range, especially in May and June in our region.

GEOGRAPHICAL DISTRIBUTION: Florida (Broward, Dade, Lee and Monroe counties) and Louisiana (Orleans Parish); also Guatemala, British Honduras, Nicaragua, Bermuda, Bahama Islands, the West Indies and Trinidad.

CULTURAL NOTES: The Rush-leaf Spiral-orchid grows in moist acid pinelands and open swamps along the Gulf Coast. There is no record of its successful cultivation. (E. T. W.)

25. **Spiranthes vernalis** Engelm. & Gray, Bost. Journ. Nat. Hist. 5: 236 (Plantae Lindheimerianae, p. 28). 1845. Type locality: Moist prairies, Galveston and Houston, Texas, April, May. (*Gyrostachys vernalis* (Engelm. & Gray) O. Ktze.; *G. Reverchonii* Small; *G. linearis* Rydb.; *G. xyridifolia* Small; × *Spiranthes intermedia* Ames; *Spiranthes neglecta* Ames; *S. Reverchonii*

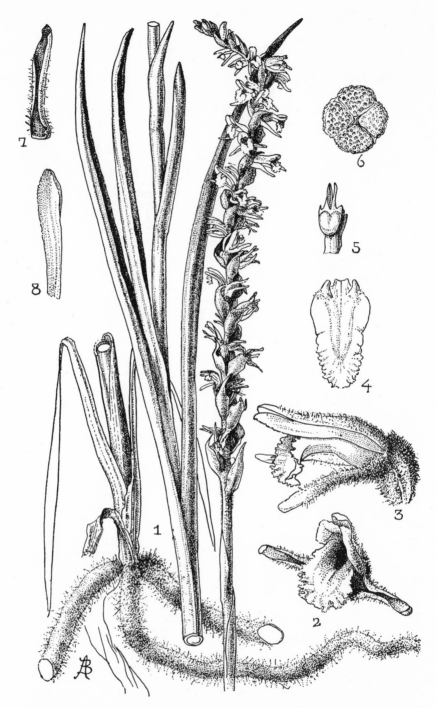

PLATE 88.—**Spiranthes vernalis.** 1, plant, natural size. 2, flower, front view, four times natural size. 3, flower, side view, four times natural size. 4, lip, spread out, four times natural size. 5, column, four times natural size. 6, pollen tetrad, highly magnified. 7, lateral sepal, four times natural size. 8, petal, four times natural size. *Drawn by Blanche Ames.*

(Small) K. Schum.; *Ibidium vernale* (Engelm. & Gray) House; *I. xyridi-folium* Small). PLATE 88

(The name, *vernalis,* is a Latin adjective meaning "spring," so-called because of the time of year this species is found in flower in the southern part of its range.)

COMMON NAMES: Spring Ladies' Tresses, Linear-leaved Ladies' Tresses, Narrow-leaved Tresses, Spring Tresses.

Plant stout or slender, densely and copiously pubescent above, 1.8-11 dm. tall. Roots fasciculate, coarse, fusiform. Leaves basal or extending partly up the stem, suberect or ascending, linear to narrowly lanceolate, acuminate, often strongly keeled or semiterete, with the basal portion sheathing the stem, up to 30 cm. or more long and 1 cm. wide. Spike densely flowered, spiraled, 3-25 cm. long, about 1.5 cm. in diameter; rachis and ovaries mostly covered with a dense mat of reddish brown articulated sharp-pointed hairs. Floral bracts broadly ovate to oblong-lanceolate, rather abruptly acuminate-elongated, concave, 7-15 mm. long. Flowers yellowish (rarely marked with green) or often white, usually fragrant, in a single rank or very rarely 2-ranked; parts of the perianth somewhat pubescent on the outer surface. Dorsal sepal oblong-lanceolate to lanceolate, obtuse to acute, concave at the base, 5.5-10 mm. long, 2.5-3 mm. wide near the base. Lateral sepals lanceolate, acute, 5-9.5 mm. long. Petals adherent to the dorsal sepal, linear to linear-elliptic, obtuse, 5-9 mm. long, 1-2 mm. wide. Lip fleshy-thickened, broadly ovate to rhombic-ovate or sometimes ovate-oblong, arcuate-recurved in natural position, often somewhat dilated and crenulate-wavy at the apex, 4.5-8 mm. long. 2.5-6 mm. wide near the base; basal callosities stout, incurved, pubescent.

The Spring Ladies' Tresses is characterized by its copiously pubescent rachis and ovaries which are provided with articulated sharp-pointed hairs. It is a rather variable and widespread species, especially on the southeastern Coastal Plain, and a number of its forms have been segregated as independent entities by some authors.

On September 5, 1942, E. J. PALMER collected some specimens near Diamond Hill, Providence County, Rhode Island. Pressed in the throat of one of the flowers was a tropical Chalcid Fly (*Eurytoma orchidiarum*) (identified by C. T. BRUES) with pollinia attached to its body. There, far from its natural clime, the little insect was still carrying on the process of pollination.

Apparently this characteristically southern species was first collected in Canada at Hatley, Quebec, by HENRY MOUSLEY in 1923. However, it was not reported by MOUSLEY as from the Dominion until 1941(A).

This species is commonly found in low swampy pastures and meadows, bogs, fresh and coastal salt marshes, low wet pine barrens and flatwoods, swamps, flood-plain areas, low prairies and savannahs, sandy beaches and dune areas, in open woods and hammocks, and occasionally in calcareous soils. It occurs from near sea level, up to 3,600 feet altitude in the mountains of North Carolina and Tennessee, where it is usually found in dry sandy soil and open fields. In Guatemala, it grows at an elevation of 9,000 feet. The Spring Ladies' Tresses has been collected in flower in every month of the year in various parts of its range. It flowers, however, mainly from January to June in the South and during July and August in the extreme North.

GEOGRAPHICAL DISTRIBUTION: Rare in Quebec (Stanstead County), eastern Massachusetts, Rhode Island and Connecticut, becoming more frequent through the Atlantic States, south to southern Florida, along the Gulf Coast to Texas (west to Brazos and Victoria counties); west infrequently through the Central and Lake States to Missouri (Jasper County), Kansas (west to Cowley, Riley and Sumner counties), Iowa (Fremont County), Nebraska (Otoe County), Oklahoma (Creek, Dewey and McCurtain counties) and New Mexico; also Mexico and Guatemala.

CULTURAL NOTES: This species differs from the closely related *S. praecox* in extending rather widely over the southeastern United States and up to latitude 45°. It grows chiefly in grassland on loamy soil of subacid reaction. If transplanted early in the season, it can be cultivated in the wild garden for a while; but it is not long-lived, on account of its susceptibility to attack by pests. (E. T. W.)

18. Centrogenium Schltr.

Centrogenium Schltr., Beihefte Bot. Centralbl. 37, Abt. 2: 451. 1920.

(The name, *Centrogenium,* is from the Greek words meaning "spur" and "jaw" or "chin," in allusion to the prominence of the chin-like spur or mentum in the flowers of this genus.)

Terrestrial scapose herbs with tuberous fasciculate roots. Leaves radical, long-petioled. Inflorescence a lax few-flowered terminal spike. Lateral sepals forming a distinct mentum with the foot of the column, the apex of the mentum being free. Lip concave and embracing the column in natural position, with its base attached to the column-foot inside the mentum formed by the lateral sepals. Column short, stout, with a prominent foot; rostellum cuspidate-setaceous; anther erect behind the rostellum; pollinia powdery-granular. Capsule suberect, ellipsoid.

This is a small genus of about ten species which are confined to the tropics and subtropics of the Western Hemisphere, mostly South American.

1. **Centrogenium setaceum** (Lindl.) Schltr., Beihefte Bot. Centralbl. 37, Abt. 2: 453. 1920. *Pelexia setacea* Lindl., Gen. and Sp. Orch. Pl. 482. 1840. Type locality and collection: Brazil, along Rio Dulce and in forests near Mandiocca, *Maximilian Alexander Philipp, Prinz zu Wied-Neuwied.*   PLATE 89

(The name, *setaceum,* is a Latin adjective meaning "bristlelike," in reference to the long tapering apex of the sepals and petals.)

COMMON NAME: Spurred Neottia.

Plant scapose, 2.3-6.8 dm. tall. Roots fleshy, rather coarse, fasciculate. Stem slender or stout, reddish purple, glabrous below, downy above, with scattered tubular sheaths having a free triangular acuminate apex. Leaves one or sometimes two, basal, long-petioled; petiole purplish, 6-18 cm. long; lamina elliptic-oblong to narrowly elliptic-lanceolate, acute to rarely obtuse, 7-17 cm. long, 2-6 cm. wide. Spike laxly few-flowered, 5-14 cm. long. Floral bracts narrowly lanceolate, acuminate, semitranslucent, 2-3.5 cm. long. Flowers greenish white. Sepals linear-lanceolate, acuminate-attenuate, 2.6-3.5 cm. long, 3-5 mm. wide near the base; lateral sepals united and forming a spur-like mentum which is adnate to the ovary for about half its length and projects into a free portion 7-16 mm. long. Petals linear-lanceolate, acuminate-attenuate, adnate to the dorsal sepal, 1.8-2.5 cm. long, 2-3 mm. wide near the base. Lip ascending-arcuate in natural position, oblong to narrowly lanceolate when expanded, acuminate-attenuate, somewhat notched on each side near the middle, laciniate above the notches almost to the apex, 2.8-4 cm. long, about 5 mm. wide at the widest point. Column stout, with a foot about 1 cm. long. Capsule ellipsoid, 2-2.7 cm. long, about 8 mm. in diameter.

This rare species was first discovered in the United States in Dade County, Florida, by A. A. EATON in February 1905. It was apparently not found again until J. B. McFARLIN collected it in a dense hammock in Highlands County, Florida, on February 4, 1936.

The spur-like mentum and attenuated floral segments are characteristics of this species.

The Spurred Neottia grows in leaf mold and rich humus in dense hammocks of southern Florida. In the tropics, it occurs on boulders and in leaf mold in deep forests, while in Puerto Rico it has been collected in sand near the sea. It grows at low elevations, flowering from January to March.

GEOGRAPHICAL DISTRIBUTION: Florida (Dade and Highlands counties); also the Bahama Islands, the West Indies, Trinidad, Colombia and Brazil.

CULTURAL NOTES: This species is reported to grow in circumneutral soil in subtropical Florida. It could doubtless be cultivated farther north in greenhouses. (E. T. W.)

The Spurred Neottia was apparently first introduced into England from Jamaica about 1835 by CHARLES HORSFIELD, Esq., of Liverpool.

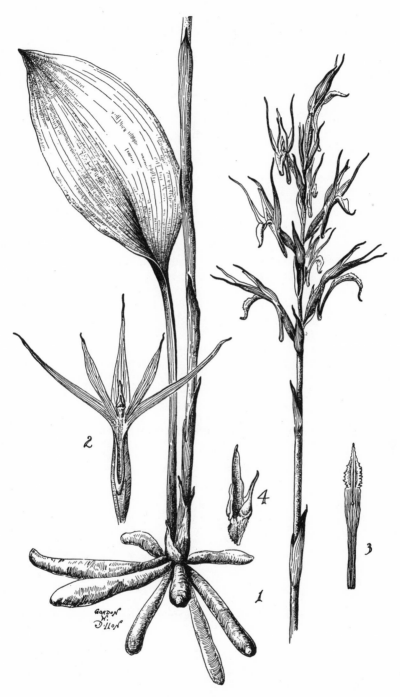

PLATE 89.—**Centrogenium setaceum.** 1, lower part of plant and inflorescence (with lip of lower right hand flower pulled away from the rest of the flower to show its attachment), one half natural size. 2, flower, with lip removed, spread open, natural size. 3, lip, natural size. 4, column, side view, twice natural size. *Drawn by Gordon W. Dillon.*

19. Goodyera R. Br.

Goodyera R. Br. in Ait., Hort. Kew., ed. 2, 5: 197. 1813, conserved name.

(The name, *Goodyera,* is in honor of JOHN GOODYER (1592-1664), an English botanist.)

Terrestrial scapose herbs with creeping rootstocks bearing several thick fibrous roots and with the alternate leaves basal or clustered on the lower part of the stem. Leaves ovate to lanceolate, dark green or bluish green, often reticulate-veined or variegated with white, rising from somewhat inflated sheaths, abruptly reduced above to sheathing bracts. Inflorescence a lax or dense cylindrical or secund terminal spicate raceme. Flowers small, white to pink, often tinged with yellow or green, the oblique petals being connivent with the dorsal sepal and forming a hood over the column and lip. Lip sessile, deeply concave or saccate at the base, straight or recurved at the apex, entire or rarely lobed; disc usually adorned with glands or fleshy processes. Column short; anther borne on the back; pollinia two, attached to a narrow gland which is held between the forked or 2-toothed beak terminating the column. Capsule erect, ovoid to ellipsoid.

This genus consists of about twenty-five species which are found in boreal, temperate and tropical regions throughout the world. The typically variegated leaves of most of our species and spurless lip are characteristics of the genus. Most of the species have been used at times for medicinal purposes.

The species in our region are rather well defined. However, the probable existence of a hybrid population (centered in the Lake States), involving *G. repens* var. *ophioides, G. tesselata* and *G. oblongifolia,* makes the determination of plants from that particular area a most unsatisfactory and perplexing task.

KEY FOR THE IDENTIFICATION OF THE SPECIES OF GOODYERA

1. Raceme loosely or densely flowered, 1-sided or spiraled...................................2
  2. Leaves always more or less reticulate-veined with white; petals less than 6.5 mm. long....3
    3. Plants small, averaging less than 1.5 dm. in height; lip and petals less than 4 mm. long; anther blunt or with a short tip; beaks of the rostellum shorter than the body of the stigma...*G. repens* var. *ophioides* (p. 238)
    3. Plants rather large, averaging about 2 dm. in height; lip and petals usually much longer than 4 mm.; anther acuminate; beaks of the rostellum as long as or longer than the body of the stigma...*G. tesselata* (p. 240)
  2. Leaves plain green or, if sparingly net-veined with white or with the mid-nerve white, with the petals 6.5 mm. or more long...4
    4. Plants small, usually less than 1.5 dm. tall; leaves always plain green; lip and petals less than 4 mm. long..*G. repens* (p. 236)
    4. Plants large, usually more than 2 dm. tall; leaves with the mid-nerve usually white; lip more than 4.5 mm. long; petals more than 6 mm. long..........*G. oblongifolia* (p. 230)
1. Raceme densely flowered on all sides, cylindrical......................................5
  5. Lip broadly globose-saccate, with a short beak; anther blunt; rostellum essentially beakless ....*G. pubescens* (p. 233)
  5. Lip narrowly saccate, with an elongated beak; anther acuminate; beaks of rostellum as long as or longer than the body of the stigma...........................*G. tesselata* (p. 240)

1. **Goodyera oblongifolia** Raf., Herb. Raf. 76. 1833. Type locality: Oregon mountains. (*Goodyera Menziesii* Lindl.; *G. decipiens* (Hook.) Hubbard; *Epipactis decipiens* (Hook.) Ames; *Peramium decipiens* (Hook.) Piper; *P. Menziesii* (Lindl.) Morong). PLATE 90

(The name, *oblongifolia,* is a Latin adjective signifying "oblong-leaved," in allusion to the shape of the leaves.)

COMMON NAMES: Menzies' Rattlesnake Plantain, Green-leaved Rattlesnake Orchid.

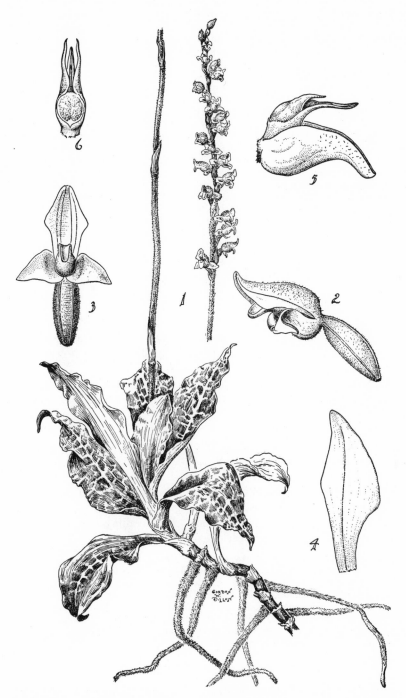

PLATE 90.— **Goodyera oblongifolia.** 1, plant, one half natural size. 2, flower, side view, three times natural size. 3, flower, front view, partly spread open, three times natural size. 4, petal, five times natural size. 5, lip and column, in natural position, side view, five times natural size. 6, column, front-ventral view, to show stigma and beak, five times natural size. *Drawn by Gordon W. Dillon.*

Plant scapose, erect, densely glandular-pubescent above, 1-4.5 dm. tall. Roots fibrous, from a short creeping rootstock. Scape rather stout, provided with closely appressed sheaths. Leaves in a basal rosette, suberect-spreading, with rather wide petioles, usually oblong-elliptic, sometimes ovate-oblong to lanceolate, obtuse to acute, somewhat rounded to tapering at the base, oblique, dark green, plain or partly reticulate-veined with white especially along the mid-nerve, 4-11 cm. long, 1.5-3.5 cm. wide. Raceme densely flowered, strongly 1-sided or loosely spiraled, tapering to the apex, 6-14 cm. long, 1-2.5 cm. in diameter. Floral bracts ovate to ovate-lanceolate, acute to acuminate, concave, 8-12 mm. long. Flowers white, tinged or streaked with green, large for the genus, the stout pedicellate ovaries being about 1 cm. long. Sepals and petals 1-nerved, with the sepals puberulent on the outer surface. Dorsal sepal triangular-lanceolate to elliptic-lanceolate, tapering to the recurved obtuse apex, deeply concave below, 6.5-10.5 mm. long, 3-4.5 mm. wide below the middle. Lateral sepals obliquely ovate-lanceolate, rather abruptly tapering to the recurved acuminate apex, 5-8 mm. long, 2.5-4 mm. wide below the middle. Petals connivent with the dorsal sepal and forming a hood over the lip, contiguous on their inner margins above the middle, dolabriform, narrowly cuneate below the middle, obliquely dilated at about the middle and then tapering to the subobtuse apex, erose-ciliate above the middle, 6.5-10 mm. long, 3-4 mm. wide at about the middle. Lip deeply concave-cymbiform, with a long beak and involute margins, 5-8 mm. long; saccate portion 1.5-2.5 mm. deep, up to 4.5 mm. wide in natural position, provided with three or four unequal rows of tubercules on the inner surface; beak sulcate, usually minutely calyptrate at the somewhat recurved apex, 2-3 mm. long. Column 4-5.5 mm. long, with the slender beak as long as or longer than the body of the stigma. Capsule obovoid-ellipsoid, about 1 cm. long.

Until recently, this species has been commonly known as *Goodyera decipiens*. FERNALD, however, in 1946, calls attention to the fact that RAFINESQUE's earlier name is the correct one for this plant. The fact that only this species of *Goodyera* occurs in Oregon, in addition to RAFINESQUE's clear description, amply support this nomenclatural change.

This transcontinental orchid, a widespread species in the far West, is locally distributed in the northeastern United States and Canada. However, once it gains a foothold it apparently multiplies and spreads rapidly. It has become exceedingly abundant in some parts of the Lake Huron region.

Some variations have been noted in the column of this species. The anther is sometimes 3-celled and tridentate at the apex, and the pollinia three with two each poorly developed caudae.

This plant is a reputed alterative.

Goodyera oblongifolia is found in dry or moist coniferous or mixed forests. It usually grows in moss or rich humus on forest slopes in mountain regions, where it grows commonly at high elevations. Menzies' Rattlesnake Plantain occurs up to 3,000 feet altitude in Montana, 4,500 feet in Alberta, California and Oregon, 6,000 feet in British Columbia, 7,500 feet in Washington and Wyoming and 10,000 feet in Arizona, Colorado, New Mexico and Utah. Its blooming season is from the last of June to the first of September in various parts of its range.

GEOGRAPHICAL DISTRIBUTION: Nova Scotia (Victoria County), New Brunswick (Madawaska County), Quebec (Bonaventure, Gaspé, Matane, Rimouski and Stanstead counties) and Ontario (Bruce and Manitoulin counties), west to Alberta (Banff, Waterton Lakes Park and Castlemont), British Columbia and Alaska (Loring and Sitka); south to northern Maine (Aroostook County), Michigan (south to Crawford County), Wisconsin (Door County), South Dakota (Lawrence County), Montana (Flathead, Glacier and Sanders counties), Idaho, Washington, Oregon, California, Wyoming (Teton County) and Colorado (Douglas, Jefferson and Larimer counties), southwest along the Rocky Mountains to New Mexico (Catron, Sandoval, San Miguel, Santa Fé and Taos counties) and Arizona (Apache, Coconino and Graham counties); also Mexico (Nuevo León).

CULTURAL NOTES: The Green-leaved Rattlesnake Orchid survived glaciation in the Rocky Mountains and perhaps in some refuge around the Great Lakes, and after the melting of the ice the species migrated far northward through Canada. Correspondingly, according to expectations, it requires soil which is cool throughout the summer. Tests as to soil-reaction indicate that it thrives best in subacid humus resulting from the thorough decay of coniferous tree litter. Whether it can be cultivated in middle-eastern gardens is doubtful, although wild flower gardeners in the northwestern states report some success. (E. T. W.)

2. **Goodyera pubescens** (Willd.) R. Br. in Ait., Hort. Kew., ed. 2, 5: 198. 1813.
   Neottia pubescens Willd., Sp. Pl. 4: 76. 1805. Type locality: Canada to Florida. (*Peramium pubescens* (Willd.) Salisb.; *Epipactis pubescens* (Willd.) A. A. Eaton).   PLATES 91 and 92

(The name, *pubescens*, is a Latin adjective meaning "downy," in allusion to the soft hairs on the scape and raceme.)

COMMON NAMES: Downy Rattlesnake Plantain, Scrofula-weed, Downy Rattlesnake Orchid.

Plant scapose, erect, densely pubescent above, 1-4.5 dm. tall. Roots fibrous, from a short or elongated creeping rootstock. Leaves three to eight, in a basal rosette, with a rather broad short petiole, ovate to oblong or ovate-lanceolate, bluish green, with several white nerves and many fine reticulating white veins, 2.5-9 cm. long, 1.2-3.5 cm. wide. Raceme densely many-flowered on all sides, cylindrical, 3-12 cm. long, 1-2 cm. in diameter. Floral bracts lanceolate, 6-9 mm. long. Flowers globose, small, white. Sepals and petals glandular-pubescent on the outer surface, with one central vein. Dorsal sepal broadly ovate to oblong-elliptic, strongly concave, with a rather abrupt beak-like obtuse apex, 4.5-5.5 mm. long, 3-4 mm. wide. Lateral sepals broadly ovate, concave, conforming to the shape of the lip, with a rather abrupt and beak-like obtuse to subacute apex, 4-5 mm. long, 3-3.5 mm. wide. Petals connivent with the dorsal sepal and forming a hood over the lip, contiguous on their inner margins above the middle, obliquely oblong-spatulate to somewhat dolabriform, obtuse, with the upper half somewhat crenulate, 5-6 mm. long, 2.5-3 mm. wide. Lip strongly bulbous-saccate, with a short blunt tip or beak, with the margins not strongly flaring or recurved, prominently 3-nerved, with the outer surface somewhat tuberculose-spinulose, 4-5 mm. long, 3-3.5 mm. wide; beak 1.5-2 mm. long; sac about 3 mm. deep. Column about 2 mm. long; anther blunt; rostellum essentially beakless.

Orchid seeds are essentially lacking an endosperm (stored food within the embryo sac) and, consequently, the growing embryo has to depend primarily upon some foreign source for its nutrition. Theoretically, this is achieved in nature through symbiosis, wherein the orchid seed is first invaded by a fungus and, in turn, is enabled to germinate and grow by absorbing the waste- or by-products produced externally on digestion or secretion by the fungus or by decomposition of the fungus.

The following account concerning the remarkable relationship existing between orchids and fungi is adapted from AMES (1947), who made a study of this strange commensalism in this species of orchid.

When the orchid fruit is ripe it dehisces and the powdery microscopic seeds fall or are blown to a receptive substratum where they either perish or lie dormant until they are invaded by a non-pathogenic fungus. The slender threadlike hyphae of the fungus enter the minute embryo of the seed (*cf.* PLATE 91, FIG. 6) and later invade certain cells of the leafless seedling (*cf.* PLATE 92, FIG. 6) where eventually they are supposedly digested and assimilated by the orchid.

Once infested by a fungus the embryo swells and increases in size by the formation of numerous tiny cells and forms a protocorm (FIG. 1; all figures refer to PLATE 92), the term protocorm simply meaning "first stem." As the protocorm develops it becomes pear-shaped (FIG. 1), and emits slender elongated rhizoids (root-like structures). Through these tubular rhizoids (FIG. 3), the hyphae of the fungus which have developed in the protocorm gain access to the humus in which the plants grow and assimilate food materials necessary for the growth of the orchid, and in exchange the fungus apparently receives some nutrition from the orchid. Later the protocorm produces a short rhizome and a pair of tiny leaves and gradually develops into a young plant (FIG. 2). When the fungus is digested in a cell, it forms a globular mass (resembling a ball of cotton twine) from which slender filaments penetrate the cell walls of the protocorm and form loose skeins of hyphae in adjacent cells where again digestion apparently takes place (FIGS. 5, 6).

Until recently, the method of producing seedling orchids in the horticultural and floral industry closely simulated the process occurring in nature. That is, the seeds were sown on a dampened substratum containing organic matter, such as sphagnum,

PLATE 91.—**Goodyera pubescens.** Flowering plant and fruiting inflorescence, natural size. 1, flower, front-side view, four times natural size. 2, flower, longitudinal cross-section to show relation of the lip and column to the ovary, sepals and petals, seven times natural size. 3, column, front-side view, to show position of stigma and anther, fifteen times natural size. 4, pollinia, greatly enlarged. 5, a pollen tetrad, greatly enlarged. 6, mature seed, greatly enlarged. *Drawn by Blanche Ames.*

peat, leaf mold, sawdust, wood or bark, or mixtures of peat and sphagnum moss. If not destroyed by pathogenic fungi, insects, algae or poisonous substances produced by decomposition of their substratum or other organisms, the seeds became infected, as in nature, by a compatible fungus which, in theory, induced germination and growth of the seeds. This haphazard method to produce hybrids from seeds commonly met with complete failure so that growers, in order to replenish or rapidly in-

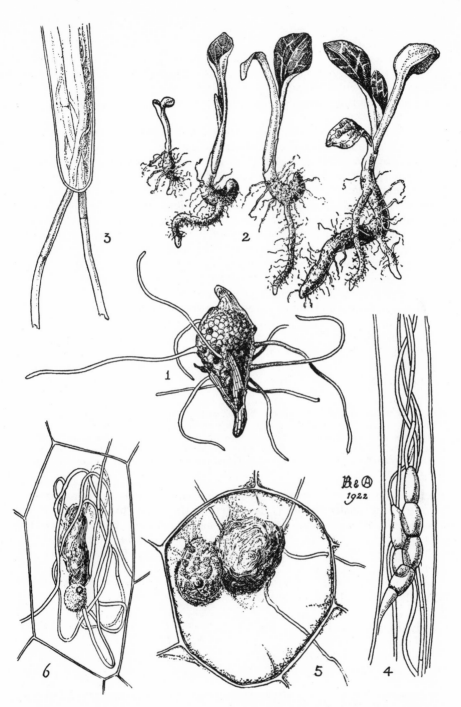

PLATE 92.— **Goodyera pubescens.** 1, protocorm (thirty times natural size), showing testa still adherent to the base; spreading hair-like structures through which the hyphae pass to and from the humus, and the growing tip, the darker portion indicates the extent of distribution of the fungus. 2, four stages in the development of young plants, two and one half times natural size. 3, the upper part of a hair-like process through the tip of which two fungal hyphae have passed, greatly enlarged. 4, part of a hair-like process in which fruit-like structures have formed, greatly enlarged. 5, a cell from the lower part of the protocorm showing a large nucleus closely appressed to a mass of digested hyphae, greatly enlarged. 6, an earlier stage of digestion than that shown in figure 5, the nucleus and partly digested fungus are surrounded by a skein of hyphae, greatly enlarged. *Figures 1-3 drawn by Blanche Ames; figures 4-6 drawn by Oakes Ames.*

crease their stock, resorted either to the practice of dividing their plants or to the importation of mature plants from the stock of other growers. In 1922, KNUDSON's great work on the nonsymbiotic germination of orchid seeds was published. He and his followers developed a method of growing seeds asymbiotically on a sterile agar medium containing a nutrient solution enriched by an appropriate sugar, thus insuring the scientific germination of seeds and the resultant growth of seedlings. Today, in the horticultural and floral industry, orchid seeds no longer depend upon the introduction of fungi for their germination and the number of seedlings produced in our greenhouses are incalculable.

In 1814, PURSH naively remarked concerning the Downy Rattlesnake Plantain, "This plant has lately made a great noise among the country people, as infallibly curing the bite of a mad dog." At another period the leaves of this plant are said to have been used in the attempted cure of scrofula.

The common name of rattlesnake plantains, especially of the species under consideration, is derived from the belief of superstitious folk that the mottled snake-striped leaves when chewed or macerated and applied to a rattlesnake bite act as a powerful antidote. It may be noted here that the common tendency of primitive or superstitious peoples to associate natural objects which resemble a part or organ of the human body with a cure for disease of that organ is called the Doctrine of Signatures—the basis for early medical practice as well as for witchcraft.

This species is most abundant in dry or moist coniferous forests, and is rather frequent in deciduous and mixed forests, in ravines along streams, on rocky well-drained wooded slopes and in rich humus in moist upland hardwoods. It is often found in thickets (especially of Rhododendron) in the mountains where it occurs up to 2,000 feet altitude in South Carolina and 4,500 feet in North Carolina and Tennessee. The Downy Rattlesnake Plantain blooms from May (in Massachusetts) to the first of October (in New York).

GEOGRAPHICAL DISTRIBUTION: Quebec and Ontario (Elgin and Wellington counties), through New England and the Atlantic States, south to South Carolina (Greenville, Oconee and Pickens counties), Georgia (Jackson, Madison, Rabun and Towns counties) and Alabama (Clarke and Winston counties), west through the Central and Lake States to Minnesota (Chisago and Houston counties), Iowa (Iowa County), Kentucky (Harlan and McCreary counties), Arkansas (*fide Demaree*) and Tennessee (west to Putnam County); also (?) British Columbia.

CULTURAL NOTES: Growing in woodlands having a wide range in temperature, the Downy Rattlesnake Orchid is the easiest of this genus to cultivate. It thrives best in moderately acid humus on a well-drained slope where the sun is screened by overhanging branches for most of the day. While it is rather susceptible to attack by soil fungi, the plant may persist in an acid-soil garden for years if its enemies are not too active. (E. T. W.)

According to BROWN (1813), this species was first introduced into England in 1802 by H. R. H. the Duke of Kent.

3. **Goodyera repens** (L.) R. Br. in Ait., Hort. Kew., ed. 2, 5: 198. 1813.
    Satyrium repens L., Sp. Pl., ed. 1, 2: 945. 1753. Type locality: In forests in Sweden, England, Siberia and Switzerland. (*Peramium repens* (L.) Salisb.; *Epipactis repens* (L.) Crantz).   PLATE 93

(The name, *repens*, is a Latin adjective meaning "creeping," in reference to the elongated growth of the rhizome.)

COMMON NAMES: Lesser Rattlesnake Plantain, Creeping Goodyera, Northern Rattlesnake Plantain.

Plant scapose, erect or somewhat flexuously erect, glandular-pubescent above, 7-35 cm. tall. Roots fibrous, from a short or elongated creeping rhizome. Leaves several in a basal rosette, with rather short broad petioles, ovate to oblong-elliptic, obtuse to subacute, dark green, with darker veins, 1-4.5 cm. long, 6-20 mm. wide. Raceme laxly flowered, strongly one-sided, 2-9 cm. long, 5-12 mm. in diameter. Floral bracts lanceolate, acuminate, 5-12 mm. long. Flowers

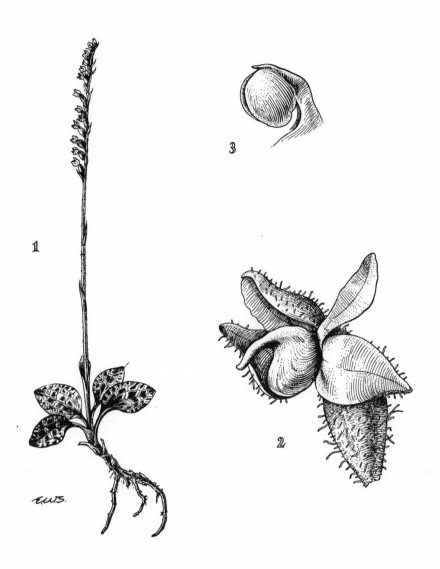

GOODYERA *repens*

var. ophioides (R.Br.) Fernald

PLATE 93.—**Goodyera repens** var. **ophioides.** 1, plant, two thirds natural size. 2, flower, side view, with one lateral sepal and one petal turned back, about eight times natural size. 3, column, side view, about ten times natural size. *Drawn by E. W. Smith.*

white, tinged with green, sometimes flushed with brownish pink. Sepals and petals puberulent on the outer surface, with a prominent central vein. Dorsal sepal broadly ovate-oblong to oblong-elliptic, slightly concave, somewhat constricted near the obtuse apex, 3-3.5 mm. long, 1-1.5 mm. wide. Lateral sepals ovate to ovate-oblong, obtuse to subacute, occasionally apiculate, shallowly concave, 3-3.5 mm. long, 2-2.5 mm. wide. Petals connivent with the dorsal sepal and forming a hood over the lip, obliquely oblong-spatulate, with the lower margin often angled and with the upper margin finely crenulate, recurved at the obliquely acute apex, 3-3.5 mm. long, 1-1.5 mm. wide. Lip deeply saccate, with an elongated tip or beak and with the margins flaring and recurved, glabrous on the outer surface, 3-3.5 mm. long, about 2 mm. wide; beak 1.5-2 mm. long, acute to acuminate; sac naked within, 2-2.5 mm. deep. Column 1-1.5 mm. long; anther short; beak shorter than the body of the stigma.

The deep green leaves with darker veins serve to separate this plant from the var. *ophioides* which is much more widespread and frequent in our region.

According to STEVENSON (1926), the rust *Phyllosticta decidua* Ferraris has been observed on the leaves of this species in Italy. However, there are no data available as to the ill effect of this fungus upon the plant.

The Lesser Rattlesnake Plantain frequently occurs in damp mossy coniferous forests or in mixed forests. It usually grows at high elevations in the Rocky Mountains, and is found up to 3,000 feet altitude in British Columbia and in the Yukon, flowering during July and August.

GEOGRAPHICAL DISTRIBUTION: Rare from New Mexico (Pecos National Forest), Arizona (Apache County) and South Dakota (Custer County), along the Rocky Mountains to British Columbia, Alberta, Saskatchewan, the Yukon and Alaska; also Anticosti, Ontario (Thunder Bay (District) and Eurasia.

CULTURAL NOTES: This species is common in Europe but on this continent it is, with few exceptions, limited to the Rocky Mountains and Canada. It has probably never been successfully cultivated in the New World. (E. T. W.)

4. **Goodyera repens** var. **ophioides** Fernald, Rhodora 1: 6. 1899. Type locality: Eastern United States and Canada. (*Peramium repens* var. *ophioides* (Fernald) Heller; *P. ophioides* (Fernald) Rydb.; *Epipactis repens* var. *ophioides* (Fernald) A. A. Eaton; *Goodyera ophioides* (Fernald) Rydb.). PLATE 93

(The name, *ophioides,* is a Greek term meaning "snake-like," in allusion to the reticulate pattern of the leaf which suggests the skin-pattern of some snakes.)

COMMON NAMES: Net-leaf, Squirrel-ear, White-blotched Rattlesnake Plantain.

Variety *ophioides* differs from the typical form of the species mainly in that the veins of the leaves, instead of being dark uniformly or darker, are conspicuously bordered with white.

Although often found in rather dry cold forests, one of the favorite haunts of this little orchid in the southern Appalachian Mountains is in deep moss of coniferous forests, especially hemlock, in the vicinity of waterfalls where a perpetual fine spray of moisture keeps its surroundings moist and cool.

This variety is commonly found in damp or dry cold woods where it is usually trailing, stoloniferously, in dense mats of moss or is lightly rooted in heavily shaded cool moist humus. It is chiefly found beneath conifers and occasionally in bogs and swamps. Variety *ophioides* usually grows at high elevations, and occurs up to 2,000 feet altitude in Massachusetts, 4,500 feet in North Carolina, Tennessee and Vermont, and 8,500 feet in Colorado and New Mexico, and blooms from June to September in various parts of its range. In the Himalaya Mountains of India it is found between 7,000 and 10,000 feet altitude.

GEOGRAPHICAL DISTRIBUTION: Newfoundland, Miquelon Islands, Nova Scotia, (?) New Brunswick, Quebec and Ontario, west to British Columbia, the Yukon and Alaska, through northern and (?) western New England, New York, Pennsylvania and West Virginia, south in the mountains to North Carolina and Tennessee, west through the Central and Lake States to Minnesota (Lake and Saint Louis counties), southwest to New Mexico (Sandoval and San Miguel counties); also Eurasia.

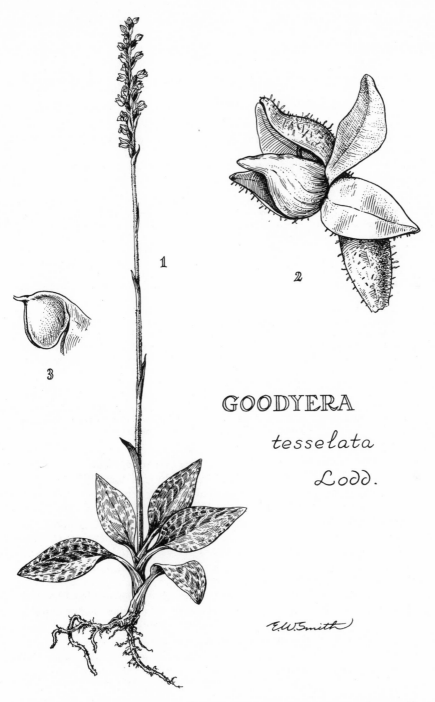

1

2

3

GOODYERA

tesselata

Lodd.

E. W. Smith

PLATE 94.—**Goodyera tesselata.** 1, plant, one half natural size. 2, flower, side view, with one lateral sepal and one petal turned back, five times natural size. 3, column, side view, about ten times natural size. *Drawn by E. W. Smith.*

CULTURAL NOTES: This variety survived glaciation in the southern Appalachians, and when the ice sheets melted away, the plant succeeded in migrating far northward. Thus, it can withstand severe winter conditions and a moderate amount of summer heat. When the acid humus in which it thrives can be supplied in a wild garden, this orchid can be maintained for a time, although it is not so resistant to parasites as could be desired. (E. T. W.)

5. **Goodyera tesselata** Lodd., Bot. Cab. 10: pl. 952. 1824. Type locality: "We received plants of it from New York and Philadelphia in 1824, . . . " (*Peramium tesselatum* (Lodd.) Heller; *Epipactis tesselata* (Lodd.) A. A. Eaton).   PLATE 94

(The name, *tesselata*, is a Latin adjective meaning "checkered," in allusion to the reticulate pattern of the leaf.)

COMMON NAMES: Loddiges' Rattlesnake Plantain, Checkered Rattlesnake Plantain, Smooth Rattlesnake Orchid.

Plant scapose, erect, densely glandular-pubescent above, 1.2-3.4 dm. tall, averaging about 2 dm. in height. Roots fibrous, from a short creeping rhizome. Scape slender or stout, provided with slender sheaths. Leaves several in a basal rosette, spreading, with short broad petioles, suborbicular-ovate to oblong-lanceolate, rounded to obtuse or subacute at the apex, broadly rounded to tapering at the base, prominently or faintly reticulate-veined with white, 2-8 cm. long, 8-28 mm. wide. Raceme laxly or densely flowered, one-sided to spiraled or occasionally cylindrical, 4.5-15 cm. long, 1-2 cm. in diameter. Floral bracts lanceolate, acuminate, 7-12 mm. long. Flowers white, with the stout pedicellate ovaries about 7 mm. long. Sepals and petals 1-nerved, with the sepals puberulent on the outer surface. Dorsal sepal elliptic-oblong to ellipitic-lanceolate, recurved at the obtuse apex, concave below, 5-6.5 mm. long, about 2.5 mm. wide below the middle. Lateral sepals suborbicular-ovate to ovate-lanceolate or elliptic-lanceolate, tapering to the recurved obtuse apex, concave below, oblique, 5-6.5 mm. long, 3-3.5 mm. wide below the middle. Petals connivent with the dorsal sepal and forming a hood over the lip, contiguous on their inner margins above the middle, dolabriform, narrowly cuneate below the middle, obliquely dilated at about the middle and tapering to the subobtuse apex, 5-6.5 mm. long, 2.2-2.5 mm. wide at about the middle. Lip strongly saccate, with a short beak and revolute margins, 4.2-6 mm. long; sac 1.5-2.5 mm. deep, about 3.5 mm. across in natural position, somewhat lamellate-thickened on the inner surface; beak shallowly sulcate, somewhat recurved at the blunt apex, 1.5-2 mm. long. Column 2-3.5 mm. long, with the slender beak as long as or longer than the body of the stigma; anther acuminate. Capsule obovoid, about 8 mm. long.

This species is often quite similar to *G. repens* var. *ophioides*, especially in the herbarium. However, quite apart from their technical floral differences, the two plants apparently differ somewhat in their habitat requirements—*Goodyera tesselata* usually (but not always) occurring in much drier situations than var. *ophioides*.

A confusing phase of this species occurs in the Lake States where it is represented by plants which show various stages of intermediacy between *G. repens* var. *ophioides* and *G. oblongifolia*. FULLER (1933) has suggested that these plants might represent a hybrid population. This idea is only conjectural, however, and the problem must await further experimental researches.

This species is commonly found in rather dry rich coniferous, hardwood or mixed forests and thickets. It rarely occurs in wet places. Loddiges' Rattlesnake Plantain grows up to 2,000 feet altitude in Massachusetts, New Hampshire and New York, and flowers from July to September in various parts of its range.

GEOGRAPHICAL DISTRIBUTION: Newfoundland, Nova Scotia, New Brunswick, Quebec and Ontario (Algoma County, Algonquin Park and Great Duck Island), south through New England to New York, west to Michigan, Wisconsin and Minnesota (Saint Louis County); also Maryland (Montgomery County).

CULTURAL NOTES: The Smooth Rattlesnake Orchid prefers moderately cool and acid soils, and has been cultivated by a few gardeners within its area of distribution. (E. T. W.)

This species was perhaps first introduced into England from New York in 1824 by ROBERT BARCLAY, when it flowered out-of-doors at Bury Hill.

20. **Erythrodes** Bl.

Erythrodes Bl., Bijdr. 410, t. 72. 1825.

(The name, *Erythrodes,* is a combination of Greek words meaning "red" and "appearing," in allusion to the color of the flowers.)

Terrestrial leafy herbs with roots at the base of the stem or from the nodes on the lower part of the rhizome. Stem erect, ascending or prostrate, often provided with sheathing bracts. Leaves with short petioles which surround the stem by a tubular base; lamina ovate to lanceolate or elliptic-lanceolate, usually reticulate-veined. Inflorescence a dense or lax spicate raceme of small subsessile flowers. Sepals free, erect or spreading Petals connivent with the dorsal sepal and forming a galea. Lip ascending from the base of the column which it lightly embraces in natural position, produced at the base into a spur; spur a simple or didymous sac, nervose, usually provided with four or more mammillate calli or callus-like structures on the interior wall near the base. Column short; anther erect, with two contiguous and distinct cells; pollinia two, sectile or granular.

This is a complex genus of about one hundred species occurring in mild temperate regions and the tropics and subtropics of both hemispheres. They are found primarily in the rich humus of damp forests. The typically spurred lip as well as the variegated leaves of many of the species are characteristics of this genus.

1. **Erythrodes querceticola** (Lindl.) Ames, Orch., fasc. 5: 29. 1915, in footnote. *Physurus querceticola* Lindl., Gen. and Sp. Orch. Pl. 505. 1840. Type locality and collection: North America, abundant in oak forests near New Aurelia [New Orleans], *Ingalls.* (*Physurus Sagraeanus* A. Rich.; *Goodyera quercicola* Chapm.). PLATE 95

(The name, *querceticola,* is a Latin term meaning "inhabiting oak woods," doubtless in reference to the habitat where this species was first found.)

COMMON NAME: Low Erythrodes.

Plant slender or rarely stout, leafy, glabrous, 6-43 cm. tall, reproducing by means of underground stolons. Roots slender or stout, arising from the nodes of the short prostrate rhizome and clustered at the base of the stem. Stem erect from a geniculate-prostrate base, leafy, light green or yellowish or brownish green. Leaves shortly petioled; lamina ovate to ovate-lanceolate or narrowly lanceolate, acute to acuminate, broadly rounded to subcordate at the base, 1.5-8 cm. long, 1-3 cm. wide near the base, light or dark green, often with whitish reticulate veins, reduced above to translucent sheathing bracts; petiole thin, translucent, surrounding the stem by a tubular base, about 2 cm. long. Raceme few- to many-flowered, densely to laxly flowered, 1.5-10 cm. long, 1-2 cm. in diameter. Floral bracts broadly ovate to lanceolate, acute to acuminate, usually scarious, 4.5-7 mm. long. Flowers subsessile, yellowish green or white. Dorsal sepal narrowly ovate-oblong to lanceolate, subacute, concave, 3-4 mm. long, 1-2 mm. wide. Lateral sepals ovate to oblong-lanceolate or linear-oblong, somewhat oblique, obtuse, 3-4.5 mm. long, 1-2 mm. wide, with a conspicuous central vein. Petals linear to linear-lanceolate, somewhat oblique, obtuse to acute, 3-4.5 mm. long, 1-1.3 mm. wide. Lip produced below into a saccate spur, 5-7 mm. long (including the spur); lamina panduriform, divided into two subequal parts by a shallow constriction on each side; basal half suborbicular, concave, thickened and partly embracing the column in natural position; upper half 3-lobed, obcordate in outline, 2-2.5 mm. wide across the lateral lobes, the lateral lobes being short, divergent and broadly rounded and the apical lobe triangular-apiculate to subulate, strongly arcuate-recurved and about 1 mm. long; spur saccate, descending, provided with three conspicuous nerves. Capsule ellipsoid, 7-9 mm. long.

This species is extremely variable, being represented by several types of habit and showing a number of variations in the apical portion of the lip.

The earliest collection I have seen of this species in our region is that obtained by a Dr. INGALLS from near New Orleans, Orleans Parish, Louisiana, in 1834—probably an isotype.

PLATE 95.—**Erythrodes querceticola.** 1, plant, natural size. 2, flower, side view, five times natural size. 3, dorsal sepal, five times natural size. 4, petal, five times natural size. 5, lateral sepal, five times natural size. 6, lip and spur, front view, five times natural size. 7, fruits, natural size. *Drawn by Gordon W. Dillon.*

In the unique and botanically rich forested ravines so common near St. Francisville, Louisiana, I have seen large colonies of these little plants intermingled with *Ponthieva racemosa* and the creeping Woodgrass.

The Low Erythrodes is found commonly in moist rich soil in densely shaded swamps and swampy forests, in various types of hammocks, wet barrens and moist hardwood forests and ravines where it is often associated with Woodgrass (*Oplismenus setarius*). In the tropics, it grows in deep humus and leaf mold of shady barrancas and wooded ravines, and in dense thickets among rocks. It occurs near sea level in Florida and Mexico, up to 2,500 feet altitude in Mexico and 5,500 feet in Guatemala, and flowers sporadically throughout the year.

GEOGRAPHICAL DISTRIBUTION: Florida (widespread), Louisiana (East Feliciana, Orleans, Rapides and West Feliciana parishes) and Texas; also Mexico, Central America, the West Indies and northern South America.

CULTURAL NOTES: This species could not be expected to thrive in gardens outside of its native Gulf Coast region, and there is no record of its cultivation. (E. T. W.)

21. Zeuxine Lindl.

Zeuxine Lindl., Orch. Scel. 9. 1826, *nomen;* Lindl., Bot. Reg. 19: sub. t. 1618. 1833, conserved name.

(The name, *Zeuxine,* is a Greek word meaning "joining," in allusion to the partial union of the lip and column.)

Terrestrial herbs with succulent glabrous stems, ascending or erect. Leaves membranaceous, ovate to lanceolate or linear. Inflorescence a dense spike or raceme of small flowers. Floral bracts membranaceous, scarious, mostly longer than the flowers. Sepals subequal; dorsal sepal erect, concave, connivent with the petals and forming a hood; lateral sepals free. Lip adnate to the base of the column, concave to subsaccate or cymbiform at the base, abruptly dilated above. Column very short; anther erect or occasionally inclined, membranaceous, oblong, short apiculate; pollinia four, large, granular and dry. Capsule small, erect, ovoid to subglobose.

This is a small genus of perhaps less than twenty species which are scattered in the tropics of Asia and Africa, with one species in Florida where it appears to have been recently and accidentally introduced.

1. **Zeuxine strateumatica** (L.) Schltr. in Engl., Bot. Jahrb. 45: 394. 1911. *Orchis strateumatica* L., Sp. Pl., ed. 1, 2: 943. 1753. Type locality: Ceylon.

PLATE 96

(The name, *strateumatica,* is a Latin adjective meaning "military," doubtless in allusion to the erect soldier-like aspect of the plant or to the ascending rigid sword-shaped or bayonet-like leaves.)

COMMON NAME: None known.

Plant erect or ascending from a decumbent base, slender, glabrous throughout, greenish, tinged with purple or brown, 4-17 cm. tall. Roots fibrous, short, clustered at the nodes on the lower part of the stem and rhizome. Leaves sessile, linear to narrowly lanceolate, long-acuminate, with the lower part inflated and sheathing the stem, semitranslucent below, 1.5-9 cm. long, up to about 5 mm. wide. Spike densely few- to many-flowered, 1-8 cm. long, 1-2 cm. in diameter. Floral bracts ovate-lanceolate to lanceolate, long-acuminate, recurved, translucent, 8-20 mm. long. Flowers small, white or yellowish with a yellow lip. Dorsal sepal erect, concave, ovate-oblong to oblong-elliptic, obtuse, 4-4.5 mm. long, 2 mm. wide. Lateral sepals free, ovate-oblong to oblong-elliptic, obtuse to subacute, 4-5 mm. long, 2-2.5 mm. wide. Petals connivent with the dorsal sepal and forming a hood over the column, oblong-lanceolate, oblique to somewhat falcate, obtuse, 4-4.5 mm. long, about 1.5 mm. wide. Lip fleshy-thickened, arising from the base of the column and adnate to it for a short distance, about 4 mm. long, more or less pandurate when spread out (widest near the apex), concave-saccate and cymbiform at the base, with the lower half oblong and slightly rounded on the lateral margins, abruptly expanded above into a suborbicular or transversely elliptic lobe. Capsule ovoid, about 7 mm. long.

This is the only Asiatic terrestrial orchid which has been introduced into the eastern part of our region. The first record of its occurrence in the United States rests on a photograph of three plants found by GEORGE NELSON on January 27, 1936, west of Felsmere, Indian River County, Florida. In 1937, AMES reported the finding of this species in Florida.

Since its original discovery, it has spread throughout Florida in a phenomenal fashion, exhibiting the behavior of a weed, being found commonly in the vicinity of human habitations. It may be of interest to trace briefly its rapid invasion of that state. In 1937, specimens were collected in Osceola and Volusia counties, and, in 1938, in Citrus, Highlands, Glades, Hendry and Collier counties. The next year, collections were made in Pinellas County and, in 1942, in Polk, Saint Lucie and Manatee counties. In 1943, Duval County was added to the list and at about the same time it was found in Orange, Lee, Sarasota and Lake counties. In 1944, Flagler and Dade counties were added to the rapidly growing list of counties in which this species has spread since it was first observed in 1936.

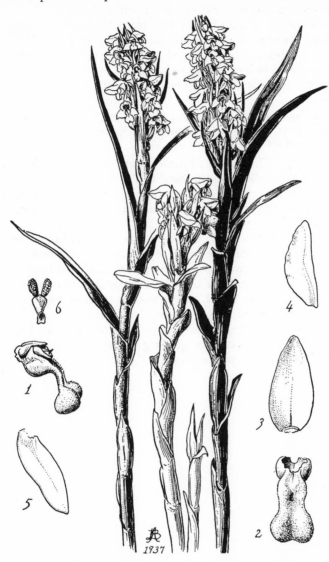

PLATE 96.— **Zeuxine strateumatica.** Three flowering plants, natural size. 1, lip and column, side view, five times natural size. 2, lip, front view, five times natural size. 3, dorsal sepal, six times natural size. 4, petal, six times natural size. 5, lateral sepal, six times natural size. 6, pollinium, much enlarged. *Drawn by Blanche Ames.*

In 1938, AMES wrote a most interesting and informative account of the introduction and spread of this species in Florida. He conjectured, and perhaps rightly so, that this species was brought from China into Florida with seeds of Centipede Grass (*Eremochloa ophiuroides*) which was first introduced in 1917 and is now a common lawn-grass in Florida and other parts of the Southern States. A more recent importation of seeds of Centipede Grass was received in 1927 from Anwhei Province, China. These seeds were widely distributed in Florida, Georgia, Louisiana and elsewhere. If the orchid was introduced with these grass seeds, it is reasonable to assume that *Zeuxine* may soon become a familiar plant along the entire

Gulf Coast. It is apparently quite hardy and can withstand much abuse. As AMES (1938) has pointed out, ". . . it exhibits the propensities of a weed and has become amenable to a diversity of conditions, growing in clipped lawns, under shrubs, along ditches, and thriving equally in sun and shade."

This species occurs in open or shrubby places in mucky soils, in moist sandy soil in ditches, on the edge of swamps and on coastal prairies. In Florida it is often associated with Bayberry (*Cerothamnus* spp.) and various species of *Baccharis*. It grows near sea level in Florida, up to 2,000 feet or more altitude in India (Punjab), and flowers sporadically throughout the year, mainly during January and February in Florida.

GEOGRAPHICAL DISTRIBUTION: Florida (Citrus, Collier, Dade, Duval, Glades, Hendry, Highlands, Indian River, Lee, Osceola, Sarasota and Volusia counties); also India to Japan, southward to Java and the Philippines.

CULTURAL NOTES: This native of southeastern Asia constitutes our only orchid weed besides *Epipactis Helleborine*. Said to thrive in waste places where the soil is circumneutral, the plant may be expected to be more or less amenable to cultivation in subtropical wild gardens. It is spontaneous on many lawns in Florida, where large colonies are formed. (E. T. W.)

Professor OAKES AMES wrote me the following from his winter home in Ormond, Florida, regarding this species: "My experience has been that this species appears unexpectedly in flower pots in the greenhouse! Although it is not at all particular with regard to locations and seems happy in acid or subneutral soils, *my efforts to transplant* it have failed, and it has not come up in my Centipede Grass lawn where I have scattered simply thousands of fertile seeds! I once dug up a great ball of earth with strong plants completely undisturbed. I inserted the ball of earth side by side with naturally growing plants. The results were sterile although the naturally present plants persisted."

22. Tropidia Lindl.

Tropidia Lindl. in Wall., Cat. n. 7386. 1831; Lindl., Bot. Reg. 19: sub. t. 1618. 1833.

(The name, *Tropidia,* is from a Greek word meaning "keel," in allusion to the boat-shaped lip.)

Terrestrial coarse leafy and often branching herbs with thick fibrous roots from a short rhizome. Leaves oblong-lanceolate to elliptic-lanceolate, membranaceous, strongly veined and plicate. Inflorescence a paniculate raceme of numerous small flowers. Lateral sepals connate at the base and forming an inconspicuous sac or mentum. Lip sessile, entire, oblong, with a broadly saccate base, canaliculate, parallel to and partly embracing the column in natural position. Column short, straight; anther and rostellum about equal in length; anther erect, lying against the rostellum; pollinia two, granulose, sectile. Capsule spreading.

This is a small genus of about thirty-five species which are natives mainly of the East Indies, Malaya, China and Japan. It is represented in this hemisphere by one species.

1. **Tropidia Polystachya** (Sw.) Ames, Orch., fasc. 2: 262. 1908. *Serapias Polystachya* Sw., Prodr. Veg. Ind. Occ. 119. 1788. Type locality: Jamaica and Hispaniola. (*Tropidia Eatonii* Ames). PLATE 97

(The name, *Polystachya,* is the Greek term meaning "many spikes," in allusion to the numerous branches of the inflorescence.)

COMMON NAME: None known.

Plant 2.5-5.3 dm. tall, with a short rhizome. Roots slender, fibrous, coarse and tough, giving rise to short lateral clavellate rootlets. Stem leafy, often branched, glabrous throughout. Leaves several, distichous, near the summit of the stem, oblong-elliptic to elliptic-lanceolate, acute to long-acuminate, 6-28 cm. long, 1.5-5.5 cm. wide, thin, plicate and membranaceous. Inflorescence densely paniculate, terminating a slender naked peduncle, 3-9 cm. long (flowers rarely occurring also in the axils of the leaves along the stem). Floral bracts subulate to ovate-lanceolate, with a prominent midrib and hyaline margins, acute to acuminate, 2-4 mm. long (bracts subtending each branch of the inflorescence much longer, narrowly lanceolate-attenuate, otherwise similar to the floral bracts). Flowers greenish white to reddish, with the sepals and petals connivent and 3-nerved. Dorsal sepal oblong-elliptic, strongly concave, acute or obtuse, often apiculate, 6-7 mm. long, 2-2.3 mm. wide. Lateral sepals somewhat obliquely oblong-elliptic to rarely linear-oblong, acute or subacute, often somewhat conduplicate or concave at the apex, gibbous at the base, 6-7 mm. long, 2-3 mm. wide. Petals subovate to oblong or linear-oblong, curved, slightly concave near the obtuse to truncate (or retuse) or rarely acute apex, 5.5-6.2 mm. long, 2-2.3 mm. wide. Lip 4.5-6.5 mm. long, oblong in outline, cymbiform, strongly concave-saccate with the basal margins strongly involute, thickened and with a median groove at the base, lightly constricted at about the middle, with the anterior half thin and somewhat expanded, broadly rounded and often retuse with an apicule in the sinus; disc pubescent at about the middle, with two intramarginal ridges that converge near the apex. Column terete, 3-5 mm. long. Capsule oblong-ellipsoid, prominently 6-ribbed, becoming dark brown or black at maturity, about 1 cm. long.

This rather coarse unorchidaceous-appearing plant was found for the first time in the United States near Miami, Dade County, Florida by A. H. CURTISS in April 1897. It is apparently a rare plant in southern Florida.

This species is found in rather thinly wooded hammocks in humus under low thickets and shrubs. In the tropics, it grows in well-drained stony soil of open woods, on shaded hillsides and in peaty soil of dense forests and brushlands. It is found near sea level in Florida, up to 1,600 feet altitude in Mexico, blooming from August to February, inclusive, in various parts of its range.

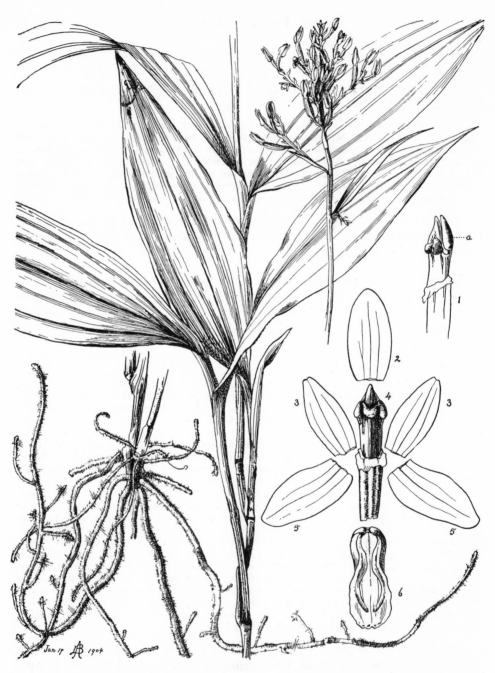

PLATE 97.— **Tropidia Polystachya.** Plant three fourths natural size. 1, column, to show anther (*a*) and upper part of ovary, four times natural size. 2, dorsal sepal, four times natural size. 3, petals, four times natural size. 4, column, front-ventral view, and upper part of ovary, four times natural size. 5, lateral sepals, four times natural size. 6, lip, from above, four times natural size. *Drawn by Blanche Ames.*

GEOGRAPHICAL DISTRIBUTION: Florida (Dade County) ; also Mexico, Guatemala, Costa Rica, Galapagos Islands, Cuba, Jamaica and Santo Domingo.

CULTURAL NOTES: This subtropical orchid is recorded as growing in circum-neutral soil in hammocks of southern peninsular Florida. It could perhaps be cultivated in wild gardens of that region. (E. T. W.)

23. Pleurothallis R. Br.

Pleurothallis R. Br. in Ait., Hort. Kew., ed. 2, 5: 211. 1813.

(The name, *Pleurothallis,* is a combination of Greek words meaning "rib" and "branch," probably in allusion to the arrangement of the short persistent pedicels along the rachis in many of the species.)

Small or medium-sized epiphytic herbs with commonly caespitose or approximate non-pseudobulbous secondary stems which are unifoliate and rise from a creeping primary stem or rhizome. Leaves mostly coriaceous, sessile or petioled. Inflorescence terminal or very rarely lateral, one or several and fasciculate, racemose or sometimes a solitary flower at the apex of a more or less elongate peduncle. Flowers small, subtended by inconspicuous bracts. Sepals about the same length or nearly so, erect or spreading; dorsal sepal free or very shortly connate with the lateral sepals, rarely clavellate at the apex; lateral sepals slightly connate at the base to entirely united, mostly concave or gibbous at the base. Petals commonly shorter and narrower than the sepals (rarely as long as the sepals), sometimes clavellate at the apex. Lip shorter or rarely a little longer than the petals, simple or 3-lobed, often contracted below and jointed with the base of the column, mostly unguiculate. Column equaling or shorter than the lip, winged or wingless, produced into a more or less distinct foot or essentially footless at the base; foot (when present) almost obsolete up to as long as the column; anther terminal, operculate, incumbent, 1- to 2-celled; pollinia two or four, waxy. Capsule subglobose to ellipsoid, often somewhat 3-angled.

Pleurothallis is a large New World genus of approximately six hundred species which commonly occur in the mountainous regions of the tropics and subtropics. The genus comprises a group of plants which are notable for their apparent dissimilarity and polymorphism. It is interesting to note that in most of the species the sepals are extremely variable (especially as to size) while the lip and petals are rather constant as to size—varying only slightly in comparison with the variation evidenced by the sepals.

1. **Pleurothallis gelida** Lindl., Bot. Reg. 27: Misc. p. 91. 1841. Type locality: Jamaica. PLATE 98

(The name, *gelida,* is a Latin adjective meaning "frosty," perhaps in allusion to the whitish shiny rachis of the inflorescence or the whitish hairs on the sepals.)
COMMON NAME: None known.

Plant erect, caespitose, 1.2-6 dm. tall. Roots from a short creeping rhizome, slender, clustered. Secondary stems several, approximate, glabrous, clothed with one or more tubular membranaceous sheaths which are 6-8 cm. long, bearing a solitary leaf at the summit. Leaf ovate-elliptic to oblong-elliptic or narrowly linear-oblong, obtuse to subacute, usually keeled through the center beneath, 7-25 cm. long (including the petiole), 1.5-7 cm. wide, coriaceous. Racemes one to fifteen clustered in the axil of the leaf, slender, many-flowered, 6-28 cm. long, about 2 cm. in diameter, enclosed at the base by a short membranaceous spathe less than 2 cm. long. Floral bracts minute, tubular, apiculate, scarious and translucent, 2-3 mm. long. Flowers pale yellow to greenish yellow, 2-ranked, with the slender arching pedicellate ovaries 4-5 mm. long. Dorsal sepal oblong-elliptic to broadly lanceolate, strongly concave and dorsally keeled at the base, obtuse to acute and somewhat reflexed at the apex, with the inner surface pilose, 5-8 mm. long, about 3 mm. wide. Lateral sepals coherent at the base and forming a cup, narrowly oblong to elliptic, obtuse, dorsally keeled, pilose on the inner surface, 5-7 mm. long, about 2.5 mm. wide near the base. Petals whitish, obliquely oblong-obovate, either acute, broadly rounded, retuse or tridentate at the apex, 3-4 mm. long, about 2.5 mm. wide. Lip small, obscurely or obsoletely 3-lobed, narrowly cuneate or sometimes pandurate in outline (rarely broadest below the middle), broadly truncate and more or less retuse at the apex, arcuate-recurved in natural position, usually with a pair of minute lateral lobes or teeth; disc with a pair of erect keels near the middle. Column short, with two minute teeth on each side at the apex. Capsule ellipsoid, strongly 3-angled and triangular in cross-section, light brown, 5-10 mm. long, 3-5 mm. in diameter.

PLATE 98.— **Pleurothallis gelida.** 1, plant, one half natural size. 2, flower, front-side view, five times natural size. 3, dorsal sepal, five times natural size. 4, petal, five times natural size. 5, lateral sepals, spread open, five times natural size. 6, lip and column, side view, five times natural size. 7, lip, spread out, ten times natural size. 8, fruiting inflorescence, one half natural size. *Drawn by Gordon W. Dillon.*

This species was probably found for the first time in the United States about ten miles northeast of Everglade in Collier County, Florida, by ALVAH AUGUSTUS EATON in March 1905.

The flowers of this orchid are deliciously fragrant, somewhat recalling the odor of hyacinth.

Pleurothallis gelida grows on trees in cypress swamps, hammocks and dense tropical forests, where it is found near sea level in Florida, up to 5,000 feet altitude in Panama. It flowers sporadically throughout the year, mainly from March to June in Florida.

GEOGRAPHICAL DISTRIBUTION: Florida (Collier and Dade counties); also Cuba, Jamaica, Santo Domingo, Puerto Rico, Panama and Peru.

CULTURAL NOTES: LINDLEY, in describing this species, stated that he had received his plant from the Messrs. Loddiges, English commercial growers. It is quite possible that Loddiges had this species under cultivation at that time, in 1841.

Professor OAKES AMES states that this species is easy to grow in the greenhouse. See this section under the generic discussion of *Epidendrum*.

24. Lepanthopsis Ames

Lepanthopsis Ames, Bot. Mus. Leafl. Harvard Univ. 1 (9) : 3. 1933.

(The name, *Lepanthopsis,* is a combination of the generic name *Lepanthes* and the Greek *opsis,* meaning "resemblance," in allusion to the similarity of the species to those in *Lepanthes.*)

Small epiphytic herbs with several clustered erect slender secondary stems arising from a minute creeping primary stem; secondary stems clothed by tubular sheaths which are longitudinally ribbed and flaring at the apex, bearing at the summit a solitary leaf. Leaf elliptic. Inflorescence consisting of a solitary or clustered few-flowered racemes in the axil of the leaf. Flowers minute, distichous. Lateral sepals connate to about the middle. Petals short, orbicular to elliptic, membranaceous. Lip simple, adnate to the base of the column. Column very short, without a foot; anther terminal, operculate, incumbent; pollinia two, pyriform, waxy. Capsule ovoid, obovoid or ellipsoid.

This is a small genus of less than half a dozen species which are confined to the American tropics and subtropics.

1. **Lepanthopsis melanantha** (Reichb. f.) Ames, Bot. Mus. Leafl. Harvard Univ. 1 (9) : 19. 1933. *Pleurothallis melanantha* Reichb. f., Flora 48: 275. 1865. Type locality and collection: Cuba, 1860-1864, *Charles Wright 3342.* (*Lepanthes Harrisii* Fawc. & Rendle). PLATE 99

(The name, *melanantha,* is Greek signifying "black flower," in reference to the dark crimson-purple flowers.)

COMMON NAME: None known.

Plant arising from a short creeping rhizome bearing slender fibrous roots, consisting of several erect secondary stems terminated by a solitary leaf, 4-8 cm. tall (to the apex of the erect leaf). Secondary stems clothed with several close tubular-funnelform imbricating sheaths which are strongly ribbed longitudinally and obliquely dilated at the apex and forming a flaring cuspidate mouth with the margins pilose. Leaf solitary, subsessile, coriaceous, oblong-elliptic to elliptic, obtuse to acute or apiculate, marginate, with the margins smooth, 5-11 mm. long, 1.2-3.5 mm. wide. Racemes arising in the axil of the leaf, few-flowered above the middle, slender, 8-20 mm. long, less than 1 cm. in diameter. Floral bracts funnelform, acute, glabrous, about 1 mm. long. Flowers crimson-purple, minute, distichous and approximate, on slender pedicels which are about 1 mm. long. Dorsal sepal ovate to oval, obtuse, 1.5-2 mm. long, about 1.3 mm. wide, 3-nerved. Lateral sepals connate to about the middle, 1.7-2.3 mm. long, with a prominent central nerve; free part lanceolate and subacute. Petals suborbicular to oblong-quadrate or elliptic, broadly rounded to obtuse at the apex, 0.3-0.6 mm. long. Lip entire, cordate to orbicular-ovate, obtuse to subacute, concave, with the margins slightly upcurved, 3-nerved, about 1 mm. long and broad. Column minute, about 0.5 mm. long. Capsule ovoid, 6-ribbed, 3-4 mm. long.

This little plant was probably found for the first time in the United States in the Big Cypress Swamp in Collier County, Florida, by D. T. TOMPKINS in December 1931. However, it was not known to occur in our region until W. M. BUSWELL reported having found it in the same locality in 1937.

This orchid grows on trees in cypress swamps, hammocks and wet forests. It occurs near sea level in Florida, up to 2,600 feet altitude in Jamaica, and blooms in May.

GEOGRAPHICAL DISTRIBUTION: Florida (Collier County) ; also Jamaica.

CULTURAL NOTES: There is no record of this species ever having been culti-vated. See this section under the generic discussion of *Epidendrum.*

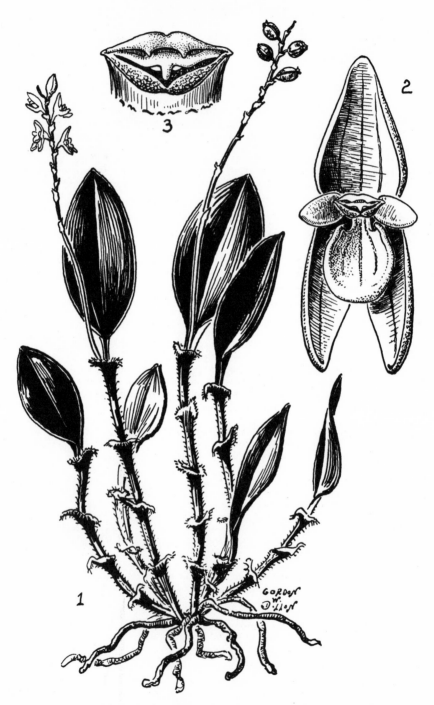

PLATE 99.—**Lepanthopsis melanantha.** 1, flowering and fruiting plant, twice natural size. 2, flower, spread out, twenty times natural size. 3, column, ventral surface, fifty times natural size. *Drawn by Gordon W. Dillon.*

25. **Malaxis** Soland.

Malaxis Soland. ex Sw., Prodr. Veg. Ind. Occ. 119. 1788.

(The name, *Malaxis,* is a Greek word meaning "softening," probably in allusion to the soft texture of the leaves.)

Inconspicuous terrestrial (rarely epiphytic) herbs arising from a slender or swollen base. Stem bearing one to five or more leaves at about the middle or near the base, occasionally with the leaves just below the inflorescence. Inflorescence terminal, either a few- to many-flowered subumbellate raceme or an elongated raceme of small flowers. Sepals free or the lateral sepals more or less connate, spreading. Petals ovate-lanceolate to narrowly linear or filiform, often strongly coiled. Lip sessile, usually the uppermost member of the perianth, erect or spreading, entire or 3-lobed, sometimes tridentate at the apex, often auriculate at the base, concave to saccate or plane, often more or less callous-thickened. Column short, terete, often toothed at the apex; anther terminal, erect or incumbent; pollinia four, waxy. Capsule small, ovoid to ellipsoid or subglobose.

This genus consists of about two hundred fifty species and attains its greatest development in Asia and Oceania. It is also widely distributed in the Western Hemisphere and sparsely so in Europe. The species are found primarily in low moist woods, swamps, bogs, ravines, thickets, wet meadows and on seepage slopes, in floodplain woods and mucky soils in strongly acid to calcareous soils.

Key for the Identification of the Species of Malaxis

1. Lip unequally tridentate at the apex, with the middle tooth minute......................2
  2. Flowers subsessile; pedicels less than 2 mm. long; raceme spicate, narrowly cylindric, densely many-flowered, usually much less than 1 cm. in diameter.......*M. Soulei* (p. 263)
  2. Flowers on slender pedicels which are more than 3 mm. long; raceme subumbellate to somewhat elongated, laxly few- to many-flowered, usually more than 1.5 cm. in diameter....
....*M. unifolia* (p. 268)
1. Lip not tridentate at the apex, obtuse to acuminate....................................3
  3. Lip distinctly 3-lobed; margin of the basal half of lip verrucose-thickened..............4
    4. Lip uppermost in the flower................................*M. monophyllos* (p. 258)
    4. Lip lowermost in the flower.................*M. monophyllos* var. *brachypoda* (p. 260)
  3. Lip not 3-lobed, at most prominently auriculate or subhastate at the base; margin of the basal half of lip not verrucose-thickened...5
    5. Leaf solitary; distribution southwestern...6
      6. Lip 3.5 mm. or more long, long-acuminate, with two green nerves in the center, ecallose; petals 4 mm. or more long..................................*M. tenuis* (p. 265)
      6. Lip 3 mm. or less long, at most shortly acuminate, provided with a callus or keel on the disc, 3-nerved; petals 3 mm. or less long..7
        7. Raceme elongate, cylindric, 7.5 cm. or more long; sepals 1-nerved, about 1 mm. wide; lip with a callus in the center at the base..................*M. Ehrenbergii* (p. 256)
        7. Raceme short, often subumbellate, 5 cm. or less long; sepals 3-nerved, 1.5 mm. or more wide; lip with a rudimentary keel in the concave portion. *M. corymbosa* (p. 255)
    5. Leaves two to five; distribution northern or southeastern...........................8
      8. Lip pale yellow to orange-vermilion, prominently auriculate, 3 mm. or more long; distribution Virginia to Florida.....................................*M. spicata* (p. 263)
      8. Lip greenish, adorned with three to five dark green nerves, dilated at the base, less than 2 mm. long; distribution northern and northwestern........*M. paludosa* (p. 261)

1. **Malaxis corymbosa** (S. Wats.) O. Ktze., Rev. Gen. Pl., pt. 2: 673. 1891. *Microstylis corymbosa* S. Wats., Proc. Am. Acad. 18: 195. 1883. Type locality and collection: In Tanner's Cañon, Huachuca Mountains, southern Arizona, July 1882, *J. G. Lemmon 2882.* (*Achroanthes corymbosa* (S. Wats.) Greene). PLATE 105

(The name, *corymbosa,* is a Latin adjective meaning "arranged like a corymb," in allusion to the corymb-like appearance of the inflorescence.)

COMMON NAME: None known.

Plant rather small, slender, glabrous, 6-30 cm. tall. Stem from a globose swollen base, broadly winged above, 5-25 cm. long, provided below with a loose tubular greenish sheath which is 2-4.3 cm. long. Leaf-blade solitary, expanded abruptly mostly above the middle of the stem, cordate-ovate to rarely elliptic-oblong, obtuse to acute, clasping the stem below, 2.8-10 cm. long, 1.2-6.5 cm. wide. Raceme subumbellate to shortly racemose, 1.5-5 cm. long. Floral bracts deltoid, acute, 1-2.5 mm. long. Flowers green or greenish yellow, on slender pedicels 6-12 mm. long. Sepals oblong-elliptic to lanceolate, subobtuse to acute, somewhat longitudinally concave, 3-nerved, dorsally thickened along the mid-nerve, 2.8-4 mm. long, 1.5-2 mm. wide; dorsal sepal recurved at the apex; lateral sepals oblique. Petals linear-filiform, obtuse, somewhat coiled, 1-nerved, 2-3 mm. long. Lip rather thin (rarely fleshy), broadly cordate-triangular, narrowly obtuse to somewhat abruptly acuminate, with a distinct upcurved auricle on each side at the base (or rarely without distinct auricles), 2-3 mm. long, 2-3 mm. wide; disc 3-nerved, shallowly concave below the middle, occasionally with a rudimentary keel in the concave portion. Column short, about 1 mm. long.

Specimens of what he considered to be this species were reported as *Malaxis fastigiata* (Reichb. f.) O. Ktze. from Arizona and New Mexico by WILLIAMS (in Journ. Arnold Arb. 25:83. 1944), who considered that the two concepts represented the same species. *Malaxis corymbosa* differs from *M. fastigiata,* however, in always having one instead of two leaves, and in the lip being shallowly concave and essentially ecallose, whereas the lip of *M. fastigiata* is deeply saccate and semi-globose with a thick central callus which divides the disc into two chambers. Since, however, *M. fastigiata* is found in Mexico in the border states of Chihuahua, Coahuila and Nuevo León, its eventual occurrence in the southwestern United States would not be unusual.

This species grows in damp copses and thickets, wet mossy places and in leaf mold in coniferous forests and on cold ledges. It usually occurs at high elevations and is found up to 7,000 feet altitude in Arizona and Guatemala and 11,000 feet in Mexico, flowering from June to September in various parts of its range.

GEOGRAPHICAL DISTRIBUTION: Arizona (Cochise County); also Mexico, Guatemala and Honduras.

CULTURAL NOTES: There is no record of this species ever having been cultivated. It is a plant of the high plateau country of Arizona and Mexico, southward.

2. **Malaxis Ehrenbergii** (Reichb. f.) O. Ktze., Rev. Gen. Pl., pt. 2: 673. 1891.
   Microstylis Ehrenbergii Reichb. f., Linnaea 22: 835. 1849. Type locality and collection: Mexico, Real del Monte, *C. Ehrenberg.* (*Microstylis purpurea* S. Wats.; *Achroanthes purpurea* (S. Wats.) Greene; *A. porphyrea* (Ridley) Woot. & Standl.). PLATE 102

(The name, *Ehrenbergii,* is in honor of CHRISTIAN GOTTFRIED EHRENBERG (1795-1876), German naturalist and writer who first collected this species.)
COMMON NAME: None known.

Plant slender, erect, glabrous, 1.5-4.8 dm. tall. Stem from a swollen base, terete, with inconspicuous longitudinal wings above, provided at the base with a purplish closely appressed leaf-sheath which is up to 6 cm. long. Leaf-blade solitary, suberect, abruptly expanded at about the middle or slightly above the middle of the stem, suborbicular to ovate or oblong-elliptic, obtuse, thin, succulent, 3-10 cm. long, 1.3-6 cm. wide. Raceme loosely many-flowered, much exceeding the leaf, cylindric, slender, 7.5-26 cm. long, 5-15 mm. in diameter. Floral bracts subulate, acute, 0.5-1.3 mm. long. Flowers minute, deep maroon to green, with the filiform pedicellate ovaries 2-3 mm. long. Sepals spreading, linear-ligulate to elliptic, obtuse to sub-acute, 1-nerved, with strongly revolute margins, 2-3 mm. long and 1 mm. wide. Petals linear, falcate, narrowly obtuse, strongly recurved, with somewhat revolute margins, 1-nerved, about 2 mm. long, up to 0.4 mm. wide. Lip extremely variable in shape, triangular-hastate to triangular-lanceolate, hastate-auriculate at the base, acute to acuminate at the apex, concave with the basal auricles erect, 2-2.5 mm. long, 1.5-2 mm. wide; disc 3-nerved below the middle,

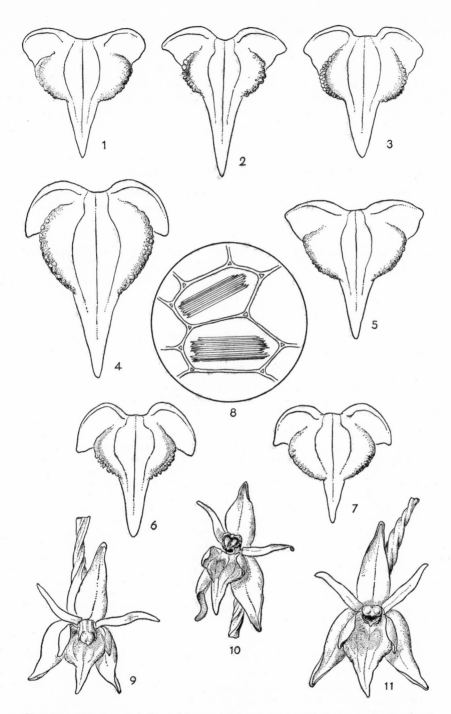

Plate 100.—**Malaxis monophyllos** and its var. **brachypoda.** All of the figures are much enlarged. Figures 1-7 represent lips taken from different plants, and so as to show variation and to aid in comparative studies they are represented in the same position. The basal lobes have been flattened out to reveal the outline. The magnification is similar throughout. 1, var. **brachypoda** from Newfoundland, 2 mm. long. 2, var. **brachypoda** from Vermont, 2.5 mm. long. 3, var. **brachypoda** from Japan, 2 mm. long. 4, **M. monophyllos** from Switzerland, 3 mm. long. 5, var. **brachypoda** from Vermont, 2 mm. long. 6, **M. monophyllos** from Japan, 2 mm. long. 7, **M. monophyllos** from China, 1.5 mm. long. 8, raphides found in the thickened margin and keels of the lip of **M. monophyllos** and var. **brachypoda,** much enlarged. 9, **M. monophyllos,** flower, front view, from Siberia, lip 2 mm. long. 10, var. **brachypoda,** flower, front view, from Vermont, lip 2.5 mm. long. 11, **M. monophyllos,** flower, front view, from Pomerania, lip 2.5 mm. long. *Drawn with the aid of the camera lucida by Blanche Ames.*

with a fleshy callus in the center at the base. Column short, stout, about 1 mm. long. Capsule obliquely subglobose, about 5 mm. long.

The long slender spike of small deep maroon to green flowers is characteristic of this species.

This species is found commonly on cool rocky slopes, in deep shady canyons, on open banks near the summit of mountains, on the wet face of cliffs and on steep slopes in dense pine-oak forests. It is usually a plant of high elevations and occurs up to 10,000 feet altitude in Guatemala and 13,000 feet in Mexico. It flowers from July to September.

GEOGRAPHICAL DISTRIBUTION: Arizona (Cochise and Pima counties) and New Mexico (Colfax, Otero and Socorro counties); also Mexico and Guatemala.

CULTURAL NOTES: There is no record of this species ever having been cultivated. It is a plant of the high plateau country from Arizona and New Mexico, southward.

3. **Malaxis monophyllos** (L.) Sw., Kongl. Svens. Vetens. Acad. Nya Handl. 21: 234, t. 3, fig. P. 1800. *Ophrys monophyllos* L., Sp. Pl., ed. 1, 2: 947. 1753. Type locality: Prussia, "Medelpadiae," swampy forests. (*Microstylis monophyllos* (L.) Lindl.; *Achroanthes monophylla* (L.) Greene; *Malaxis diphyllos* Cham.). PLATE 100

(The name, *monophyllos*, is a Greek term meaning "single-leaved," referring to the typically solitary leaf.)

COMMON NAME: White Adder's-mouth.

Plant small to rather large, glabrous, pale green, 5-33 cm. tall (rarely less than 3 cm. tall). Stem slender, arising from an ovoid corm surrounded by grayish white sheaths, angled above, with one or (rarely) two long-sheathing leaves near the base or at about the middle, the tubular sheathing base up to 7 cm. long. Leaf-blades one or two (if two subopposite), abruptly spreading, broadly ovate, suborbicular-oval to elliptic or lanceolate, broadly rounded to narrowly acute at the apex, 1-10 cm. long, 1-5 cm. wide. Raceme narrowly cylindric, elongated, commonly loosely many-flowered above, 2-25 cm. long, 7-13 mm. in diameter. Floral bracts subulate to lanceolate, acuminate, 1.5-3 mm. long. Flowers non-resupinate, minute, pale greenish white to greenish or yellowish green, occasionally marked with red, on filiform pedicels which are 1-3.5 mm. long. Sepals linear-oblong to oblong-lanceolate, subacute to acuminate, 1-nerved, 2-3 mm. long, 0.7-1 mm. wide below the middle, commonly with revolute margins and minutely calyptrate at the apex; lateral sepals slightly oblique. Petals linear, acute, strongly reflexed, somewhat oblique, 1-nerved, 1.8-2.5 mm. long, about 0.2 mm. wide. Lip uppermost in the flower, concave, 3-lobed, when expanded triangular-ovate in outline, with the basal portion broadly rounded with an auriculate inrolled lobe on each side, abruptly contracted above and forming a linear-lanceolate apical lobe which tapers to a sharp point, 3-nerved in the center, 2-2.5 mm. long, 1.5-2 mm. wide across the lateral lobes when spread out; margins of the basal half verrucose-thickened, with the thickenings passing into short keels on each side of the disc beneath each membranaceous inrolled lateral lobe. Column short, fleshy. Capsule obliquely ovoid, 3-5.5 mm. long.

It is interesting to note that most of the plants which I have seen from Alaska and the Aleutian Islands had two more or less well developed leaves, instead of the solitary leaf which typifies this species. This two-leaved plant was described from Unalaska as *Malaxis diphyllos* by CHAMISSO in 1828. However, that plant seems to be no more than a minor geographical variant.

In the Orchidaceae, those flowers which are considered to have the most primitive and "normal" position in the inflorescence (in respect to the rachis) usually have an untwisted pedicel or pedicellate ovary. The flowers in this position are called "non-resupinate"—the lip being in the uppermost position in the flower and the dorsal sepal the lowermost floral segment. On the other hand, the more advanced floral position is one in which the lip becomes the lowermost segment in the perianth by a twisting of the pedicel or pedicellate ovary through 90-180 degrees. The majority of the orchids in our region exemplify the more advanced

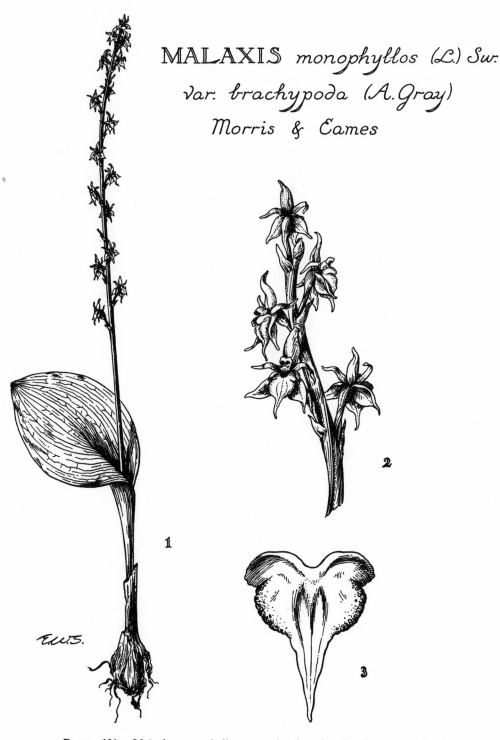

MALAXIS *monophyllos* (L.) Sw.
var. *brachypoda* (A. Gray)
Morris & Eames

PLATE 101.—**Malaxis monophyllos var. brachypoda.** 1, plant, natural size. 2, portion of raceme, about five times natural size. 3, lip, front view, much enlarged. *Drawn by E. W. Smith.*

condition for, with few exceptions, our species have the lip lowermost in the flower, and the flowers are thus called "resupinate."

In *Malaxis monophyllos,* as in *M. paludosa,* the pedicellate ovary twists through 360 degrees and thus the lip is brought to rest in its original uppermost position in the flower. However, the var. *brachypoda,* which is much the commoner form in most of our range, has the lip in the lowermost position by reason of the pedicellate ovary making only the 180 degree twist. It may be of interest to note that twisting of the pedicel or pedicellate ovary may be either to the left or to the right.

Various theories have been advanced to explain resupination and non-resupination in the Orchidaceae, and, in 1938(A), AMES wrote a most interesting and illuminating paper in regard to resupination as a diagnostic taxonomic character in the Orchidaceae. He concluded that "Resupination is a purely physiological phenomenon which should be treated with circumspection in taxonomic work."

Since the lip is considered to be closely correlated with insect-pollination in the Orchidaceae, and, in fact, functions as a landing platform for insects when they visit the flower, DARWIN was of the opinion that the reverting of the lip to the lowermost position was perhaps a symbiotic response—". . . so that insects can easily visit the flower." Whatever may be the reason for this peculiar trait in orchids, it is interesting to know that it exists. Like so many puzzling problems in Nature, perhaps the real reason for its existence may remain to us an unfathomable mystery.

This species is found along mountain streams in shady places, in bogs, swamps and forests. In Alaska, it grows on high sandy beaches and on rather dry hillsides. It occurs up to 2,000 feet altitude in Germany, 8,000 feet in China and 10,500 feet in India, blooming from June to August in various parts of its range.

GEOGRAPHICAL DISTRIBUTION: Uncommon in Alaska and the Aleutian Islands; widespread and rather frequent throughout Eurasia; erroneously reported from Texas.

CULTURAL NOTES: There is no record of this species ever having been cultivated. See this section under *M. paludosa.*

4. **Malaxis monophyllos** var. **brachypoda** (A. Gray) Morris & Eames, Our Wild Orchids 358, pls. 110 and 111. 1929. *Microstylis brachypoda* A. Gray, Ann. Lyc. Nat. Hist. N. Y. 3: 228. 1835. Type locality and collection: New York, in deep shady swamps, Fairfield, Herkimer County, *Prof. Hadley;* New York, Oneida County, Bridgewater. (*Malaxis brachypoda* (A. Gray) Fernald). PLATES 100 and 101

(The name, *brachypoda,* is a Greek term signifying "short-pediceled," referring to that organ in this variety which, because of its brevity, causes the inflorescence to appear very slender and wand-like.)

COMMON NAME: White Malaxis.

Although an effort has been made by some to maintain this plant as specifically distinct from *M. monophyllos,* based upon its supposedly smaller capsules and shorter pedicels, in addition to the lowermost position of the lip in the flower, the fact remains that the latter feature is the only readily diagnostic character which separates this orchid from the typical form.

This variety is found commonly in cold bogs, swamps, boggy swales, wet meadows and in crevices of wet shaded cliffs and ledges. It occurs up to 550 feet altitude in Vermont and 9,000 feet in the San Bernardino Mountains of California, flowering from June to August.

GEOGRAPHICAL DISTRIBUTION: Newfoundland, Labrador, New Brunswick, Quebec and Ontario, west to Manitoba (Lake Winnipegoosis) and Alaska, south through New England to New York, Pennsylvania (Blair and Bradford counties) and New Jersey (Sussex County), west through the Lake States to Minnesota (Itasca County); also California (San Bernardino County) and Japan.

CULTURAL NOTES: Variety *brachypoda* evidently survived glaciation close to the margins of the ice sheet, and after the ice melted this little orchid migrated far north into Canada. Its present southern limit is reached in northern New Jersey and Pennsylvania. Correspondingly, it is completely winter hardy and is tolerant of little warming of the soil in summer. This plant grows chiefly in circumneutral, more or less calcareous swamps, and has been cultivated to some extent in northern gardens where similar conditions exist. (E.T.W.)

5. **Malaxis paludosa** (L.) Sw., Kongl. Svens. Vetens. Acad. Nya Handl. 21: 235. 1800. *Ophrys paludosa* L., Sp. Pl., ed. 1, 2: 947. 1753. Type locality and collection: Sweden, in grassy swamps, *Bergius*.   PLATE 102

(The name, *paludosa,* is a Latin adjective meaning "boggy," referring to the habitat where this species was originally found.)

COMMON NAMES: Marsh Malaxis, Bog Adder's Mouth, Bog Tenderwort.

Plant small, glabrous, stoloniferous, 4.5-22 cm. tall, produced from a small globose corm which is 4-10 mm. long, with the old corms usually persisting and surrounded by whitish scales. Stem slender, pale yellowish green, angled above. Leaves two to five in a basal cluster, ovate to obovate or elliptic, often provided with coarse yellow teeth or excrescences at the rounded to obtuse apex, fleshy, pale green, 3-30 mm. long, 3-8 mm. wide. Raceme elongated, narrowly cylindric, rather densely flowered, 1.8-11.5 cm. long, usually exceeding the peduncle in length, 5-8 mm. in diameter. Floral bracts small, lanceolate, acuminate, closely appressed to the pedicels, 2-3 mm. long. Flowers non-resupinate, small, yellowish green, thirty or less, with the filiform pedicels 2-3 mm. long. Sepals ovate-elliptic to elliptic-lanceolate, obtuse, spreading, 2-2.5 mm. long, about 1 mm. wide. Petals ovate-lanceolate to lanceolate, acute to acuminate, falcate, widespreading and reflexed, 1.2-1.5 mm. long, about 0.3 mm. wide. Lip uppermost in the flower, trulliform, triangular-ovate, apiculate, concave, often dilated at the base so as to appear 3-lobulate, 1.2-1.5 mm. long, 0.7-1 mm. wide across the base when expanded, adorned through the center with three to five dark green veins. Column minute, about 0.3 mm. long. Capsule obliquely ovoid, 2.5-4 mm. long.

This Eurasian bog orchid is exceedingly rare and elusive. Even where it is considered to be definitely established, it is seldom found without a diligent search of its native haunts. This is partly because of its small size and partly due to its apparent preference for inaccessible and often dangerous and treacherous habitats.

It was not until the first decade of the present century that the Bog Adder's Mouth was discovered in North America, being found for the first time in northern Minnesota about 1905 by Dr. H. L. LYON. Two years later, HENRY C. COWLES found it near Ketchican, Alaska. Subsequently, it has been collected only a few times, and it is still very sparsely represented in our region. On the other hand, this *Malaxis* is frequent in northern Europe.

Because of its tendency to grow poised upon mosses or other minute bog plants or on stumps and logs, it has been designated by some authors as the only European "epiphytic orchid."

A peculiar characteristic of this plant is the development of bulbil-like excrescences at the apex of the leaves.

The Bog Adder's Mouth is apparently confined to spongy turfy bogs and muskegs or exceedingly wet forests. It occurs up to 1,600 feet altitude in Scotland. While the normal blooming period is July and August, in Europe it has been found in flower as late as the first of October.

GEOGRAPHICAL DISTRIBUTION: Minnesota (Clearwater, Itasca and Otter Tail counties), Ontario (Thunder Bay District) and Alaska (Juneau, Ketchican and Wrangell); also Eurasia.

CULTURAL NOTES: This arctic species extends into the United States only around the northern Great Lakes, having apparently entirely vanished from any more southern points in which it may have survived glaciation on this continent. It is recorded as growing in acid bogs, and is evidently intolerant of any considerable warming of its soil in summer. Its cultivation, if at all possible, would be attended with great difficulty. (E. T. W.)

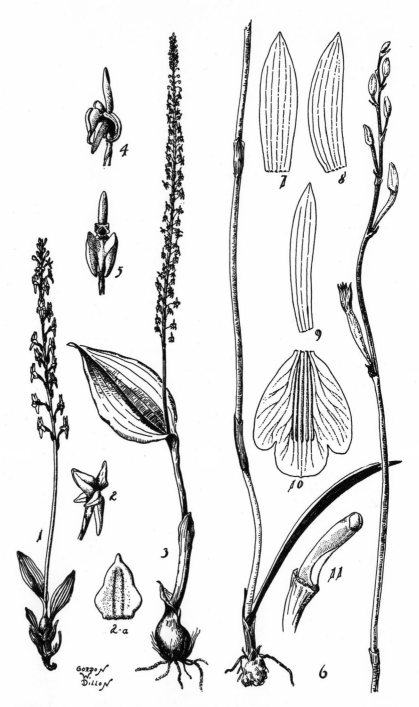

PLATE 102.— **Malaxis paludosa.** 1, plant, natural size. 2, flower, side view, five times natural size. 2a, lip, front view, spread open, ten times natural size.

Malaxis Ehrenbergii. 3, plant, one half natural size. 4, flower, side view, five times natural size. 5, flower, front view, five times natural size.

Basiphyllaea corallicola. 6, plant, natural size. 7, dorsal sepal, five times natural size. 8, lateral sepal, five times natural size. 9, petal, five times natural size. 10, lip, spread out, front view, five times natural size. 11, column and upper part of ovary, front-side view, five times natural size. *Drawn by Gordon W. Dillon.*

6. **Malaxis Soulei** L. O. Wms., Ann. Mo. Bot. Gard. 21: 343. 1934. *Microstylis montana* Rothr. in Wheeler, Rept. U. S. Geogr. Surv. W. 100th Merid. (Bot.) 6: 264. 1878. Type locality and collection: Mount Graham, Arizona, at an elevation of 9,500 feet, September 1874, *J. T. Rothrock*. (*Achroanthes montana* (Rothr.) Greene; *Malaxis montana* (Rothr.) O. Ktze., not Blume, 1825). PLATE 103

(The name, *Soulei*, is in honor of JUSTUS F. SOULE (1862-1939), Professor of Greek and Latin, University of Wyoming.)

COMMON NAMES: Mountain Malaxis, Rat-tail.

Plant glabrous, slender or stout, erect or ascending, usually flexuous above, 1.4-5 dm. tall. Stem arising from a short globose base, provided below with a loose tubular leaf-sheath which is marginate, obtuse or apiculate and 2-10.5 cm. long. Leaf-blade solitary, expanded abruptly at about the middle of the stem, cordate-ovate to elliptic-oblong or oblong-lanceolate, obtuse to obtuse and apiculate, dark bluish green, usually somewhat marginate, 2.5-16 cm. long, 1.3-6 cm. wide. Raceme densely many-flowered, spicate, narrowly cylindric, 4.5-24 cm. long, 3-10 mm. in diameter; rachis minutely grooved. Floral bracts deltoid to broadly lanceolate, acute, up to 1.5 mm. long. Flowers non-resupinate, minute, yellowish green, subsessile, on short pedicels up to 2 mm. long. Sepals ovate-oblong to elliptic-oblong, obtuse and often minutely cucullate at the apex, 1- to 3-nerved, 1.5-2.8 mm. long, 0.8-1.3 mm. wide; lateral sepals oblique, slightly shorter than the dorsal sepal. Petals obliquely linear, obtuse, strongly coiled, 1-nerved, 1.3-2.2 mm. long. Lip uppermost in the flower, suborbicular-ovate to triangular-.ovate or subquadrate-ovate, obliquely tridentate at the apex or retuse with an apicule in the sinus, mostly with a prominent spreading obtuse auricle on each side at the base, 1.5-2.8 mm. long, 1.3-2.5 mm. wide across the base; disc 5-nerved, rather deeply concave. Column short, fleshy. Capsule obliquely ellipsoid, about 7 mm. long.

The slender wand-like inflorescence, consisting of numerous minute approximate flowers closely appressed to the rachis, is characteristic of this species. Although its habit closely resembles that of the Mexican *M. streptopetala* (Robins. & Greenm.) Ames, the flowers of the two species are quite different.

The Mountain Malaxis is usually found in humus in moist canyons and ravines, on rocky slopes or dry or moist coniferous, hardwood or mixed forests, in open pine savannahs, in rain forests or along shaded streams. It commonly occurs at high elevations and is recorded from 5,000 feet altitude in northern Mexico (Baja California), up to 10,000 feet in Arizona and 12,000 feet in southern Mexico. It blooms from July to October in various parts of its range.

GEOGRAPHICAL DISTRIBUTION: Texas (Jeff Davis County), New Mexico (Grant County, Pinos Altos Mountains and near Sulphur Springs (Valle Grande)) and Arizona (Cochise, Coconino, Graham, Navajo, Pima and Santa Cruz counties); also Mexico, through Central America to Panama.

CULTURAL NOTES: There is no record of this species ever having been cultivated.

7. **Malaxis spicata** Sw., Prodr. Veg. Ind. Occ. 119. 1788. Type locality: Jamaica. (*Microstylis spicata* (Sw.) Lindl.; *M. floridana* Chapm.; *Malaxis floridana* (Chapm.) O. Ktze.; *Achroanthes floridana* (Chapm.) Greene). PLATE 104

(The name, *spicata*, is a Latin adjective meaning "spicate," in allusion to the usually very slender wand-like inflorescence.)

COMMON NAMES: Florida Adder's Mouth, Little Orange-lip, Slender Malaxis, Brown Malaxis.

Plant erect, glabrous, naked except for two approximate leaves below the middle of the stem, 7-45 cm. tall. Roots few, fibrous. Stem with a swollen base (becoming pseudobulbous in the fruiting stage), enveloped below by one or two loose tubular leaf-sheaths, inconspicuously angled and winged above the leaves. Leaf-blades two (rarely three), subopposite, abruptly spreading near the base or just below the middle of the stem, ovate to suborbicular, obtuse to acute, glossy and strongly keeled along the midrib beneath, 2.5-10 cm. long, 1.2-5.5 cm. wide. Raceme laxly few- to many-flowered, subumbellate to elongate, 1.5-20 cm. long, about 7 mm. in diameter. Floral bracts linear-lanceolate, acute, 2-4 mm. long. Flowers non-resupinate, small, with the very slender pedicellate ovaries about 8 mm. long. Sepals and petals green. Sepals ovate-elliptic to elliptic, concave, with strongly involute margins and a prominent mid-nerve,

2.5-3.5 mm. long, 1.5-2 mm. wide. Petals narrowly linear to filiform, strongly recurved, 2-3 mm. long. Lip pale yellow to orange-vermilion, uppermost in the flower, entire or sub-entire, cordate-ovate, prominently and obtusely auricled on each side at the base, with the

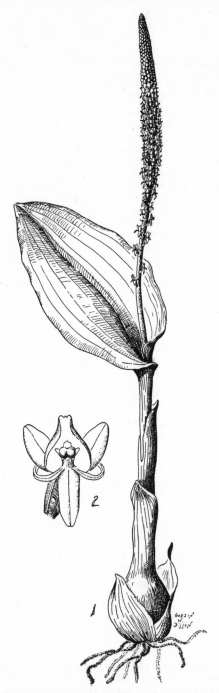

PLATE 103.— **Malaxis Soulei.** 1, plant, natural size. 2, flower, front view, six times natural size. *Drawn by Gordon W. Dillon.*

apical portion strongly upcurved and subacute, shallowly saccate at the base with the rim of the sac thickened, 3-4 mm. long (including the auricles) 2.5-3.3 mm. wide near the base; disc with three prominent nerves and the lateral margins revolute. Column short, about 1 mm.

long, with two short rounded teeth on each side near the apex. Capsule ellipsoid, 7-8 mm. long, about 4 mm. in diameter.

This species has been known from the United States since 1860, at which time A. W. CHAPMAN described (as *Microstylis floridana*) a collection of this plant from Florida. Although considered to be a subtropical species, it appears to be quite hardy in that it extends along the Atlantic seaboard as far north as southeastern Virginia, a region now famous for its yield of unique plants as the result of the extensive field work in recent years of MERRITT LYNDON FERNALD and his associate, BAYARD LONG.

Malaxis spicata grows in hammocks, swamps, low moist woods, in mucky soil of low floodplain areas and on rich wooded slopes, on shady ledges in hammocks and on river bottom-lands. It is also found on rotting wood and in calcareous soils, and is rarely semiepiphytic on the roots and lower parts of the trunks of trees. The Slender Malaxis occurs near sea level in Florida, up to 3,000 feet altitude in Haiti and 5,000 feet in Jamaica, blooming sporadically throughout the year, mainly from August to February in various parts of its range.

GEOGRAPHICAL DISTRIBUTION: Virginia (Gloucester, Isle of Wight and Surry counties), South Carolina (Berkeley and Georgetown counties), Georgia (Jenkins County) and Florida (throughout the peninsula); also the Bahama Islands and the West Indies.

CULTURAL NOTES: In the United States this species extends from Florida to southeastern Virginia, and accordingly is able to survive freezing conditions. It prefers moist, circumneutral or limy soil where a moderate accumulation of humus has developed. Attempts to cultivate it outside of its native range have not been successful, for, even though it could readily be protected from severe winter conditions, no way has been found to keep parasitic fungi from destroying it in the garden. (E. T. W.)

8. **Malaxis tenuis** (S. Wats.) Ames, Proc. Biol. Soc. Wash. 35: 85. 1922.
   Microstylis tenuis S. Wats., Proc. Am. Acad. 26: 152. 1891. Type locality and collection: Mexico, in low meadows, Flor de Maria, State of México, July 1890, *C. G. Pringle*. PLATE 105

(The name, *tenuis,* is a Latin adjective meaning "thin," in allusion to the slender attenuated floral segments.)

COMMON NAME: None known.

Plant erect, glabrous, 11-25 cm. tall. Stem from a small swollen base, slender, the basal portion being concealed by a closely appressed leaf-sheath which is 3-6 cm. long. Leaf-blade solitary, usually (but not always) expanded just below the middle of the stem, elliptic to broadly ovate, rounded to obtuse at the apex, clasping the stem below, 3.5-8 cm. long, 1.5-4 cm. wide. Raceme many-flowered, loose, cylindric, 4.5-9 cm. long, 2-3 cm. in diameter. Floral bracts minute, triangular, acute, about 1 mm. long. Flowers small, greenish yellow, on filiform pedicels which are up to 1 cm. long. Sepals spreading, narrowly lanceolate, long-acuminate (often attenuate), 3-nerved, 4-6 mm. long, 1.2-2 mm. wide; lateral sepals oblique, free or sometimes united to about the middle, with the margins usually revolute, conduplicate and somewhat recurved at the apex. Petals linear-attenuate to filiform, 1-nerved, 4-4.5 mm. long, less than 0.5 mm. wide. Lip triangular-lanceolate, long-acuminate (and often attenuate) at the apex, 3-nerved, concave below, angled or rounded on each side at the base, 3.5-4.2 mm. long, 1.5-2 mm. wide across the base when expanded; disc usually adorned with two broad green stripes in the center. Column minute, less than 1 mm. long.

The thin, long-acuminate floral segments are characteristic of this rare species.

Malaxis tenuis was first discovered in the United States in New Mexico by EDWARD LEE GREENE on September 14, 1880.

This species grows in meadows and on shaded rocky hills. It occurs up to 10,000 feet altitude in Mexico, blooming from July to October in various parts of its range.

GEOGRAPHICAL DISTRIBUTION: New Mexico (Grant and Socorro counties) and Arizona (Pima County); also Mexico.

PLATE 104.—**Malaxis spicata.** 1 and 2, plants, natural size. 3, flower, front view, six times natural size. 4, dorsal sepal, six times natural size. 5, petal, six times natural size. 6, fruits, natural size. *Drawn by Blanche Ames.*

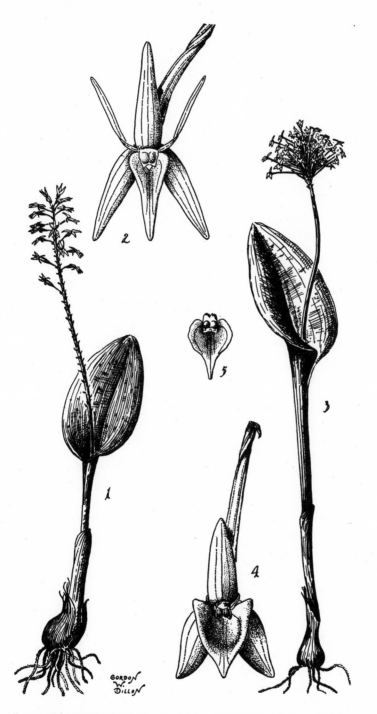

PLATE 105.— **Malaxis tenuis.** 1, plant, one half natural size. 2, flower, front view, five times natural size.

Malaxis corymbosa. 3, plant, one half natural size. 4, flower, front view, five times natural size. 5, lip, from the type specimen, five times natural size. *Drawn by Gordon W. Dillon.*

CULTURAL NOTES: There is no record of this species ever having been cultivated.

9. **Malaxis unifolia** Michx., Fl. Bor.-am. 2: 157. 1803. Type locality: In dense woods, Pennsylvania, Carolina and Florida. (*Malaxis ophioglossoides* Muhl. ex Willd.; *M. Bayardi* Fernald; *M. Grisebachiana* Fawc. & Rendle; *Achroanthes unifolia* (Michx.) Raf.; *Microstylis unifolia* (Michx.) BSP.; *M. ophioglossoides* (Muhl. ex Willd.) Nutt.). PLATE 106

(The name, *unifolia*, means "one-leaved" in Latin, referring to the typically solitary leaf.)

COMMON NAMES: Green Adder's Mouth, Adder's Mouth, Adder's Tongue Tenderwort, Green Malaxis, Tenderwort, Wide Adder's Mouth.

Plant bright green, erect, glabrous, 6-55 cm. tall. Stem from a bulbous corm, concealed below by a close tubular leaf-sheath, somewhat angled and winged above. Leaf-blade solitary, abruptly spreading (usually near the middle) from the stem, orbicular-ovate to ovate-lanceolate, obtuse to acute, sessile and clasping the stem, 1-9 cm. long, 0.6-6.5 cm. wide. Raceme subumbellate to slender-elongated, densely flowered, 1-16 cm. long, 0.7-2.5 cm. in diameter. Floral bracts minute, subulate, 1-3 mm. long. Flowers minute, green, with the filiform pedicellate ovaries 3-10 mm. long. Sepals spreading, linear-oblong to oblong-elliptic, subacute, 1-nerved, with the margins often somewhat involute, 1.8-3.5 mm. long, 0.8-1.5 mm. wide. Petals narrowly linear to filiform, strongly recurved, 1.4-3 mm. wide. Lip lowermost in the flower at maturity, variable in shape, cordate-deltoid to cordate-ovate or oblong-quadrate, 2-4 mm. long, 1.5-3 mm. wide, cordate or auricled on each side at the base with the auricles broadly rounded to acute and occasionally deeply notched, obliquely tridentate at the apex with the two lateral teeth more or less elongated and obtuse to acute and the median tooth minute, thickened and apiculate. Column minute, 0.5-1 mm. long, with two short lateral teeth at the apex. Capsule obliquely ovoid, 3-6 mm. long, 2-3 mm. in diameter.

As in most of the species of *Malaxis,* the lip of *M. unifolia* is exceedingly variable—in fact, the lips of individual flowers on the same raceme often differ markedly from one another. In some flowers the lip may have the basal auricles much longer than the apical lateral teeth or lobules, whereas in other flowers the lip will have an almost truncate base with the apical lateral teeth or lobules conspicuously elongated. Furthermore, the lip is sometimes noticeably constricted near the apex. Based primarily upon such variations in the lip, several specific proposals have been made for this species.

A peculiarity of this species, as well as that of many other orchids, is the apparent growth-stimulation that follows fertilization. In the Green Adder's Mouth, growth seems to be momentarily arrested at anthesis, but upon fertilization of the flowers and consequent setting of the fruit, vegetative growth is resumed and the leaf frequently increases noticeably in size. This phenomenon also seems to be the case in other species of *Malaxis* as well as in the genus *Isotria*. In the Australasian genus *Corybas,* the peduncle of many of the species elongates greatly after the occurrence of fertilization. In these low herbaceous plants, the solitary flower is borne near the ground and the elongation of the peduncle, so as to elevate the fruit, would seem to be "effort" on the part of the plant to raise its fruit into higher air-currents so as to insure the dispersal of its powdery seeds.

Although no true scientist would dare attribute to plants teleological virtues to explain the above responses, it is, indeed, often difficult to determine causes and effects on an entirely mechanical basis.

The Green Adder's Mouth is found commonly on moist wooded slopes along streams (mostly in mixed pine-hardwood forests), in hammocks, peaty or sandy soil of bogs, meadows, swamps, deep shaded ravines, on the edge of woods and in thickets or on open grassy seepage slopes. It also occurs in clay soil of dense floodplain woods, in mountain ravines and on heavily forested mountain slopes. In Mexico, it also grows in lava-fields in mixed forests. It occurs near sea level on the Coastal Plain, up to 2,000 feet altitude in Massachusetts and Vermont, 5,000

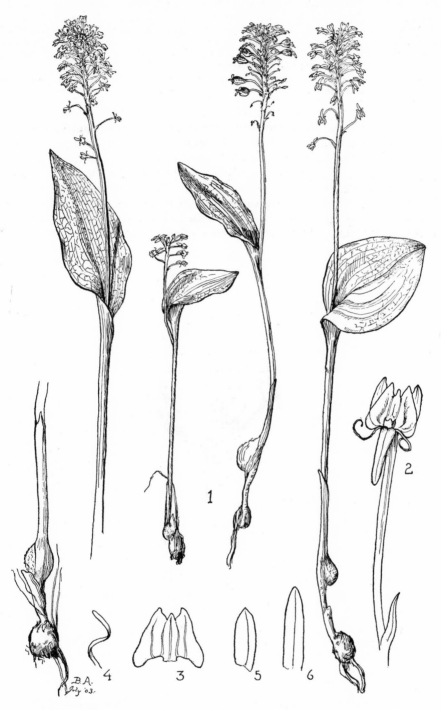

PLATE 106.— **Malaxis unifolia.** 1, plants, natural size. 2, flower, front view, five times natural size. 3, lip, spread out, six times natural size. 4, petal, seven times natural size. 5, lateral sepal, seven times natural size. 6, dorsal sepal, seven times natural size. *Drawn by Blanche Ames.*

feet in Jamaica and in the mountains of North Carolina and Tennessee, and 8,500 feet in Mexico. The Green Adder's Mouth flowers throughout the year, especially from March to August in the United States and Canada.

GEOGRAPHICAL DISTRIBUTION: Occasional from Newfoundland, Nova Scotia, New Brunswick, Prince Edward Island, Quebec and Ontario (Algoma County and Temagami) and through New England, rather frequent through the Atlantic States, south to northern Florida (Alachua and Gadsden counties), along the Gulf Coast to Texas (Harris and Nacogdoches counties), west through the Central and Lake States to (?) Manitoba, Minnesota (Clearwater and Ramsey counties), Missouri (Shannon County) and Arkansas (Clark County); also Mexico, Guatemala, Cuba and Jamaica.

CULTURAL NOTES: Considering the vast area of distribution of this species, it is evidently indifferent to temperature conditions. It does require, however, intensely acid humus-rich soil. When transplanted to acid-soil gardens it grows for a time until its pseudobulbous corms are found by rodents or slugs. (E. T. W.)

Apparently the first attempt to cultivate this species was that of Conrad Loddiges & Sons in England sometime before 1832. They wrote as follows: "With us it is difficult to preserve; we have succeeded best by placing it in a cold frame during winter, and in summer in the shade, potted in a mixture of peat earth, loam, and decayed sawdust. We have never been able to propagate the plant."

26. Liparis L. C. Rich.

Liparis L. C. Rich., De Orch. Europ. Annot. 21, 30, 38. 1817 (in Mém. Mus. Hist. Nat. Par. 4: 43, 52, 60. 1818), conserved name.

(The name, *Liparis,* is from a Greek word meaning "fat" or "greasy," in allusion to the typically fleshy-thickened shiny leaves.)

Inconspicuous terrestrial (or rarely epiphytic) scapose herbs arising from corms or pseudobulbs. Leaves one or more, basal, sheathing the stem below, fleshy or plicate. Inflorescence a lax few- to many-flowered raceme terminating the scape. Sepals mostly oblong-lanceolate, free, spreading. Petals narrowly linear to filiform. Lip entire to emarginate or 3-lobed, mostly arcuate-recurved in natural position, attached to the base of the column. Column strongly incurved, with narrow lateral wings above; anther terminal, incumbent, operculate; pollinia four (two in each anther-cell), waxy, ovoid. Capsule ellipsoid or obovoid.

This is a rather large and complex genus of approximately two hundred sixty species which are widely dispersed through the temperate and warmer regions of the world, with the greatest concentration in tropical Asia and Oceania. It is closely allied to *Malaxis* from which it differs chiefly in having an elongate column.

KEY FOR THE IDENTIFICATION OF THE SPECIES OF LIPARIS

1. Leaves three or more, membranaceous, plicate..........................*L. elata* (p. 271)
1. Leaves two, succulent, smooth..2
   2. Lip 10 mm. or more long, translucent, madder-purple................*L. liliifolia* (p. 273)
   2. Lip less than 5 mm. long, opaque, yellowish green..................*L. Loeselii* (p. 274)

1. Liparis elata Lindl., Bot. Reg. 14: t. 1175. 1828. Type locality: Near Rio de Janeiro, Brazil. (*Liparis elata* var. *latifolia* Ridley; *Leptorchis elata* (Lindl.) O. Ktze.). PLATE 107

(The name, *elata,* is a Latin adjective meaning "tall," in allusion to the unusual height of the flowering spike.)

COMMON NAME: Tall Liparis.

Plant essentially erect, scapose, glabrous, slender or stout, 1.2-6 dm. tall. Pseudobulb conical, producing numerous fibrous roots. Scape naked (except for several remote bracts), angled and prominently winged above, suffused with madder-purple. Leaves three to five (very rarely two), subtended by scarious sheaths which envelope the pseudobulbs, situated near the base of the scape, ovate to elliptic or oblong-lanceolate, broadly rounded to abruptly acuminate above, sheathing the stem at the base, plicate, 6-30 cm. long, 5.5-12 cm. wide, reduced above to minute bracts. Raceme laxly few- to many-flowered, 3-26 cm. long, 2-3 cm. in diameter. Floral bracts subulate to triangular-lanceolate, acuminate, 6-12 mm. long. Flowers small, with the rather stout pedicellate ovaries 7-12 mm. long. Sepals greenish, streaked with madder-purple, with five prominent nerves; dorsal sepal oblong-elliptic to linear-oblong, broadly rounded to obtuse at the apex, 5-8 mm. long, 1.8-4 mm. wide; lateral sepals obliquely ovate-oblong to elliptic, obtuse to subacute, with the margins strongly revolute, 4-7 mm. long, 2-3.5 mm. wide. Petals greenish, streaked with madder-purple, linear-oblanceolate to narrowly spatulate, prominently 2- to 3-nerved, 5-7.5 mm. long, 1-2 mm. wide near the apex. Lip madder-purple, obcordate to broadly cuneate or oblong-flabellate, emarginate, occasionally with a small apicule in the sinus, strongly arcuate-recurved in natural position, obsoletely auricled on each side at the base, 4-5.5 mm. long when expanded, 3.5-5.3 mm. wide; disc with two fleshy tubercles on the basal portion, prominently 5-nerved, the nerves giving rise to numerous veinlets. Column stout, strongly incurved above, with broad lateral wings and a small tooth on each side at the apex, 3.5-5 mm. long. Capsule obovoid, 1.2-1.5 cm. long, 5-6 mm. in diameter.

The following interesting note by AMES (1947) not only concerns the discovery of this species in the United States, but gives a little insight into the intriguing personality of one of our great botanical collectors, ALVAH AUGUSTUS EATON.

PLATE 107.—**Liparis elata.** 1, plant, one fourth natural size. 2, inflorescence, one and one third times natural size. 3, flower, front view, five times natural size. 4, flower, side view, five times natural size. 5, petal, five times natural size. 6, lateral sepal, five times natural size. 7, pollinia, enlarged. *Redrawn from Blanche Ames by Gordon W. Dillon.*

"The discovery of *Liparis elata* in the United States we owe to James E. Layne who gathered budding specimens in Fahkahatchie Swamp, near Everglade, in southwestern Florida in July, 1903. These specimens behaved very badly in my greenhouse and, before a sure diagnosis could be made, they perished. At this time, Alvah Augustus Eaton was a member of my herbarium staff. At my request he went to Florida in June 1904 to meet Layne and under his guidance to procure additional specimens of the *Liparis* in flower. In the meantime Layne died. Now it must be told that Eaton claimed to have Indian blood in his veins and that through his heritage he possessed unusual powers of woodcraft. On his return home he told me that he had learned something about Layne's botanical activities, and in going afield had endeavored to collect over the same ground that Layne had been accustomed to cover. One day, despairing of success in the purpose of his visit to Florida, he sat down on a log to drink water sweetened with sugar, his chief means of sustenance when on a prolonged field trip. And then he observed some nearly obliterated footprints. As these footprints were in a place which it was unlikely that anybody but a plant collector would visit, he decided that they might have been made by Layne and he decided to follow them. This he did and found *Liparis elata* in flower. As Eaton found orchids in Florida that nobody else had seen up to that time or since, perhaps, after all, he had in his blood something of the uncanny ability that made the aborigines keen observers of nature. In any event he was a master field botanist."

On July 18, 1936, I collected this species on a stump in the Royal Palm Hammock, a few miles west of Deep Lake, Collier County, Florida. The country surrounding Deep Lake is known as the Big Cypress Swamp and consists mainly of a vast flat grassland or "prairie" having scattered depressions filled with water and cypress trees. The Royal Palm Hammock, an oasis in a desert of water, is an elevated area of limerock. At that time, the entire country, except for the elevated roads and a few isolated high spots, was inundated.

The Tall Liparis is found usually in cypress swamps on decaying logs and stumps, in rich humus of hammocks or in wet muck. In the tropics, it grows in leaf mold or on logs, stumps, rocks or even trees in shady forests and barrancas, in thickets, crevices of cliffs and on high grassy ridges. It occurs near sea level in Florida and Panama, up to 2,500 feet altitude in Honduras, Panama and the West Indies, 3,500 feet in Costa Rica, Guatemala and Mexico, and 5,000 feet in Peru. The Tall Liparis blooms sporadically throughout the year, mainly from June to September in Florida.

Geographical distribution: Widespread from southern Florida (Collier and Hernando counties), through Mexico and Central America to Panama, the West Indies, Venezuela, Brazil, Ecuador and Peru.

Cultural notes: This species occurs in circumneutral soil in hammocks of southern Florida. (E. T. W.)

The Tall Liparis was first introduced into England from Brazil in 1826 by Sir Henry Chamberlain.

2. **Liparis lilifolia** (L.) L. C. Rich. ex Lindl., Bot. Reg. 11: sub. t. 882. 1825.
  Ophrys lilifolia L., Sp. Pl., ed. 1, 2: 946. 1753. Type locality: In swamps in Virginia, "Canada and Sweden." (*Malaxis lilifolia* (L.) Sw.; *Leptorchis lilifolia* (L.) O. Ktze.). Plate 108

(The name, *lilifolia*, means "lily-leaved" in Latin, and was so-called for the Section Lilia in the family Liliaceae, including such plants as the Dog-tooth Violet (*Erythronium americanum*) which somewhat resembles this plant vegetatively.)

Common names: Mauve Sleekwort, Large Twayblade, Purple Scutcheon.

Plant erect or ascending, scapose, succulent, slender or stout, 4-25 cm. tall. Rootstock a bulbous corm with short spongy roots. Stem angled and obscurely winged above, bright green and often tinged with purplish brown. Leaves two, basal, ovate to elliptic, obtuse to acute, sheathing the stem below, glossy, keeled beneath, 4-18 cm. long, 2-6 cm. wide. Raceme laxly few-flowered, 4-15 cm. long, 3-5 cm. in diameter. Floral bracts minute, subulate, about 2 mm. long. Flowers five or usually more, with the slender pedicellate ovaries about 1.5 cm. long. Sepals pale greenish white, translucent, oblong-lanceolate to lanceolate, obtuse to acute, with three prominent veins, 1-1.1 cm. long, 2-3 mm. wide when expanded; dorsal sepal with the margins strongly revolute; lateral sepals with the margins strongly involute. Petals madder-purple, narrowly linear to filiform, pendent and curved, with a single prominent vein, 1-1.2 cm. long. Lip mauve-purple tinged with green, cuneate-obovate to suborbicular, abruptly mucronate at the subtruncate apex, slightly auricled on each side at the base, finely erose-serrulate along the apical margin, translucent, with five prominent reddish purple veins which give rise to dichotomously branching veinlets, 1-1.1 cm. long when expanded, 7.5-10 mm. wide. Column thick, clavate, incurved, about 3 mm. long, with two blunt tubercles on the inner surface near the base. Capsule ellipsoid, about 1.5 cm. long.

One of the favorite haunts of this little woodland orchid is along the mossy crown of ravines and deeply cut stream banks. There, the small corms are at first firmly imbedded in moss but gradually, through offsets, the plants elevate themselves so as finally to nestle on the surface of the mossy mat—a semiepiphytic tendency. The low inconspicuous plants, with their watery mauve flowers, are easily overlooked and usually only the most persistent and patient searcher has the good fortune to see *Liparis lilifolia* in its idyllic settings.

LINNAEUS, in describing *Ophrys lilifolia,* the basis for our North American plant, for some reason erroneously included Canada and Sweden in its area of distribution. So far as I know, this species has never been found in either Europe or Canada.

According to STEVENSON (1926), the rust *Cylindrina delavarji* Pat. has been recorded in China as attacking the leaves of this species. However, there are no data available as to the ill effect this fungus has on the plants infected.

This species is found in low moist floodplain woods and in thickets along streams, in rocky sandy well-drained soil on moist forested slopes, in rich humus or moss along wooded streams and in mountain ravines. It occurs up to 2,000 feet altitude in Georgia and South Carolina and 5,000 feet in North Carolina, blooming from May to July in various parts of its range.

GEOGRAPHICAL DISTRIBUTION: Rare in Maine (*T. James*), Vermont (Addison County), Massachusetts, Connecticut, New York (north to Essex and Washington counties), Pennsylvania and New Jersey, more frequent along the Atlantic States south to South Carolina (Oconee, Pickens and Richland counties), Georgia (Rabun County) and Alabama (Franklin and Lee counties), west through the Central and Lake States to Wisconsin (Iowa, Lafayette and Walworth counties), Minnesota, Iowa (Johnson County), Missouri (west to Jasper, Mercer and Sullivan counties), Kentucky (Estill and Union counties), Arkansas and Tennessee (Davidson, Gibson, Madison and McNairy counties); also China (Kwangsi, Kwangtung).

CULTURAL NOTES: The Mauve Sleekwort occurs over much of the eastern half of the United States, being thus indifferent to temperature conditions. Its pseudobulbs grow loosely imbedded in litter or mosses of chiefly subacid reaction. Accordingly, it should be relatively easy to cultivate, and such is the case in the absence of rodents. The pseudobulbs, however, form a favorite food of these creatures, and will soon be devoured by them if not protected. A method which has met with fair success is to surround the pseudobulbs completely by a mixture of humus-rich soil and sharp-edged chips of trap-rock or other stone (avoiding limestone as too alkaline). (E. T. W.)

According to BROWN (1813), this species was first introduced and cultivated in England in 1758 by PETER COLLINSON, Esq.

3. **Liparis Loeselii** (L.) L. C. Rich., De Orch. Europ. Annot. 38. 1817 (in Mém. Mus. Hist. Nat. Par. 4: 60. 1818). *Ophrys Loeselii* L., Sp. Pl., ed. 1, 2: 947. 1753. Type locality: In swamps in Sweden and Prussia. (*Leptorchis Loeselii* (L.) MacM.). PLATE 108

PLATE 108.— **Liparis Loeselii.** 1, flowering plant, with last year's fruiting inflorescence persisting, natural size. 2, flower, front view, spread out, one and one half times natural size. 3, column, with basal part of lip, side view, five times natural size.

Liparis lilifolia. 4, plant, natural size. 5, flower, front view, spread out, one and one half times natural size. 6, column, with basal part of lip, side view, five times natural size. *Drawn by Gordon W. Dillon.*

(The name, *Loeselii,* is in honor of JOHANN LOESEL (1607-1655), a German botanist.)

COMMON NAMES: Fen Orchid, Olive Scutcheon, Loesel's Twayblade, Russet-witch.

Plant erect, scapose, succulent, glabrous, mostly slender, pale green or yellowish green, 6-26 cm. tall. Rootstock a bulbous corm producing slender whitish roots. Stems somewhat angled above. Leaves two, basal, oblong-elliptic to elliptic-lanceolate, obtuse to subacute, sheathing the scape below, keeled beneath, 3-19 cm. long, 1-6 cm. wide. Raceme slender, laxly few-flowered (very rarely one-flowered), 2-10 cm. long, 1-2 cm. in diameter. Floral bracts minute, subulate, less than 3 mm. long. Flowers yellowish green or whitish, with the slender pedicellate ovaries 3-6 mm. long. Dorsal sepal erect, obelisk in outline, arising from a rather broad hastate base, prominently 3-nerved, with the margins revolute, 5-6 mm. long, 1.5-2 mm. wide at about the middle. Lateral sepals oblong-lanceolate to lanceolate, somewhat incurved, with the margins involute, prominently 3-nerved, 5-5.5 mm. long, 1.5-2.2 mm. wide at about the middle. Petals filiform, tubular, with a single prominent nerve, 4.5-5 mm. long. Lip arcuate-recurved in natural position, narrowly cuneate, obovate to oblong or suborbicular when expanded, with an apiculate apex, slightly hastate or subauriculate on each side at the base, with the margins finely crenulate-wavy and with five prominent veins which give rise to numerous veinlets, 4.3-5 mm. long, 3-3.5 mm. wide above the middle. Column short, stout, about 2 mm. long. Capsule ellipsoid, about 1.2 cm. long.

It is noteworthy that this typically northern plant extends along the Allegheny Mountains to North Carolina, with a disjunct station on the Piedmont Plateau in Alabama (Lee County), and westward to Washington (Falcon Valley). On the other hand, the more southern *L. lilifolia* extends sparingly northward to an apparently lone station in Maine and one in Vermont. Such disconnected distributional patterns may be the result of the irregularity of botanical collecting or they may represent an invasion or recession of a species at its outermost limits of distribution.

This species is found usually in cool mountain ravines and on moist grassy seepage slopes and banks, along streams in forests, in cedar, spruce and tamarack swamps, peat bogs, wet meadows, thickets and occasionally in dry fields and on marshy shores. It occurs up to 600 feet altitude in Ontario and Vermont and 3,500 feet in the mountains of North Carolina. It flowers from May to the first of August in various parts of its range.

GEOGRAPHICAL DISTRIBUTION: Nova Scotia, New Brunswick, Prince Edward Island, Quebec and Ontario (Bruce, Carleton, Elgin, Norfolk and Wellington counties), through New England, New York, New Jersey and Virginia (Bedford and Henrico counties), south in the mountains to North Carolina (Avery and Rutherford counties) and on the Piedmont Plateau in Alabama (Lee County), west through the Central and Lake States to Illinois (Grundy, Lake and Peoria counties), Minnesota (Hennepin, Hubbard, Otter Tail and Saint Louis counties), Iowa, Kansas (Pottawatomie County), North Dakota (Pembina County), Manitoba (Carberry), (?) Saskatchewan to Washington (Falcon Valley).

CULTURAL NOTES: The Fen Orchid has a more restricted range in our region than its relative *L. lilifolia,* being less tolerant of summer heat and also requiring more moist conditions. Its soils are usually slightly to moderately acid. Like its relative, it must have protection from rodents, but it is more susceptible to fungus attacks so is less likely to survive in the average wild garden. (E. T. W.)

27. **Tipularia** Nutt.

.

Tipularia Nutt., Gen. N. Am. Pl. 2: 195. 1818.

(The name, *Tipularia,* is derived from *Tipula,* the generic name for the crane-flies, and is so named because of the similarity of the straggly long-spurred flowers to the appearance of a crane-fly in mid-air.)

Inconspicuous terrestrial scapose herbs arising from a corm (forming a horizontal series) which alternately produce a leaf in autumn and a slender scapose inflorescence in summer. Leaf solitary, fugacious before the arrival of the inflorescence, cordate-ovate, green above, purplish beneath. Inflorescence an elongated lax raceme terminating the slender scape. Flowers varying in color from greenish yellow to purplish. Sepals and petal similar. Lip 3-lobed, producing a long slender spur at the base. Column suberect, without lateral wings; anther terminal, operculate; pollinia two, waxy. Capsule ovoid, pendent.

This genus consists of two species, one in America, the other in Asia. Both occur primarily in the humus of hardwood forests in moderately to strongly acid soils.

1. **Tipularia discolor** (Pursh) Nutt., Gen. N. Am. Pl. 2: 195. 1818. *Orchis discolor* Pursh, Fl. Am. Sept. 2: 586. 1814. Type locality: In pine barrens, New Jersey to South Carolina. (*Tipularia unifolia* (Muhl.) BSP.).

PLATE 109

(The name, *discolor,* is a Latin adjective meaning "mottled," perhaps referring to the coloration of the flowers of some of the plants. The leaf often has a mottled appearance also.)

COMMON NAMES: Crippled Crane-fly (this name would seem to describe the flowers of this species very well because, as far as I know, this is the only species in the Orchidaceae in which the petals are arranged asymmetrically in the perianth. One of the petals distinctly overlaps the dorsal sepal for about half its width, resulting in a "crippled" appearance of the flower), Crane-fly Orchid, Elfin-spur, Mottled Crane-fly.

Plant scapose, very slender and erect, glabrous, 1-6.5 dm. tall, from a corm (later forming a horizontal series of corms) producing a few slender spongy velamentous roots. Stem naked except for a long tubular sheath at the base, brownish green, suffused with bronze or purple. Leaf solitary, produced in the autumn, cordate to ovate-elliptic, acute to acuminate, with a slender petiole, dull green above and often blotched with purple, purplish beneath, 5-10.5 cm. long, 2.5-7 cm. wide. Raceme laxly many-flowered, slender, apparently devoid of floral bracts, 8-28 cm. long, 2.5-3.5 cm. in diameter. Flowers variously colored, greenish, lemon yellow, rust-bronze or purplish, pendent, with the slender pedicellate ovaries 8-12 mm. long. Sepals oblong-oval to oblong-elliptic, obtuse, 5-8 mm. long, 1.5-2.8 mm. wide; lateral sepals occasionally narrowly spatulate, shorter than the dorsal sepal. Petals narrowly linear-oblong to oblong-elliptic or rarely narrowly spatulate, obtuse, 4-7 mm. long, 1-1.8 mm. wide, asymmetrically placed in the perianth (one petal partially overlaps the dorsal sepal). Lip 3-lobed, produced into a slender spur at the base, 5-8 mm. long, 2.5-3 mm. wide across the lateral lobes; lateral lobes basal, short, broadly rounded with an obtuse to acute or subacute apex, erose or crenulate along the margins, extending about 2 mm. above the base of the lip; apical lobe linear-oblong, to oblong-lanceolate, somewhat dilated or obtuse (rarely acute) at the apex, with the lateral margins undulate and coarsely erose or crenulate above; spur horizontal or ascending, strongly upcurved, 1.5-2.2 cm. long. Column 3-4 mm. long, 1-2 mm. wide. Capsule drooping to a position parallel to the rachis, ovoid, 1-1.2 cm. long, 4-5 mm. in diameter.

The rootstock of this plant consists of a chain of subterranean irregular solid corms which send out an offset in midsummer, from which is formed a new corm. This new corm gives rise to a single ovate leaf in the autumn which survives the winter. In the spring the leaf withers and dies and, in midsummer, the corm sends up a slender scapose inflorescence of small greenish flowers usually mottled with brownish purple.

PLATE 109.— **Tipularia discolor.** 1, plant, natural size. 2, lateral sepal, three times natural size. 3, petal, three times natural size. 4, dorsal sepal, three times natural size. 5, flower, with sepals and petals removed, side view, three times natural size. 6, lip, spread out, three times natural size. 7, fruits, natural size. *Drawn by Blanche Ames.*

In the illustration of this species the phenomenon of resupination is graphically demonstrated. As will be noted from a glance at the drawing, the buds show that in the early stage of floral development the lip, with its slender elongated spur, is uppermost in the flower. As each bud develops and approaches anthesis, the pedicellate ovary of the flower twists through 180 degrees, and by thus rotating the flower, the lip with its spur becomes the lowermost segment of the flower.

The following amusing incident occurred along the Apalachicola River in West Florida while HERMAN KURZ, of the Florida State College for Women at Tallahassee, and I were looking for this elusive orchid and other unique plants in that fascinating hill-country in 1936.

The old roadbed down which we were exploring had eaten deeply into the limestone, and, since its abandonment after logging operations ceased many years before, it had become a forested dry streambed. On each side rose ragged dull gray walls of pitted rock, and from the deeper clefts bristled depauperate yellowish green fronds of spleenworts. Enormous serpentine muscadine vines groped and twisted over the trail to eventually grasp a support and snake their sinuous way to the uppermost branches of the forest.

I was about to step over one of these ancient vines when a sudden slight movement beneath my uplifted foot caused me to whirl around and rush away. Looking back, I could see beneath and parallel to the repent vine the largest Southern Copperhead snake I had ever seen. KURZ, a rather large man, saw the snake as soon as I did. He called to me and started running around hunting for a rock or club—all the while yelling for me to kill it. I was more than willing to oblige—but how? My shotgun pistol, which I frequently carried for just this sort of occasion, had been left behind and, characteristic of most eroded limestone regions, there were no loose small stones at hand nor were there any large sticks nearby. I grabbed a rotten branch and swung it at the creature but the innocuous weapon went to pieces in my hands as the snake slithered from beneath the vine and disappeared into a hole in a rotten stump. KURZ was worked up to a high pitch, and well he might be since this, I understand, was the second time on record that a Copperhead had been observed in Florida, and RAYMOND L. DITMARS was just in the process of completing his final great work on the snakes of North America!

This species is found commonly in the humus of rich damp woods, in hammocks, along banks of streams, on pine-hardwood slopes, pine flatwoods, and in wooded floodplain areas. It occurs from near sea level in Virginia, up to 1,500 feet altitude in Alabama and 3,000 feet in North and South Carolina and Tennessee, blooming from the middle of June to September in various parts of its range.

GEOGRAPHICAL DISTRIBUTION: Rather frequent from North Carolina south through the Atlantic States to northern Florida (Alachua, Columbia, Gadsden and Leon counties), along the Gulf Coast to Texas (Hardin and Jasper counties), west to Ohio (Cuyahoga and Medina counties), Indiana (Perry County), Kentucky (Edmonson and Jefferson counties), and Arkansas (Garland and Hempstead counties), rare and local from North Carolina along the Atlantic seaboard to New Jersey (Cape May, Gloucester and Morris counties), Pennsylvania (Delaware County), New York and Massachusetts (Dukes County).

CULTURAL NOTES: While *T. discolor* is chiefly southern in distribution and tolerant of high summer heat, it ranges locally across Pennsylvania and New York and so is able to withstand winter conditions. It thrives best in subacid humus-rich soil, but it is not especially particular in this respect. The greatest difficulty in cultivating the plant lies in the fact that its corms are sought out and devoured by pine mice and their numerous relatives. Surrounding the corms with a mass of sharp-edged stone chips is about all that can be done. Slugs often get what the rodents miss, the succulent leaves being one of their favorite foods. In the garden, then, a preparation containing metaldehyde may have to be dusted over the soil when it is time for growth to start. (E. T. W.)

28. Calypso Salisb.

Calypso Salisb., Par. Lond. Pl. 89. 1807 (not Thouars, 1805), conserved name.

(The orchid, *Calypso,* is named for HOMER's sea nymph in the Odyssey, whose appelation signifies "concealment" in that she kept ODYSSEUS seven years on her island Ogygia. This little orchid is probably so named not only because of the singular beauty of the flowers, but because of its rarity and its usually secluded haunts.)

Plant terrestrial, small, consisting of a corm with fleshy roots or a coralloid rhizome (or both) giving rise to a solitary leaf and a 1-flowered scape. Sepals and petals similar, linear-oblong to lanceolate, spreading. Lip larger than the rest of the flower, deeply saccate, bicornute at the apex of the sac, dilated at the anterior margin of the orifice and forming an apron which is adorned with hairs at the base. Column broadly winged, having the operculate anther just below the apex; pollen-masses two, bipartite, waxy, sessile on a square gland.

This is a monotypic genus found in boreal and temperate regions of North America and Eurasia.

1. **Calypso bulbosa** (L.) Oakes in Thompson, Hist. of Vt., pt. 1: 200. 1842. *Cypripedium bulbosum* L., Sp. Pl., ed. 1, 2: 951. 1753. Type locality: Lapland, Russia and Siberia. (*Calypso borealis* (Sw.) Salisb.; *Cytherea bulbosa* (L.) House; *C. occidentalis* (Holz.) Heller). PLATE 110

(The name, *bulbosa,* is a Latin adjective meaning "with a bulb," in reference to the corm at the base of the plant.)

COMMON NAMES: Fairy Slipper, Calypso, Cytherea, Hider-of-the-north, Pink Slipper-orchid. (The var. *japonica* (Maxim.) Makino, of Asia, is known in Japan as *Hotei-ran* or "Ventricose Orchid.")

Plant erect, glabrous, 6-22 cm. tall, rising from a fleshy corm. Corm globose to ellipsoid, sometimes depressed, more or less clothed with sheaths, 1-2.5 cm. long, up to 2 cm. in diameter, giving rise to slender fleshy roots or a coralloid rhizome (or both). Leaf solitary, produced from the summit of the corm late in the first season and persisting through the winter, petiolate; petiole semiterete and sulcate, 1-6 cm. long; lamina variously shaped, cordate-ovate, suborbicular-ovate, cordate-elliptic or rarely elliptic, rounded to acute at the apex, plicate, with the margin wavy, dark green or bluish green, 2-6.5 cm. long, 1.5-5.2 cm. wide. Scape from the summit of the corm, produced (contiguous with the leaf) early in the second season, fleshy, slender or stout, pale yellowish purple to brownish purple, clothed below with two or more membranaceous tubular closely appressed obtuse sheaths which are up to 5 cm. long. Floral bracts lanceolate, acuminate to attenuate, convolute, 7-25 mm. long. Flower solitary (very rarely two), rather showy, pendent, with the slender arcuate pedicellate ovary 1.5-2.5 cm. long. Sepals and petals similar, spreading, purplish, rarely white, narrowly lanceolate to linear-oblong, subobtuse to acuminate, 1.2-2.3 cm. long, 2.7 mm. wide below the middle; lateral sepals slightly oblique. Petals slightly oblique, usually somewhat broader than the sepals. Lip pendent, calceolate, ovate-oblong in outline, 1.5-2.3 cm. long, 7-13 mm. wide; sac expanded in front and forming a pellucid whitish apron which spreads above the bicornute apex of the sac, whitish or yellowish to pale reddish brown, vividly marked on the inner surface with reddish brown spots and lines; apron bearded at its base in the middle with three longitudinal rows of golden yellow or brown-spotted (rarely white) hairs, more or less spotted with purple. Column petaloid, suborbicular, convex, inverted over the orifice of the lip, 7-12 mm. long and about as wide. Capsule erect, ellipsoid-cylindric, 2-3 cm. long.

The form rather frequent in the West, originally segregated as forma *occidentalis* Holz., has the beard white, instead of yellow as in the eastern plant. The hairs also appear to be less numerous, straighter and more slender. Concerning further variability of this plant, it is noteworthy that the corms may be either globose and depressed or ellipsoid, and quite often a coralloid rhizome, such as is characteristic of *Hexalectris* and *Corallorhiza,* occurs in this species. The above characteristics are shown in the illustration.

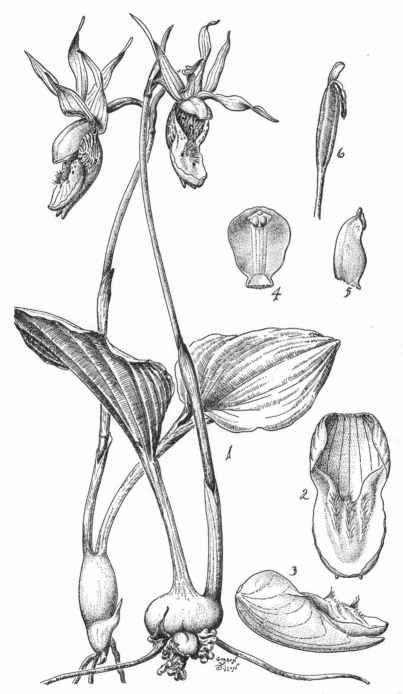

PLATE 110.—**Calypso bulbosa.** 1, plants, note two types of corms, natural size. 2, lip, front view, twice natural size. 3, lip, side view, twice natural size. 4, column, front-ventral view, twice natural size. 5, column, side view, twice natural size. 6, fruit, natural size. *Drawn by Gordon W. Dillon.*

JOSEPH T. ROTHROCK noted that the corms, which contain a large amount of a mucilaginous substance, are eaten by the Indians in British Columbia.

In his study of the northern orchids, NYLANDER (1935) recorded the following interesting observations about *Calypso:* "It is one of our first spring flowers, and I have collected it the first part of May on my farm in Woodland [Maine] . . . The plant has a very enduring blossom for I have had one standing in a little damp moss in my room for three weeks before it has begun to wither, and any ordinary frost common with us in May or June seems not to affect it at all.

"The flower of the *Calypso* is attacked by many birds and other animals, and in over forty years of careful observation of it on my farm, and elsewhere, I have not seen a dozen seed pods fully ripened."

Few if any of our native orchids possess the sheer beauty and loveliness of the Fairy Slipper. The first time I came upon this little orchid in a dense primeval forest in northern British Columbia, I looked at the flowers with the feeling that at last I was indeed looking upon the most beautiful terrestrial orchid in North America. The following paragraph concerns the location of a colony of these plants which grew on the summit of a high ridge along the Beatton River in northern British Columbia.

An inviting coolness seeped from the forest as I strolled between the rough corrugated trunks, and an undisturbed quietude lay over the green plateau. The feet of heavy forest denizens had left their impressions in the lush cover of lichens and mosses. All animate life lay still in its retreat. Beneath low hanging bows of conifers could be seen the bearded lips of the Fairy Slipper—the delicate nymphal orchid which hides in wet bogs in our eastern states and trails in deep moss of woodlands in the Rocky Mountains. The solitary pastel pink-purple flowers, touched here and there with white and yellow, diffidently nodded on the tips of short slender stems. Myriads of these dainty little plants grew in a mossy cushion in the dense shadow of low horizontal spruce branches. As if to secrete their beauty for some sylvan sprite, they had hidden themselves in solitude, for no other herb kept them company. A low rumble from the East and scattered drops of rain hurried me from the privacy of this elfin garden, and I turned and hastened from the thick sheltering woods as the storm broke.

This species is found commonly growing in mosses on the floor of cool moist coniferous forests, in tamarack and cedar swamps, bogs, and in damp spruce-aspen forests. It also occurs on mossy banks and on subalpine slopes in the West and Northwest. The Fairy Slipper usually grows at high elevations and occurs up to 450 feet altitude in Vermont, 3,500 feet in Idaho, 5,000 feet in Alberta and British Columbia, 9,000 feet in Montana and New Mexico and 10,000 feet in Arizona, Colorado and Utah. It flowers from the first of April (in Oregon) and May (in Maine) to the middle of July (in Alberta and British Columbia).

GEOGRAPHICAL DISTRIBUTION: Labrador, across Canada to British Columbia, Alaska and the Aleutian Islands, south to southern Maine, northern New Hampshire (Coös County), Vermont (Addison County), New York (Herkimer, Jefferson and Onondaga counties), Michigan, Minnesota (Carlton County), Montana, Idaho, Wyoming (Albany, Carbon, Teton and Yellowstone National Park counties), Colorado (Boulder, Custer, Huerfano and Larimer counties), Arizona (Apache, Coconino and Greenlee counties), New Mexico (Colfax and Lincoln counties), Utah (San Juan County), California (Del Norte, Humboldt, Mendocino and Sonoma counties), Oregon and Washington; also Eurasia.

CULTURAL NOTES: There are two forms of the Fairy Slipper, one eastern and one western, which, while they may not be recognized by taxonomists, are horticulturally rather different. The eastern form prefers a moist, circumneutral, humus-soil where the sun does not heat the litter above 60° F. in summer. Since it is highly susceptible to attack by rodents, slugs and fungi, its successful cultivation is dubious. The western form thrives in moderately dry coniferous litter of subacid reaction, and seems able to withstand higher summer temperatures in addition to being less subject to destruction by pests. It has been cultivated with some degree of success in a few western gardens, though it rarely persists more than a year or two. The wholesale marketing of corms of these plants by dealers represent little but wild life destruction. (E. T. W.)

According to BROWN (1813), this species was first introduced into England in 1805, by R. A. SALISBURY, Esq.

29. Epidendrum L.

Epidendrum L., Syst. Nat., ed. 10, 2: 1246. 1759, *pro parte* (*E. ciliare*); emend. Necker, Elem. 3: 132. 1790, *ex parte;* Ames, Hubbard & Schweinfurth, Gen. Epid. in U. S. & Mid. Am. 6: 1936, *non* Linnaeus (1753), conserved name.

(The name, *Epidendrum,* is a combination of Greek words meaning "upon trees," referring to the usual habitat of the species comprising this genus. Many unrelated genera and species of the Orchidaceae were originally erroneously included in the genus *Epidendrum,* simply because they happened to grow on trees.)

Epiphytic herbs of various habits. Stem either more or less erect, slender (rarely slightly swollen) and leafy or consisting of a pseudobulb bearing leaves at its summit. Leaves coriaceous or thick-membranaceous, mostly slender and elongated. Inflorescence a simple or compound raceme or panicle terminating the stem (very rarely on a lateral shoot), often with a long peduncle. Flowers small to large, inconspicuous or showy, variously arranged in the inflorescence. Sepals and petals free, spreading or reflexed. Lip entire or more or less 3-lobed, with the erect claw mostly adnate to the column; disc variously crested or callose. Column subfree or adnate to the claw of the lip (often to the apex), semiterete, either wingless, 2-winged or 2-auricled; anther terminal, operculate, incumbent, 2-celled (the cells divided again longitudinally); pollinia four, waxy. Capsule ovoid to ellipsoid, suberect or pendent, with prominent ribs which are occasionally winged.

This is the largest genus of New World neotropical orchids, comprising about eight hundred species. It is widely dispersed from southeastern North Carolina to Florida and Louisiana, through Mexico, Central America and the West Indies to Argentina, and is by far the most widely distributed of epiphytic orchids in the Western Hemisphere. Its component species are variable and polymorphic. Most of the species are epiphytic or lithophytic, growing on trees, shrubs and rocks, and derive their nourishment from the air and from the humus accumulated on the substratum upon which they grow. They, as well as all other epiphytic orchids, are not parasites, as is often commonly thought, but gain only their support from the trees or shrubs upon which they occur.

Two of the three sections comprising the genus are found in our flora, namely: *Encyclium,* characterized by having stems with true pseudobulbs that are provided above with one to several leaves, and a column which is subfree or only slightly adnate to the lip; *Euepidendrum,* characterized by having non-thickened, leafy, reed-like stems without pseudobulbs, and a column which is strongly (usually entirely) adnate to the lip.

CULTURAL NOTES: Of special interest to amateur growers because of its ease of culture, this group of small-flowered epiphytes has representatives in almost every collection of orchids. Both winter- and summer-flowering, the several species are extremely variable in habit of growth and size, in coloration of flowers, and in size and form of the pseudobulbs. After flowering, the old flowers should be clipped off as the formation of fruits and seeds devitalize the plants. Standard pot culture in which cleaned wild plants are packed firmly in clay pots with blocks of brown osmundine suits the members of this easily grown Florida genus. Wire baskets, cypress knees, cypress boards or the boots of cabbage palms may be used as a substratum or containers for large colonies. Osmundine may be packed about the roots and held in place on vertical supports by strips of bronze screen wire.

As growth commences in late winter, the plants should be soaked at least once each week when there is no rain. When the summer rainy season begins, growth is very rapid, flowering is luxuriant and no attention is needed. In the autumn only enough water should be given to keep the plants from shrinking, and a summer oil at half the recommended strength should be applied as a protection against scale insects. Thrips may be troublesome at times, especially with the Clam-shell

PLATE 111.— **Epidendrum anceps.** 1, plant, one half natural size. 2, flower, front view, two and one half times natural size. 3, flower, side view, two and one half times natural size. *Drawn by Gordon W. Dillon.*

Orchid (*E. cochleatum* var. *triandrum*). Daily syringing with a hose will usually be helpful against these pests if it is started soon after a dry spell begins and is continued until natural precipitation gives control.

As a minimum temperature of 38° F. is the extreme limit of safety for all species except *E. conopseum* and *E. tampense* (which stands 28° or less), specimens growing on lawn trees in southern Florida must be protected on nights during which lower temperatures are anticipated. Hoods of several thicknesses of burlap or cotton cloth, inside of which electric lights can be burned, will usually furnish adequate protection. (J. V. W.)

KEY FOR THE IDENTIFICATION OF THE SPECIES OF EPIDENDRUM

1. Stems with true pseudobulbs surrounded by scarious non-leaf-bearing sheaths; leaves only at the summit of the pseudobulbs 2
   2. Lip deeply 3-lobed; mid-lobe orbicular; lateral lobes ovate-oblong....*E. tampense* (p. 301)
   2. Lip not deeply 3-lobed, entire or at most shallowly lobed or angled 3
      3. Lip entire, broadly orbicular-cordate, dark purple; sepals more than 2 cm. long........
      ....*E. cochleatum* var. *triandrum* (p. 289)
      3. Lip angled or shallowly 3-lobed, not purple; sepals less than 1.5 cm. long 4
         4. Lip rhombic or trapeziform; sepals and petals yellow with reddish brown blotches; pseudobulbs strongly flattened, suborbicular.................*E. Boothianum* (p. 287)
         4. Lip with broadly rounded lateral lobes and a small triangular mid-lobe; sepals and petals yellowish white, unblotched; pseudobulbs terete, fusiform........*E. pygmaeum* (p. 297)
1. Stem without true pseudobulbs, slender or stout and leafy throughout 5
   5. Lip undivided, on the upper side of the flower; floral bracts large, concave, enclosing the ovary and most of the flower 6
      6. Flowers distant, green; lip broadly ovate to suborbicular, at most acute; floral bracts separated ....*E. rigidum* (p. 299)
      6. Flowers in a close raceme, yellowish white; lip ovate-cordate, subacuminate; floral bracts imbricate ....*E. strobiliferum* (p. 299)
   5. Lip deeply or shallowly 3-lobed, on the lower side of the flower; floral bracts not enclosing the flowers 7
      7. Lip much longer than wide, deeply 3-lobed; mid-lobe linear-filiform and mostly more than 2 cm. long ....*E. nocturnum* (p. 295)
      7. Lip wider than long, shallowly 3-lobed; mid-lobe short and blunt 8
         8. Flower-cluster sessile or nearly so; lip usually broadly reniform and emarginate, more than 9 mm. wide...*E. difforme* (p. 293)
         8. Flower-cluster (or clusters) terminating a more or less elongate peduncle...........9
            9. Flowers in a crowded subcapitate raceme or panicle which terminates an elongated compressed peduncle; stem strongly compressed and leafy (mostly with more than six leaves) ....*E. anceps* (p. 286)
            9. Flowers in a loose few- to many-flowered simple (or rarely compound) raceme which terminates a more or less elongate terete peduncle; stem not compressed, with a few leaves (mostly less than four)......................*E. conopseum* (p. 291)

1. **Epidendrum anceps** Jacq., Select. Stirp. Am. Hist. 224, t. 138. 1763. Type locality: Forests in Martinique. (*Amphiglottis anceps* (Jacq.) Britton).

PLATE 111

(The name, *anceps,* is a Latin adjective meaning "two-edged," referring to the compressed peduncle.)

COMMON NAMES: Dingy-flowered Epidendrum, Brown Epidendrum.

Plant erect, leafy, glabrous, often stout, up to 10 dm. tall. Stem compressed, slender or stout but not pseudobulbous, entirely concealed by tubular leaf-sheaths. Leaves distichous, linear-elliptic to oblong-elliptic, obtuse to acute-apiculate, coriaceous and somewhat rigid, sessile and articulated at the base to the leaf-sheaths, occasionally tinged with purple, 5-20 cm. long, up to 4.5 cm. wide. Inflorescence a compact subcapitate raceme or few-branched panicle, 2-7 cm. long, 3-5.5 cm. in diameter, terminating a commonly elongate peduncle which is enveloped by close scarious tubular bracts. Floral bracts small, ovate to lanceolate, acute to acuminate, up to 6 mm. long. Flowers small, fleshy, light greenish brown to dull red or tawny yellow, with the slender pedicellate ovaries 8-16 mm. long. Sepals obovate to broadly oblong-elliptic, obtuse to subacuminate at the apex, strongly 3-nerved, 4.5-9.5 mm. long, 3.5-4 mm. wide above the middle; lateral sepals oblique. Petals linear-oblanceolate to oblong-spatulate, subacute to acute, somewhat oblique, 1-nerved, 5-8.5 mm. long, up to 1.5 mm. wide near the apex. Lip adnate to the column almost to its apex, up to 1.1 cm. long from the apex to the base of the column; lamina spreading from the apex of the column, cordate-reniform, more or less shallowly 3-lobed, up to 5.5 mm. long and 8 mm. wide across the lateral lobes; lateral lobes broadly rounded to subquadrate; mid-lobe short, with a truncate-retuse apex, usually with an apicule in the sinus; disc with a thickened ridge in the middle but without calli. Column dilated upward, lavender at the truncate tip, 4-5 mm. long. Capsule ovoid, about 1.5 cm. long and 1 cm. in diameter.

This species varies considerably in its leaves, inflorescence and flowers. The inflorescence is usually long-pedunculate (rarely short-pedunculate) and is shortly racemose to almost subcapitate when young, but becomes branched by proliferation as it develops. The flowers are malodorous and vary in having the lip nearly simple to noticeably 3-lobed, with the apical portion of the lip (or mid-lobe) rounded to retuse or somewhat bilobulate.

The earliest collection I have seen of this species in our region is that obtained by OAKES AMES and BLANCHE AMES from Gobbler's Head near Naples, Collier County, Florida, on March 12, 1904.

Epidendrum anceps grows on trees in cypress swamps and hammocks of southern peninsular Florida. It is especially frequent on oaks (*Quercus* spp.), Bald Cypress (*Taxodium distichum*) and ashes (*Fraxinus* spp.). In the tropics, it is found on trees in dense forests and on rocks in thickets and along streams. It usually grows at low elevations and occurs near sea level in Florida, up to 6,500 feet altitude in Central America. It flowers sporadically throughout the year, especially from February to July in Florida.

GEOGRAPHICAL DISTRIBUTION: Widespread and frequent in southern Florida (Collier, Dade, Lee and Monroe counties); also Mexico, through Central America to Panama, throughout the West Indies and northern South America.

CULTURAL NOTES: I had this species, as well as a number of the other epiphytic orchids which I collected in Florida, under cultivation in the Duke University Greenhouses for several years and, as far as I know, they are still surviving there. These epiphytes were grown on a section of an old oak tree trunk suspended over a small pool in the greenhouse. There they thrived with very little attention, and proved to be exceedingly hardy.

This species was first introduced into England from the West Indies in 1790 by Lord GARDNER. See this section under the generic discussion.

2. **Epidendrum Boothianum** Lindl., Bot. Reg. 24: Misc. p. 5. 1838. Type locality and collection: "native of Havannah," Cuba, 1835, *Sutton*. (*Epidendrum erythronioides* Small; *Epicladium Boothianum* (Lindl.) Small).

PLATE 112

(The name, *Boothianum,* is in honor of WILLIAM BEATTIE BOOTH (*circa* 1804-1874), noted English gardener who furnished LINDLEY with a drawing and description of this species.)

COMMON NAMES: Dollar-orchid, Booth's Epidendrum, Epicladium.

Plant glabrous, up to 3 dm. tall, consisting of short clustered pseudobulbs which bear at the summit one to three leaves and in the center between them a flowering branch. Rootstock a short rhizome which gives rise to slender flexuous whitish roots. Pseudobulbs suborbicular, strongly flattened, often inclined, smooth and glossy, yellow-green, subtended by several short fibrous sheaths, 2.5-3 cm. long, 1-2.5 cm. wide. Leaves one to three, oblanceolate, obtuse to acute, sessile, thin, rather rigid, somewhat twisted, keeled on the back and recurved at the apex, 7-17 cm. long, 1-2.5 cm. wide above the middle. Raceme laxly few-flowered, borne on a slender peduncle which is clothed below by one or more slender linear-oblong conduplicate foliaceous sheaths; peduncle up to 25 cm. long. Floral bracts minute, subulate, less than 2 mm. long. Flowers up to eight, small but rather showy, with the slender pedicellate ovaries up to 1.7 cm. long. Sepals and petals yellow with reddish brown to magenta-purple irregular blotches. Sepals broadly to narrowly oblanceolate, acute to subacuminate, with the margins slightly revolute, 1-1.4 cm. long, 3-3.5 mm. wide; lateral sepals slightly oblique. Petals narrowly oblanceolate, obtuse to acute, 1-1.3 cm. long, 1-2 mm. wide near the apex. Lip greenish yellow or white, occasionally marked with magenta, free from the column except at the base, entire or obscurely 3-lobed, rhombic or trapeziform in outline, with all of the lobes or angles obtuse and with the lateral angles strongly reflexed, about 1 cm. long and 7 mm. wide; disc with a white tridentate callus under the column, the middle tooth being extended into a clavate or bulbous-thickened termination reaching to the apex of the mid-lobe. Column greenish at the base, with purplish blotches, whitish above, strongly longitudinally grooved on each side, 6-7 mm. long. Capsule ovoid, conspicuously 3-winged, tan-colored and shining, pendent, 2-3 cm. long, 1.5-2 cm. in diameter.

PLATE 112.— **Epidendrum Boothianum.** 1, plant, natural size. 2, lip and column, from above, four times natural size. 3, lip and column, front-side view, four times natural size. 4, fruit, showing three-winged capsule, natural size. *Drawn by Gordon W. Dillon.*

This species was apparently first found in the United States "on small trees" on Key Largo, Monroe County, Florida, by ALLEN HIRAM CURTISS, probably before 1890. It was next collected by J. H. SIMPSON in February 1892. In fact, although originally found on the Florida Keys, the Cape Sable region on the mainland in Monroe County is the place where this species most frequently occurs. It is an attractive little plant with rather showy flowers, and the peculiar flat round pseudobulbs have given rise to its common name, Dollar-orchid.

The Dollar-orchid is found on trees in hammocks and thickets of southern peninsular Florida. It usually occurs on small trees, having been collected on Jamaica-dogwood (*Piscidia piscipula*), Buttonwood (*Conocarpus erecta*), Live Oak (*Quercus virginiana*) and Buckthorn (*Bumelia* spp.). This species usually grows at low elevations and has not been found to grow above 175 feet altitude in Mexico, blooming from July to November in various parts of its range.

GEOGRAPHICAL DISTRIBUTION: Florida (Dade and Monroe counties); also Mexico, British Honduras, the Bahama Islands and Cuba.

CULTURAL NOTES: This species was first introduced into England from Cuba by Captain Sutton of Flushing in the spring of 1835. It flowered the following September in the collection of Sir CHARLES LEMON at Carclew. See this section under the generic discussion.

3. **Epidendrum cochleatum** L. var. **triandrum** Ames, Contrib. Knowl. Orch. Fl. South. Florida 16, t. 8. 1904. Type locality: Florida, common in hammocks nearly everywhere from Ft. Lauderdale south. Rare on the Keys. (*Epidendrum triandrum* (Ames) House; *Anacheilium cochleatum* (L.) Small, not Hoffmannsegg, 1840). PLATE 113

(The name, *cochleatum,* is a Latin adjective meaning "shell-shaped," in allusion to the lip which resembles in shape one valve of a clam shell. The name, *triandrum,* is a Greek term meaning "three anthers," designating the number of anthers found in the variety, instead of the usual single one of the typical form.)

COMMON NAME: Clamshell Orchid.

Plant glabrous, stout, 0.8-5.8 dm. tall. Pseudobulbs more or less stipitate, ovoid to cylindrical-ellipsoid, strongly compressed, bearing one to three leaves at the summit, 3.5-21 cm. long, 2.5-3.5 cm. wide, clothed with scarious fugacious sheaths when young. Leaves oblong-lanceolate to linear-lanceolate, acute to shortly acuminate, sessile, 1-4.6 dm. long, 1.3-6 cm. wide. Inflorescence a loosely few-flowered raceme or rarely a panicle with several branches, up to 45 cm. long (including the peduncle); peduncle subtended at the base by one or two spathaceous sheaths which are up to 10 cm. long, provided with scattered bracts above. Floral bracts triangular-lanceolate, acute to acuminate, concave, membranaceous, 5-11 mm. long. Flowers showy, with the rather stout pedicellate ovaries 1-4 cm. long. Sepals and petals greenish white or greenish yellow, with purplish blotches near the base, linear-lanceolate, long-acuminate, twisted and spreading-reflexed, somewhat triangular-thickened at the apex, sepals 2.8-7 cm. long, 4-7 mm. wide near the base; petals 2.3-5.5 cm. long, 3-5 mm. wide near the base. Lamina of lip spreading from the middle of the column, entire, deep purple with the basal central portion whitish marked with conspicuous radiating purple veins, broadly orbicular-cordate (shape similar to one valve of a clam shell), deeply concave, sharply mucronate at the apex and with the margins somewhat undulate, 1.2-2.3 cm. long, 1.5-3 cm. wide; disc with two yellowish cushion-like calli at the base. Column short, stout, somewhat dilated above, 5-toothed at the apex, flecked with purple below, greenish yellow or whitish above, 6-10 mm. long; anthers three. Capsule yellowish brown, ellipsoid to obovoid, recurved and pendent, 3-angled, with the angles broadly winged, 2-4 cm. long, 8-15 mm. in diameter.

All of the Florida plants examined have three anthers, instead of one as in the typical form. In addition to having three anthers, var. *triandrum* also has the apex of the column 5-toothed instead of being 3-toothed, the two additional teeth being accounted for by the two additional lateral anthers.

AMES, in describing this variety, made the following interesting observation: "In an examination of specimens from many parts of South Florida, not a single one has been seen with a 'normal' column, so that it may be safely assumed that *Epidendrum cochleatum* has given rise to a three-anthered race exclusively occupying this part of the state, at least. The pollen of the lateral anthers—which are applied to the stigma—germinates *in situ,* as proven by microscopic examination, while the pollen of the third or normal anther does not reach the stigmatic surface. Plants growing in my greenhouse and thus removed from the possi-

PLATE 113.—**Epidendrum cochleatum** var. **triandrum.** Plant, two thirds natural size. 1, column, front view, to show the three anthers, twice natural size. 2, cross-section of capsule, natural size. 3, fruits, natural size. *Drawn by Blanche Ames.*

bility of insect fertilization, have produced seeds freely. It is, therefore, safe to conclude that the variety is self-fertilized. When an anomaly is sporadic and found only in a few individuals, it is merely of phytoteratological interest; but when the 'anomaly' becomes constant in plants occurring over a large area, it seems worthy of recognition as a varietal character."

In 1947, AMES made the following additional observation concerning this variety: "It might be argued, on the basis of this variety, that the epiphytic orchids which have entered Florida from the West Indies have depended on one or a few introductions. If so, it would seem that *Epidendrum cochleatum* var. *triandrum* represents in Florida a single introduction from which all the Floridian specimens have descended. If this supposition is true, it would throw interesting light on the history of the introduction of orchids into Florida from the West Indies and other parts of the tropics."

The earliest collection I have seen of this variety in our region is that obtained by A. P. GARBER from near Miami, Dade County, Florida, sometime between March and June 1877.

This variety is found on trees in low woods, hammocks and cypress swamps in southern peninsular Florida. It flowers sporadically throughout the year, especially from October to July, inclusive.

GEOGRAPHICAL DISTRIBUTION: Florida (Collier, Dade, Lee and Monroe counties). The typical form occurs in Mexico, Central America, the Bahama Islands, the West Indies and South America.

CULTURAL NOTES: According to BROWN (1813), the typical form of this species was first introduced into England in 1786 by ALEXANDER ANDERSON. See this section under the generic discussion.

4. **Epidendrum conopseum** R. Br. in Ait., Hort. Kew., ed. 2, 5: 219. 1813.
   Type locality and collection: Florida, *William Bartram*. (*Amphiglottis conopsea* (R. Br.) Small). PLATE 114

(The name, *conopseum,* is a Greek term meaning "gnat-like," probably in reference to the small inconspicuous flowers.)

COMMON NAMES: Green-fly Orchid, Tree Orchid, Florida Epidendrum.

Plant without pseudobulbs, slender, glabrous, erect or ascending, 5.5-40 cm. tall. Roots fibrous, thick, spongy, matted. Leaves one to three or rarely more, distichous, above the lower part of the stem, narrowly oblong to linear-lanceolate, acute to cuspidate, coriaceous, sessile, articulated to closely appressed leaf-sheaths at the base, 3-9 cm. long, 4-14 mm. wide. Raceme simple or rarely compound, borne on a slender more or less elongate peduncle, laxly few- to many-flowered, 5-16.5 cm. long, 4-7 cm. in diameter; peduncle bearing a few remote sheathing bracts. Floral bracts linear-lanceolate, acuminate, 5-12 mm. long. Flowers fragrant, grayish green, occasionally tinged with purple, with the slender pedicellate ovaries 1.5-2.5 cm. long. Dorsal sepal broadly oblong-spatulate to oblanceolate, obtuse to subacute, 9-12.5 mm. long, 3-4 mm. wide near the apex. Lateral sepals somewhat obliquely oblong-spatulate or obovate-oblong, obtuse to subacute, with the margins involute, 8-13 mm. long, about 4 mm. wide near the apex. Petals narrowly oblanceolate to linear-spatulate, obtuse to subtruncate, 8-12 mm. long, 1.5-2 mm. wide near the apex. Lamina of lip spreading from near the apex of the column, shallowly 3-lobed, irregularly cordate-reniform to cordate-ovate in outline, 4-6 mm. long, about 7.5 mm. wide across the lateral lobes; lateral lobes broadly rounded; mid-lobe narrower than the lateral lobes, subtruncate to truncate or sometimes retuse at the apex; disc with two short fleshy calli near the base. Column slender, adnate to the lip for almost its entire length, about 8 mm. long. Capsule pendent, 1.5-2.3 cm. long, 7-9 mm. in diameter.

For several reasons, this species is unique among the epiphytic orchids in our region. It is not only the most frequent and widespread epiphytic orchid in the southeastern United States, but it is also the only one in this country occurring outside of Florida. Thus, it is the northernmost epiphytic orchid in the Western Hemisphere.

Its range in our region, based on extant botanical specimens, extends from the Lake Waccamaw region, Columbus County, in southeastern North Carolina (where it is apparently frost-resistant), southward along a narrow strip of the Atlantic Coastal Plain, through all of northern Florida to Palm Beach, Highlands, Polk, Hillsborough and Pinellas counties in south-central Florida and to Calhoun County in West Florida. Its distribution then jumps to several stations in Mobile County,

Sketched in 1902. Finished Dec. 1946.

PLATE 114.—**Epidendrum conopseum.** Flowering plant and fruiting inflorescence, natural size. In extreme left hand corner, a lateral sepal, about
three times natural size; just above the lateral sepal, a petal (at left) and
lip adnate to the column (at right), from above, about three times natural
size. *Drawn by Blanche Ames.*

Alabama, and then, skipping Mississippi, to southeastern Louisiana where it is fairly abundant. There is a wide gap in south-central Louisiana where no collections have been made (or where the species does not occur) and then a lone station occurs near Lake Charles, Calcasieu Parish, in southwestern Louisiana.

I have collected this orchid at both extremities of its range. On December 13, 1935, Dr. H. L. BLOMQUIST of Duke University and I found the Green-fly Orchid at Lake Waccamaw, North Carolina, where it was growing in a mass with the common epiphytic fern, *Polypodium polypodioides* var. *Michauxianum,* on a large limb of a sweet gum tree about fifteen feet from the ground. On July 21, 1938, my wife and I obtained plants of this species from near Lake Charles, Louisiana, where it was rather abundant high up in trees in a swamp. This station is only thirty miles from the Texas state line.

In the *Flora of Texas* (1944), I stated that it is very likely that with further exploration this epiphytic orchid will be found in some of the swamp-forests in southeastern Texas. Accordingly, in June and July 1946, my wife and I undertook to make a "further exploration" for this orchid in Orange and Jefferson counties in southeastern Texas. Although swamp-forests were explored along the Sabine and Neches rivers, Cow Bayou and other streams, no specimen of *E. conopseum* was taken. The prolific growth of the epiphytic fern, *Polypodium polypodioides,* and Spanish Moss, *Tillandsia usneoides,* very often proved to be a great hindrance in our looking for the orchid, not to mention the fiery stings and insidious annoyances of countless flies and mosquitoes which haunt the swamps of that part of the state. Notwithstanding our failure to find the orchid, there is little doubt in my mind that it will eventually be discovered in southeastern Texas.

The earliest collection I have seen of this species in our region is that obtained by W. M. CANBY from Hibernia, Clay County, Florida, in March 1869. However, an undated collection from Louisiana by a Dr. CARPENTER, labeled "Parasitic particularly upon *Magnolia grandiflora,* May . . ." is perhaps still earlier.

Epidendrum conopseum has been found on the bark of various species of trees and rarely on rocks, in hammocks, low woods and cypress swamps. It grows primarily on old trees of Southern Magnolia (*Magnolia grandiflora*) and Live Oak (*Quercus virginiana*). It has also been collected on Beech (*Fagus grandifolia*), Sweet Gum (*Liquidambar styraciflua*), Ironwood (*Carpinus caroliniana*), Red Maple (*Acer rubrum*), Bald Cypress (*Taxodium distichum*), Red Cedar (*Juniperus virginiana*) and species of Gum (*Nyssa* spp.). It is quite probable that this species grows also on many other of our southern trees. The Green-fly Orchid flowers sporadically throughout the year, mainly from January to August.

GEOGRAPHICAL DISTRIBUTION: Local and rare from southeastern North Carolina (Columbus and Pender (*fide Wood & McCarthy*) counties), becoming more frequent southward along the Atlantic seaboard to south-central Florida (south to Highlands and Palm Beach counties), locally along the Gulf Coast to Louisiana (west to Calcasieu Parish). It is represented in Mexico by the recently discovered var. *mexicana* L. O. Wms.

CULTURAL NOTES: This is the hardiest epiphytic orchid found in the United States. It occurs on trees in swamps and on the edge of lakes in Southeastern North Carolina, where it is apparently frost-resistant. According to Brown (1813), this species was first introduced into England in 1775 by John Fothergill, thirty-eight years before it was known to science. See this section under the generic discussion.

5. **Epidendrum difforme** Jacq., Enum. Syst. Pl. Carib. 29. 1760 and Select. Stirp. Am. Hist. 223, t. 136. 1763. Type locality: Everywhere in extensive forests in Martinique. (*Epidendrum umbellatum* Sw.; *Auliza difformis* (Jacq.) Small; *Amphiglottis difformis* (Jacq.) Britton).   PLATE 115

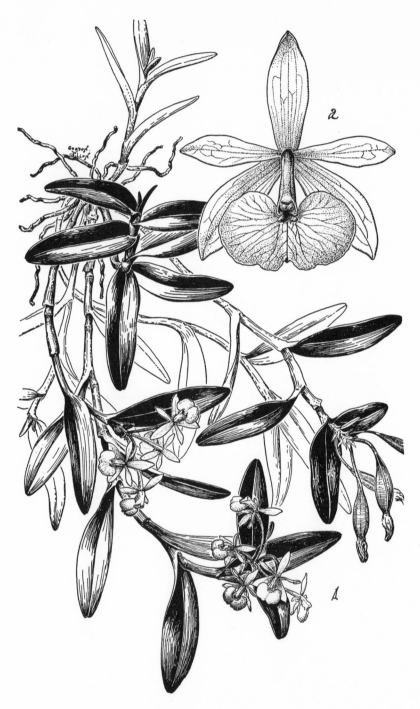

PLATE 115.— **Epidendrum difforme.** 1, flowering and fruiting plants, one third natural size. 2, flower, front view, twice natural size. *Drawn by Gordon W. Dillon.*

(The name, *difforme,* is a Latin term meaning "of unusual form," apparently in allusion to the straggly, zig-zag stems which are often entwined.)

COMMON NAME: Umbelled Epidendrum.

Plant ascending, 6-47 cm. tall, glabrous, caespitose. Stem without pseudobulbs, leafy, often more or less flexuous, entirely concealed by the persistent flaring leaf-sheaths, Leaves distichous, variable in shape, oval or ovate-elliptic to oblong-lanceolate, rounded to somewhat obtuse and retuse at the apex, rigid and coriaceous, 1.3-11 cm. long, up to 3.5 cm. wide. Raceme sessile, terminal, umbelliform, several- to many-flowered (rarely one-flowered). Floral bracts scarious, semitranslucent, lanceolate, acute to acuminate, 7-15 mm. long. Flowers very variable in size, pale green or whitish, with the slender pedicellate ovaries up to 4 cm. long. Dorsal sepal variable in shape, lanceolate to oblong-obovate, subobtuse to short-acuminate, 1.1-3.4 cm. long, 3.8-8 mm. wide. Lateral sepals somewhat obliquely oblong-lanceolate to obovate, obtuse to short-acuminate, 1.1-3.2 cm. long, 3.5-9 mm. wide. Petals filiform to narrowly oblanceolate, obtuse to rarely acuminate, 1-3 cm. long, 0.8-7 mm. wide near the apex. Lip adnate to the column to its apex with the lamina spreading from the apex of the column; lamina nearly simple to trilobulate, transversely subquadrate to reniform or transversely oval in general outline, 6-18 mm. long, 1-3.4 cm. wide; mid-lobe wanting or obscure to rather well-developed, when developed usually transversely oblong to semi-elliptic, either entire to crenate or bilobulate, retuse, truncate or apiculate at the apex; disc with two basal erect calli and more or less thickened nerves. Column dilated above, 7-10 mm. long. Capsule ellipsoid, up to 4.5 cm. long, about 1.5 cm. in diameter.

This species is extremely variable, particularly in the form of the leaves and in the size and shape of the lip. A number of varieties and specific proposals have been made in this species based on minor variations. In Latin American countries, where it is commonly called "Maria Izabel" and "flora garbanzo," this orchid is exceedingly abundant.

According to STEVENSON (1926), the rust, *Uredo guacae* Mayor., has been observed on this species and on *Epidendrum rigidum* in Ecuador. However, no data are available to show what effect this infection has on the plant.

The earliest collection I have seen of this species in our region is that obtained by A. P. GARBER in the Everglades near Miami, Dade County, Florida, sometime in April or May 1877.

The Umbelled Epidendrum is found on trees in cypress swamps and low hammocks of southern peninsular Florida. In the tropics, it is terrestrial or epiphytic in dense tropical forests, open mountain forests and pine-oak forests. In Mexico it often occurs on fence posts bordering coffee plantations. Although this species usually grows at low elevations, it is found up to 10,000 feet altitude in Guatemala, and flowers sporadically throughout the year, especially from August to November in Florida.

GEOGRAPHICAL DISTRIBUTION: Widespread and frequent in southern Florida (Collier, Dade, Lee, Monroe and Palm Beach counties); also Mexico, through Central America to Panama, throughout the West Indies and northern South America.

CULTURAL NOTES: According to BROWN (1813), this species was first introduced into England in 1793 by Rear Admiral WILLIAM BLIGH in H. M. S. *Providence.* See this section under the generic discussion.

6. **Epidendrum nocturnum** Jacq., Enum. Syst. Pl. Carib. 29. 1760 and Select. Stirp. Am. Hist. 225, t. 139. 1763. Type locality: Mountain forests, Martinique. (*Auliza nocturna* (Jacq.) Small; *Amphiglottis nocturna* (Jacq.) Britton). PLATE 116

(The name, *nocturnum,* is a Latin adjective meaning "nocturnal" or "by night," in allusion to the fragrance of the flowers which is especially noticeable at night.)

COMMON NAME: Night-smelling Epidendrum.

Plant erect, slender to stout, caespitose, up to 10 dm. tall. Stem without pseudobulbs, leafy, terete below, compressed above, up to 1.5 cm. in diameter, concealed by subcoriaceous leaf-sheaths. Leaves distichous, broadly oval to elliptic, linear-elliptic or lanceolate, broadly rounded to subacute at the apex (occasionally emarginate), sessile, articulated to closely appressed sheaths at the base, coriaceous, 7-15 cm. long, 1-5.5 cm. wide. Raceme one or more, very compact and abbreviated, terminal, composed of four or five flowers (rarely more). Floral bracts ovate-cucullate, acute, with hyaline margins, 4-9 mm. long. Flowers large, showy, more or less nodding, with the slender pedicellate ovaries 4.5-12 cm. long. Sepals

PLATE 116.— **Epidendrum nocturnum.** Flowering and fruiting plants, natural size. *Drawn by Blanche Ames.*

greenish white, linear-lanceolate, long-acuminate, somewhat twisted above, 3.6-9 cm. long, 3-8.5 mm. wide near the base. Petals whitish, filiform, 3.5-8.5 cm. long, 2-3 mm. wide near the base. Lip white, adnate to the column to its apex, deeply and unequally 3-lobed; lateral lobes directed forward, semioval to semiovate or obliquely ovate-lanceolate, semicordate at the base, obtuse to long-acuminate at the apex, with the margins entire or rarely denticulate,

1.2-3.8 cm. long, 4-10 mm. wide below the middle; mid-lobe linear-filiform, setaceous and long-attenuate, 2.2-5.7 cm. long, up to 3 mm. wide near the base; disc with two elongate parallel lamellae extending from the base of the lip to the base of the mid-lobe. Column somewhat dilated above, entire to dentate at the apex, 1.5-2 cm. long. Capsule ellipsoid-fusiform, 3-5.5 cm. long, 1.5-2 cm. in diameter.

This species is variable in the size of the plant, in the shape of the leaves, in the size of the flowers, and in the shape of the lateral lobes of the lip. The flowers, which are the largest in the genus in our region, are extraordinarily fragrant, especially at night — hence the common name.

The earliest collection I have seen of this species in our region is that obtained by A. P. Garber from near Miami, Dade County, Florida, in April 1877.

The Night-smelling Epidendrum grows on trees, as Holly (*Ilex* spp.), Live Oak (*Quercus virginiana*), other species of oaks, etc. in low hammocks of southern peninsular Florida. In the tropics, it is found on trees and rocks in dry or wet forests, on trees in dense jungles along the coast and on the edge of thickets. It usually occurs at low elevations and grows near sea level in Florida and Panama, up to 4,000 feet altitude in Honduras and 5,000 feet in Mexico. The blooming season is sporadic throughout the year, but mainly from July to December in Florida.

Geographical distribution: Widespread and rather frequent in southern Florida (Collier, Dade, Lee, Monroe, Okeechobee and Palm Beach counties); also from Mexico, through Central America to Panama, throughout the West Indies and northern South America.

Cultural notes: This species was first cultivated in England about 1824 by Conrad Loddiges & Sons. See this section under the generic discussion.

7. **Epidendrum pygmaeum** Hook., Bot. Mag. 60: t. 3233. 1833. Type locality: Brazil. (*Hormidium tripterum* (Brongn.) Cogn.; *H. pygmaeum* (Hook.) Benth. & Hook. f. ex Hemsl.).   Plate 117

(The name, *pygmaeum,* is a Latin term meaning "dwarf," in allusion to the small size of the plant.)

Common name: Dwarf Epidendrum.

Plant glabrous, consisting of a creeping branched rhizome which produces numerous remote ascending or erect pseudobulbs. Rhizome concealed by inflated imbricating brown scarious sheaths. Pseudobulbs slender, fusiform, terete, 2- (rarely 3-) leaved at the apex, 2.5-10 cm. long, subtended by one or more brownish sheaths which are ovate, acute to acuminate and cuspidate, scarious and 1.5-4.5 cm. long. Leaves subopposite, erect-spreading, linear to oblong-elliptic or oblong-lanceolate, obtuse to acute or cuspidate, sessile, coriaceous, with fine conspicuous ribs, 1.5-14 cm. long, 8-20 mm. wide. Inflorescence terminal, consisting of one to several flowers in an abbreviated raceme, the peduncle being more or less fractiflex, up to 3 cm. long and subtended by scarious sheaths which are up to 2 cm. long. Floral bracts small, broadly ovate, acute, 3-5 mm. long, scarious. Flowers small, one to several, with the pedicellate ovaries up to 1.7 cm. long. Sepals spreading, greenish or brownish green, often tinged with lavender, thick and fleshy, dorsally keeled; dorsal sepal oblong-elliptic to oblong-lanceolate, rather abruptly acuminate, 5-11 mm. long, 1.5-4 mm. wide near the base; lateral sepals ovate-triangular to rhombic-ovate or oblong-lanceolate, acuminate, oblique, shortly connate at the base, 5-12 mm. long, 1.7-4 mm. wide. Petals linear, abruptly acute to acuminate, thickened at the apex, 4-9 mm. long, 2 mm. or less wide, similar to the sepals in color and often whitish at the base. Lip adnate to the column through the lower half and forming a cup, more or less distinctly 3-lobed, with the central portion sulcate, 2.5-7.5 mm. long from the apex of the mid-lobe to the base of the column, 3.2-8 mm. wide across the lateral lobes when spread out, white with a purple blotch at the base of the mid-lobe; lateral lobes broadly oblong to suborbicular, upcurved, with the margins finely erose, 1.5-3 mm. long, about 2 mm. wide; mid-lobe minute, subulate, apiculate, 1-3 mm. long. Column 2-5 mm. long, trilobulate at the apex. Capsule ellipsoid, broadly 3-angled and winged along the angles, 1-2 cm. long.

This species is exceedingly variable as to the size of the plant and flowers and shape of the leaves. It often forms large colonies on trees by means of its creeping elongated branching rhizome.

As far as I know, the Dwarf Epidendrum has been collected only once in our region when it was found by A. A. Eaton in March 1905. Eaton found this species growing on a Pop-ash (*Fraxinus caroliniana*) tree ten miles northeast of the town of Everglade in Collier County, Florida.

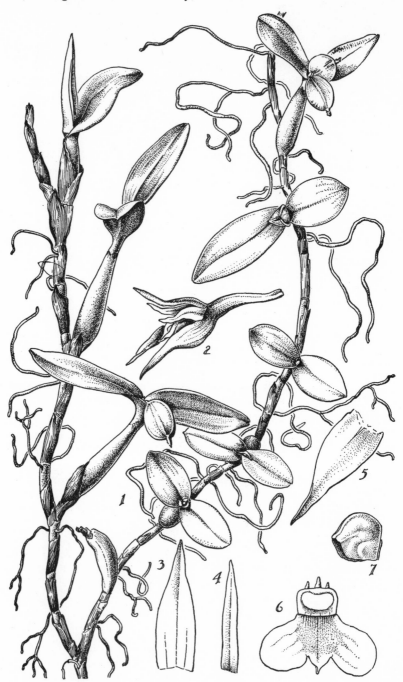

PLATE 117.—**Epidendrum pygmaeum.** 1, fruiting plant, two thirds natural size. 2, flower, side view, three times natural size. 3, dorsal sepal, four times natural size. 4, petal, four times natural size. 5, lateral sepal, four times natural size. 6, lip and column, front view, lip spread out, four times natural size. 7, anther cap, enlarged. *Redrawn from Blanche Ames by Gordon W. Dillon.*

In the tropics, this species occurs on trees and rocks in dense humid forests where it grows up to 2,500 feet altitude in Haiti and 6,200 feet in Honduras. The blooming season extends primarily from July to November, but it may flower sporadically throughout the year.

GEOGRAPHICAL DISTRIBUTION: Florida (Collier County); also Mexico through Central America to Panama, the West Indies and northern South America.

CULTURAL NOTES: Cultivation of this species was first undertaken in England about 1832 by a Mrs. ARNOLD HARRISON. See this section under the generic discussion.

8. **Epidendrum rigidum** Jacq., Enum. Syst. Pl. Carib. 29. 1760 and Select. Stirp. Am. Hist. 222, t. 134. 1763. Type locality: Forests of Martinique. (*Spathiger rigidus* (Jacq.) Small). PLATE 118

(The name, *rigidum,* is a Latin adjective meaning "stiff" or "rigid," in reference to the condition of the inflorescence.)

COMMON NAME: None known.

Plant consisting of a creeping more or less branched rhizome which produces at intervals erect or ascending stems. Stems entirely concealed by the leaf-sheaths, up to 3 dm. tall. Leaves several, distichous, sessile, articulated with the leaf-sheaths, oblong-elliptic to linear-oblong, obtuse and usually obliquely retuse at the apex, coriaceous, 2.5-12.5 cm. long, 6-22 mm. wide. Raceme spicate, slender and rigid, somewhat fractiflex, few- to many-flowered, up to 15 cm. long (including the short peduncle). Floral bracts distichous and equitant, concave-conduplicate with a prominent keel on the back, membranaceous, ovate to broadly triangular when spread out, subobtuse to acuminate, concealing the ovary and often most of the flower, green or brownish, with scarious hyaline margins, 9-15 mm. long, 7-10 mm. wide at the base when expanded. Flowers non-resupinate, inconspicuous, green or yellowish green, sessile, leathery. Sepals ovate to ovate-oblong or oblong-elliptic, obtuse to subacute, 4.5-10 mm. long, 2.5-4 mm. wide; lateral sepals oblique. Petals linear to linear-oblanceolate, obtuse, more or less denticulate on the margins, 4-9 mm. long, 1-2.5 mm. wide near the apex. Lip uppermost in the flower, adnate to the column up to its apex; lamina broadly cordate-ovate to suborbicular, obtuse to occasionally retuse at the apex, with the margins usually crenulate-denticulate, 2.5-6 mm. long, 3-5.5 mm. wide; disc with a pair of small calli at the base. Column short, stout, 2-3 mm. long, dentate at the apex. Capsule ellipsoid, 1-2 cm. long.

In the way of beauty, this scraggly orchid has little to recommend it, but it is of interest, however, in that it is an "ugly duckling" in a family of "swans." In some hammocks of southern peninsular Florida it is an epiphytic weed.

The earliest collections of this species which I have seen from our region are those obtained by J. K. SMALL, J. J. CARTER and A. A. EATON from between Cutler and Longview Camp, Dade County, Florida, in November 1903. However, an undated collection by A. H. CURTISS from "west of Everglades" is probably a much earlier record than those above since that botanist collected in Florida as early as 1880.

This species is found on various species of trees in cypress swamps, hammocks and low swampy woods in southern peninsular Florida. In the tropics, it grows on trees in open or dense wet forests and cypress swamps. Although it is usually found at low elevations, it occurs up to 2,500 feet altitude in Honduras and 3,500 feet in Mexico and Guatemala. It blooms sporadically throughout the year, mainly from November to May.

GEOGRAPHICAL DISTRIBUTION: Widespread and quite frequent in southern Florida (Broward, Collier, Dade and Monroe counties); also Mexico, through Central America to Panama, throughout the West Indies and northern South America.

CULTURAL NOTES: See this section under the generic discussion.

9. **Epidendrum strobiliferum** Reichb. f., Nederl. Kruidk. Arch. 4: 333. 1858. Type locality and collection: Dutch Guiana (Surinam), *Splitgerber 426.* (*Spathiger strobiliferus* (Reichb. f.) Small). PLATE 119

(The name, *strobiliferum,* is a Latin adjective meaning "cone-bearing," in allu-

PLATE 118.— **Epidendrum rigidum.** 1, plant, natural size. 2, lip and column, front-side view, five times natural size. 3, flower, side view, three times natural size. 4, anther, enlarged. *Drawn by Blanche Ames.*

sion to the short, compact inflorescence which superficially resembles the strobile or cone of some conifers.)

COMMON NAME: None known.

Plant much-branched, caespitose, leafy, creeping to pendent or erect-ascending, small, up to 23 cm. tall. Stem somewhat terete below, compressed above, often fractiflex, entirely concealed by the greenish or purplish leaf-sheaths. Leaves distichous, widely spreading, rigidly coriaceous, elliptic to elliptic-lanceolate or linear-lanceolate, obtuse or retuse at the apex, sessile, articulate at the base, 1-4.5 cm. long, 3-10 mm. wide. Raceme at the tips of the branches, short, compact, few-flowered, up to 3.5 cm. long. Floral bracts broadly ovate-cucullate, acute, distichous, more or less imbricating, scarious, strongly ribbed, with erose hyaline margins, often purplish brown, concealing the ovary and often the flower, 4-9 mm. long. Flowers non-resupinate, white or yellowish white, occasionally marked with reddish lines, sessile, with the segments coriaceous and strongly nervose. Dorsal sepal oblong to elliptic-lanceolate, obtuse to acute, 3.5-4 (rarely up to 5.5) mm. long, 1.2-1.4 mm. wide. Lateral sepals obliquely ovate-oblong to oblong-lanceolate, subobtuse to acute, about 4 (rarely up to 5.3) mm. long, 1.8-2 mm. wide. Petals linear-spatulate to linear-oblanceolate, subacute to acute, slightly oblique, 3.5-4 (rarely up to 5.2) mm. long, about 0.5 mm. wide above the middle. Lip uppermost in the flower, adnate to the column nearly to its apex; lamina simple, ovate-cordate to triangular-cordate, acute to subacuminate, concave, 3-4 mm. long, 2.5-3 mm. wide; disc with two small lamellae at the base, nervose. Column stout, about 1.5 mm. long, somewhat dilated at the middle, with a triangular tooth on each side and two smaller teeth on the posterior surface at the apex. Ovary with a small vesicle at the summit beneath the lip and lateral sepals. Capsule ovoid-ellipsoid, 6-9 mm. long, 3-6 mm. in diameter, with the dehiscing ribs broad with scarious wings.

This species was first discovered in the United States near Naples, Collier County, Florida, by OAKES AMES on March 19, 1904. It was found in the Fahkah-natchee Swamp near Everglade, Florida, by A. A. EATON on June 10 of the same year. There have been very few collections made since then; the last, as far as I know, having been obtained in the Big Cypress Swamp, Collier County, on May 2, 1937 by W. M. BUSWELL.

Epidendrum strobiliferum occurs on trees with smooth bark, such as ashes (*Fraxinus* spp.), in cypress swamps and "heads" in southern peninsular Florida. In the tropics, it grows on trees in open or dense wet forests and thickets where it occurs up to 2,000 feet altitude. It usually flowers from March to May in Florida and elsewhere sporadically throughout the year.

GEOGRAPHICAL DISTRIBUTION: Southern Florida (Collier and Lee counties); also Mexico through Central America to Panama, throughout the West Indies and northern South America.

CULTURAL NOTES: See this section under the generic discussion.

10. **Epidendrum tampense** Lindl., Bot. Reg. 33: sub. t. 35. 1847. Type locality and collection: "It occurs near Tampa Bay [Florida], . . . Dr. Torrey, . . ." (*Encyclia tampensis* (Lindl.) Small).   PLATE 120

The name, *tampense,* designates the region of Tampa, Florida, as the locality where this species was first discovered.)

COMMON NAMES: Florida Butterfly Orchid, Tampa Encyclia.

Plant glabrous, 0.8-7.5 dm. tall, consisting of a short stout pseudobulb bearing at the summit one to rarely three leaves and a flowering branch between them. Roots stout, fibrous, whitish, matted. Pseudobulb ovoid to suborbicular, shining, green, often suffused with madder-purple, 3-8 cm. long, clothed with scarious sheaths which are fugacious. Leaves one to rarely three, linear to linear-lanceolate, subacute to acute, rigidly coriaceous, spreading, longitudinally sulcate, sometimes twisted, 4.5-42 cm. long, 4-15 mm. wide. Inflorescence terminal, racemose or paniculate; peduncle slender, long, brownish, smooth or warty; flower cluster few- to many-flowered. Floral bracts minute, subulate, closely appressed, less than 3 mm. long. Flowers showy, fragrant, variable in color, with the slender pedicellate ovaries 1.5-2.5 cm. long. Sepals and petals yellowish brown or yellowish green, somewhat veined and suffused with madder-purple. Sepals oblong to oblong-oblanceolate or oblong-spatulate, obtuse to subacute, 1.4-2.1 cm. long, 4.5-6.5 mm. wide above the middle. Petals oblanceolate to narrowly spatulate, obtuse to subacute, 1.4-2 cm. long, 4-5.5 mm. wide near the apex. Lip almost free from the column, white to magenta-purple, deeply 3-lobed, 1.4-1.8 cm. long; lateral lobes erect and porrect in natural position, obliquely ovate-oblong, obtuse to broadly rounded at the apex, with several crimson-magenta veins or suffused with magenta-crimson, 7-10 mm. long, 4-5 mm. wide; mid-

PLATE 119.— **Epidendrum strobiliferum.** 1, plant, natural size. 2, inflorescence, four times natural size. 3, dorsal sepal, six times natural size. 4, petal, six times natural size. 5, lateral sepal, six times natural size. 6, lip, six times natural size. 7, column and upper part of ovary, side view, ten times natural size. 8, column, front-ventral view, ten times natural size. 9, anther, enlarged. 10, pollinia, enlarged. *Redrawn from Blanche Ames by Gordon W. Dillon.*

lobe separated from the lateral lobes by a short isthmus, orbicular, rounded or retuse and often apiculate at the apex, slightly undulate on the margins, with numerous radiating veins of magenta-purple which become confluent into a large blotch of the same color near the base;

disc traversed in the center by two fleshy ridges extending from the base of the lip to the lower part of the mid-lobe, with a third short ridge between the others near the apex. Column with a pair of incurved wings or auricles near the summit, irregularly crenulate at the apex, 8-10 mm. long. Capsule ellipsoid, 2-3 cm. long, 1-1.5 cm. in diameter.

This is the most abundant epiphytic orchid found in southern peninsular Florida, and, with *Epidendrum conopseum,* which takes its place in northern Florida, it shares the honor of being our most frequent epiphytic orchid. Sometimes there are enormous colonies in which hundreds of attractive long-lasting flowers may be produced at the same time. The flowers are pleasantly fragrant, especially at night, and remain in good condition for as long as several weeks if sprays are kept in water at ordinary room temperature. The flowers are also exceedingly variable in color and are quite beautiful, making this species by far the most attractive of our Epidendrums.

The Florida Butterfly Orchid was apparently discovered in the United States for the first time in the vicinity of Tampa, Hillsborough County, Florida, by JOHN TORREY, who sent plants from this station to JOHN LINDLEY as early as 1846-47. For many years this species was thought to be endemic to Florida, but in recent years it has been found in the Bahama Islands, with var. *Amesianum* Correll occurring in Cuba.

This species doubtless owes its abundance to its extreme hardiness, for it not only occurs in dense moist forests but also in extraordinarily dry habitats. While exploring along the Homosassa River in Florida, I came across this species growing in an exceedingly xerophytic brushland near Hell's Gate, at the mouth of the river. The following brief account of my trip down this river may be of interest.

The Homosassa River, a short though large river, rises in Citrus County less than ten miles from the Gulf of Mexico. Its source is a group of tremendous artesian wells—the famous Homosassa Springs. The river meanders through a densely forested country to break out eventually into the Gulf from a slightly elevated dry hot country covered with a stunted vegetation.

In places the river is almost impassable, even to canoes, except for narrow channels cutting through the dense growth of under-water vegetation which threatens everywhere to choke the stream. Great carpets of aquatic plants gradually sweep up from the banks on each side, giving the impression of a long tortuous lawn approaching the inner depths of the silent forest. Except for a gentle, though well-nigh inaudible, whispering hum made by the tiny forest creatures, and the rhythmic dip of our paddles, no sound can be heard. The stillness is pierced now and then by some warning cry of our approach, and the thrashing of great schools of fish, which spread fan-like from the bow of our boat, give rise to little rippling waves over the otherwise placid water. Cormorants and Water Turkeys perch, as though in silhouette, on branches of dead trees, draped with grayish white Spanish Moss, and dart their snake-like necks upward into the brilliant sky. Especially sharp bends in the river have gradually eaten away prehistoric Indian shell-mounds which are so frequent in this vicinity. In one of these bends we ride a swift current which suddenly brings us out into a small cove where the surrounding country is dry and desert-like, being almost impenetrable because of its cover of shrubby thorny vegetation. There Spanish Bayonets (*Yucca* spp.) grow so thickly and have attained such large proportions that to attempt to travel through this impregnable growth might prove a difficult task. Nevertheless, a brief foray into the thicket reveals the Florida Butterfly Orchid growing in large clumps on cedars and Live Oak trees, and numerous unique herbaceous plants growing in the dry barren soil.

This species grows on trees in cypress swamps and "heads," low hammocks, dense swampy woods and in open dry woods. It has been collected on various species of oaks (*Quercus* spp.), cedars (*Juniperus* spp.) and pawpaws (*Annona* spp.), and on Bald Cypress (*Taxodium distichum*), Buttonwood (*Conocarpus*

PLATE 120.—**Epidendrum tampense.** 1, plant, natural size. 2, lip and column, spread out, one and one half times natural size. 3, pollinia, much enlarged. 4, fruits, natural size. *Redrawn from Blanche Ames by Gordon W. Dillon.*

erecta), Cabbage-palm (*Sabal palmetto*) and Gumbo-limbo (*Elaphrium simaruba*). Although it usually occurs near sea level, the var. *Amesianum* is found up to 800 feet altitude in Cuba. Its blooming period is from April to December in various parts of its range.

GEOGRAPHICAL DISTRIBUTION: Florida (in all of the state in and south of Flagler, Volusia, Seminole, Lake and Citrus counties) ; also Bahama Islands. It is represented in Cuba by var. *Amesianum*.

CULTURAL NOTES: The Florida Butterfly Orchid is perhaps the most widely cultivated in Florida of all the native epiphytic orchids. It is often seen on trees in yards where it has been naturally or artificially introduced, and is sometimes used for adornment by commercial establishments, such as hotels and amusement centers. See this section under the generic discussion.

30. **Basiphyllaea** Schltr.

Basiphyllaea Schltr. in Fedde, Repert. 17: 77. 1921.

(The name, *Basiphyllaea,* is a combination of Greek terms meaning "leaf" and "base," in allusion to the position of this organ on the plant.)

Terrestrial slender scapose herbs arising from a cluster of tuberous roots. Leaf solitary (rarely more) at the base of the scape, ovate to linear-oblanceolate, short. Inflorescence a slender few-flowered spicate raceme terminating a long peduncle. Flowers small, remote. Sepals and petals free, parallel and porrect. Lip sessile, free from the column, 3-lobed, 5-crested through the center of the disc. Column free, slender. Capsule cylindrical, recurved.

There are three species in this genus which occur either in southern Florida, Cuba or the Bahama Islands.

1. **Basiphyllaea corallicola** (Small) Ames, Sched. Orch., No. 7: 1. 1924. *Carteria corallicola* Small, Torreya 10: 188. 1910. Type locality and collection: Florida, Long Prairie, October 31, 1906, *J. K. Small, J. J. Carter & A. A. Eaton.* PLATE 102

(The name, *corallicola,* is a Latin term meaning, "growing on coral," in reference to the type of rock upon which this species was found growing.)

COMMON NAME: Carter's Orchid.

Plant scapose, very slender, erect, glabrous, 2-3.8 dm. tall. Roots fasciculate, fleshy, tuberous. Leaf one (rarely more), basal, linear-oblanceolate to linear, acute to subacuminate, rather fleshy and conduplicate, somewhat succulent, 4-10 cm. long. Stem provided with remote tubular sheaths, much exceeding the leaves. Raceme slender, spicate, few-flowered, 5-10 cm. long. Floral bracts minute, ovate, with a subulate tip, less than 4 mm. long. Flowers small, suberect, with the slender pedicellate ovaries 1.1-1.5 cm. long. Sepals and petals yellow-green or tinged with magenta-pink. Dorsal sepal linear-oblong to narrowly oblong-lanceolate, obtuse to acute, 7-8 mm. long, about 1.5 mm. wide. Lateral sepals obliquely linear-lanceolate, falcate, obtuse to acute, 7-8.5 mm. long, 1.5-2 mm. wide. Petals linear, somewhat falcate, acute, 7-8 mm. long, about 1 mm. wide. Lip 3-lobed above the middle, sessile, broadly cuneate to obovate in outline, 6-7 mm. long, 4-5 mm. wide across the lateral lobes, yellow-green with the apex of each lobe magenta-pink; lateral lobes short, rounded (free part about 1 mm. long); mid-lobe semi-orbicular; disc with five longitudinal crests traversing the center. Column slender, cylindrical, 3-4 mm. long. Capsule cylindrical, curved, 1-1.2 cm. long.

During the first decade of the present century, OAKES AMES, just beginning his extensive work on the Orchidaceae, sent his assistant, ALVAH AUGUSTUS EATON, into southern peninsular Florida during 1903-05 to explore that region for orchids. As has been noted throughout this work, EATON discovered during this period a number of orchids for the first and (often) only time in our region. While in Florida, EATON spent several months in the field with J. K. SMALL, authority on the flora of the southeastern United States, and others. On November 12, 1903, EATON sent to AMES a hastily written report of his explorations, a part of which report is included below. The report graphically describes the intense rivalry (typical of many field botanists) which existed between EATON and SMALL for honor in the field of new discoveries. The report not only reveals EATON's enthusiastic personality, but is descriptive of the country at that comparatively pioneer time in Florida and of some of the difficulties of plant collecting. It is also directly concerned with the discovery of *Basiphyllaea corallicola* in the United States.

"To summarize: you can't kill [JOHN KUNKEL] SMALL by walking. He is as good at that as I am. I feel he is not above a beat if he can make one, but honors are easy between us, as I find most of the ferns and orchids. I am much chagrined to fail in one instance, however, but CARTER made that find. [This find, an orchid, was later described as *Carteria corallicola* by Small in honor of J. J. Carter, and is the basis for the genus *Carteria*.]

"The first find was Triorchis [*Eulophia ecristata*], in fruit. S. [Small] found this first as it was on his side of the team. After that I got plenty, and had to give him enough to make up a sheet. It grows in the limerock country, in little pockets of earth. Its leaf-scheme appears to be as S. [Small] figures *Calopogon* to be. *Bletia* is abundant, but not in bloom. It grows as everything else does in the South country, in little patches, all derived from one seed, probably. It is very exasperating collecting things in the pines. The road is lime-rock, with no work done but fall the trees. You can judge how uneven it is. Every now and then you come to a 'glade,' open, rocky, with 1-3' of mud. Here they grow tomatoes for market, are getting them in now. . . .

"Several of the 'glades' are wet, and some have Corduroy roads over them, under water often, tilted more or less: and yet it is not so rough as the pines. You will find a single plant of a thing, and then for miles see no more, possibly not at all. It is the way of the country. I think it is the wrong time of the year. Everything has gone to seed save here and there, for some cause, an individual is in bloom. All orchids but [*Epidendrum*] *nocturnum* and [*E.*] *cochleatum* [var. *triandrum*] are out of bloom. *Rigidum* [*Epidendrum rigidum*] just coming on. I found two Calopogons and S. [Small] had found a *Bletia* in bloom before I came, but they are accident and won't be in full blast till Spring. Then one could do wonders collecting. No one has been here at that time, and it is just the time they should be.

"But to continue: about 15 miles from Cutler we found a hammock in the pine woods. These hammocks are peculiar. They are from a small patch to 10 or 12 acres: don't appear to be depresst much, sometimes elevated, but the trees are hardwood, they usually have 'sinks' from 6' to several feet across and 2-6 ft. deep, at the bottom of which is water. In these hammocks grow all kinds of epiphytes and ferns, usually one kind or another predominating. For instance: in this [*Epidendrum*] *cochleatum* [var. *triandrum*] was everywhere, [*E.*] *rigidum* common, but [*E.*] *tampense* was rare . . .

"Found a small rattler on one of the glades, a 'brown rattler' never more than a foot long. I killed him with my trowel. We got to 'Jenkins' just before dark . . . Jenkins is off at work on the railroad. So we took possession. We had never heard of him, but that didn't matter. A Swede lived near and gave us the freedom of the country with Jenkins' orders. The house is made of 5-8' logs cut in at ends till they fit with 2-4" and are not chinkt. I drank two cups of coffee and slept about 15 minutes all night. I had been awake since 3.30 A.M. the day before. We started out at 6 and had just gone 400 yrds or so when Carter spotted the orchid I spoke of [*Carteria corallicola*]. Usually they workt it by having Carter ride the middle seat on my side and Small the back one with me, but this time they were both on the same side. A most extended search failed to reveal more, and it was my luck to have it on the wrong side of the wagon. Small gave me a piece and you may be able to get an idea of it and grow the root on. The spike [all were in bud] lookt much like *Calopogon*: the bulb like *Triorchis*: one radical leaf, conduplicate, thick, horizontal. I hope you may be able to make something of it.

"One horse had lost a shoe, and soon went lame. We could outwalk him anyway and so started on. We went to the end of the road, then off into a hammock on the left. This was barren. I wanted S. [Small] to go into another ½ mi. away. He didn't want to, but concluded to. He stoppt halfway to consider if it were best to go on. As I kept on, he did too. Before we got into it I saw a tree loaded with [*Epidendrum*] *Boothianum*. I presume there is other there, but we lookt no more on the edge, where it grew, and I noticed it took dead or unshaded limbs. It was in fruit, but enough flower persisted to show its color.

". . . SMALL had begun to fuss to get away, and I reluctantly turned back, before we had more than dippt in it. I soon found *Hab. Garberi* [*Habenaria strictissima* var. *odontopetala*], 2 plants. He [SMALL] could find none, tho both returned and searched while I 'shinned' the oak for the [*E.*] *Boothianum*. The tree was 2 ft. through, and I didn't have the irons along, but I got there. . . .

"After coming out of the hammock yesterday I said to SMALL 'we havn't said anything about it, but I suppose when a person finds a thing it is his to handle.' He drawled out ye-e-ess. I then said I wanted it settled as I wanted to handle all the ferns I had found. He said 'It is pretty hard to tell who found them first.' I then called to his mind that I had announced every one of my finds but one, and told him just when I found that, which I knew was before he did. When CARTER found the orchid S. [SMALL] clincht that as if afraid I would claim it for you by duffing it 'Carteria.' I see what he intended, but he knows now what I intend—any breach will receive a kick."

This species grows in shallow sand-filled pockets of rocks in dry pinelands of southern peninsular Florida. It flowers from September to December.

GEOGRAPHICAL DISTRIBUTION: Florida (Dade County); also the Bahama Islands.

CULTURAL NOTES: While this orchid grows in the so-called coral-rock (a porous limestone) in Florida, as its specific epithet implies, its tuberous roots are embedded in humus and sand which fill the hollows in the rock, and the soil-reaction of this material is more or less acid. It is quite possible that it could be cultivated in Florida wild gardens, although its habit of remaining dormant for many years without blooming makes it rather unsatisfactory as a horticultural subject. (E. T. W.)

31. Polystachya Hook.

Polystachya Hook., Exot. Fl. 2: t. 103. 1824, conserved name.

(The name, *Polystachya,* is a combination of Greek words meaning "many spikes," in allusion to the typically numerous branches of the inflorescence.)

Epiphytic or rock-inhabiting caespitose plants with small thickened or pseudobulbous leafy stems. Leaves one or several, distichous, articulated with the sheaths. Inflorescence a simple or paniculate raceme terminating a more or less long closely sheathed peduncle. Flowers small, non-resupinate. Dorsal sepal free. Lateral sepals larger than the dorsal sepal, attached to the column-foot and forming a more or less prominent mentum. Petals usually linear. Lip uppermost in the flower, nearly entire to deeply 3-lobed; disc usually with a conspicuous callus, mostly covered with mealy hairs. Column short, not winged, with a more or less prominent foot; pollinia four, waxy. Capsule ellipsoid.

There are about one hundred species in *Polystachya.* This genus attains its maximum development in tropical and southern Africa, though it also occurs in India and Malaya, and sparsely so in the American tropics and subtropics. The single species in our area is closely allied to several other Mexican, Central American and West Indian species.

1. **Polystachya luteola** (Sw.) Hook., Exot. Fl. 2: t. 103. 1824. *Cranichis luteola* Sw., Fl. Ind. Occ. 3: 1433. 1804 (?). Type locality: "Parasitica" on trees in mountains of Hispaniola and Jamaica. (*Polystachya minuta* (Aublet) Frappier, not A. Richard & Galeotti, 1845). PLATE 121

(The name, *luteola,* is a Latin adjective meaning "yellowish," in allusion to the color of the flowers.)

COMMON NAME: Pale-flowered Polystachya, Large Polystachya.

Plant erect, often growing in large clumps, 1-6 dm. tall, from a swollen pseudobulbous base. Pseudobulbs tapering from a thickened base, concealed by imbricating scarious sheaths and producing coarse fibrous roots. Leaves one to several, oblong-elliptic to linear-lanceolate or oblong-lanceolate, obtuse to acute, subcoriaceous, 4-30 cm. long, 1-4 cm. wide. Raceme simple or branched, 3- to many-flowered, slender, often unilateral; peduncle compressed, up to 5.5 dm. long (including the inflorescence), more or less concealed by long tubular imbricating membranaceous sheaths which are glaucous and semitranslucent. Floral bracts suborbicular-ovate, acuminate, with hyaline margins, about 3 mm. long. Flowers yellowish green, fragrant, with slender glabrous arcuate pedicellate ovaries 4-5 mm. long. Dorsal sepal triangular-ovate to ovate-oblong, acute to apiculate, shallowly concave, 4-5 mm. long, about 3 mm. wide. Lateral sepals obliquely and broadly triangular, acute to apiculate, with the margins somewhat involute, adnate to the column-foot and forming a prominent saccate mentum, about 6 mm. long and 4 mm. wide across the base. Petals narrowly linear-spatulate, subobtuse, apiculate, about 3 mm. long, mostly less than 0.5 mm. wide. Lip uppermost in the flower, parallel with the column and arcuate-recurved in natural position, obovate to broadly cuneate in outline when spread out, deeply 3-lobed above the middle, 4-4.5 mm. long, 3.5-4 mm. wide across the lateral lobes; lateral lobes entire, incurved, obtuse, with the free part about 1 mm. long; mid-lobe oblong-quadrate to suborbicular, often slightly dilated at the apex, truncate, with irregularly undulate-crenulate margins; disc entirely covered with inconspicuous glandular hairs, with a prominent solitary fleshy ridge, prominently crested on the central portion from the base to about the middle. Capsule ellipsoid, 8-12 mm. long, glabrous.

When SWARTZ first described this species (as *Cranichis luteola*) he stated that it was parasitic on trees. In SWARTZ's time it was the common belief that all plants which grew upon others were parasites, irrespective of how firmly or loosely they were attached to the "host." As noted before, there is no proof that any orchid is parasitic.

B. Ames. 1905.

PLATE 121

The earliest collection I have seen of this species in our region is that obtained by A. P. GARBER from near Miami, Dade County, Florida, sometime between March and July 1877.

This species grows on trees and on the dead trunks of trees in hammocks and cypress swamps of southern peninsular Florida. In the tropics, it is found on trees, rocks, rotten logs and stumps. While it usually grows at low elevations, it is found near sea level in Florida and the Philippines, up to 2,500 feet altitude in Cuba and 4,000 feet in the Philippines. The blooming period extends throughout the year in various parts of its range.

GEOGRAPHICAL DISTRIBUTION: Widespread and rather frequent in Florida (Broward, Collier, Dade, Lee, Monroe, Okeechobee, Orange and Palm Beach counties), uncommon in Mexico, Central America, the West Indies, the Bahama Islands and South America; also in the Old World tropics and subtropics.

CULTURAL NOTES: This species was cultivated in England before 1824 by Conrad Loddiges & Sons. See this section under the genus *Epidendrum*.

PLATE 121.—**Polystachya luteola.** Flowering plant, slightly less than natural size. Fruits, natural size. 1, flower, side view, about four times natural size. 2, lateral sepals, spread out to show their attachment to the column-foot, and column, four times natural size. 3, petal, five times natural size. 4, lip, spread out to reveal the lateral lobes and farinaceous callus, five times natural size. *Drawn by Blanche Ames.*

32. Galeandra Lindl.

Galeandra Lindl. in Bauer, Ill. Orch. Pl. Gen. t. 8. 1830 (?) ; Lindl., Gen. and Sp. Orch. Pl. 186. 1833.

(The name, *Galeandra,* is a combination of classical words meaning "male" and "helmet," doubtless in reference to the hooded anther.)

Terrestrial or epiphytic herbs. Stem pseudobulbous, fusiform, short or elongated, concealed by leaf-sheaths. Leaves distichous, articulated with a large sheath, narrow, plicate. Inflorescence terminal, a simple or paniculate raceme. Flowers showy. Sepals free, spreading, equal. Petals similar to the sepals but a little wider. Lip rising from the base of the column, entire or more or less lobed, produced at the base into a prominent spur; disc crested or lamellate along the center. Column short to somewhat elongated, with a short foot, shortly 2-winged at the apex and dorsally rostrate; clinandrium oblique; anther terminal, operculate, incumbent, imperfectly 2-celled; pollinia four, ovoid, waxy. Capsule erostrate.

This is a small genus composed of about twenty-five species which are confined to the American tropics and subtropics.

1. **Galeandra Beyrichii** Reichb. f., Linnaea 22: 854. 1849. Type locality: Shady woods around New Freiburg, Province of Rio de Janeiro, Brazil.

PLATE 122

(The name, *Beyrichii,* is in honor of HEINRICH CARL BEYRICH (1796-1834), German botanical collector who presumably first found this species.)

COMMON NAME: None known.

Plant up to 12 dm. tall, glabrous. Rhizome short, stout, entirely covered with scales, bearing numerous roots. Stem robust, pseudobulbous-thickened, several-jointed, invested by sheaths. Sheaths twelve to fifteen, large, loosely tubular, scarious, somewhat imbricate, with the free portion triangular-oblong, acute to shortly acuminate, 3-10 cm. long, becoming bract-like above. Leaves not present at time of flowering but appearing after the flowering time, erect, rather large, lanceolate to elliptic-lanceolate, elongate, acute to acuminate, with three thick ribs, about 3 dm. long, 3-3.5 cm. wide, tapering below into a stout petiole which is about 1 dm. long. Inflorescence terminal, rather short, laxly racemose and few-flowered above with usually about twelve flowers. Floral bracts oblong-elliptic, tapering to an acute or shortly acuminate apex, shorter than the pedicellate ovary. Flowers greenish or yellowish green, erect-spreading, rather large, with the slender pedicellate ovaries up to 2.5 cm. long. Sepals linear-oblong to elliptic-oblanceolate, tapering to the base and apex, keeled, 5-nerved, 1.9-2.8 cm. long; dorsal sepal about 5 mm. wide, obtuse; lateral sepals about 6 mm. wide, with a blunt apiculate apex. Petals obliquely oblanceolate, obtuse to abruptly acute, 5- to 7-nerved, a little shorter and broader than the sepals. Lip with numerous nerves, almost orbicular to orbicular-subquadrate when expanded, shorter than the sepals, broader than long, about 1.6-2 cm. long, 2.1-2.5 cm. wide when expanded, irregularly undulate at the broad apex, green with lines of crimson in front, produced into a prominent short blunt spur at the base; disc with four crests running from the base to about the middle, pubescent between the crests and in the middle and along the nerves above the crests. Column about 1 cm. long, stout, thickened above, concave in front, with short hairs on the apex. Capsule ellipsoid, reflexed, about 2.5 cm. long.

This species was found for the first time in the United States in Costello Hammock near Silver Palm, Dade County, Florida, by KARL O. KRAMER while attending a botanical field party from Miami University (Coral Gables) on November 2, 1946. This is the most recent addition to our orchid flora, and it is literally an invitation to adventurous naturalists and botanists not only to explore more thoroughly the less accessible regions but even those, like Costello Hammock, which are thought to be exhausted of all botanical interest and possibilities in the way of new discoveries. The finding of this species assures us that from time to time additional previously overlooked introductions from tropical America will be discovered in southern peninsular Florida and in those states adjacent to Mexico.

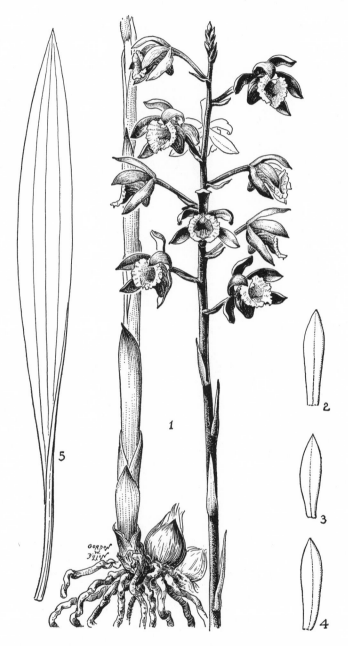

PLATE 122.—**Galeandra Beyrichii.** 1, flowering plant, one half
natural size. 2, dorsal sepal, natural size. 3, petal, natural size.
4, lateral sepal, natural size. 5, leaf, one half natural size (redrawn
from Cogniaux). *Drawn by Gordon W. Dillon.*

This species occurs as a terrestrial in forests, hammocks and along roadsides from near sea level in Florida, up to 3,500 feet altitude in Costa Rica. It has been found in flower from July to December in various parts of its range.

GEOGRAPHICAL DISTRIBUTION: Florida (Dade County), Costa Rica, the West Indies and throughout northern South America.

CULTURAL NOTES: See this section under *Bletia purpurea*.

33. Aplectrum Nutt.

Aplectrum Nutt., Gen. N. Am. Pl. 2: 197. 1818.

(The name, *Aplectrum,* is a Greek word meaning "spurless," referring to the lack of that organ in the flowers.)

Terrestrial scapose herbs arising from the side (near the summit) of a globose corm. Leaf solitary, with a short petiole, appearing in autumn and persisting until spring. Inflorescence vernal, consisting of a lax terminal raceme of several flowers. Sepals and petals free, somewhat spreading. Lip 3-lobed, free, with a lamellate crest on the disc. Column nearly straight, compressed; pollinia four. Capsule ellipsoid, pendent.

This is a monotypic genus which is confined to temperate North America.

1. **Aplectrum hyemale** (Muhl. ex Willd.) Torr., Comp. Fl. North. and Middle States 322. 1826. *Cymbidium hyemale* Muhl. ex Willd., Sp. Pl. 4: 107. 1805. Type locality: Pennsylvania. (*Aplectrum spicatum* BSP., not *Arethusa spicata* Walt.). PLATE 123

(The name, *hyemale,* is a Latin term meaning "of winter," in allusion to the leaf which is persistent during this time of year.)

COMMON NAMES: Puttyroot, Adam-and-Eve, Short's Puttyroot.

Plant scapose, glabrous, 2.8-5.5 dm. tall. Rootstock moniliform, horizontal, normally consisting of several subglobose glutinous corms (connected by slender naked stolons) which produce slender fibrous roots at the base and (near the apex) a flowering scape in spring and a leaf in autumn. Leaf solitary, basal, appearing in autumn and decaying in early spring before the appearance of the scape, with a short petiole; lamina elliptic to broadly elliptic, acute, plicate, dark green, with whitish nerves, often tinged with purple, 1-1.7 dm. long, 3-8 cm. wide. Scape with the lower part entirely clothed by tubular membranaceous sheaths. Raceme terminal, loosely few- (up to 15) flowered, 4-14 cm. long, 2-5 cm. in diameter. Floral bracts small, subulate, 3-6 mm. long. Flowers greenish, yellowish or whitish, variously marked with madder-purple (occasionally albino forms occur), with the rather stout pedicellate ovaries 8-10 mm. long. Sepals oblong-elliptic to narrowly oblong-spatulate, obtuse to acute, spreading, 1.1-1.4 cm. long, 3-4 mm. wide; lateral sepals somewhat falcate. Petals narrowly oblong-spatulate, obtuse to subacute, 1.1-1.2 cm. long, 2.8-3.5 mm. wide. Lip 3-lobed, broadly obovate-cuneate in outline, white, marked with magenta, 1-1.2 cm. long, 7-7.5 mm. wide across the lateral lobes when spread out; lateral lobes obliquely ovate-oblong, obtuse to subacute, with the free part about 2 mm. long; mid-lobe suborbicular, with the margins slightly involute and crenulate-undulate, 5-5.5 mm. wide; disc with three longitudinal crests (lamellae) on the lower half. Column compressed, minutely undulate-crenulate at the apex, about 7 mm. long and 2 mm. in diameter. Capsule ellipsoid, pendent, 1.5-2.3 cm. long, about 8 mm. in diameter.

THEODOR HOLM (unpublished mss.) writes the following concerning this species: "Very interesting is the fact that *Aplectrum,* at least for some years, possesses a coralloid rhizome of the same structure as that of *Corallorhiza, Calypso* and *Hexalectris,* thus a saprophytic stage may be found in genera of no immediate relationship. It seems indeed remarkable to observe this saprophytic structure, even though merely temporary, in *Aplectrum* which, otherwise, shares so many, and very obvious characters with the epiphytes, to which a saprophytic stage would be rather uncalled for . . . each tuber of *Aplectrum* represents a monopodium, and several such monopodiums are connected with each other into a sympodium, a structure known so well from epiphytic genera; nevertheless this highly specialized type of rhizome is in *Aplectrum* preceded by a coral-like, creeping rhizome, destitute of roots, but covered with hairy papillae, and performing the function of a root. Furthermore, when *Aplectrum* reaches the autophytic stage, it sends up a green leaf

PLATE 123.—**Aplectrum hyemale.** 1, flowering plant, two thirds natural size. 2, plant, with leaf, winter phase, two thirds natural size. 3, leaf-shoot, natural size. 4, fruiting inflorescence, natural size. 5, lip, spread out, two and one half times natural size. *Drawn by Gordon W. Dillon.*

which winters over, and of which the structure is approximately isolateral, the stomata being distributed over both faces of the blade. . . ."

According to TAYLOR (1940), the Catawba Indians, of the southeastern United States, beat and macerate the rootstock and corms of this plant and apply the resulting paste to boils. The corms of this species have also been used in New England and in other parts of its range for medicinal purposes. PURSH (1814) wrote concerning this species, "The roots bruised, with a small addition of water, give a strong cement, which when applied to broken china and glass is exceedingly durable."

GIBSON (1905) stated that the two joined corms, typical of most of the plants, are worn as amulets by the negroes and poor whites of the southeastern states who tell each other's fortunes by placing the separated corms in water, ". . . and according as 'Adam or Eve pops up calculate the chances of retaining a friend's affection, getting work, or living in peace with neighbors.' "

A pale-flowered plant, originally found in Onondaga County, New York, is known as forma *pallidum* House (1924). It is similar to the typical form, but the flowers are lemon yellow or greenish yellow and the white lip is without the usual magenta spots.

The Puttyroot is found commonly in mucky wet soil in wooded floodplains, in peat bogs and tamarack swamps, rich low moist hardwoods and moist ravines, from near sea level in Pennsylvania, New Jersey and Maryland, up to 4,000 feet altitude in the Smoky Mountains of North Carolina and Tennessee. It flowers from May to early June.

GEOGRAPHICAL DISTRIBUTION: Uncommon from Quebec (Two Mountains County) and Ontario (Lambton County), through New England, New York, Pennsylvania and New Jersey, more frequent south to North Carolina, South Carolina (*fide Ravenel*), Georgia (Decatur County), Alabama (Lawrence County, *fide Mohr*) and Tennessee, west through the Central and Lake States to Minnesota (Stearns County), Saskatchewan (*fide Rydberg*), Iowa (Fayette and Johnson counties), Kansas (Leavenworth County), Missouri (Dunklin and St. Louis counties) and Arkansas; also Arizona (Santa Rita Mountains). (This species is included in Abram's *Illustrated Flora of the Pacific States* (p. 482) with the note: "Said to have been collected by NUTTALL in Oregon, but not since reported from west of the Rocky Mountains.")

CULTURAL NOTES: Puttyroot can stand a wide range of climatic conditions, for it extends from the uplands of Georgia to Saskatchewan and Quebec. Moreover, it is relatively indifferent to soil-reaction, thriving best in circumneutral humus-rich wood loam but withstanding moderate acidity. The single white-striate leaf is evergreen, and the plants can best be found when a light covering of snow is on the ground. They can readily be transplanted to a shaded garden, and will produce leaves year after year until discovered by one of the pests which feeds on bulbous-rooted plants. In nature only about two or three plants out of every hundred are likely to bloom in any one year, so flowering is not to be expected often from a small group. (E. T. W.)

34. Hexalectris Raf.

Hexalectris Raf., Neogenyton 4. 1825.

(The name, *Hexalectris,* is a Greek term meaning "six cock's combs," referring to the several fleshy ridges on the disc of the lip.)

Terrestrial scapose saprophytic herbs arising from a slender or stout coralloid and annulated rhizome. Stem flesh-colored or purplish, apparently lacking in chlorophyll, simple or occasionally branched. Leaves reduced to flesh-colored or purplish sheathing scales. Inflorescence a lax terminal few-flowered raceme. Flowers usually showy, rose-lavender, purplish, red or yellowish, often variously striped or mottled with purple, rarely nearly white. Sepals and petals free, spreading or somewhat revolute. Lip 3-lobed, crested on the disc with several longitudinal central lamellae or ridges. Column slender, shallowly winged on each side at the summit; pollinia eight, four in each cell of the anther, waxy, fasciculate.

This genus consists of only six species which are found primarily in the United States and Mexico, with one species in Guatemala. Most of the species comprising the genus have been described within the last ten years. They occur primarily in leaf mold in forests, ravines, rocky well-drained slopes and on limestone outcrops, commonly in calcareous soils.

True parasitism is not known to occur in the Orchidaceae. Although, as pointed out previously, at one time many orchids were thought to be parasitic because of the epiphytic habitat of some of the species. Partial parasitism is considered by some as likely to exist in the saprophytic genera. Only recently, G. B. HINTON, a collector of Mexican plants, reported in one instance of finding plants of this genus which seemed to be firmly attached to the roots of trees. Although orchids in nature are known to be involved in a state of symbiosis with fungi there still remains the fact that there is no definite proof that they have ever parasitized any of the seed-bearing plants.

KEY FOR THE IDENTIFICATION OF THE SPECIES OF HEXALECTRIS

1. Mid-lobe of lip adorned with three irregularly scalloped and broken lamellae..............
....*H. Warnockii* (p. 324)
1. Mid-lobe of lip without prominent broken lamellae 2
  2. Lateral lobes of lip free for 3 mm. or more 3
    3. Lateral lobes of lip oblong, obtuse; lip broadly elliptic in outline, 1.4 cm. or more
    long ....*H. revoluta* (p. 320)
    3. Lateral lobes of lip subquadrate to suborbicular-obovate, broad at the apex; lip obovate
    in outline, 1.3 cm. or less long..................................*H. grandiflora* (p. 318)
  2. Lateral lobes of lip free for 2 mm. or less 4
    4. Lip less than 1 cm. long...*H. nitida* (p. 320)
    4. Lip more than 1.2 cm. long.......................................*H. spicata* (p. 322)

1. **Hexalectris grandiflora** (A. Rich. & Gal.) L. O. Wms. in Johnston, Journ. Arn. Arb. 25: 81. 1944. *Corallorhiza grandiflora* A. Rich. & Gal., Ann. Sci. Nat., sér. 3, 3: 19. 1845. Type locality: Mexico. (*Hexalectris mexicana* Greenm.). PLATE 124

(The name, *grandiflora,* is a Latin adjective meaning "large-flowered," apparently used as a comparative term.)

COMMON NAME: Greenman's Hexalectris.

Plant glabrous and purplish throughout, 1-6 dm. tall. Stem aphyllous, simple or sometimes branched, slender or stout, provided with several short sheathing bracts. Raceme few-flowered, up to 20 cm. long. Floral bracts ovate to ovate-lanceolate, acute to shortly acuminate, 6-12 mm. long. Flowers deep rose-lavender to purplish red, sometimes nearly white, with the slender pedicellate ovaries about 1.2 cm. long, at first erect-ascending, later reflexed. Dorsal sepal linear-oblong to oblong-elliptic, obtuse to acute, 1.4-2.7 cm. long, 4-7 mm. wide. Lateral sepals oblong-elliptic, obtuse to subacute, somewhat falcate, 1.2-2.3 cm. long, 4-7 mm. wide.

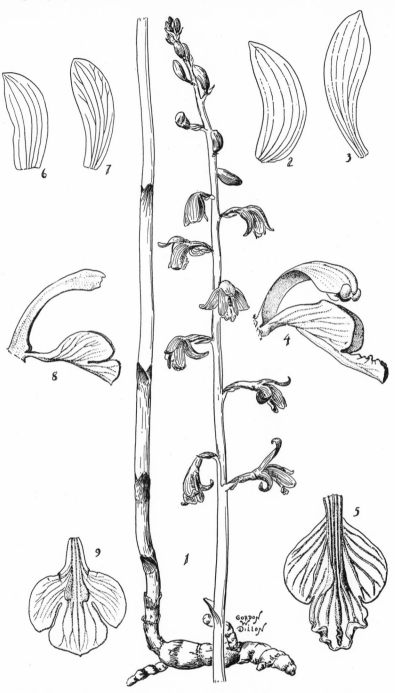

PLATE 124.— **Hexalectris spicata.** 1, plant, one half natural size. 2, lateral sepal, twice natural size. 3, petal, twice natural size. 4, lip and column, front-side view, two and one half times natural size. 5, lip, spread out, two and one half times natural size.
Hexalectris grandiflora. 6, lateral sepal, twice natural size. 7, petal, twice natural size. 8, lip and column, side view, two and one half times natural size. 9, lip, spread out, two and one half times natural size. *Drawn by Gordon W. Dillon.*

Petals oblong-lanceolate, obtuse to subacute, slightly oblique, 1.2-2.3 cm. long, 4-6.5 mm. wide. Lip rather deeply 3-lobed, concave, obovate in outline, clawed, abruptly rounded at the base,

1-1.3 cm. long (including the slender claw), 1-1.2 cm. wide across the lateral lobes when expanded, adorned with one or two short lamellae on each side opposite the lateral sinuses; lateral lobes subquadrate to semiorbicular or suborbicular-obovate, broadly obtuse to subtruncate at the apex, about 3 mm. wide; mid-lobe broadly subquadrate-cuneate to oblong-cuneate or suborbicular-flabellate, broadly rounded to retuse or slightly apiculate at the apex, more or less verrucose-tuberculate on the upper surface, about 4 mm. long and 6 mm. wide. Column slender-clavellate, arcuate, narrowly winged above, about 1.2 cm. long.

This species was apparently found for the first time in the United States a little more than twenty years ago. It was collected in Fern Canyon near Alpine, Brewster County, Texas, by Mr. and Mrs. W. W. WIMBERLEY on July 7, 1925.

Greenman's Hexalectris is found in rich humus and leaf mold of coniferous or hardwood forests in ravines, moist canyons and on stream banks. It usually grows at high elevations and occurs up to 8,000 feet altitude in Mexico. The blooming season is from May to September in various parts of its range.

GEOGRAPHICAL DISTRIBUTION: Texas (Brewster and Jeff Davis counties); also Mexico.

CULTURAL NOTES: There is no record of this species ever having been cultivated. See this section under *Hexalectris spicata.*

2. **Hexalectris nitida** L. O. Wms. in Johnston, Journ. Arn. Arb. 25: 81. 1944. Type locality and collection: Mexico, State of Coahuila, Sierra Mojada, Cañon de Hidalgo, shaded canyon below crest at top of canyon, among rocks, August 4, 1941, *R. M. Stewart 1068.* PLATE 125

(The name, *nitida,* is a Latin adjective meaning "shining," in allusion to the varnished appearance of the deeply colored flowers.)

COMMON NAME: None known.

Plant saprophytic, erect-ascending from a slender fleshy rhizome, up to 3.2 dm. tall. Stem rather stout, simple, aphyllous, provided with several short broad clasping apiculate sheaths, apparently purplish. Raceme composed of about twenty flowers, short or elongated, up to 15 cm. long. Floral bracts ovate-oblong, acute, about 5 mm. long. Flowers small, apparently deep purple and vernicose. Dorsal sepal narrowly oblong-elliptic, obtuse, 8-11.5 mm. long, 3-4.5 mm. wide. Lateral sepals obliquely elliptic, broadly rounded at the apex, 7-9 mm. long, 3-4 mm. wide. Petals somewhat oblique, narrowly obovate to oblanceolate, broadly rounded at the apex, 8-10.5 mm. long, 3-3.5 mm. wide above the middle. Lip obovate in outline, deeply 3-lobed above the middle, tapering to the base, 7-9 mm. long, 4-6.5 mm. wide across the lateral lobes when expanded; lateral lobes semielliptic, broadly rounded at the apex, free for 1-1.5 mm.; mid-lobe suborbicular to suborbicular-cuneate, slightly retuse with a small apicule in the sinus at the apex, 2.5-3.5 mm. long, 2.5-3 mm. wide near the apex; lamina prominently nervose, with the five central nerves more or less lamellate. Column arcuate, about 6 mm. long. Capsule ellipsoid, pendent, about 1.5 cm. long.

This, the smallest flowered species in the genus, has been known from the United States only since November 1946. Although it was collected in Texas in August 1940 by BARTON H. WARNOCK, it remained unidentified for six years.

This species is found among rocks in shaded canyons. It flowers in August.

GEOGRAPHICAL DISTRIBUTION: Known only from Panther Hill in the Glass Mountains of Brewster County, Texas, and in the Sierra Mojada in the State of Coahuila, Mexico.

CULTURAL NOTES: So far as known, this species has never been cultivated. See this section under *Hexalectris spicata.*

3. **Hexalectris revoluta** Correll, Bot. Mus. Leafl. Harvard Univ. 10: 19, fig. 2. 1941. Type locality and collection: Mexico, State of Nuevo León, Sierra Madre Oriental, lower San Francisco Canyon, about 15 miles southwest of Galeana, altitude 7500-8000 feet, sparse in oak wood, June 10, 1934, *C. H. & M. T. Mueller 767.* PLATE 125

(The name, *revoluta,* is a Latin term meaning "rolled back," in reference to the typical condition of the sepals and petals.)

COMMON NAME: None known.

Plant saprophytic, erect from a fleshy rhizome, 3-4.5 dm. tall. Stem stout, simple, aphyllous, provided with several short broad clasping sheaths, apparently purplish. Raceme few-

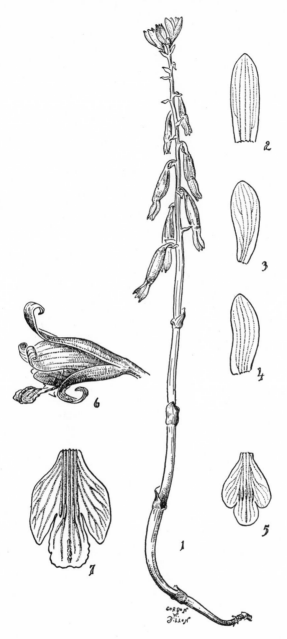

PLATE 125.—**Hexalectris nitida.** 1, plant, two thirds natural size. 2, dorsal sepal, twice natural size. 3, petal, twice natural size. 4, lateral sepal, twice natural size. 5, lip, spread out, twice natural size.

Hexalectris revoluta. 6, flower, front-side view, in natural position, twice natural size. 7, lip, spread out, twice natural size. *Drawn by Gordon W. Dillon.*

flowered, up to 12-flowered, 20 cm. or less long. Floral bracts broadly ovate, acute, concave, 1-1.4 cm. long. Flowers with the rather stout pedicellate ovaries about 1.5 cm. long. Sepals and petals usually conspicuously revolute toward the apex, probably purplish (no color notes available). Dorsal sepal oblong-elliptic, bluntly obtuse, concave, 1.6-2.1 cm. long, 3-7 mm. wide.

Lateral sepals oblique, elliptic to elliptic-lanceolate, obtuse to subacute or rarely minutely retuse at the apex, 1.5-2 cm. long, 3.5-7.5 mm. wide. Petals oblique, elliptic to elliptic-obovate, bluntly obtuse, 1.5-1.9 cm. long, 4.5-7.5 mm. wide. Lip concave in natural position, broadly elliptic in outline, deeply 3-lobed, broadly cuneate at the base, 1.4-1.8 cm. long, 9-13 mm. wide across the lateral lobes when expanded; lateral lobes oblong, obtuse, with the free part 3-6 mm. long and 3.5-4.5 mm. wide; mid-lobe obovate-cuneate, truncate or retuse at the apex, undulate on the upper margin, with the central nerve prominently thickened above, 7-8.5 mm. long, 5-6 mm. wide across the apex; lamina prominently nervose, with all the nerves more or less raised and thickened, adorned with four or five subequal lamellae at the base of the mid-lobe. Column clavate, arcuate, about 1.5 cm. long. Capsule ellipsoid, pendent, about 2 cm. long.

This species has been known from the United States only since November 1946. Although it was collected in Texas in July 1937 by BARTON H. WARNOCK, it remained unidentified for nine years.

This rather large plant bears relatively few distant flowers. When the flowers are fully expanded in typical material the sepals and petals are conspicuously revolute, often being tightly rolled back a third or more of their length. As shown by the illustration, the lip is distinctly different in shape and lobing from that of *H. spicata,* to which it is most nearly allied. Although the lamellation of the lip is somewhat similar in the two species, it is not so prominent in *H. revoluta.* Instead of five prominent keels at the base of the mid-lobe of the lip as in *H. spicata,* the lip of *H. revoluta* has four or rarely five keels which are only slightly raised.

This species is found in moist or dry oak woods in canyons. It flowers in June and July.

GEOGRAPHICAL DISTRIBUTION: Found in the lower Willow Creek basin of the Chisos Mountains in Brewster County, Texas, and in the Sierra Madre Oriental in the State of Nuevo León, Mexico.

CULTURAL NOTE: So far as known, this species has never been cultivated. See this section under *Hexalectris spicata.*

4. **Hexalectris spicata** (Walt.) Barnh., Torreya 4: 121. 1904. *Arethusa spicata* Walt., Fl. Carol. 222. 1788. Type locality: Not given; probably eastern Carolina. (*Bletia aphylla* Nutt.; *Hexalectris aphylla* (Nutt.) Raf.; *Corallorhiza arizonica* S. Wats.; *C. spicata* (Walt.) Tidestrom). PLATE 124

(The name, *spicata,* is a Latin adjective meaning "spiked," in allusion to the commonly elongated spicate inflorescence.)

COMMON NAMES: Crested Coral-root, Brunetta, Buff-crest, Cock's-comb, Leafless Orchid.

Plant saprophytic, scapose, slender to very stout, 1.6-8 dm. tall. Stem flesh-colored to light madder-purple, up to 1 cm. in diameter. Leaves reduced to sheathing scale-like bracts along the stem, broadly ovate, acute. Raceme laxly few- to several-flowered, 5-35 cm. long, 4-6 cm. in diameter. Floral bracts purplish, triangular-ovate, acute to acuminate, partly clasping the rachis, 5-10 mm. long, 2-6 mm. wide. Flowers showy, with the rather stout pedicels 4-6 mm. long. Sepals and petals yellowish with purplish brown striations, strongly 5-nerved, free, spreading. Dorsal sepal oblong-elliptic, obtuse, 2-2.4 cm. long, 5-8 mm. wide. Lateral sepals ovate-oblong to oblong-lanceolate, obtuse to subacute, oblique, 1.4-1.8 cm. long, 5.5-8 mm. wide. Petals oblong-elliptic to narrowly oblong-spatulate, obtuse, somewhat falcate, 1.8-2 cm. long, 5-7 mm. wide. Lip concave, obovate in outline when expanded, shallowly 3-lobed, recurved in natural position, yellowish white with purple striations, 1.4-1.7 cm. long, 1-1.4 cm. wide across the lateral lobes when spread out; lateral lobes entire, with the apex broadly rounded to obtuse, incurved and clasping the column in natural position, with the free part 1-1.5 mm. long; mid-lobe suborbicular-ovate, subtruncate to occasionally notched at the apex, with crisped-undulate margins, about 8 mm. wide; disc with the five to seven central nerves crested with longitudinal fleshy ridges extending from the base of the lip nearly to the apex of the mid-lobe and three additional fleshy-ridged nerves spreading out into the lateral lobes. Column strongly arcuate, 1.3-1.6 cm. long, with shallow lateral wings at the apex which are 3-4 mm. wide. Capsule ellipsoid, strongly 3-ribbed, pendent, about 2.5 cm. long.

The Crested Coral-root is by far the most attractive saprophytic orchid found in our region. The flesh-colored to madder-purple succulent stem supports a spike of lurid richly colored flowers which are beautifully marked with yellow, deep purple, brownish purple and white.

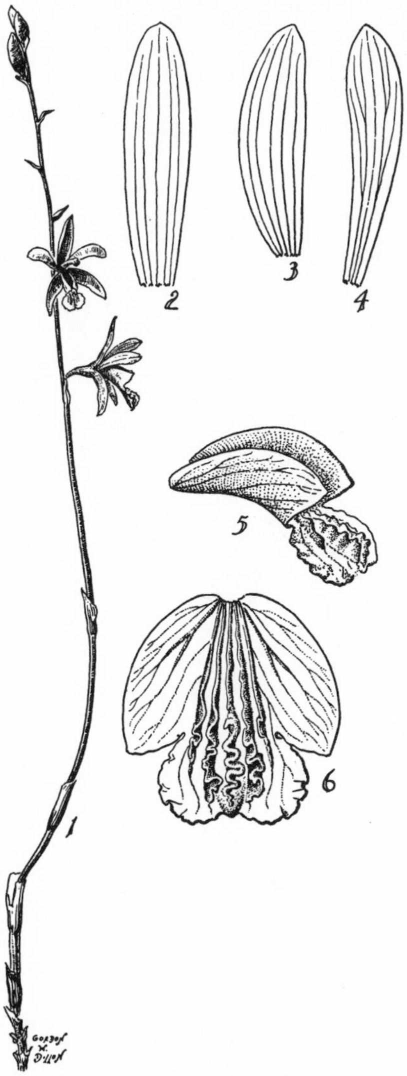

This orchid is rather abundant in some parts of Florida, especially where coquina shell banks and shell marls occur in cedar hammocks and thickets. One such place is found near Anastasia, St. Johns County, where I counted several hundred plants growing in close proximity. It is also found frequently in such places as the remarkable sink-hole, known as the Devil's Millhopper, near Gainesville in Alachua County, where it grows in deep humus under hardwood trees. The species apparently attains its most luxuriant development around Knoxville, Tennessee, where some extremely robust plants reach 8 dm. in height.

This orchid is found on hardwood slopes in calcareous soils, on rocky well-drained hardwood or pine slopes, borders of swamps in low rich woods and in leaf mold in sandy loam of mixed pine-hardwood forests. In Florida, it occurs on coquina shell banks and shell marls of cedar hammocks and thickets. In Mexico, it grows in moist shady soil on stream banks, in creek basins, grassy woodlands, canyons, coniferous and hardwood forests, thickets and on limestone slopes. The Crested Coral-root occurs near sea level in Florida, up to 1,000 feet altitude in Alabama and Georgia, 2,000 feet in North Carolina and Tennessee and 7,000 feet in Mexico. It blooms from June to the latter part of August, rarely to the first of October in Florida.

PLATE 126.— **Hexalectris Warnockii.** 1, plant, one half natural size. 2, dorsal sepal, twice natural size. 3, lateral sepal, twice natural size. 4, petal, twice natural size. 5, lip, side view, twice natural size. 6, lip, spread out, twice natural size. *Drawn by Gordon W. Dillon.*

GEOGRAPHICAL DISTRIBUTION: Locally frequent from West Virginia (Pendleton County), Maryland and Virginia (Bedford and James City counties), through the Atlantic States to south-central Florida (south to Sarasota County), along the Gulf Coast to Texas, west to Indiana (Floyd County), Kentucky (Edmonson and Wayne counties), Missouri (Barry, Dunklin and Franklin counties), Arkansas (Craighead, Hempstead and Pulaski counties), Arizona and New Mexico; also Mexico (Nuevo León).

CULTURAL NOTES: The Crested Coral-root is tolerant of a rather wide range of temperature conditions. The reaction of the humus-rich soil into which its coralloid rhizome extends is most often neutral, owing to the nearby presence of lime-stone or shells, although in mineral-rich loam it can withstand subacid conditions. Like most saprophytes, it exists in such a delicate equilibrium with its environment that successful transplanting is practically impossible. (E. T. W.)

5. **Hexalectris Warnockii** Ames & Correll, Bot. Mus. Leafl. Harvard Univ. 11 : 8, t. 2. 1943. Type locality and collection: Texas, Brewster County, rare in upper Blue Creek Canyon, Chisos Mountains, June 25, 1937, *Barton H. Warnock.* PLATE 126

(The name, *Warnockii,* is in honor of BARTON HOLLAND WARNOCK (1911-   ), Texas botanist and botanical collector.)

COMMON NAME: Texas Purple-spike.

Plant saprophytic, erect or ascending from a slender rhizome, 1.5-3 dm. tall. Stem slender, simple or occasionally branched, aphyllous, provided with several short tubular sheaths, maroon or deep purple, vernicose, often becoming flesh-colored in age. Raceme 3- to 8-flowered, up to 12 cm. long. Floral bracts ovate to elliptic, acute, concave, 5-9 mm. long. Flowers with the slender pedicellate ovaries about 7 mm. long. Sepals and petals only slightly spread-ing, maroon or deep purple, vernicose. Sepals linear-elliptic to linear-oblanceolate, obtuse to subacuminate, 1.5-1.8 cm. long, 3.8-4.5 mm. wide at the widest point; dorsal sepal channelled; lateral sepals more or less falcate. Petals oblanceolate to linear-spatulate, obtuse to subacute, falcate, 1.6-2 cm. long, 2.8-3.8 mm. wide above the middle. Lip concave, prominently or shallowly 3-lobed above the middle, suborbicular to broadly cuneate-obovate in outline when expanded, rounded to broadly cuneate at the base, white with the lateral lobes veined with purple, adorned with orange-yellow lamellae and purple at the apex, 1.5-1.8 cm. long, 1.5-1.6 cm. wide across the lateral lobes when spread out; lateral lobes obtuse to broadly rounded, upcurved in natural position, with the free part up to 4.5 mm. long; mid-lobe variable, broadly obcordate to subquadrate, somewhat emarginate, with the margins crenulate-dentate, 4-6 mm. long, 6-11 mm. wide; lamina prominently nervose, adorned with five parallel lamellae, the three central lamellae prominent, irregularly scalloped and broken on the mid-lobe, extending from below the middle of the lip nearly to the apex of the mid-lobe and surrounded on each side by a shorter lamella which terminates near the base of the mid-lobe. Column somewhat clavate, arcuate, compressed, about 1 cm. long. Capsule ellipsoid, pendent, about 1.5 cm. long.

The Texas Purple-spike was apparently found for the first time in the United States in Love Peak Basin, Chisos Mountains, Brewster County, Texas, by C. H. MUELLER on July 20, 1932.

When seen in the field, the striking flowers of this little orchid appear to be too large for the weak slender stem. While the species is probably rather widespread in the Southwest, it is difficult to see the maroon plant in its favorite habitat—shady cedar-oak groves—and it is thus easily overlooked. Consequently, it was not dis-covered until fairly recently and very few collections have been made.

This species grows under oaks in mountain canyons and in cedar-oak groves in limestone soil. It is found up to 6,500 feet or more altitude, and flowers from June to August.

GEOGRAPHICAL DISTRIBUTION: Texas (Brewster, Gillespie and Jeff Davis counties) and Arizona (Chiricahua National Monument).

CULTURAL NOTES: There is no record of this species ever having been cultivated. See this section under *Hexalectris spicata.*

35. Corallorhiza [Hall.] Chat.

Corallorhiza [Hall.] Chat., Spéc. Inaug. de Corallorhiza 6. 1760.

(The name, *Corallorhiza,* is a Greek term meaning "coral-root," in allusion to the brittle coral-like rhizome.)

Inconspicuous terrestrial saprophytic scapose herbs with short or somewhat elongated rhizomes which are much-branched, toothed and coralloid. Stem brownish, yellowish or purplish, destitute of green foliage, clothed with several membranaceous sheaths. Inflorescence terminating the simple naked scape, consisting of a lax or subdense raceme of yellowish, brownish or purplish (less commonly greenish or whitish) flowers. Sepals subequal, ascending, spreading or connivent; lateral sepals united at the base and forming a short mentum which is more or less adnate to the ovary. Lip simple to 3-lobed, slightly adherent to the base of the column. Column compressed; anther terminal; pollinia four, waxy, free. Capsule ovoid to ellipsoid, pendent.

This is a small genus of about twelve species, mainly in North and Central America. The largest number of species is in Mexico and the greatest development of the genus is in the United States and Canada. One species is found in Eurasia. The favorite habitats are rich decaying humus in forests, dry wooded slopes, thickets, ravines and swampy woods in intensely acid to calcareous soils.

This genus appears to be devoid of chlorophyll, the substance which gives to most plants their green color. Because of this apparent lack of green coloring matter and the predominance of other pigments, saprophytic (as well as parasitic) plants are often vegetatively and florally rich in color and exceedingly attractive. Orchids in this category may vary from almost pure white, as exemplified by *Cephalanthera Austinae,* to deep maroon, as exhibited by some species of *Hexalectris.* The colors are for the most part gay and lurid, and their intensity is obviously greatly affected by several factors, such as age, light and shade, soil constituency, genetic composition, etc. This variation in the intensity of color, as well as in the color-pattern, itself, has given rise to a number of named forms and variants in some of the species. I have taken cognizance of the more striking variants which have been described, not so much because they are worthy of taxonomic consideration as because they are widely diverse and of interest.

Most of the species in this genus have been used at one time or another for medicinal purposes.

CULTURAL NOTES: Saprophytic plants, as the coral-roots, live in such delicate equilibrium with fungi and other factors of their environment that transplanting is out of the question. They may be raised from seed, however, if soil conditions are suitable, and they attain blooming size in from five to ten years. (E. T. W.)

KEY FOR THE IDENTIFICATION OF THE SPECIES OF CORALLORHIZA

1. Lip 3-lobed or with a curved tooth on each side at or near the base 2
   2. Lateral sepals 1-nerved; plant small, usually less than 1.5 dm. tall; lip 3-5 mm. long....
   ....*C. trifida* (p. 333)
   2. Lateral sepals 3-nerved; plant mostly large, usually much more than 1.5 dm. tall; lip 5-9.5 mm. long 3
      3. Lip usually reddish purple, scarcely 3-lobed; mentum always more or less free from the ovary and conspicuously exserted; flowers erect or ascending; perianth segments widely spreading...*C. Mertensiana* (p. 328)
      3. Lip usually white and spotted with magenta-crimson, deeply 3-lobed; mentum usually inconspicuous or (at most) a gibbous swelling; flowers widely spreading from the rachis; perianth segments scarcely spreading ....*C. maculata* (p. 326)

1. Lip not 3-lobed, at most notched, erose-denticulate or undulate on the margins 4
    4. Sepals always 1-nerved; plant small, usually less than 1.5 dm. tall; lip 3-5 mm. long;
        petals 5.5 mm. or less long 5
        5. Stem bulbous-thickened at the base; petals 3-4 mm. long, 1- to 3-nerved; lip
            blotched with madder-purple.................................*C. odontorhiza* (p. 330)
        5. Stem not bulbous-thickened at the base; petals 4.5-5.5 mm. long, always 1-nerved; lip
            white, rarely spotted with purple ....*C. trifida* (p. 333)
    4. Sepals usually 3-nerved (rarely 1-nerved); plant mostly large, usually much more than
        1.5 dm. tall; lip and petals 5.5 mm. or more long 6
        6. Lip linguiform, with conspicuously involute margins which are much thickened at the
            base; disc with a fleshy bilobed callus in the middle of the base; perianth segments
            usually conspicuously striate-veined ....*C. striata* (p. 331)
        6. Lip not linguiform, with flat margins which are not thickened at the base; disc with a
            pair of separate lamellae on the lower half; perianth segments without prominent stria-
            tions 7
            7. Plant essentially southern in distribution but extending westward, usually short and
                slender, mostly less than 2 dm. tall; blooming time February to May (rarely June);
                without an evident mentum ....*C. Wisteriana* (p. 336)
            7. Plant essentially northern and western in distribution, usually tall and stout or some-
                times slender, mostly more than 2 dm. tall; blooming time June to September (rarely
                May); with a conspicuous or obsolescent mentum 8
                8. Lip usually reddish purple; mentum always more or less free from the ovary and con-
                    spicuously exserted; flowers erect or ascending; perianth segments widely spreading
                    (plant entirely far western in distribution)...............*C. Mertensiana* (p. 328)
                8. Lip usually white and spotted with magenta-crimson; mentum usually inconspicuous
                    or (at most) a gibbous swelling; flowers widely spreading from the rachis; perianth
                    segments scarcely spreading ....*C. maculata* (p. 326)

1. Corallorhiza maculata Raf., Am. Month. Mag. & Crit. Rev. 2: 119. 1817.
Type locality: Shady woods of Long Island, near Flatbush, Flushing, Oyster Bay, etc., New York. (*Corallorhiza multiflora* Nutt.). PLATE 127

(The name, *maculata,* is a Latin adjective meaning "spotted," in allusion to the typically dark purplish spots on the lip.)

COMMON NAMES: Spotted Coral-root, Large Coral-root, Many-flowered Coral-root.

Plant stout or slender, erect, glabrous, leafless, madder-purple or yellowish, 1.5-7.5 dm. tall. Stem succulent, provided with several tubular sheaths which are 4-9 cm. long. Raceme laxly few- to many-flowered, 4-23 cm. long. 2.5-3.5 cm. in diameter. Floral bracts minute, subulate, translucent, 1.5-3 mm. long. Flowers spreading, on rather stout pedicels which are about 3 mm. long. Sepals and petals crimson-purple or rarely greenish, 3-nerved. Dorsal sepal linear, obtuse to broadly rounded at the apex, 7-8.5 mm. long, 1.5-2 mm. wide. Lateral sepals spreading, linear to oblong-lanceolate, obtuse to acute, concave, oblique, 7-8.5 mm. long, 1.5-2.5 mm. wide, united at the base and forming an obsolescent mentum which is adnate to the ovary or only slightly projecting. Petals oblong-lanceolate to oblong-elliptic or oblanceolate, broadly rounded to obtuse or acute at the apex, 5.5-7.5 mm. long, 1.5-3 mm. wide near the apex. Lip deeply but unequally 3-lobed, 5-8 mm. long, 3.5-5 mm. wide across the lateral lobes when spread out, nearly white to white and spotted with magenta-crimson; lateral lobes relatively small, directed forward, somewhat curved, obtuse to acute (rarely bifid) at the apex, 1-1.5 mm. long; mid-lobe oblong-quadrate to obovate or suborbicular, retuse, broadly rounded or abruptly obtuse (rarely somewhat apiculate) at the apex; disc with two narrow longitudinal lamellae near or below the middle. Column yellow, with magenta spots on the ventral surface, strongly curved, compressed, 4-5 mm. long. Capsule nodding, ovoid, 1.5-2.5 cm. long, about 6 mm. in diameter.

This species and *C. trifida* are the most widespread coral-roots in the genus. In the United States, the Spotted Coral-root is the most widely distributed and frequent, while in Canada its place is taken by *C. trifida.*

Corallorhiza maculata has flowers whose segments, particularly the lip, are quite variable in size and shape. The lip of some flowers is occasionally entire or with only one lateral lobe present. The mentum is usually more or less decurrent on the ovary. However, a form occurring in the West, segregated as var. *occidentalis* (Lindl.) Cockerell (1916), has the mentum gibbous and bluntly spur-like.

Several color-variants have been described in this species. Briefly, these are—

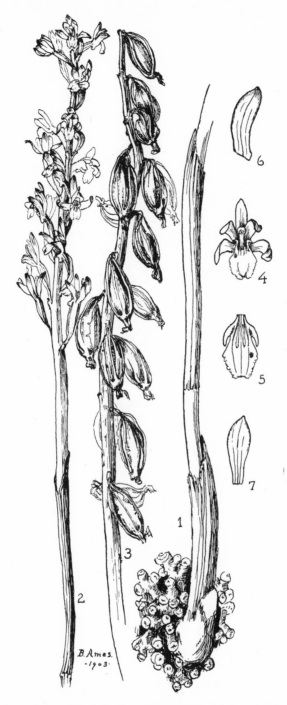

PLATE 127.—**Corallorhiza maculata.** 1, basal half of plant, to
show the coralloid rhizome, natural size. 2, inflorescence, four
fifths natural size. 3, fruits, natural size. 4, flower, front view,
one and one half times natural size. 5, lip, spread out, two and
one half times natural size. 6, lateral sepal, two and one half
times natural size. 7, petal, two and one half times natural size.
Drawn by Blanche Ames.

1) var. *flavida* (Peck) Cockerell (1916), with dark orange-yellow stem and sheaths, and lemon-yellow flowers with an unspotted white lip; 2) var. *intermedia* Farwell (1917), a prevailingly brown plant, with the stem and fruits light grayish brown, and the sheaths dark purplish brown; 3) var. *punicea* H. H. Bartlett (1922), a plant without a trace of brown, but with the stem and fruit dark lavender-purple, and the sheaths much paler than the stem.

The rhizome of this orchid has been used as a diaphoretic, febrifuge and sedative, and the dried stems are said to be used by the Paiute and Shoshone Indians of Nevada to make a tea so as to build up the blood in pneumonia patients. Doubtless this latter fancied attribute rests on the existence of a reddish tone and coloration in some of the plants.

The Spotted Coral-root is found commonly in rich decaying humus of moist upland coniferous, deciduous or mixed forests and along shaded stream banks and occasionally in dry forests and on grassy mossy banks. The Spotted Coral-root occurs near sea level in Washington, up to 1,000 feet altitude in Vermont, 2,000 feet in British Columbia, 5,000 feet in North Carolina and Tennessee, 8,500 feet in California, South Dakota and Wyoming, 10,000 feet in Arizona, Colorado, Nevada and Utah and 12,000 feet in New Mexico and Mexico. It flowers from April (in California) to September (especially during July and August) in various parts of its range.

GEOGRAPHICAL DISTRIBUTION: This species is found from Newfoundland, St. Pierre Island, Miquelon Island, Nova Scotia, New Brunswick, Prince Edward Island, Quebec and Ontario, west to Alberta (Castlemont, Clive, Cypress Hills, Elkwater and Waterton Lakes Park) and British Columbia (Vancouver Island, Trail, Greenwood, Armstrong and Chilliwack Valley); south through New England and the Atlantic States to central and western North Carolina; west through the Central and Lake States to Washington, Oregon and California; southwest to New Mexico (Catron, Colfax, San Miguel, Río Arriba and Santa Fé counties), Arizona (Apache, Coconino, Gila, Graham, Greenlee and Pima counties) and Texas (Jeff Davis County); also Mexico and Guatemala.

CULTURAL NOTES: The Spotted Coral-root ranges over much of the United States except in the drier and warmer lowlands, so it is evidently tolerant of a wide variety of temperature conditions. Its soil-reaction is most often subacid, the litter in which it grows being well decomposed and fairly rich in nutrient elements. (E. T. W.)

2. **Corallorhiza Mertensiana** Bongard, Mém. Acad. Imp. Sci. St. Pétersbourg, ser. 6, Sci. math., phys. et nat. 2: 165. 1832. Type locality: Sitka, Alaska.

PLATE 128

(The name, *Mertensiana,* is in honor of FRANZ CARL MERTENS (1764-1831), noted German botanist. The genus *Mertensia* in the family Boraginaceae is also named for him.)

COMMON NAMES: Western Coral-root, Mertens' Coral-root.

Plant erect, glabrous, leafless, 1.5-5.5 dm. tall. Stem slender or rather stout, purple, reddish or brownish purple, succulent, provided with two or three tubular sheaths, 2-6 mm. in diameter near the base. Raceme laxly or densely 10- to 40-flowered, 6-27 cm. long, 2-3 cm. in diameter. Floral bracts minute, triangular-subulate, acute to acuminate, usually much less than 2 mm. long. Flowers erect-spreading, greenish or purplish, on slender pedicels which are 2-3 mm. long. Sepals spreading and reflexed, linear-oblanceolate, obtuse, concave, 3-nerved, 6-10.5 mm. long, 1.5-2.5 mm. wide; lateral sepals falcate, decurrent on the ovary, united at the base and forming a prominent blunt mentum which is free from the ovary for about 1 mm. Petals linear-oblong to linear-oblanceolate, obtuse to subacute, 3-nerved, entire to somewhat crenulate on the upper margins, 6-9 mm. long, 1.5-2.2 mm. wide. Lip reddish purple, oblong-subquadrate to broadly obovate-elliptic, rounded to truncate or retuse at the apex, narrowed at the base, entire or provided with a short incurved tooth on each side at or near the base, usually somewhat serrated, 3-nerved, concave, 7.5-9.5 mm. long, 4-5.2 mm. wide; disc provided on the lower half with a pair of small parallel lamellae. Column slender-clavellate, 4-7.5 mm. long. Capsule obovoid, 1.5-1.8 cm. long.

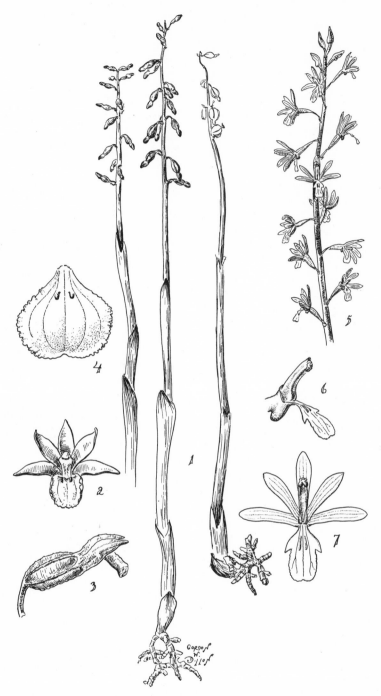

PLATE 128.— **Corallorhiza odontorhiza.** 1, plants, two in flower and one in fruit, one half natural size. 2, flower, spread open, two and one half times natural size. 3, flower, side view, two and one half times natural size. 4, lip, spread out, eight times natural size.

Corallorhiza Mertensiana. 5, inflorescence, one half natural size. 6, lip and column, front-side view, one and two thirds natural size. 7, flower, spread open, one and two thirds natural size. *Drawn by Gordon W. Dillon.*

This is our only distinctly western and northwestern *Corallorhiza,* being also the most restricted in range of any of the species.

The Western Coral-root usually occurs in rich wet coniferous forests and alpine woods, but it also grows in dry forests, along boggy streams and (in Oregon) on serpentine ridges. It is found near sea level in Alaska, up to 5,000 feet altitude in California, Oregon and Washington and 7,500 feet in Wyoming. The blooming season is from June to August.

GEOGRAPHICAL DISTRIBUTION: British Columbia, Alaska and the Aleutian Islands, south to Montana (Flathead County), Washington, Oregon and northwestern California (Del Norte, Humboldt, Siskiyou and Trinity counties), Idaho (Bonner and Idaho counties), and Wyoming (Lincoln, Teton and Yellowstone National Park counties).

CULTURAL NOTES: The Western Coral-root grows chiefly in coniferous forests at moderate to high altitudes. From the temperature standpoint, it is to be classed as a cool-climate plant. Tests of its soils have shown predominantly subacid reaction. (E. T. W.)

3. **Corallorhiza odontorhiza** (Willd.) Nutt., Gen. N. Am. Pl. 2: 197. 1818.
Cymbidium odontorhizon Willd., Sp. Pl. 4: 110. 1805. Type locality: Canada, New England, Pennsylvania and Virginia. (*Corallorhiza micrantha* Chapm.). PLATE 128

(The name, *odontorhiza,* is a Greek term meaning "toothed-root," referring to the numerous small knobs projecting from the coralloid rhizome.)

COMMON NAMES: Late Southern Coral-root, Autumn Coral-root, Fall Coral-root, Crawley-root, Small Coral-root, Small-flowered Coral-root, Dragon's-claw, Chicken-toes.

Plant frail, slender, rather abruptly bulbous-thickened at the base, erect, leafless, glabrous, light brown to madder-purple, 1-4 dm. tall. Rootstock a coralloid underground elongated rhizome. Stem more or less concealed by several closely appressed tubular sheaths. Raceme laxly few- to many-flowered, 2-11 cm. long, 1-2 cm. in diameter. Floral bracts minute, subulate, mostly less than 1 mm. long. Flowers small, with the segments connivent (not spreading), on filiform pedicels which are 2-3 mm. long. Sepals and petals purple or purplish green. Dorsal sepal linear-lanceolate to narrowly spatulate, obtuse to subacute, 3-4.5 mm. long, 1.2-1.5 mm. wide. Lateral sepals linear to linear-lanceolate, obtuse to acute, oblique, somewhat incurved and concave, often involute near the apex, 1-nerved, not produced into a mentum, 3-5 mm. long, 1-1.5 mm. wide. Petals with a short claw, oblong-elliptic, subacute, somewhat concave, with the lateral margins nearly entire to crenulate-erose, 1- to rarely 3-nerved, 3-4 mm. long, 1.3-2 mm. wide. Lip with a short slender claw, arcuate and recurved near the base in natural position, obovate to suborbicular-quadrate or broadly oval, often wider than long, retuse to obtuse or somewhat apiculate at the apex, irregularly crenulate or erose along the somewhat undulate margins, white, spotted with magenta-crimson, 3-4.5 mm. long (including the claw), 3-5.2 mm. wide; disc with two short somewhat divergent lamellae near the base, 3- to 5-nerved. Column slender, slightly curved, compressed, about 2 mm. long. Capsule ovoid to ellipsoid, nodding, 6-8 mm. long, about 4 mm. in diameter.

This little saprophyte is closely allied to the Mexican *C. Williamsii* Correll, but it differs from that species in floral structure. A distinctive color-variant, forma *flavida* Wherry (1927), has been found in Fairfax County, Virginia, and the District of Columbia. It is described as follows: "Plant in every respect like the typical form of the species except in the lack of all traces of purple color, the lip being pure white without spots, and the sepals, ovaries, bracts, and stem being dull yellow, . . ."

The roots of this species have a rather strong peculiar odor, and have been used as a diaphoretic and sedative.

At one of its southernmost stations, in virgin mountain forests in the vicinity of Jocassee, Oconee County, South Carolina, I have seen this slender insignificant plant holding its own with the rare and legendary *Shortia galacifolia.* In this picturesque and botanically rich region numerous turbulent streams, upper tributaries of the Keowee River, cut their way down the southern slopes of the Appalachian

Mountains to form deep ravines. The slopes of some of these ravines are completely covered by Shortia, while other nearby ravines harbor not a single plant—a peculiar characteristic of the species and a prime factor for its rarity. Scattered through the forests are many of the orchids occurring in the southern Appalachians, while along nearby Big Eastatoe Creek is the only North American station for the filmy fern, *Hymenophyllum tunbridgense*. To one interested in nature, this primeval preserve is a veritable paradise.

The Late Southern Coral-root is found usually in light soil or rich humus in coniferous, deciduous or mixed forests, in dry or moist soil, on slopes, in ravines or floodplain regions and in low shady woods along streams. It occurs near sea level in North Carolina, up to 4,000 feet altitude in the mountains of North Carolina and Tennessee and 9,000 feet in Mexico and Guatemala. The flowering season is from early June to October in various parts of its range.

GEOGRAPHICAL DISTRIBUTION: Uncommon from Maine (York County), Vermont (Bennington and Windham counties), Massachusetts, Rhode Island and Connecticut, more frequent through New York, Pennsylvania and New Jersey, south to northwest South Carolina (Greenville, Oconee and Pickens counties) and Georgia (DeKalb, Madison, Rabun, Union and White counties), southwest to Alabama (Butler, Calhoun, Cullman and Morgan counties) and Mississippi (Adams County), west through Ohio, Michigan (Cass and St. Clair counties) and Wisconsin (Dane County) to Iowa (Johnson County), Missouri (Jasper and Shannon counties) and Arkansas (*fide Demaree*); also Mexico, Guatemala and Honduras.

CULTURAL NOTES: The Late Southern Coral-root ranges widely over the south-central United States, and after the melting of the glacial ice, the orchid migrated north to the lower Great Lakes and the lowlands of New England. Accordingly, it is essentially indifferent to temperature conditions. In common with the other coral-roots, it favors subacid soils and is the easiest of the group to grow, at least in middle latitudes. The root-system gradually increases in size for several years without sending up any superficial structures. Then, when sufficient nutrients have accumulated, a blooming stalk is produced and seed-pods develop. As a rule, the vitality of the root-system is so exhausted by this effort that the plant succumbs to the fungi which it previously had been able to withstand, so that a given clump rarely blooms a second year. (E. T. W.)

4. **Corallorhiza striata** Lindl., Gen. and Sp. Orch. Pl. 534. 1840; emend. by L. O. Wms., Bot. Mus. Leafl. Harvard Univ. 5: 171. 1938. Type locality and collection: Western North America, *Douglas*. (*Corallorhiza Macraei* A. Gray; *C. Bigelovii* S. Wats.; *C. Vreelandii* Rydb.; *C. striata* var. *Vreelandii* (Rydb.) L. O. Wms.). PLATE 129

(The name, *striata,* is a Latin adjective meaning "striped," in allusion to the conspicuous purple stripes of the floral segments.)

COMMON NAMES: Striped Coral-root, Bigelow's Coral-root, Macrae's Coral-root.

Plant erect, glabrous, leafless, 1.5-5 dm. tall. Stem madder-purple to brownish purple, usually stout, succulent, provided with three or four whitish to purplish sheaths, up to 8 mm. in diameter near the base. Raceme laxly few- to many-flowered, 5-25 cm. long, 2-4 cm. in diameter. Floral bracts minute, triangular-subulate, acute to acuminate, about 2 mm. long. Flowers usually rather large for the genus, variable in size, somewhat arcuate when viewed from the side, pinkish yellow or whitish, tinged and conspicuously striped with reddish purple, on short pedicels which are about 2 mm. long. Sepals oblong-elliptic to oblong-lanceolate or linear-lanceolate, rounded to obtuse at the apex, 3- to 5-nerved, with the nerves reddish purple, 6.5-16 mm. long, 2.3-5 mm. wide; lateral sepals somewhat falcate, not producing a mentum. Petals linear-oblong to obovate-elliptic, broadly rounded to obtuse at the apex, 3- to 5-nerved, with the nerves reddish purple, 6-15 mm. long, 2.5-5.5 mm. wide above the middle. Lip somewhat reflexed near the base in natural position, entire, suborbicular-elliptic to obovate-elliptic, concave-cymbiform, fleshy, with the thickened margins involute, white, conspicuoulsy striate-veined with reddish purple, with the stripes nearly confluent, 6-12 mm. long, up to 8.5 mm. wide when spread out; disc adorned with a fleshy bilobed callus near the middle of the base. Column slender, arcuate, thickened at the base, 3-5 mm. long. Capsule ellipsoid, 1.2-2 cm. long.

This is by far our most attractive coral-root. Its striking raceme of commonly large, richly colored flowers is a handsome spectacle when seen in its native haunts.

PLATE 129.— **Corallorhiza striata.** 1, basal half of plant, one half natural size. 2, inflorescence, one half natural size. 3, flower, spread open, one and one half times natural size. *Drawn by Gordon W. Dillon.*

It is noteworthy that two typically western species, the one under consideration and *Habenaria unalascensis,* are found quite frequently on Manitoulin Island and the Bruce Peninsula in the Lake Huron region, as well as infrequently in several other eastern localities. Since most of these easterly stations occur near water, it is quite possible that migratory waterfowl have accidentally carried seeds of these species from the West. Other suppositions are that these orchids may represent a relict population or that in the course of time they are gradually spreading eastward. However, at present the causes responsible for these unique patterns of distribution are purely conjectural.

FERNALD (1946) segregated a color-variant of this species, occurring in Gaspé County, Quebec, as forma *fulva,* on the basis of the stem, sheaths and perianth being yellow- or orange-brown instead of being madder-purple with a purple-striped perianth as in the typical form. Miss ALICE EASTWOOD found an albino form on the West Coast in 1931.

This species grows in moist soil and humus in dense hardwood and mixed forests, canyons and on shaded stream banks. It occurs up to 5,000 feet altitude in Wyoming, 7,500 feet in California and New Mexico and 8,500 feet in Arizona and Colorado. It flowers from March to August (rarely September) in various parts of its range.

GEOGRAPHICAL DISTRIBUTION: Found sparingly from Quebec, New Brunswick and Ontario (Bruce and Manitoulin counties), west through Saskatchewan (Bourgeau) and Alberta (Castlemont, Cypress Hills and Salicetum) to British Columbia (Vancouver Island), southwest through northern Michigan, Wisconsin (Bayfield, Door and Manitowac counties), Minnesota (Lake of the Woods County), North Dakota (Stark County), Wyoming (Lincoln and Yellowstone National Park counties), Colorado, Oklahoma (Jackson County), Arizona (Pima County), New Mexico (Otero and Socorro counties) and Texas (Presidio County), west to Washington, Oregon and California where it is common; also Mexico (Nuevo León).

CULTURAL NOTES: The showy Striped Coral-root apparently survived glaciation close to the margins of the ice sheet in the East and in the higher mountains in the West. Then, after the ice vanished, this orchid spread out through the northern part of North America. The humus in which it grows is usually thoroughly decomposed, so that the reaction is neutral or but slightly acid, and nutrient elements are available in considerable amounts. Since it can withstand severe winter conditions, but is intolerant of summer heat, it cannot be expected to thrive in gardens south of its natural area of distribution. (E. T. W.)

5. Corallorhiza trifida Chat., Spéc. Inaug. de Corallorhiza 8. 1760. Type locality: Not given. (*Corallorhiza innata* R. Br.; *C. ericetorum* Drejer; *C. Corallorhiza* (L.) Karst.; *C. Corallorhiza* var. *coloradensis* Cockerell). PLATE 130

(The name, *trifida,* is a Latin term meaning "trifid" or "split into three," in reference to the 3-lobed lip.)

COMMON NAMES: Northern Coral-root, Early Northern Coral-root, Little Yellow Coral-root.

Plant erect, glabrous, leafless, 4-36 cm. tall. Stem pale yellow, greenish yellow or deep yellow, usually very slender, succulent, provided with two to five pale tubular sheaths, up to 3 dm. long, 1-4 mm. in diameter near the base. Raceme laxly 3- to 20-flowered, 2.5-9 cm. long, 1.5-2.5 cm. in diameter. Floral bracts minute, deltoid to subulate, acute to acuminate, 1-2 mm. long. Flowers small, erect-spreading, varying from yellowish white to dull purple or greenish, on slender pedicels which are about 2 mm. long. Sepals linear-oblong to linear-oblanceolate, obtuse, concave, 1-nerved, 4.5-6.5 mm. long, 1-1.8 mm. wide above the middle; lateral sepals oblique, spreading, decurrent on the ovary and usually forming an inconspicuous mentum. Petals connivent with the dorsal sepal and forming a hood over the column, linear-oblanceolate, obtuse, 1-nerved, oblique, 4.5-5.5 mm. long, 1.4-2 mm. wide. Lip arcuate-recurved in natural position, broadly or narrowly oblong-quadrate in outline, subtruncate to obtuse, narrowed at the base, usually with a small triangular upcurved tooth on each side near the base, with the more or less upcurved margins lightly undulate, white, unspotted or sometimes spotted with purple, 3-5 mm. long, 2-3 mm. wide; disc provided below or at about the middle with a pair of small subparallel lamellae. Column slightly clavate, arcuate, 3.5-7 mm. long. Capsule obovoid-ellipsoid, pendent, green until mature, 8-12 mm. long.

FERNALD (1946) follows NUTTALL in segregating the more southern form and the plant most frequent in our region (characterized by having light yellowish

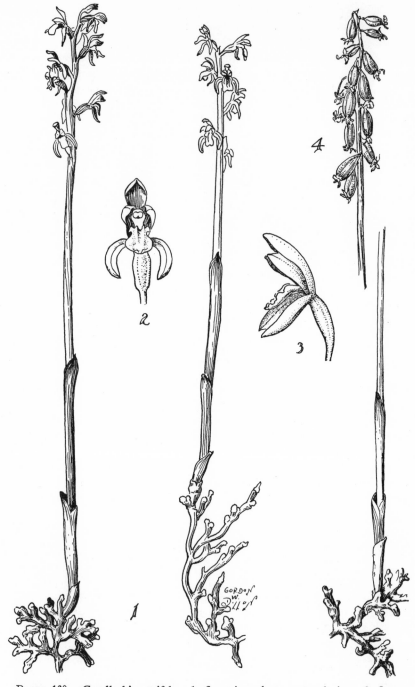

PLATE 130.— **Corallorhiza trifida.** 1, flowering plants, natural size. 2, flower, front view, three times natural size. 3, flower, side view, three times natural size. 4, fruiting plant, natural size. *Drawn by Gordon W. Dillon.*

green flowers with an unspotted lip) as var. *verna* (Nutt.) Fernald. FERNALD includes "mountains to Georgia and Tennessee" in the range of the var. *verna.* However, since I have seen no actual specimens of this plant south of Pennsylvania,

I seriously question its occurrence as far south as Georgia. The typical form (frequent in Eurasia) with a spotted lip tends to be more northern in distribution in North America.

This little orchid usually threads its slender brittle rhizome through loose thick mosses or humus, and it often occurs quite abundantly in boggy areas. The following incident occurred while I was searching in a boggy region for the Northern Coral-root. The location is along the Beatton River in northern British Columbia, where the country is particularly picturesque at this point along the Alaskan Highway.

After working my way back up the Road in short stages from our camp on the Beatton, I finally arrived on a high bluff near Mile 97 (above Fort St. John) where I had noted some large ragged ledges rising above the young secondary forest. Breaking through the thick growth to the ledges and climbing over them, I came out onto a large upland trapped peat bog surrounded by a low palisade of granitic rock. Enormous segments had fallen away from the palisades and the wall, itself, was split into numerous deep fissures in which grew lacy fronds of fragile bladder ferns and northern shield ferns. Climbing Polypody sent its slender rhizomes into humus-filled crevices, and neat little Woodsias nestled primly in shallow holes. The entrances to larger and deeper openings at the base of the wall were rubbed smooth, apparently by the passage of some small animal, and uneven platforms of little bones and fresh pine cone strippings formed miniature terraces before many of these acrid dens. A pungent stench pervading the air indicated that probably a weasel, that blood-thirsty little glutton of the woods and fields, or some one of its cousins, lived within some of the crevices.

The overflow from the hidden bog seeped across a sloping granite table to form a small moss-clogged pool in a virgin stand of spruce farther down the slope. Upon entering this dimly lit grove from the glare of the scrub land which surrounded it, I hesitated for my eyes to become adjusted to the darkness. I felt as though I had just stepped into a tomb, and so it would appear to be. For, as things began to take form, I saw across the pool the freshly killed body of an adult lynx. Its body, as well as the mossy turf about it, showed signs of a fierce struggle. One of the animal's tough tufted ears had been ripped away. The short stumpy tail contrasted ludicrously with the long sprawling heavy legs. Glancing down, I saw growing about my feet great clumps of the Northern Coral-root. Feeling uncomfortable in such morbid surroundings, I quickly gathered some of the little orchids and was glad to go back again into the open scrub land.

This species occurs in deep moss on coniferous forest slopes, in cedar, tamarack or spruce swamps, bogs, wet meadows, along streams in forests and in low boggy woods. It usually grows at high elevations and is found up to 2,500 feet altitude in New York and Vermont, 4,000 feet in British Columbia, 8,000 feet in New Mexico and 10,000 feet in Colorado and Idaho. The blooming season is from March (in Alberta) to July or rarely to the first of August in various parts of its range.

GEOGRAPHICAL DISTRIBUTION: Greenland (head of Söndre Strömfjord), Newfoundland, Miquelon Island, Labrador, Nova Scotia, New Brunswick, Prince Edward Island, Quebec and Ontario, west to British Columbia, the Yukon, Alaska and the Aleutian Islands; through New England south to New York (Herkimer, Oneida and Tompkins counties), New Jersey, Pennsylvania (Monroe County) and (?) Virginia, through the Central and Lake States, west to South Dakota (Custer and Lawrence counties), Montana (Gallatin and Madison counties), Wyoming (Albany and Sublette counties), Colorado (Boulder, Chaffee, Gilpin, Gunnison, Jefferson and Larimer counties), Utah (Grand, Salt Lake and Summit counties), New Mexico (Río Arriba County), Idaho (Custer and Fremont counties), Washington (Columbia, Skamania and Spokane counties) and Oregon (Hood River and Union counties); also Eurasia.

CULTURAL NOTES: The Northern Coral-root is somewhat more tolerant of warm soil in summer than *C. striata*. It is, however, unable to survive in the lowlands south of Pennsylvania. Its remarkable indifference to environmental conditions is further indicated by its having spread not only over northern North America, but also throughout the cooler parts of Eurasia. In like manner, it shows no special preference from the soil-reaction standpoint, thriving in both strongly and weakly acid soils, and even sometimes appearing in neutral humus. It is, however, very susceptible to attacks by slugs and other garden pests, so must be classed as difficult to cultivate. (E. T. W.)

6. **Corallorhiza Wisteriana** Conrad, Journ. Acad. Nat. Sci. Phila. 6: 145. 1829. Type locality and collection: In a wood bordering the eastern side of the Schuylkill River, between the Falls and the mouth of the Wissahickon Creek, Pennsylvania, 1828, *Charles J. Wister.* (*Corallorhiza odontorhiza sensu* Chapm., not Nuttall, 1818; *C. ochroleuca* Rydb.).   PLATE 131

(The name, *Wisteriana,* is in honor of CHARLES J. WISTER (1782-1865), American amateur botanist who collected the type of this species.)

COMMON NAMES: Spring Coral-root, Wister's Coral-root, Early Southern Coral-root.

Plant stout or slender, erect, glabrous, from a slightly thickened base, leafless, yellowish or madder-purple, 1-4.3 dm. tall. Stem with several tubular sheaths which are 2-8 cm. long. Raceme laxly few-flowered, 2.5-14 cm. long, 2-3 cm. in diameter. Floral bracts minute, subulate, mostly 1-2 mm. long. Flowers ringent and spreading, on slender pedicels which are 2-4 mm. long. Sepals and petals greenish yellow, tinged with purplish brown, 1- to 3-nerved. Dorsal sepal linear, broadly rounded to obtuse or acute (rarely retuse or toothed) at the apex, 6-9 mm. long, 1.3-2.2 mm. wide. Lateral sepals linear to linear-lanceolate, oblique, subacute to acute, not forming a mentum, 6-9 mm. long, 1.2-2 mm. wide. Petals linear to narrowly oblong-elliptic or narrowly ovate-oblong, subacute to acute or rarely toothed or apiculate at the apex, often with somewhat erose margins, 5.5-7.5 mm. long, 2-2.5 mm. wide. Lip with a short claw, strongly arcuate and recurved in natural position, broadly elliptic to suborbicular, truncate and often retuse at the apex, with two intramarginal linear lamellae on the disc near the base, erose-denticulate or undulate on the margins, rarely with an obsolescent tooth on each side near the base, white, spotted with magenta-purple, 5.5-7 mm. long, 4-5 mm. wide. Column compressed, 3-4 mm. long. Capsule ovoid, 9-11 mm. long, about 6 mm. in diameter.

As late as 1924, the year of the publication of AMES' *Enumeration of the Orchids of the United States and Canada,* this species (originally described from Pennsylvania) was considered to be almost confined to the southern United States. On the basis of our present knowledge, however, it appears to occur as frequently in some parts of the West as it does in the South. Indeed, its most luxuriant development is attained in some of its westernmost stations. This "mushroom" distributional growth is the result of several factors, foremost of which has been the examination and reidentification of numerous herbarium specimens. The western collections have been rather badly treated in the past, and for no accountable reason this species has been confused with *C. maculata* which has a much different lip.

The Spring Coral-root is usually found in rich shady forests of oak, pine and magnolia, in upland or swampy woods, on the edge of cypress swamps, in low woods and in various types of hammocks, on rocky wooded slopes, in thickets, cedar brakes, canyons, subalpine meadows or on river bluffs. It occurs near sea level in Florida (where I have found it in low palm hammocks), up to 9,000 feet altitude in Arizona and 10,000 feet in Colorado and Utah where it grows in subalpine meadows. The Spring Coral-root flowers from February (in Florida and Louisiana) to the middle of August (in Wyoming).

GEOGRAPHICAL DISTRIBUTION: This species is found sparingly from Pennsylvania (Philadelphia County), West Virginia (Cabell and Wayne counties) and Virginia (Frederick, Page and Surry counties), south through the Atlantic States to central Florida (south to High-

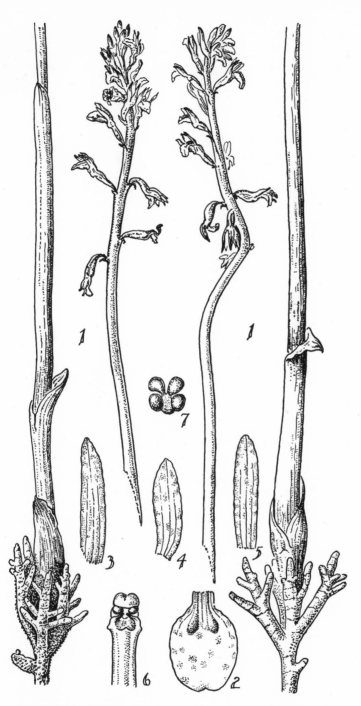

PLATE 131.— **Corallorhiza Wisteriana.** 1, plants, natural size. 2, lip, spread out, four times natural size. 3, lateral sepal, four times natural size. 4, petal, four times natural size. 5, dorsal sepal, four times natural size. 6, column, seven times natural size. 7, pollinia, highly magnified. *Redrawn from Blanche Ames by Gordon W. Dillon.*

lands County), along the Gulf Coast to Texas and Arkansas (Hempstead County), west through Ohio (Highland County) and Indiana (Jackson, Perry and Posey counties) to (?) Wisconsin (Blue Lick, *D. Houghton*), Kentucky (*Short*), Tennessee, Missouri (Jasper and St. Louis counties), Kansas (Cherokee County), South Dakota (Custer, Lawrence and Pennington counties), Montana (Gallatin County), Idaho (Fremont County), (?) Washington, Wyoming (Lincoln and Yellowstone National Park counties), Utah (Summit and Washington counties), Colorado (Boulder and La Plata counties) and Arizona (Coconino, Gila and Pima counties); also Mexico (México).

CULTURAL NOTES: The Spring Coral-root is not only tolerant of summer heat, but it is also winter-hardy. Tests of its soil-reaction have shown it to prefer circumneutral conditions, the litter in which it grows being decomposed to nutrient-rich leaf mold. Although it might be expected to be relatively easy to cultivate in mid-latitude gardens, its inability to resist parasitic fungi and animals prevents its cultivation. (E. T. W.)

36. **Bletia** Ruiz & Pavon

Bletia Ruiz & Pavon, Fl. Peruv. & Chil. Prodr. 119, t. 26. 1794.

(The name, *Bletia,* is in honor of Don Luis Blet, a Spanish herbalist and apothecary of the 18th century.)

Erect terrestrial herbs with the leaves rising from the top of a corm and the inflorescence borne on a sublateral leafless flowering branch. Leaves one or several, often early-fugacious, plicate, more or less petiolate. Peduncle produced from the upper node of the corm. Inflorescence a simple or paniculate raceme, rarely one-flowered. Sepals free, subequal, with the lateral sepals somewhat connivent and gibbous at the base. Petals free, similar to the sepals. Lip attached to the base of the column, free, entire or commonly 3-lobed, arcuate-recurved or spreading in natural position; lateral lobes usually broad, upcurved and clasping the column in natural position; mid-lobe often recurved, spreading, sometimes emarginate or bilobed; disc mostly bearing keels or papillae. Column elongated, semiterete, arcuate, winged above, often biauriculate at the base, essentially without a foot; anther operculate, incumbent; pollinia eight, waxy. Capsule cylindric or ellipsoid.

This genus contains about fifty species which are confined to the American tropics and subtropics. It consists of a number of accepted species which are often difficult to distinguish because of apparent intergradations.

1. **Bletia purpurea** (Lam.) DC., Mém. Soc. Phys. et Hist. Nat. Genève 9, pt. 1, pp. 97 and 100. 1841 and Huit. Not. Pl. Rares Jard. Genève 23. 1841. *Limodorum purpureum* Lam., Encycl. Méth. Bot. 3: 515. 1791. Type locality: In the Antilles and tropical America. (*Limodorum tuberosum* L., in part; *Bletia tuberosa* (L.) Ames). PLATE 132

(The name, *purpurea,* is a Latin adjective meaning "purple," in reference to the rich color of the flowers.)

Common names: Pine-pink, Purple Bletia, Sharp-petaled Bletia.

Plant glabrous, consisting of a short thick depressed corm bearing at the summit a few approximate leaves and a sublateral flowering branch, up to about 18 dm. tall. Corm 2-3 cm. in diameter, producing numerous fibrous velamentous roots. Leaves linear to narrowly elliptic-lanceolate, plicate, long-acuminate, with the lower part sheathing the scape, 2-9 dm. long, 1-5 cm. wide. Inflorescence a simple or paniculate raceme borne on a long slender sublateral peduncle; peduncle provided with remote tubular sheaths, 2.5-17 dm. long; raceme or panicle loosely few- to many-flowered. Floral bracts mostly small, ovate-triangular to ovate-lanceolate, acute to acuminate, 2-9 mm. long. Flowers pink, rose-purple or deep purple, rarely almost white, showy, with the slender pedicellate ovaries 9-18 mm. long, variable in size. Dorsal sepal oblong-elliptic to ovate-lanceolate, subobtuse to acute, 1.5-2.6 cm. long, 5-9 mm. wide. Lateral sepals obliquely ovate-oblong to elliptic-oblong, abruptly acute to acuminate, with the margins involute, 1.2-2 cm. long, 5-8 mm. wide. Petals obliquely ovate-oblong to elliptic or oblong-lanceolate, obtuse to acute, 1.2-2.1 cm. long, 7-11 mm. wide. Lip concave below, broadly cordate to ovate-cordate or cordate-subquadrate when spread out, conspicuously 3-lobed above the middle, strongly recurved in natural position, with the base truncate to subcordate, 1-1.8 cm. long, 8-14 mm. wide across the lateral lobes when expanded; lateral lobes incurved in natural position, broadly rounded at the base, tapering to a triangular-obtuse to rounded apex; mid-lobe suborbicular, truncate to deeply emarginate at the apex, with the margins undulate-crenate, 5-10 mm. wide; disc prominently veined, with five to seven yellowish lamellae extending from near the base of the lip to near the apex of the mid-lobe and with two shorter lamellae on the lateral lobes. Column strongly arcuate, clavellate, with narrow lateral wings, 8-12 mm. long. Capsule obliquely cylindric, erect or essentially so, reddish or chocolate-brown, 2-4.5 cm. long, 8-10 mm. in diameter.

Although the Pine-pink is considered to be a terrestrial species, its fibrous roots are heavily coated with velamentous tissue such as is characteristic of epiphytic orchids. It is one of a large number of borderline species which do not fall definitely into either the "terrestrial" or the "epiphytic" category, and thus is an example of the artificiality of those categories. Perhaps, after all, the Pine-pink should

PLATE 132.— **Bletia purpurea.** 1, plant, one half natural size. 2, flower, front view, spread open, one and one half times natural size. 3, lip and column, side view, twice natural size. 4, lip, spread out, two and one half times natural size. 5, fruiting inflorescence, one half natural size. *Drawn by Gordon W. Dillon.*

be designated as a semiterrestrial or semiepiphyte. For I have seen it growing on rock ledges in thinly wooded pinelands on Big Pine Key, Monroe County, Florida, where half the length of its roots trailed over the bare hot rocks while the other half were lightly threaded through the surrounding loose litter.

The corms of this widespread tropical orchid are commonly called "wild ginger" because they contain an irritating and bitter juice, and are used medicinally by primitive peoples in various parts of its range. When dried, these corms are steeped to make a tea which is used as a tonic, for stomachic purposes and as an antidote for fish-poisoning. The fresh corms are also used as a curative for cuts and abrasions of the skin.

According to STEVENSON (1926), a natural enemy affecting the Pine-pink is the rust, *Uredo nigropunctata* P. Henn. which apparently causes devitalization of the plants affected.

The Pine-pink is found commonly in dry pinelands or flatwoods, rocky woods, or on palmetto roots. It also occurs in cypress swamps on the base of tree trunks and on stumps and "knees" of cypress trees. In the tropics, the Pine-pink grows on grassy hills, wet cliffs, on rocks in dry woods and fields, in barrancas and pine barrens, as well as on the base of tree trunks, on logs and stumps or on floating clumps of weeds and grasses in water. It occurs near sea level in Florida and Panama, up to 2,000 feet altitude in Cuba and Colombia and 4,000 feet in Jamaica and Guatemala. The Pine-pink blooms sporadically throughout the year, especially from November to June.

GEOGRAPHICAL DISTRIBUTION: Widespread and rather frequent in southern Florida (Broward, Collier, Dade, Highlands, Lee and Monroe Counties), Mexico, through Central America to Panama, the Bahama Islands, the West Indies, Colombia and Venezuela.

CULTURAL NOTES: Many well-meaning motorist-gardeners have collected large numbers of the Pine-pink and moved the plants to their gardens and greenhouses where they have been placed in a haphazard manner. Almost certain to be a failure under this treatment, *Bletia* cannot be recommended as a garden plant. Even with the best of expert care, it passes from the subacid humus-rich soils of the pinelands or flatwoods to the artificial environment of a clay flower-pot and a greenhouse bench with extreme reluctance. Not a plant for casual gardeners, the Pine-pink should be left in its native pinelands.

Most of the Florida terrestrial orchids may be considered in the same class as *Bletia* or as the northern Pink Moccasin-flower (*Cypripedium acaule*) in regard to their likelihood of being transplanted and successfully cultivated. The grower who wishes to succeed with these plants will have to adapt his soil mixture, watering and shading to the requirements of each species. Close attention is needed as experiments with different combinations of treatments are carried out for the growing of our native terrestrial orchids in the out-of-door garden. (J. V. W.)

In 1824, ELLIOTT made the following interesting remark concerning this species, "With this species I am unacquainted . . . MICHAUX who cultivated it near Charleston [South Carolina] where it flowered in the Autumn, received it from the Bahama Islands."

37. Eulophia R. Br.

Eulophia R. Br., Bot. Reg. 8: t. 686. 1823, conserved name.

(The name, *Eulophia,* is a Greek term meaning "well crested," in allusion to the crest on the lip of the type species of the genus.)

Rather large terrestrial (rarely epiphytic) scapose herbs rising from thickened rhizomes or corms. Leaves several, clustered, sheathing the lower part of the scape. Inflorescence a loose or dense few- to many-flowered lateral raceme, rising at or near the base of the root-stock. Sepals and petals free; lateral sepals sometimes adnate to the base of the column. Lip articulated to the foot of the column, saccate at the base, 3-lobed; lateral lobes erect and embracing the column; mid-lobe spreading or recurved, mostly entire (occasionally bilobed); disc crested or naked. Column short, often with two lateral wings; anther terminal, oper-culate, incumbent, imperfectly 2-celled; pollinia two or four, waxy. Capsule ellipsoid to ovoid, erect or pendent.

This is a large genus comprising about two hundred species which are widely dispersed throughout the tropics and warm regions of both hemispheres. It is most numerous in Africa, and is rare in Malaya, Polynesia, Australia and America.

KEY FOR THE IDENTIFICATION OF THE SPECIES OF EULOPHIA

1. Lip papillose-crested on the central veins, more than 1.5 cm. long............*E. alta* (p. 342)
1. Lip naked, not papillose-crested, less than 1.2 cm. long.................*E. ecristata* (p. 344)

1. **Eulophia alta** (L.) Fawc. & Rendle, Fl. Jam. 1: 112, t. 22, figs. 4-8. 1910.
   Limodorum altum L., Syst. Nat., ed. 12, 2: 594. 1767. Type locality: Not
   given. (*Cyrtopodium Woodfordii* Sims; *Eulophia Woodfordii* (Sims)
   Rolfe; *Platypus altus* (L.) Small; *P. papilliferus* Small & Nash).

PLATE 133

(The name, *alta,* is a Latin adjective meaning "high," in reference to the tall conspicuous inflorescence.)

COMMON NAMES: Wild Coco, Ground Coco, Woodford's Cyrtopodium.

Plant erect, coarse, from a bulbous corm, 7.5-17 dm. tall. Corn 4-6 cm. in diameter. Stem short, mostly concealed by the elongated tubular membranaceous leaf-sheaths. Leaves three to four, clustered at the summit of the corm, sheathing the short stem, elliptic-lanceolate, plicate, acute to acuminate, 2-12 dm. long, 3-11 cm. wide. Inflorescence a lax many-flowered lateral raceme, from near the base of the corm, up to 10.5 dm. long (including the peduncle); peduncle up to 1 cm. in diameter. Floral bracts ovate-lanceolate to linear-subulate, acuminate, 1-3 cm. long. Flowers numerous, up to sixty or more, greenish or bronze-colored with the lip marked with purple, often opposite or in whorls along the rachis, the slender arcuate pedicellate ovaries being 1.5-2 cm. long. Sepals elliptic-oblong to oblong-lanceolate, acute to acuminate, often slightly dilated above the middle, 1.5-2.6 cm. long, 5-7.5 mm. wide above the middle; dorsal sepal shorter than the lateral sepals; lateral sepals oblique, adnate to the column-foot. Petals wider than the sepals, broadly oblong-spatulate to oblanceolate, obtuse to broadly rounded at the apex, 1.5-1.8 cm. long, 6-8 mm. wide above the middle. Lip articu-lated to the column-foot, 3-lobed, saccate at the base, with the terminal half strongly recurved in natural position, brownish green, tinged and veined with purple, 1.8-2.5 cm. long, 1.4-1.6 cm. wide across the lateral lobes when spread out; lateral lobes relatively small, incurved and embracing the column in natural position, with the free part short and broadly rounded at the apex; mid-lobe ovate-semiorbicular, broadly rounded at the apex, with the margins undulate-crisped and somewhat erose, 8-12 mm. wide; disc with two erect short flap-like subquadrate keels in front of the saccate basal portion, papillose-crested along the central veins of the mid-lobe. Column erect and somewhat arcuate, compressed, dilated below, with a broad shallow foot at the base and shallow lateral wings above, 7-9 mm. long. Capsule ellipsoid, pendent, 3-3.5 cm. long, about 1.2 cm. in diameter.

Probably the first collection of this species in the United States is that of A. W. CHAPMAN discovered along the Caloosahatchee River in southwest Florida in 1875.

The occurrence of two species of this essentially African genus in the Western Hemisphere is another mystery in the realm of plant distribution. As in the case

PLATE 133.—**Eulophia alta.** 1, plant, one sixth natural size. 2, inflorescence, three fourths natural size. 3, lip and column, front view, lip spread open, one and two thirds times natural size. *Drawn by Blanche Ames.*

of a number of anomalous species found in the West Indies and other parts of tropical America, it is thought that some of these plants were introduced into the

New World by slaves in the early days of the slave trade, either for their supposed healing powers, for use in voodooistic practices or for food.

The Wild Coco grows in rather acid humus-rich sandy soils in coastal prairies, open pinelands, on the banks of rivers, on the margin of ponds, on the border-line of sawgrass ponds and hammocks, and in hammocks. In the tropics, it is found in swamps, savannahs, open fields, open pinelands, hammocks, shady places along streams and on open grassy hillsides. While it is usually found at low elevations, it occurs up to 2,000 feet altitude in Cuba and 4,000 feet in the British West Indies (Antigua). The blooming season extends from September to December and also May (in Florida).

GEOGRAPHICAL DISTRIBUTION: Widely distributed in southern Florida (Broward, Collier, Dade, Glades, Highlands, Lee, Manatee and St. Lucie counties); Mexico through Central America to Panama, throughout the West Indies, Trinidad and northern South America; also Africa.

CULTURAL NOTES: There is no record of this species ever having been cultivated. See this section under *Bletia purpurea*.

2. **Eulophia ecristata** (Fernald) Ames, Contrib. Knowl. Orch. Fl. South. Florida 19. 1904. *Cyrtopodium ecristatum* Fernald, Bot. Gaz. 24: 433. 1897. Type locality and collection: Near Jacksonville and borders of the Indian River, Florida, *A. H. Curtiss 2808.* (*Bletia verecunda* Chapm., not R. Brown, 1813; *Triorchos ecristatus* (Fernald) Small). PLATE 134

(The name, *ecristata*, is a Latin term meaning "without a crest," in allusion to the crestless lip.)

COMMON NAME: None known.

Plant erect, scapose, glabrous, 3.4-13.5 dm. tall, from a thickened corm producing slender fibrous roots. Stem entirely concealed by membranaceous imbricating leaf-sheaths. Leaves several, clustered at the base of the plant, linear-lanceolate, long-acuminate, with the lower part sheathing the stem, plicate, 1.5-7 dm. long, 1-3.5 cm. wide. Raceme lateral, loosely or densely few- to many-flowered, 3-17 cm. long, 2-2.5 cm. in diameter. Floral bracts linear-lanceolate, long-acuminate, scarious, 3-5.5 cm. long, 3-4 mm. wide at the base. Flowers brown, variously tinged and marked with deep purple, with the rather stout pedicellate ovaries about 1 cm. long. Dorsal sepal linear-oblong, obtuse to acute or occasionally abruptly acuminate and involute at the apex, 9-12 mm. long, 4-5 mm. wide. Lateral sepals spreading, adnate to the base of the column, linear-oblong to oblong-lanceolate, acute to acuminate, slightly falcate, with the margins strongly involute near the apex, 1.1-1.4 cm. long, 4-5 mm. wide. Petals oblong-elliptic, obtuse or occasionally abruptly acute, 9-12 mm. long, 4-5 mm. wide. Lip concave below, deeply 3-lobed, naked, slightly crenate-erose on the margins, varying from light brown to deep purple, strongly veined, 8-11 mm. long, 7-13 mm. wide across the lateral lobes when spread out; lateral lobes relatively small, incurved in natural position, orbicular-oblong, truncate to broadly rounded at the apex, as wide as long; mid-lobe suborbicular to orbicular, broadly rounded and strongly involute at the apex, 5-8 mm. wide. Column short, blunt, about 3 mm. long. Capsule ovoid, erect and appressed to the rachis, 1.5-2 cm. long, about 1 cm. in diameter.

The earliest collection of this species which I have seen from our region is that obtained in Florida by F. RUGEL in 1842. ALVAN W. CHAPMAN states that he found it in Gadsden County, Florida, in 1845.

This orchid has an exceedingly disrupted range. While frequent throughout Florida, it is very local elsewhere, being recorded in only two localities in Louisiana, in southeastern North Carolina, and in the mountains of North Carolina where it was collected in August 1892 by C. S. WILLIAMSON. There seems to be no satisfactory explanation for this extraordinary distribution. However, since it is a rather inconspicuous plant and usually grows in company with various tall grasses (*Andropogon* spp., *Paspalum* spp., etc.) and weedy plants (which it somewhat resembles), it is quite possible that it has been overlooked in the vast areas intervening between Florida and the other stations in Louisiana and North Carolina.

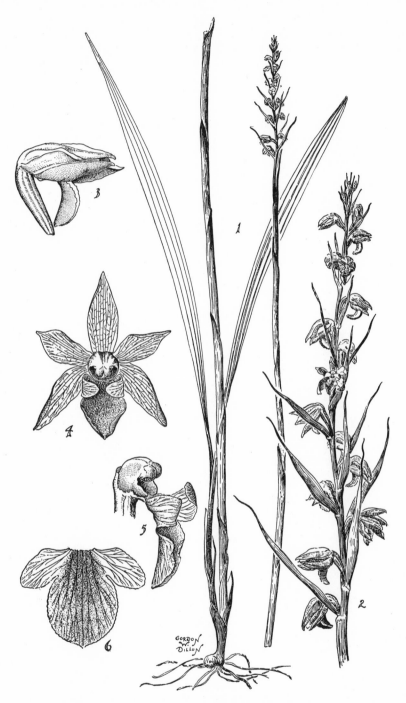

PLATE 134.—**Eulophia ecristata.** 1, plant, one fourth natural size. 2, inflorescence, natural size. 3, flower, side view, twice natural size. 4, flower, front view, partly spread open, twice natural size. 5, lip and column, frontside view, three times natural size. 6, lip, spread out, six times natural size. *Drawn by Gordon W. Dillon.*

For this reason, it provides us another intriguing problem in the study of the distribution of our native orchids.

This species occurs usually in dry acid humus-rich sand in open pine barrens and flatwoods, waste places, in scrub oak lands, open dry fields and fallow cultivated fields. It is also found in moist sandy-clay soil, open rocky soil, thin soil on lime-rock and in moist woods on the edge of swamps. It is commonly associated with Saw-palmetto (*Serenoa serrulata*) and Broom-grass (*Andropogon* spp.). Its blooming season is from June to September.

GEOGRAPHICAL DISTRIBUTION: Rare and local in North Carolina (Bladen and New Hanover counties; also "Mountains of North Carolina") and Louisiana (Jefferson Davis and Tangipahoa parishes), widespread and rather frequent in Florida; also Cuba.

CULTURAL NOTES: There is no record of this species ever having been cultivated. See this section under *Bletia purpurea*.

38. Cyrtopodium R. Br.

Cyrtopodium R. Br. in Ait., Hort. Kew., ed. 2, 5 : 216. 1813.

(The name, *Cyrtopodium,* is a combination of Greek terms meaning "curved foot," in allusion to the prominently upcurved foot of the column.)

Large epiphytic, terrestrial or rock-inhabiting plants with long fusiform pseudobulbs which bear several plicate leaves near the summit and a lateral flowering branch at the base. Inflorescence a large spreading panicle of numerous flowers. Flowers rather large but inconspicuous because of their coloration. Perianth parts free, spreading. Lip inserted on the foot of the column, 3-lobed; lateral lobes incurved over the column; mide-lobe with a verrucose apical margin; disc adorned with a warty callus. Column semiterete, dilated above, produced into a foot at the base; anther terminal, incumbent, operculate; pollinia two or four, contiguous, waxy.

This is a small genus of about twenty species which are confined to the tropics and subtropics of the Western Hemisphere.

1. **Cyrtopodium punctatum** (L.) Lindl., Gen. and Sp. Orch. Pl. 188. 1833.
   Epidendrum punctatum L., Syst. Nat., ed. 10, 2 : 1246. 1759. Type locality :
   Not given.   PLATE 135

(The name, *punctatum,* is a Latin term meaning "marked with dots," in reference to the spotted flowers and bracts of the inflorescence.)

COMMON NAMES : Bee-swarm Orchid, Cowhorn Orchid, Cigar Orchid, Spotted-flowered Cyrtopodium.

Plant large, glabrous, spreading and much-branched above, up to 1.2 m. or more tall. Pseudobulbs erect, rigid, elongate-fusiform, with numerous articulations, leafy above when young, 1.5-4 dm. long, 1.5-3.5 cm. in diameter, at first concealed by large grayish white inflated scarious sheaths, the sheaths (which are early-fugacious) being distichously imbricating. Leaves linear to linear-lanceolate or linear-elliptic, acute to long-acuminate, plicate, distichous, approximately, spreading, recurved and finally drooping above, 1-6.5 dm. long, 1-5 cm. wide. Inflorescence lateral, paniculate, with a stout peduncle; peduncle provided with large scarious sheaths. Floral bracts and bracts subtending the branches of the inflorescence similar, ovate-oblong to oblong-lanceolate, acute to acuminate, with strongly undulate margins, similar to the sepals in coloration and markings, 1.5-5 cm. long, 7-20 mm. wide. Flowers numerous, lax, with the slender pedicellate ovaries 2.5-3.5 cm. long. Sepals greenish yellow, irregularly marked with madder-purple spots; dorsal sepal oblong-lanceolate, acute, with the margins strongly undulate, up to 2.6 cm. long, 7.5-11 mm. wide; lateral sepals ovate-lanceolate to oblong-lanceolate, acute to abruptly apiculate, with the margins strongly undulate, 1.5-2 cm. long, 7-9 mm. wide. Petals broadly oblong-ovate to oblong-obovate, mostly with a short claw, somewhat undulate-crisped on the margins, with the apex subtruncate to broadly rounded or obtuse (rarely mucronate), bright yellow, sparingly spotted with madder-brown, 1.3-2.1 cm. long, 8.5-12 mm. wide. Lip inserted on the foot of the column by a narrow claw, 3-lobed, almost twice as wide as long, 1.1-1.6 cm. long, 1.7-2.2 cm. wide when expanded; lateral lobes obliquely and very broadly obovate or rounded, erect and arching over the column in natural position, matter-brown, with yellow at the base, 8-9 mm. long, 8-10 mm. wide; mid-lobe short, rigid, much broader than long, with a crisped erose-tuberculate broadly rounded apical margin, madder-purple with a yellow center, 7.5-10 mm. wide; disc provided with a fleshy grooved callus along the center from the base to a point midway between the lateral lobes where it terminates in a tuberculate thickening; sinus between the lateral lobes and mid-lobe narrow, 2-3 mm. deep. Column compressed, clavellate in outline, subapiculate, with a prominent foot projected forward at a right angle to the column, about 7 mm. long. Capsule large, broadly ellipsoid, up to 8 cm. or more long, 3-5 cm. in diameter.

This species was probably collected for the first time in our region near Miami, Dade County, Florida, by A. P. GARBER in March 1877.

The Bee-swarm Orchid is so named because of the fancied appearance of the numerous attractive flowers of the large loose inflorescence to a swarm of bees in

PLATE 135. — **Cyrtopodium punctatum.** 1, plant, one fourth natural size. 2, inflorescence, one half natural size. 3, lip and column, spread out, one and one half times natural size. 4, column, front-side view, four times natural size. 5, pollinia, much enlarged. *Drawn by Gordon W. Dillon.*

flight. It is a rather ungainly plant, and often grows in dense masses in low crotches of trees or in shallow soil on boulders exposed to full or partial sunlight. It is rather extensively distributed over the southern tip of Florida, and at one time it was of frequent occurrence. In recent years, however, the wholesale removal of plants from their native haunts by Indians and others who sell the plants to tourists and well-meaning gardeners, has greatly depleted the Bee-swarm Orchid in places where it was once quite abundant.

The pseudobulbs, containing a mucilaginous glue, are utilized in sundry ways in various parts of the species range. A glue used in book-binding and to make the soles of boots and shoes more durable is extracted from the pseudobulbs and, in Honduras, the pseudobulbs are used in place of resin to besmear the strings of guitars. In Brazil, the pseudobulbs are said to be used medicinally.

This species is found on tree trunks or rotten logs and stumps, etc., in hammocks and cypress swamps of southern peninsular Florida. In the tropics, it occurs on various species of dead or living trees, logs and stumps, in savannahs, on boulders or in soil of crevasses between rocks and ledges. While it usually grows at low elevations, it occurs up to 4,500 feet altitude in Central America, 2,500 feet in Venezuela and 3,500 feet in Argentina. It ordinarily flowers from March to May, but has been collected in flower during August in Paraguay.

GEOGRAPHICAL DISTRIBUTION: Southern Florida (Collier, Dade, Lee and Monroe counties); also Mexico, Guatemala, Costa Rica, throughout the West Indies, and in South America (south to Argentina).

CULTURAL NOTES: The great Bee-swarm Orchid is a favorite in many collections of both amateur and commercial growers alike. Culture is extremely easy, and, given protection from severe winds and low temperatures, this robust orchid is almost certain to be a success. Either pot culture with brown osmundine, or board- or post-culture in which the plants are secured against a blanket of osmunda fiber and then wired to a horizontal piece of cypress will suffice. Very often huge colonies of this species are collected from the Florida swamps by sawing through the trees on which they are growing. These three- to four-foot sections of trees are carried to the garden and secured to a post in the lath-house or greenhouse. If it is desired to grow the Cowhorn Orchid in clay pots, about one third of the pot should be filled with potsherds, and then blocks of cut osmunda fiber should be firmly packed about its root-system. Very firm potting is essential, and as this orchid has an extensive root-system, rather larger containers are needed for it than for a plant of corresponding size with a less extensive root-system. Although *C. punctatum* is commonly a terrestrial in the American tropics where it is often found in rock crevasses on the arid Pacific slope, it certainly has become an epiphyte in Florida. In cultivation it is always grown as an epiphyte in the experience of this writer.

During dry periods (from January to October) the plants should be soaked once a week. During the winter, when the leaves are shed, only enough water should be provided so as to keep the pseudobulbs from shrivelling. In cultivation, this orchid, like so many other wildlings, is most subject to attack by scale. A summer oil, at one-half the recommended concentration, should be applied under strong pressure or with a small stiff-bristled brush at the first sign of this trying pest. If scale becomes established, it will be difficult to eradicate and it may kill some of the growths and prevent the plant from setting normal blossoms. (J. V. W.)

According to VEITCH (1893), this species was first introduced to horticulture by SWAINSON, who sent it to the Botanic Garden at Glasgow, Scotland, where it was cultivated for many years before it could be induced to flower in 1835.

39. **Maxillaria** Ruiz & Pavon

Maxillaria Ruiz & Pavon, Fl. Peruv. & Chil. Prodr. 116, t. 25. 1794.

(The name, *Maxillaria,* is from the Latin noun *maxilla,* meaning "jaw," in allusion to the gaping flowers and fancied resemblance of the column and lip to the jaws of an insect.)

Epiphytic herbs with an elongated or abbreviated stem (in our species) which are represented by flattened pseudobulbs enveloped by distichously imbricating leaf-bearing sheaths. Pseudobulbs inconspicuous, bearing at the summit one or more leaves. Leaves fleshy-coriaceous, linear-oblong. Inflorescences one or more, consisting of a short 1-flowered peduncle which originates in the axil of a leaf. Flowers inconspicuous. Sepals and petals subequal, free, mostly parallel in natural position; lateral sepals adnate to the base of the column-foot and forming a short mentum. Lip attached to the foot of the column, simple or more or less 3-lobed, concave; disc usually traversed in the center by a callus. Column erect, with a short foot, wingless, mostly arcuate and concave on the anterior surface; anther terminal, operculate, incumbent; pollinia four, waxy, ovoid, compressed, attached to an oblong stipe. Capsule ovoid or ellipsoid.

This large polymorphic genus comprises about two hundred eighty species which are variable and often difficult to separate. It is widely scattered in the tropical and subtropical regions of the Western Hemisphere.

1. **Maxillaria crassifolia** (Lindl.) Reichb. f., Bonpl. 2: 16. 1854. *Heterotaxis crassifolia* Lindl., Bot. Reg. 12: t. 1028. 1826. Type locality and collection: Jamaica, 1823, *Lee.* (*Maxillaria sessilis* (Sw.) Fawc. & Rendle, not Lindley, 1845). PLATE 136

(The name, *crassifolia,* is a combination of Latin terms meaning "thick-leaved," in allusion to the fleshy-coriaceous leaves.)

COMMON NAME: None known.

Plant from a short rhizome, terminating in an inconspicuous pseudobulb which is mostly concealed by distichously imbricating cataphyll-sheaths. Pseudobulbs oblong, compressed, unifoliate, 1.5-3 cm. long, about 1.5 cm. wide. Leaves coriaceous, mostly articulated with the leaf-sheaths; outermost leaves (cataphylls) short and poorly developed; inner leaves (cataphylls) on each side of and terminating the pseudobulb linear to linear-oblong, obtuse to subacute and apiculate, conduplicate at the base, 7-45 cm. long, 1.2-4 cm. wide. Inflorescences from the axil of a leaf, one to three; peduncle short, 1-flowered, usually about 1 cm. long (rarely up to 3 cm. long), provided with a scarious bract near the middle, mostly nearly hidden by the leaf-sheaths. Floral bracts small, triangular to broadly lanceolate, acute, deeply concave, scarious, rarely up to 1.5 cm. long, clasping the pedicellate ovary. Flower solitary, campanulate, with the perianth parts fleshy-coriaceous, subparallel, yellow to orange, usually, marked with purple, the stout pedicellate ovary being about as long as the peduncle. Dorsal sepal oblong-elliptic to lanceolate, subacute to acute, conspicuously concave, 1.4-1.8 cm. long, about 5 mm. wide near the base. Lateral sepals rising from a broad somewhat concave base, obliquely ovate-oblong to broadly lanceolate, acute, usually dorsally keeled and somewhat concave at the apex, 1.5-1.8 cm. long, about 6 mm. wide near the base, forming an inconspicuous mentum with the short column-foot. Petals linear-oblanceolate, subacute to acute, with the margins entire or denticulate, occasionally lightly falcate, 1.2-1.5 cm. long, 3-3.5 mm. wide. Lip obscurely 3-lobed above the middle, elliptic to elliptic-lanceolate or rarely obovate in outline, with the margins entire or denticulate, yellow or orange with reddish purple dots or tinged lavender, 1.3-1.5 cm. long, 6.5-8 mm. wide when spread out; lateral lobes shallow, involute; disc with a broad densely tomentose or somewhat farinose callus along the central portion. Column arcuate, semiterete, 8-10 mm. long (including the short foot). Capsule ellipsoid, 2.5-3.5 cm. long.

This species was probably collected for the first time in the United States in the Big Cypress Hammock about 6 miles west of Deep Lake, Collier County, Florida, by J. B. McFARLIN in April 1934. However, it was not known to occur from con-

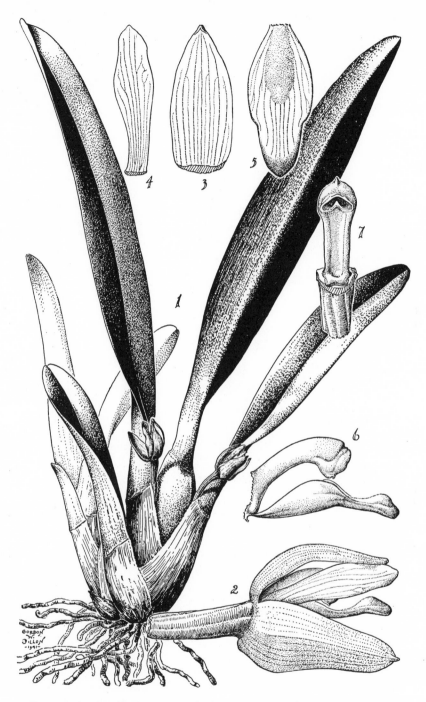

PLATE 136.— **Maxillaria crassifolia.** 1, plant, one half natural size. 2, flower, side view, two and one half times natural size. 3, dorsal sepal, two and one half times natural size. 4, petal, two and one half times natural size. 5, lip, front view, spread out, two and one half times natural size. 6, lip and column, side view, two and one half times natural size. 7, column, with upper part of ovary, front-ventral view, two and one half times natural size. *Drawn by Gordon W. Dillon.*

tinental North America until W. M. BUSWELL reported it in 1937. BUSWELL, in writing of this species, gives the following picturesque description of the Big Cypress—the haunt of many of the interesting orchids found in Florida.

"One of the most interesting spots in all Florida is the wild orchid gardens of the Big Cypress forest. A green roofed cathedral with columns decorated, often from base to top, with orchids, ferns and other epiphytic plants. A labyrinth of leafy aisles through giant ferns, beautifully draped stumps and Cypress knees and an occasional woodland pool. During the late summer months when there are fre-

TEXTFIGURE 7. — Sterile plant and front-side view of lip of *Maxillaria sanguinea*. The plant has been drawn ½ natural size. The lip is drawn about 3 times natural size. *Drawn by Gordon W. Dillon.*

quent rains these slightly lower spots are more or less under water, but wading is quite refreshing in this tropical forest. At other times the ground is fairly dry and, as the water prevents the rank growth of vines and shrubs that are almost impassable on the higher ground outside, the walking is much easier at all times of the year. Only a botanist would be willing to climb and push and crawl through miles of thorny vines and dense shrubbery to gain admission to this cathedral, but to some of us it is well worth the price. . . .

"In all of the area of the proposed [Everglades] National Park there is no other spot where so many rare plants are found and the only spot in the United States where we can see and realize the wonderful beauty of a tropical jungle. Mammoth Royal Palms are scattered through the forest, the green plumes often far above all the other trees. After spending a day in a spot like this the man-made parks outside seem very artificial and uninteresting."

This orchid grows on trees in the Big Cypress Swamp of southern peninsular Florida. In the tropics, it is found in open humid mountain forests, damp thickets and on cliffs, and it occurs up to 2,000 feet altitude in Cuba and 4,500 feet in Panama. It flowers from February to August in various parts of its range.

GEOGRAPHICAL DISTRIBUTION: Florida (Collier County); also Mexico through Central America to Panama, throughout the West Indies, Venezuela and Brazil.

PLATE 137.—**Ionopsis utricularioides.** 1, plant, natural size. 2, lip, front view, three times natural size. 3, lateral sepals, three and one fourth times natural size. 4, petal, three times natural size. 5, dorsal sepal, three times natural size. 6, column, with the anther raised, front-side view, ten times natural size. 7, pollinia and pedicel, enlarged. *Redrawn from Blanche Ames by Gordon W. Dillon.*

CULTURAL NOTES: This species was first introduced into English horticulture from Jamaica by a Mr. LEE from Hammersmith in 1823. See this section under the genus *Epidendrum*.

*   *   *   *   *

Late in February 1947, GEORGE M. WAGNER, JR., found a sterile plant of a species of *Maxillaria* growing on a small tree in the Pinecrest region of southwest peninsular Florida. Since the plant bore no flowers, it could only be tentatively identified as *Maxillaria sanguinea* Rolfe, a native of Costa Rica and Panama. Assuming that this orchid is *M. sanguinea,* its occurrence in southern peninsular Florida is most unusual, especially in consideration of the fact that it is not known to occur in the West Indies.

A habit sketch of the plant (*cf.* FIG. 7), as well as a drawing of the lip of authentic material of *M. sanguinea* together with a brief description, is included here to aid in identifying this species if it should be found in our region in the future.

Plant with a creeping sheath-covered rhizome which produces at short intervals small ancipitous pseudobulbs which are ellipsoid, unifoliate and are 2-3 cm. long. Leaves grasslike, very narrowly linear, up to 40 cm. long and 2-3 mm. wide. Inflorescence one-flowered, from the base of the pseudobulb, very short, scarcely exceeding the pseudobulb; peduncle concealed by scarious imbricating acuminate sheaths. Flowers fleshy-fibrous, deep red or bronze-colored with yellowish blotches. Sepals oblong-elliptic, subacute, 1.5-2.5 cm. long; lateral sepals falcate. Petals elliptic-oblanceolate, subobtuse, oblique, 1.5-2 cm. long. Lip from the base of the column, arcuate-recurved in natural position, entire or obscurely 3-lobed, broadly oblong-elliptic in outline when expanded, truncate to broadly rounded at the apex, with a whitish tip, about 1.5 cm. long and 8 mm. wide; disc with an oblong fleshy thickening in the center below the middle.

40. Ionopsis HBK.

Ionopsis HBK., Nov. Gen. et Sp. Pl. 1: 348, t. 83. 1815.

(The name, *Ionopsis,* is a combination of Greek terms meaning "the appearance of a violet," in allusion to the resemblance of the flowers to a violet in form and color.)

Epiphytic or rarely terrestrial plants with short or elongated leafy rhizomes which produce small pseudobulbs and long slender or stout lateral peduncles. Pseudobulbs small, leafless or unifoliate. Leaves from the rhizomes, narrow, coriaceous, rigid, distichous, articulated to imbricating sheaths. Peduncles one to three to a plant, slender, bearing a laxly flowered raceme or panicle. Flowers showy, small to medium-sized. Sepals subequal, erect, spreading; dorsal sepal free; lateral sepals united at the base and forming a short sac surrounding the base of the lip. Petals similar to the dorsal sepal. Lip attached to the base of the column, shortly and broadly clawed, much larger than the sepals and petals, minutely bicallose below. Column short, stout, wingless, footless; anther terminal, operculate, incumbent; pollinia two, waxy. Capsule ovoid to ellipsoid.

This is a small genus of about ten species which are confined to tropical and subtropical regions of the Western Hemisphere. The single species in our area is widespread and rather frequent in Florida; the others are local and rare.

1. Ionopsis utricularioides (Sw.) Lindl., Collect. Bot., t. 39, fig. A. 1825. *Epidendrum utricularioides* Sw., Prodr. Veg. Ind. Occ. 122. 1788. Type locality: Jamaica and Hispaniola.   PLATE 137

(The name, *utricularioides,* is a classic term meaning "like a Utricularia," in allusion to the resemblance of the flowers to those of some species of the lentibulariaceous Bladderwort (*Utricularia*).

COMMON NAME: Delicate Ionopsis.

Plant glabrous, 0.7-7.5 dm. tall from a short or elongated rhizome. Pseudobulbs small, smooth, ellipsoid-conical, up to 3 cm. long, leafless or bearing a solitary small leaf at its apex, often completely concealed by the leaf-bearing sheaths surrounding them. Leaves from the rhizomes, two or three (rarely more), articulated with imbricating leaf-sheaths, oblong-lanceolate to linear or linear-lanceolate, obtuse to acute and cuspidate, dorsally carinate, rigidly coriaceous, often reddish brown on the lower surface, 3-17 cm. long, 6-18 mm. wide. Inflorescence lateral, from the base of the pseudobulb, a simple raceme or spreading panicle, laxly few- to many-flowered, up to 7.5 dm. long (including the long peduncle), up to 25 cm. in diameter; peduncle slender or stout, brownish green, provided at the several nodes with closely appressed tubular sheaths which are up to 1.2 cm. long. Floral bracts minute, triangular to lanceolate, acute, less than 3 mm. long. Flowers whitish to rose-red, variegated or tinged with lavender, deep magenta or purple, showy, with the slender pedicellate ovaries 6-14 mm. long. Dorsal sepal oblong to oblong-elliptic or rarely oblanceolate, obtuse to apiculate, more or less concave-conduplicate, 3.2-6 mm. long, 1.5-3 mm. wide. Lateral sepals ovate-lanceolate to oblong-lanceolate, acute, oblique, 3.5-6 mm. long, 1.5-2 mm. wide, united at the base and forming a small sac. Petals ovate-oblong to oblong or rarely obovate-oblong, broadly rounded to acute and shortly apiculate at the recurved apex, 6-7 mm. long, 3-3.5 mm. wide. Lip with a short broad claw, broadly flabellate-obcordate, deeply emarginate, with the margins entire to sinuate or somewhat crenulate, 7-16 mm. long, 7-18 mm. wide across the subquadrate terminal lobules; claw with obsolescent lateral auricles; disc with two small thin calli or keels in the middle near the base. Column stout, truncate, about 2 mm. long. Capsule ovoid or ellipsoid, long-beaked, 1.2-1.6 cm. long, 5-7 mm. in diameter.

This species was probably collected for the first time in the United States at Gobbler's Head near Naples, Collier County, Florida, by OAKES AMES and BLANCHE AMES on March 12, 1904.

The Delicate Ionopsis is one of the most widely distributed of all American orchids, and is one of the six orchids known to occur on the Galapagos Islands. It is commonly found in regions of dry atmospheric conditions.

This species is found on Pop-ash (*Fraxinus caroliniana*) and other trees on the edge of and in thinly wooded hammocks and swamps. In the tropics, it is epiphytic on trees and shrubs in dry or dense moist forests or on citrus trees in groves, and is rarely terrestrial on grassy banks. In British Honduras, it has been observed to be especially common on Grapefruit trees. Although usually at low elevations, it occurs up to 2,000 feet altitude in Honduras and 3,500 feet in British Honduras. The flowering time is from December to March throughout its range.

GEOGRAPHICAL DISTRIBUTION : Florida (Collier and Lee counties), from Mexico, through Central America to Panama, throughout the West Indies, south to central South America and the Galapagos Islands.

CULTURAL NOTES : This is one of the daintiest of the Florida epiphytes and is a universal favorite when in flower. Widely admired by orchidists, it has been collected and brought into Florida in great numbers, but does not seem to thrive under conditions existing in Florida orchid houses. In the experience of the writer and of other orchid growers, *Ionopsis* goes into a decline during its second season in an orchid house and seldom recovers. Possibly under out-of-door garden conditions in sections near its native habitat greater success can be expected. (J. V. W.)

This species was first introduced into English horticulture by Sir RALPH WOODFORD, who sent it from Trinidad. It flowered in the Horticultural Society's garden at Chiswick in May 1824.

41. **Brassia** R. Br.

Brassia R. Br. in Ait., Hort. Kew., ed. 2, 5: 215. 1813.

(The name, *Brassia,* is in honor of WILLIAM BRASS (who died at sea in 1783), skilled English botanical draughtsman and collector.)

Epiphytic or rarely terrestrial plants with stout creeping rhizomes which produce large one- to the three-leaved pseudobulbs and lateral inflorescences. Leaves coriaceous, at the apex of the pseudobulbs or on sheaths, clasping the pseudobulbs. Inflorescence a loose few- to many-flowered raceme. Flowers usually showy. Sepals and petals free, spreading, long-acuminate or caudate; petals usually more or less shorter than the sepals. Lip sessile at the base of the column, simple, flat or convex, usually adorned at the base with a bilamellate or sulcate callus. Column short, erect, wingless, footless; anther terminal, operculate, incumbent; pollinia two, waxy. Capsule ellipsoid, obovoid or cylindric.

This genus is composed of about fifty species which are natives of tropical and subtropical America, from southern Florida, Mexico and the West Indies to Brazil and Peru. They are easily recognized by their commonly elongate-attenuate sepals. The floral segments are extremely variable in length, especially the sepals.

1. **Brassia caudata** (L.) Lindl., Bot. Reg. 10: t. 832. 1824. *Epidendrum caudatum* L., Syst. Nat., ed. 10, 2: 1246. 1759. Type locality: Not given. PLATE 138

(The name, *caudata,* is a Latin term meaning "with a tail," in allusion to the elongated narrow sepals and petals.)

COMMON NAMES: Spider Orchid, Long-tailed Brassia.

Plant up to 5 dm. or more tall. Pseudobulbs oblong-ellipsoid, compressed, two- to three-leaved at the apex, 6-15.5 cm. long, 2-3.5 cm. wide, subtended by two or more conduplicate scarious sheaths which are often leaf-bearing. Leaves from the apex of the pseudobulbs and often from sheaths surrounding the pseudobulbs, oblong-elliptic to oblong-lanceolate or oblanceolate, obtuse to acute, coriaceous, conduplicate at the base, 1.3-3.5 dm. long, 2-6 cm. wide. Peduncle lateral, from the base of the pseudobulb, in the axil of a leaf-sheath, provided with remote tubular scarious bracts, up to 4 dm. or more long (including the loosely few- (about 12) flowered raceme). Floral bracts triangular-cucullate, acute to subacuminate, scarious, spreading, 5-10 mm. long. Flowers showy, distichously arranged on the rachis, with the slender pedicellate ovaries 1.2-1.5 cm. long. Sepals and petals orange-yellow, spotted with reddish brown. Sepals linear-lanceolate, gradually becoming long-acuminate to filiform-setaceous or caudate, 3-5 mm. wide near the base; dorsal sepal 3.5-7.5 cm. long; lateral sepals oblique, 7.5-18 cm. long. Petals narrowly lanceolate, long-acuminate, 1.5-3.5 cm. long, 3-4 mm. wide near the base. Lip sessile, yellowish or greenish, with reddish brown blotches near the base, ovate-lanceolate to oblong-elliptic or broadly elliptic-obovate, more or less abruptly long-acuminate, with the upper margins crenulate and involute, 1.5-4 cm. long, 7-13 mm. wide at about the middle; disc with a pair of approximate pubescent lamellae at the base which have a tooth in front of each. Column short, erect, stout, about 4 mm. long. Capsule ellipsoid or cylindric, stipitate, 4-5 cm. long, 1-1.5 cm. in diameter.

This species was found for the first time in the United States in the Nixon-Lewis Hammock, Dade County, Florida, by J. K. SMALL and C. A. MOSIER on March 16, 1915. As far as I know, it has not been observed in Florida since April 1917 when J. K. SMALL found it again in a hammock at the eastern end of Long Key in the Everglades.

The Spider Orchid is of particular interest in being one of the few epiphytic orchids known to Linnaeus. Its flowers are variable in size, and those of the plants found in Florida are usually smaller than those occurring in Central America.

This species is found on trunks and limbs of trees in hammocks of southern peninsular Florida. In the tropics, it usually grows at low elevations on trees in dense humid forests. However, it occurs up to 1,700 feet altitude in the Dominican

Republic, 2,000 feet in Honduras and 4,000 feet in Mexico. The flowering season is from January to August throughout its range.

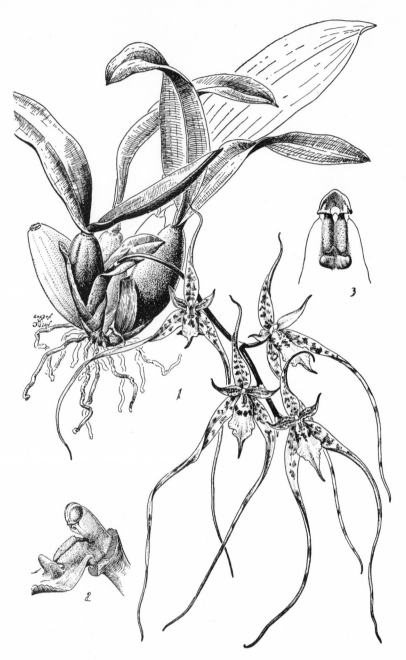

PLATE 138.— **Brassia caudata.** 1, plant, one half natural size. 2, base of lip, to show calli, and column, front-side view, two and one half times natural size. 3, base of lip, to show calli, with column removed, front view, two and one half times natural size. *Drawn by Gordon W. Dillon.*

GEOGRAPHICAL DISTRIBUTION: Florida (Dade County), from Mexico, through Central America to Panama, throughout the West Indies and northern South America.

CULTURAL NOTES: If a plant of *Brassia* is found growing on a branch suitable to be collected, it may be brought in undisturbed and grown on this natural support indefinitely. Careful watering should be provided, with an abundance of water during the spring and summer months and very little during winter. If plants cannot be collected as above, they may be potted firmly in clay flower containers filled with blocks of brown osmundine fiber. It must be borne in mind that *very firm* potting is essential for success in growing orchids and the potting stick must be applied with considerable force to assure a firm growing medium. The plants should be watched for signs of scale and a summer oil of one-half the strength recommended for palms should be used. Wild orchids are very susceptible to scale when brought into collections of greenhouse plants. (J. V. W.)

This species, one of the first Brassias to be horticulturally grown, was introduced into England from the West Indies about 1823 by a Mr. LEE of Hammersmith.

42. Oncidium Sw.

Oncidium Sw., Kongl. Svens. Vetens. Acad. Nya Handl. 21 : 239, t. 3, Q. 1800.

(The name, *Oncidium,* is a Greek term meaning "a little swelling," in allusion to the cluster of warty excrescences or calli which are always present on the lip.)

Epiphytic, terrestrial or rock-inhabiting plants with variously shaped more or less conspicuous (often minute) pseudobulbs from a short or elongated rhizome. Pseudobulbs terminated by one or more leaves. Leaves from the apex of the pseudobulbs or surrounding the pseudobulbs, either equitant, flat or terete, membranaceous to fleshy-coriaceous. Peduncle lateral, from the base of the pseudobulbs in the axil of sheaths. Inflorescence a raceme or panicle, often much-branched and elongated, few- to many-flowered. Flowers variously colored, showy or inconspicuous. Sepals usually subequal, spreading or reflexed, rarely connivent, free or with the lateral sepals more or less connate. Petals similar to the dorsal sepal or sometimes larger. Lip adnate to the base of the column and usually forming a right angle with the column, either entire or three- or more-lobed, with the apical lobe usually much larger than the other lobes, commonly with a variously tuberculate callus at the base of the lamina. Column short, thick, usually but not always provided with petal-like wings or auricles on each side at the apex, footless or occasionally with an incipient foot; anther terminal, operculate, incumbent; pollinia two, waxy, usually deeply sulcate. Capsule ovoid to ellipsoid or fusiform, more or less beaked.

This is a large and polymorphic genus of more than five hundred species, all of which are native of the American tropics and subtropics. They are extremely complex and form a closely allied group of plants, many of which approach *Odontoglossum,* another large New World genus. A great many species are cultivated for their attractive and striking flowers and constitute what are known as "spray orchids" in the market.

As I have already stated, the English were pioneers in the cultivation of orchids as a hobby, as well as for commercial purposes. The beginning of cultivation of orchids in England and its popularity is perhaps due to a species of *Oncidium.* For, more than a hundred years ago, the striking Butterfly Orchid (*Oncidium papilio*) so impressed the Duke of Devonshire that he began to assemble a collection of orchids. This undertaking started a fad which was soon followed by others and resulted in the formation of many notable orchid collections in England and throughout Europe.

CULTURAL NOTES: Like many of the spray orchids, Oncidiums are grown on trees in southern peninsular Florida where they are highly prized for their splendid decorative effect. Plants collected in the wild or acquired from collectors may be fastened to a tree against blankets of osmundine with strips of bronze screen wire, or they may be forced into cabbage palm "boots" with pieces of clean brown osmundine. Clay pots of generous size are widely used for Oncidiums, into which the plants are firmly embedded in masses of the fern rhizome. In potting orchids, a stick should be used to force the osmundine always toward the center with the purpose of obtaining a very firm potting. A pot large enough to accommodate two-years' growth is usually selected. (J. V. W.)

KEY FOR THE IDENTIFICATION OF THE SPECIES OF ONCIDIUM

1. Pseudobulb prominent, elongate-ovoid, mostly more than 1 dm. long; leaf narrowly linear-oblong .... *O. floridanum* (p. 361)
1. Pseudobulb obsolescent, rarely more than 1 cm. long; leaf not linear-oblong...............2
   2. Lateral sepals connate nearly to the apex; leaf equitant, oblong-lanceolate, with the margins more or less cartilaginous and serrulate........................*O. variegatum* (p. 367)
   2. Lateral sepals free; leaf flat, broadly oblong or elliptic, with the margins smooth........3

3. Width of mid-lobe of lip much greater than that across the lateral lobes at the base (when spread out), more than 1.5 cm. wide ....*O. luridum* (p. 363)

3. Width of mide-lobe of lip about equal to that across the lateral lobes at the base (when spread out), less than 1.5 cm. wide.........................*O. carthagenense* (p. 361)

1. **Oncidium carthagenense** (Jacq.) Sw., Kongl. Svens. Vetens. Acad. Nya Handl. 21 : 240. 1800 (as *chartaginense*). *Epidendrum carthagenense* Jacq., Enum. Syst. Pl. Carib. 30. 1760 and Select. Stirp. Am. 228, t. 133, fig. 4. 1763. Type locality : Dense forest, Cartagena, Colombia. PLATE 139

(The name, *carthagenense,* is derived from the city of Cartagena, on the Caribbean coast of Colombia, where it was first found by the Austrian botanist, N. J. JACQUIN.)

COMMON NAME: Spread-eagle Oncidium.

Plant usually large, up to 2 m. or more tall. Pseudobulbs small, less than 2.5 cm. long, arising from a short stout rhizome, unifoliate, concealed by scarious sheaths. Leaf solitary at the apex of the abbreviated pseudobulb, elliptic to oblong-elliptic or lanceolate, subobtuse to acute or subacuminate, rigid and coriaceous, sometimes marginate, 9-40 cm. long, 3-7 cm. wide. Inflorescence lateral from the base of the pseudobulb, arising from the axil of a scarious sheath, loosely paniculate; peduncle up to 2 m. long (including the inflorescence), provided at the nodes with small scarious tubular sheaths which are 7-10 mm. long. Floral bracts small, scarious, ovate to ovate-lanceolate, acute, about 4 mm. long. Flowers small, showy, yellowish white, thickly blotched with lavender, magenta or reddish brown, with the filiform pedicellate ovaries 1.5-2 cm. long. Sepals clawed, conspicuously undulate-crisped on the upper margin, 8-13 mm. long; claw slender, with the involute margins forming a channel; dorsal sepal suborbicular above, rounded at the apex, 5-8 mm. wide; lateral sepals broadly spatulate, 4-6 mm. wide. Petals with a short broad claw, broadly obovate, broadly rounded and occasionally retuse at the apex, conspicuously undulate-crisped on the margins, 7-12 mm. long, 6-8 mm. wide. Lip panduriform, 3-lobed, 9-16 mm. long, 7-14 mm. wide at the widest point (about as wide across the lateral lobes as across the large mid-lobe); lateral lobes basal, semiorbicular, broadly rounded at the apex, with strongly revolute margins; mid-lobe reniform to broadly flabellate, broadly rounded and more or less retuse at the apex, separated from the lateral lobes by a broad isthmus; callus near base of disc, composed of a pair of porrect mammillate swellings below with a short fleshy trilobulate thickening above. Column very short, fleshy, 3-4 mm. long, provided at the apex with a pair of bilobulate wings which project outward for 2-3 mm. Capsule large, ellipsoid, up to 8 cm. long.

As far as I know, this species has been found only once in our region, and that was by J. K. SMALL who collected it south of Coot Bay in Monroe County, Florida, on April 1, 1916.

This species was found on trees in hammocks of southern peninsular Florida. In the tropics, it grows on trees in low humid forests or in open mountain forests, sometimes on rocks, from near sea level up to 3,500 feet altitude. It flowers sporadically throughout the year in various parts of its range. In Florida, plants of the original collection from Monroe County were grown and flowered in April.

GEOGRAPHICAL DISTRIBUTION: Rare in Florida (Monroe County), more frequent in Mexico through Central America to Panama, throughout the West Indies and northern South America.

CULTURAL NOTES: According to BROWN (1813), this species was first introduced from the West Indies into England in 1791 by EDWARD ELCOCK, Esq. VEITCH (1892) further states that this was one of the first Oncidiums to be cultivated in England, ". . . it having flowered in the garden of EDWARD WOODFORD at Vauxhall in May, 1804." See this section under the generic discussion.

2. **Oncidium floridanum** Ames, Sched. Orch. No. 7: 13, fig. 2. 1924. Type locality and collection: Florida, Dade County, Black Point Creek, edge of pine woods in damp rocky soil, May 22, 1904, *A. A. Eaton 957.* (*Oncidium sphacelatum sensu* Ames, not Lindley, 1841). PLATE 140

(The name, *floridanum,* designates Florida as the region where this species was discovered.)

COMMON NAME: Florida Oncidium.

Plant slender, often growing in clumps, up to 2.5 m. or more tall. Pseudobulbs oblong-ovoid, gradually tapering from a broad thickened base, compressed, 2- to 3-leaved, enveloped by distichous leaf-bearing sheaths, 1-1.3 dm. long. Leaves from the apex of the pseudobulbs

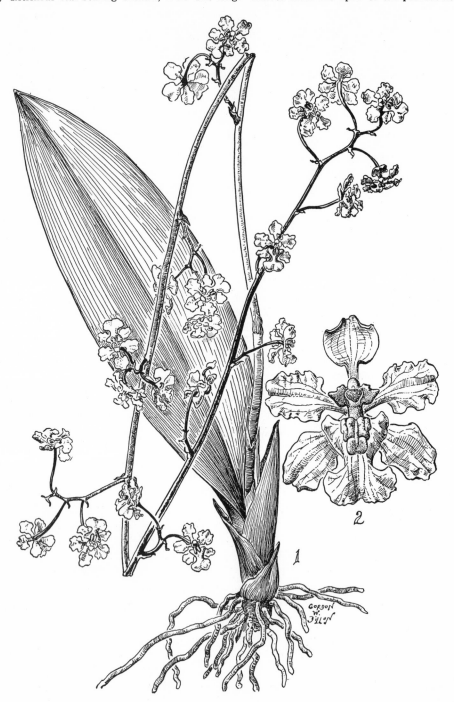

PLATE 139.— **Oncidium carthagenense.** 1, plant, two thirds natural size. 2, flower, twice natural size. *Drawn by Gordon W. Dillon.*

and from the surrounding sheaths, narrowly linear-oblong, subobtuse to acute, coriaceous, 2.5-10.5 dm. long, 1.2-2.7 cm. wide. Inflorescence lateral from the base of the pseudobulb, erect, glabrous, loosely paniculate; peduncle up to 2.5 m. long (including the inflorescence), provided at the nodes with tubular membranaceous acute sheaths which are about 1.5 cm. long. Floral bracts small, ovate, acuminate, 5-8 mm. long. Flowers rather small, yellow, marked with brown, with the slender pedicellate ovaries 1.5-2.5 cm. long. Sepals with an indistinct claw, ovate-oblong to oblong-elliptic or oblong-lanceolate, subacute to acute, somewhat undulate on the margins, reflexed at the apex, 1.1-1.4 cm. long, 4-5.5 mm. wide; lateral sepals narrower than the dorsal sepal and slightly oblique. Petals broadly ovate-oblong to elliptic, subacute to acute, reflexed at the apex, 1-1.3 cm. long, 5-6 mm. wide. Lip subpanduriform, lightly 3-lobed, 1-1.3 cm. long, 8.5-9 mm. wide near the base and slightly wider across the apical lobe; lateral lobes basal, semicordate to semiorbicular; mid-lobe separated from the lateral lobes by a broad isthmus (which is about 3 mm. long and 5.5 mm. wide), semiorbicular-reniform, shallowly retuse and often with an apicule in the sinus, rarely with crenulate margins, 9-11 mm. wide; disc with a tuberculate callus in the center at the base. Column short, 3-4 mm. long, constricted near the middle, provided with a pair of apical wings having retuse or erose margins. Capsule ellipsoid-ovoid, strongly 6-ribbed, 1.8-2.3 cm. long, 8-10 mm. in diameter.

The Florida Oncidium was probably found for the first time in the United States between Cutler and Black Point, Dade County, Florida, by J. K. Small and J. J. Carter in November (13-16), 1903. It is the only endemic epiphytic orchid occurring in our region, and is confined to southern peninsular Florida.

When first found in Florida this orchid was reported as the rather common Central American *O. sphacelatum* Lindl., which species it very closely resembles. However, in 1924, as the result of further study, Ames gave to the plant its present name. Both Small, in his Floras, and Buswell (1945) give for our endemic *O. floridanum* the range of *O. sphacelatum,* and thus impute to *O. floridanum* a much wider range than it actually has.

This species is terrestrial in rich humus or occurs as an epiphyte in low pinelands and hammocks; it is often found on rotten logs and cypress knees. It flowers sporadically throughout the year, but mainly from May to August and during November and December.

GEOGRAPHICAL DISTRIBUTION: Florida (Collier, Dade and Monroe counties).

CULTURAL NOTES: See this section under the generic discussion.

3. **Oncidium luridum** Lindl., Bot. Reg. 9: t. 727. 1823. Type locality: South America. (*Oncidium undulatum* (Sw.) Salisb.). PLATE 141

(The name, *luridum,* is a Latin adjective meaning "sallow" or "wan," in allusion to the characteristic dingy brown flowers.)

COMMON NAME: Dingy-flowered Oncidium.

Plant usually large and coarse. Pseudobulbs very small, short-cylindric, usually less than 1.5 cm. long, arising from a short stout rhizome, unifoliate, concealed by scarious imbricating sheaths. Leaf solitary at the apex of the abbreviated pseudobulb, oblong-elliptic to elliptic-lanceolate, obtuse to acute, rigid and coriaceous, more or less marginate, 1.2-8.5 dm. long, 3.5-15 cm. wide. Inflorescence lateral from the base of the pseudobulb, in the axil of a scarious sheath, loosely paniculate; peduncle up to 2 m. long (including the inflorescence), provided at the nodes with tubular scarious closely appressed sheaths which are about 1.5 cm. long. Floral bracts small, scarious, triangular-lanceolate, acute to acuminate, up to 1 cm. long. Flowers variously colored, commonly greenish yellow or dull yellow, blotched and spotted with reddish brown, with the slender pedicellate ovaries 1.5-3 cm. long. Sepals free, with a slender claw, 1.5-2 cm. long; claw with the involute margins forming a channel; dorsal sepal broadly spatulate to obovate or suborbicular above, rounded at the apex, with the margins somewhat undulate and entire to crenulate, 7.5-12.5 mm. wide; lateral sepals broadly or narrowly spatulate to obovate or subelliptic, obtuse to rarely subacute at the apex, with conspicuously undulate margins, 5-11 mm. wide. Petals clawed, 1.2-1.8 cm. long; lamina suborbicular to oblong-quadrate, truncate to broadly rounded or occasionally retuse at the apex, conspicuously undulate-crenulate on the margins, 7-12 mm. wide. Lip broadly panduriform, 3-lobed, 1.4-2 cm. long, 6.5-8.5 mm. wide across the lateral lobes at the base and 1.5-2.6 cm. wide across the apical lobe; lateral lobes basal, small, auricle-like, obtuse, with the margins strongly revolute; mid-lobe separated from the lateral lobes by a short broad isthmus (which is 5-6.5 mm. wide), semiorbicular-reniform, more or less retuse to entire or crenulate on the margins; disc with a callus at the base usually consisting of five fleshy lobules which are variously tuberculate, yellow in center with violet-stained whitish terminal and lateral tubercles. Column short, about 5 mm. long, white, faintly tinged with violet, yellow at base in front with a few brown spots, provided at the apex with a pair of bilobulate wings which project outward for about 3 mm. Capsule ellipsoid, 3.5-4 cm. long, about 1.5 cm. in diameter.

ONCIDIUM
floridanum Ames

PLATE 140.— **Oncidium floridanum.** Plant, in background, about one sixth natural size. Part of inflorescence, in foreground, about natural size. *Drawn by Blanche Ames.*

The Dingy-flowered Oncidium, when in flower, is one of the largest and most conspicuous orchid plants in our flora. Although somewhat resembling *O. cartha-*

genense, it differs from that species in the mid-lobe of the lip being much broader than the width across the basal lateral lobes. In *O. carthagenense,* on the other hand, the basal and apical portions of the lip are about equally wide.

PLATE 141.— **Oncidium luridum.** 1, basal portion of plant and part of inflorescence, one half natural size. 2, flower, one and one half times natural size. 3, basal portion of lip, to show callus and column, spread out, two and one half times natural size. *Drawn by Gordon W. Dillon.*

This species was collected for the first time in the United States on Royal Palm Key, Dade County, Florida by A. A. EATON and J. SOAR in December 1903.

Oncidium luridum occurs on Bald Cypress (*Taxodium distichum*) and other trees usually in the crotch of a limb (or some other support) in cypress swamps

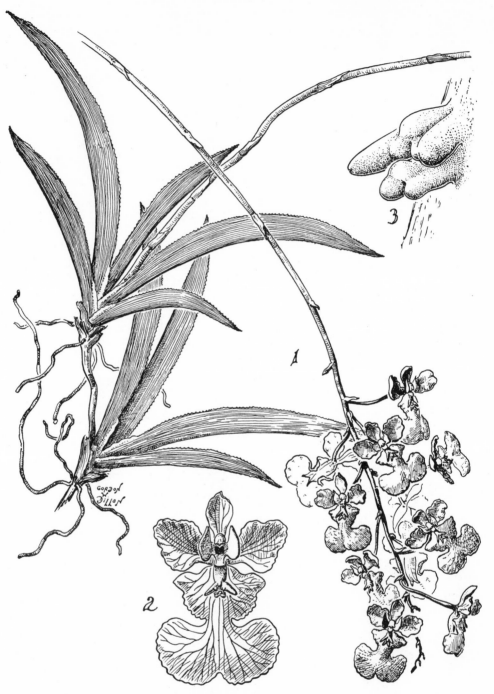

PLATE 142.— **Oncidium variegatum.** 1, plant, natural size. 2, flower, two and one half times natural size. 3, front portion of callus at base of lip, front-side view, ten times natural size. *Drawn by Gordon W. Dillon.*

and hammocks of southern peninsular Florida. In the tropics, it is found on trees in swampy woods, open forests and in pasture lands, sometimes on rocks, from near sea level up to 4,500 feet altitude. It flowers from December to June throughout its range.

GEOGRAPHICAL DISTRIBUTION: Florida (Dade and Monroe counties), from Mexico through Central America to Honduras, throughout the West Indies and northern South America.

CULTURAL NOTES: This species was being cultivated in England by a Mr. GRIF-FIN of South Lambeth shortly before it was known to science. See this section under the generic discussion.

4. **Oncidium variegatum** Sw., Kongl. Svens. Vetens. Acad. Nya Handl. 21: 240. 1800. Type locality: Hispaniola. PLATE 142

(The name, *variegatum,* is a Latin term meaning "irregularly colored" in patches, in allusion to the coloration of the flowers.)

COMMON NAME: Variegated Oncidium.

Plant glabrous, arising from an obsolescent unifoliate pseudobulb which is surrounded by several leaf-bearing sheaths with a flowering branch arising from the base. Leaves several, usually four to six, crowded, distichous, basal, lanceolate and conduplicate, acute, recurved, rigid, with the margins cartilaginous and serrulate, 3-8 cm. long, reduced above. Inflorescence slender, racemose or rarely paniculate, few- to many-flowered, 4-18 cm. long, 4-5 cm. in diameter; peduncle adorned with remote tubular sheaths, purplish below. Floral bracts small, scarious or purplish, 2-6 mm. long. Flowers greenish white, suffused with purplish brown or crimson-purple, with the slender pedicellate ovaries 1-2 cm. long. Dorsal sepal with a short claw, broadly spatulate to orbicular-obovate, truncate and retuse to broadly rounded or with a reflexed apicule at the apex, concave, 4.5-9 mm. long, 2.5-3.5 mm. wide. Lateral sepals connate nearly to the apex; lamina oblanceolate to narrowly spatulate-cuneate, retuse or bifid at the apex, concave, 4-11 mm. long, 2-5 mm. wide. Petals with a short oblong claw, broadly obovate to suborbicular, subtruncate to broadly rounded or crenulate-retuse (rarely apiculate or tridentate) at the apex, often crenulate along the margins, 5.5-9 mm. long, 3.5-7 mm. wide. Lip pandurate, 3-lobed, 8-16 mm. long, 8-14 mm. wide across the basal lateral lobes (when spread out), 1.1-2.1 cm. wide across the terminal lobe; lateral lobes basal, obovate-suborbicular, broadly rounded to obtuse, reflexed, with the margins denticulate-crenulate; mid-lobe separated from the lateral lobes by a short broad yellow-spotted isthmus with serrate margins, broadly reniform, rather deeply emarginate at the apex and with an apicule in the sinus, irregularly crenulate, more or less wider than the basal portion; disc with a prominent tuberculate yellow crest in the middle at the base, the three posterior tubercles being larger than the two anterior ones. Column short, 2.5-3 mm. long, with conspicuous lateral wings at the apex projecting 1-2 mm.; wings obscurely bilobed, acinaciform, with the margins denticulate or crenulate. Capsule ellipsoid, 1.5-2 cm. long.

This species was collected for the first time in the United States in the vicinity of West Palm Beach in Palm Beach County, Florida, by FRANK IDNER in December 1904. It was not found again until 1926 when it was obtained in the same county, and since then, as far as I know, it has not been observed in Florida. This is one of a number of species of Oncidiums which may be classified as xerophytes, being found in exceptionally dry regions with low atmospheric moisture.

The Variegated Oncidium is terrestrial or sometimes occurs as an epiphyte in scrub forests, thickets and among Saw Palmetto (*Serenoa serrulata*) in dry situations. In the West Indies, it grows on rocky slopes, on rocks in thickets and in dry or coastal forests. In the Dominican Republic, it is particularly frequent on Calabash trees (*Crescentia cujete*) near sea level and, in Haiti, it occurs up to 5,500 feet altitude. *Oncidium variegatum* blooms from November to June throughout its range.

GEOGRAPHICAL DISTRIBUTION: Florida (Palm Beach County); also the West Indies.

CULTURAL NOTES: See this section under the generic discussion.

43. Macradenia R. Br.

Macradenia R. Br., Bot. Reg. 8: t. 612. 1822.

(The name, *Macradenia,* is a combination of Greek terms meaning "large gland," in allusion to the large gland to which the·pollinia are attached.)

Inconspicuous epiphytic herbs consisting of a slender pseudobulb with a single leaf at the apex and a short lateral pendent inflorescence at the base. Leaves fleshy or coriaceous. Inflorescence a loose few-flowered raceme of small flowers. Sepals and petals free and somewhat spreading. Lip continuous with the base of the column, 3-lobed; lateral lobes broad, erect and embracing the column in natural position. Column without a foot, terete, more or less sulcate on the ventral surface; anther erect, imperfectly 2-celled; pollinia two, waxy, attached to the viscid disc or gland by a long membranaceous linear-spatulate stipe which is filamentous below. Capsule ellipsoid, more or less 3-angled.

This is a small genus of about a dozen species which are confined to the American tropics and subtropics.

1. **Macradenia lutescens** R. Br., Bot. Reg. 8: t. 612. 1822. Type locality: Trinidad.   PLATE 143

(The name, *lutescens,* is a Latin term meaning "becoming yellow," probably in allusion to the yellowing of the flowers in age.)

COMMON NAME: Trinidad Macradenia.

Plant glabrous, with a slender pseudobulb concealed at the base by scarious non-leaf-bearing sheaths and at the summit producing one leaf. Roots slender, fibrous. Pseudobulb narrowly cylindric, somewhat compressed, 2-4.5 cm. long. Leaf at the apex of the pseudobulb, oblong-lanceolate, acute, thinly coriaceous, 9-16 cm. long, 1-2.7 cm. wide. Peduncle arising from the base of the pseudobulb, in the axil of a membranaceous sheath, pendent, 5-17 cm. long. Raceme loosely few-flowered. Floral bracts ovate-lanceolate, acuminate, membranaceous, 3-11 mm. long. Flowers small, whitish and salmon-colored with reddish purple markings, with the slender pedicellate ovaries 1.2-2 cm. long. Dorsal sepal broadly oblong-elliptic, obtuse to acute, deeply concave, 8-12 mm. long, 3.5-6 mm. wide. Lateral sepals obliquely oblong-elliptic to elliptic-lanceolate, subacute to acute, 7-12 mm. long, 3-4 mm. wide. Petals elliptic-oblong, acute, somewhat falcate, 7-11.5 mm. long, about 3 mm. wide. Lip prominently 3-lobed, 7.5-10 mm. long, 6-7.5 mm. wide across the lateral lobes when expanded; lateral lobes semiobcordate to semiorbicular, incurved and embracing the column in natural position; apical lobe linear-lanceolate to linear-elliptic, acute, strongly recurved and pendent in natural position, with the margins revolute, 3.5-5 mm. long, 1-1.5 mm. wide; disc with three central keels extending from the base to the base of the mid-lobe. Column thickened above the middle, irregularly toothed and lobed at the apex, up to 8 mm. long. Capsule ellipsoid, somewhat 3-angled, 1.5-2 cm. long.

The Trinidad Macradenia was first found in the United States in Royal Palm Hammock (Paradise Key), Dade County, Florida, by A. A. EATON on December 11, 1903. It has been observed only a few times since then, the last collection apparently having been obtained by me in Sykes Hammock, about 3 miles west of Homestead in Dade County, Florida, on July 28, 1936.

This species occurs on the trunks and lower branches of small trees in hammocks of southern peninsular Florida. It flowers in December and January.

GEOGRAPHICAL DISTRIBUTION: Uncommon in Florida (Dade County), Cuba, Jamaica, Trinidad, Colombia and Venezuela.

CULTURAL NOTES: Although the blossoms of this species are very small and have little to recommend the plant except as a botanical curiosity, a few expert growers have small colonies in Florida greenhouses. *Macradenia* seems to do quite well when left on its native branch or when potted firmly in brown or black osmundine.

If scale is controlled intelligently and proper watering is provided, this tiny-flowered orchid should thrive in collections of "botanicals." (J. V. W.)

PLATE 143.— **Macradenia lutescens.** Plant, natural size. 1, pollinia and cauda, highly magnified. 2, column, side view, three times natural size. 3, lip, spread out, three times natural size. 4, lateral sepal, four times natural size. 5, petal, four times natural size. 6, lip, side view, in natural position, five times natural size. *Drawn by Oakes Ames.*

It is of interest to note that this species was first cultivated in England in 1821 by a Mr. GRIFFITH at South Lambeth, a year before it was known to science.

44. Campylocentrum Benth.

Campylocentrum Benth., Journ. Linn. Soc. 18: 337. 1881.

(The name, *Campylocentrum,* is a combination of Greek terms meaning "crooked spur," in allusion to the shape and position of that organ in the flower.)

Small epiphytic herbs either with elongated leafy stems or with abbreviated leafless stems having clustered roots which are often relatively thick and chlorophyllous. Leaves (when present) distichous, elliptic to linear, fleshy, deciduous. Inflorescence spicate, either radical or in the axil of leaves. Floral bracts small, persistent. Flowers non-resupinate, minute, in two ranks, crowded, with the floral segments more or less parallel or connivent. Sepals free, subequal. Petals similar to the sepals but usually shorter. Lip uppermost in the flower, sessile at the base of the column, about as long as the sepals or longer, simple or 3-lobed, concave, produced at the base into a saccate, cylindric or clavate more or less curved and porrect spur. Column short, footless; anther terminal, operculate, incumbent, convex; pollinia two, waxy, globose, with filiform stalks. Capsule small, obliquely ellipsoid, dehiscing in the middle by three valves.

This is a small genus of less than forty species which are confined to the American tropics and subtropics.

1. Campylocentrum pachyrrhizum (Reichb. f.) Rolfe, Orch. Rev. 11: 246. 1903.

Aëranthus pachyrrhizus Reichb. f., Flora 48: 279. 1865. Type locality:
Not given.   PLATE 144

(The name, *pachyrrhizum,* is a combination of Greek words meaning "thick roots," in allusion·to these thickened organs which grow over the surface of the bark of trees and form the most prominent vegetative part of this essentially stemless plant.)

COMMON NAME: None known.

Plant minute, essentially stemless, glabrous, leafless, consisting chiefly of thick roots. Roots aerial and clustered, free or firmly attached to the bark of trees, chlorophyllous, thick, coarse, compressed, flexuous, up to 4 mm. in diameter. Inflorescence consisting of four to seven radical short rigid spikes, 2-3.5 cm. long. Bracts (floral and cauline) broadly ovate, clasping the stem and rachis, somewhat spathaceous, acuminate, with irregularly denticulate-erose margins, reddish brown, 3-4 mm. long, rarely longer. Flowers sessile or nearly so, non-resupinate, two-ranked, very small, yellow-green. Dorsal sepal oblong-lanceolate, acute, 3.5-4 mm. long, about 1 mm. wide. Lateral sepals lanceolate, acute to acuminate, slightly oblique, 3.5-4.5 mm. long, about 1 mm. wide. Petals linear-lanceolate, acuminate, 3-4 mm. long, about 1 mm. wide. Lip uppermost in the flower, obscurely 3-lobed, partially adnate to the minute column, 3-3.5 mm. long, about 1.5 mm. wide near the base, provided with a spur; lateral lobes forming a suborbicular lightly concave basal portion; mid-lobe triangular, acuminate, with revolute margins; spur saccate, somewhat curved, erect, about 2 mm. long. Capsule ellipsoid, sessile, strongly 6-ribbed, with minute bristly hairs along the crest of the ribs, 7-9 mm. long, dehiscing in the middle by three valves.

This species was found for the first time in the United States northeast of Everglade in Collier County, Florida, by A. A. EATON in March (23-26), 1905. Subsequently, it has been observed only a few times.

This orchid and the two following species, *Harrisella porrecta* and *Polyrrhiza Lindenii,* belong to a highly specialized group in the orchid family in that they have transferred the function of photosynthesis, normally performed by the leaves and stem, to the root-system. The plants are rather difficult to see in the field because of their inconspicuous inflorescence (except *Polyrrhiza*) as well as their leafless habit.

This species is found on the bark of deciduous trees and shrubs (hardwoods) in cypress swamps and low hammocks of southern peninsular Florida. In Mexico, it occurs up to 1,500 feet altitude. Its flowering season is February and March.

GEOGRAPHICAL DISTRIBUTION: Florida (Collier County); also Cuba, Jamaica, Trinidad and French Guiana.

CULTURAL NOTES: W. M. BUSWELL states that he has tried to grow this species on logs and artificial substrata, but without success. He has expressed the opinion

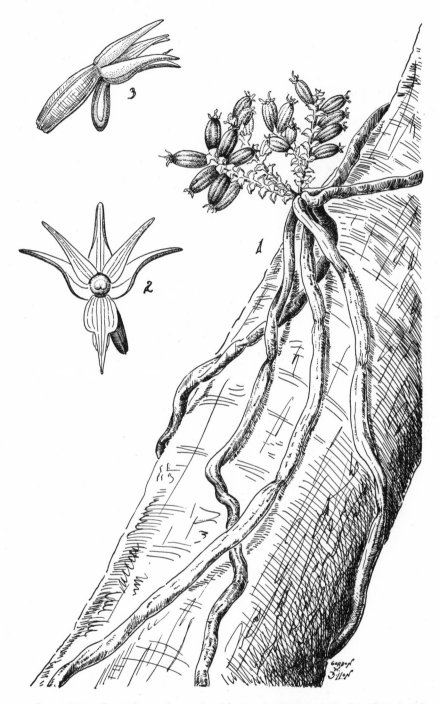

PLATE 144.—**Campylocentrum pachyrrhizum.** 1, plant, in natural habitat on tree limb, natural size. 2, flower, spread open, five times natural size. 3, flower, side view, five times natural size. *Drawn by Gordon W. Dillon.*

that a living tree is perhaps necessary for its growth. See this section under *Polyrrhiza Lindenii.*

45. **Harrisella** Fawc. & Rendle

Harrisella Fawc. & Rendle, Journ. Bot. 47: 265. 1909.

(The name, *Harrisella,* is dedicated to WILLIAM HARRIS, F. L. S. (1860-1920), Superintendent of the Public Gardens, Jamaica, an indefatigable collector of the flora of that island.)

Small epiphytic stemless and leafless herbs with clustered chlorophyllous roots. Inflorescence a few-flowered lax raceme or panicle, radical. Floral bracts minute, persistent. Flowers minute, non-resupinate, in two loose ranks, on a short jointed pedicel which is swollen above. Sepals free, subequal. Petals similar to and as long as the sepals but narrower. Lip uppermost in the flower, sessile at the base of the column, produced at the base into a spur which is constricted below and globose above; lamina deeply concave or subglobose and enveloping the column. Column short, footless; anther terminal, operculate, incumbent, somewhat flat; pollinia two, waxy, globose, with short filiform stalks. Capsule small, shortly ellipsoid to oblong-ovoid, dehiscing from the apex by six valves which are alternately broad and narrow.

This monotypic genus is confined to the American tropics and subtropics.

1. **Harrisella porrecta** (Reichb. f.) Fawc. & Rendle, Journ. Bot. 47: 266. 1909. *Aëranthus porrectus* Reichb. f., Flora 48: 279. 1865. Type locality: Not given. (*Campylocentrum porrectum* (Reichb. f.) Rolfe; *Harrisella Amesiana* Cogn.).   PLATE 145

(The name, *porrecta,* is a Latin term meaning "directed" or "stretched" out, probably named for the more or less outthrust flowers or for the spreading roots of this aphyllous plant.)

COMMON NAME: None known.

Plant leafless and essentially stemless, glabrous (except for the ovaries). Roots aerial and clustered, free or attached to the bark of trees, slender, flexuous, glaucous, chlorophyllous, simple, less than 1 mm. in diameter. Inflorescence (including the peduncle) 1.5-7 cm. long, several, clustered, radical, very slender, zig-zag, often with aborted flower-buds present; peduncle with a scarious acute scale at each node; racemes simple or paniculate, loose. Floral bracts minute, up to 1 mm. long. Flowers minute, yellow-green, with the rather stout pedicellate ovaries about 2 mm. long. Dorsal sepal broadly ovate to oblong-quadrate, obtuse to acute, 2-2.2 mm. long, about 1 mm. wide. Lateral sepals oblong-ovate to oblong-elliptic, lightly oblique, obtuse to acute-apiculate, up to 2.5 mm. long, little more than 1 mm. wide. Petals somewhat obliquely linear-oblong to oblong-elliptic or oblong-lanceolate, obtuse to subacute and apiculate, 1.8-2.5 mm. long, up to 1 mm. wide. Lip broadly ovate in outline, deeply saccate or subglobose in natural position, with the rim of the sac thin and incurved, terminating in a more or less acute small beak (similar to that of *Goodyera*), with a tubercle at the origin of the beak, 2-2.5 mm. long, little exceeding 1 mm. across the sac, provided with a spur at the base; spur constricted below, globose above. Column minute, terete, with obscure wings near the summit. Ovary glandular. Capsules clustered, shortly oblong-ellipsoid, strongly 3-angled, 4-7 mm. long, 4-5 mm. in diameter, dehiscing at the apex by six valves.

This tiny orchid was probably collected for the first time in the United States at Manatee, Manatee County, Florida, by E. N. REASONER on August 28, 1888. It was next found by T. L. MEAD at Oneco, Manatee County in 1902. Very few collections have been made since then.

This is the smallest epiphytic orchid in our flora. Because of its floral structure it is placed among the most advanced genera in the Orchidaceae.

This species is found on shrubs and trees in hammocks, cypress "heads," citrus groves, river swamps and mesophytic forest of the south-central west coast of Florida. It has been collected on various species of oaks (*Quercus* spp.) and cedars (*Juniperus* spp.), and on Red Maple (*Acer rubrum*), Pop-ash (*Fraxinus carolini-*

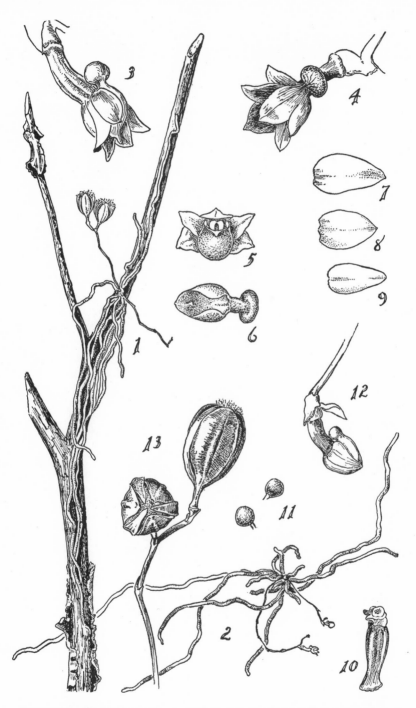

PLATE 145.—**Harrisella porrecta.** 1, fruiting plant, in natural habitat, natural size. 2, flowering plant, natural size. 3, flower, side view, eight times natural size. 4, flower, under-side view, eight times natural size. 5, flower, front view, eight times natural size. 6, lip and spur, from above, eight times natural size. 7, lateral sepal, eight times natural size. 8, dorsal sepal, eight times natural size. 9, petal, eight times natural size. 10, column and ovary, eight times natural size. 11, pollinia, highly magnified. 12, flower, unopened, eight times natural size. 13, fruits, four times natural size. *Redrawn from Blanche Ames by Gordon W. Dillon.*

ana), Buttonbush (*Cephalanthus occidentalis*) and citrus trees. In Mexico, it occurs up to 1,500 feet altitude. It flowers from September to November in various parts of its range.

GEOGRAPHICAL DISTRIBUTION: Florida (Collier, De Soto, Hernando, Highlands, Hillsborough, Manatee, Polk and Sumter counties); also Mexico (Vera Cruz, Yucatan), Salvador, Cuba, Jamaica and Puerto Rico.

CULTURAL NOTES: There is no record of this species ever having been intentionally cultivated. However, there are instances where citrus growers from curiosity have allowed this insignificant little plant to remain undisturbed on trees in their groves.

46. Polyrrhiza Pfitz.

Polyrrhiza Pfitz. in Engl. & Prantl, Nat. Pflanzenfam. 2, Abt. 6: 215. 1889.

(The name, *Polyrrhiza,* is a combination of Greek words meaning "many roots," in allusion to these organs which grow on the bark of trees and are the most prominent vegetative part of the plant.)

Epiphytic leafless herbs with abbreviated stems and very long densely clustered stout and entwined chlorophyllous roots. Inflorescence consisting of several large conspicuous flowers terminating a short bracted peduncle. Sepals and petals free, spreading. Lip sessile at the base of the column, complex, produced below into a long spur. Column short, 2-winged; anther terminal, operculate, incumbent, imperfectly 2-celled; pollinia two, waxy, on simple stipes. Capsule cylindric.

This is a small genus of less than half a dozen species which are confined to the tropics and subtropics of the Western Hemisphere.

1. **Polyrrhiza Lindenii** (Lindl.) Cogn. in Urban, Symb. Antill. 6: 680. 1910.
   Angraecum Lindenii Lindl., Gard. Chron. 135, in text. 1846. Type locality and collection: Cuba, St. Jago, September 1844, *Linden.* (*Aëranthus Lindenii* (Lindl.) Reichb. f.; *Dendrophylax Lindenii* (Lindl.) Benth. ex Rolfe).

PLATE 146

(The name, *Lindenii,* is in honor of JEAN JULES LINDEN (1817-1898), Belgian botanist and horticulturist who first collected this species.)

COMMON NAMES: Palm-polly, Linden's Angurek, White Butterfly-orchid.

Plant with an abbreviated stem, leafless. Roots very long and coarse, flexuous, chlorophyllous, glaucous-green, closely appressed to the bark of trees, about 3 mm. in diameter. Peduncle rather stout, glabrous, brownish black, abruptly ascending at the base, 6-22 cm. long, provided at the nodes with tubular sheathing bracts which are obtuse and 5-7 mm. long. Inflorescence consisting of several flowers blooming in succession. Flowers large, showy, fragrant, with the slender pedicellate ovaries about 3 cm. long. Sepals and petals white suffused with green. Dorsal sepal elliptic-lanceolate to lanceolate, subacute to acute, about 2 cm. long, 5-6 mm. wide. Lateral sepals obliquely linear-lanceolate, obtuse to acute, 2.5-3 cm. long, about 4 mm. wide. Petals linear-lanceolate, acute, falcate-recurved, 2.2-2.7 cm. long, about 4 mm. wide. Lip white, 3-lobed, cymbiform at the base, 2.3-3 cm. long; lateral lobes semicuneate, spreading, obtuse, about 2.5 cm. wide at the widest point (when spread out); mid-lobe from an abruptly contracted base, suddenly dilated into a pair of retrorse elongate-linear acuminate lobes which are 4.5-7 cm. long, the lobes being arcuate and descending in natural position but retrorsely curved when expanded; disc with a narrow fleshy callus below the middle. Column very short, about 3 mm. long, with two triangular auricles which project down into the lip. Spur slender, filiform, elongate, 11-17 cm. long. Capsule narrowly cylindric, elongated, 6-9 cm. long, about 5 mm. in diameter.

This unusual orchid was probably collected for the first time in the United States in Palm Hammock near Cape Romano, Collier County, Florida, by A. H. CURTISS in July 1880.

About Deep Lake and in the Royal Palm Hammock in Collier County, the Palm-polly is frequently found in dense shade on rough-barked trees and native royal palms. When one looks up into the gloom of a thickly leaved tree and sees the extraordinary flowers of this little orchid for the first time, one is instantly impressed with its likeness to a thin flat snow-white frog suspended in mid-air—caught, as it were, in the middle of a leap from one branch to another. Suspended as it is above its leafless base of coarse tortuous roots, the bright flower is markedly contrasted with its somber surroundings.

PLATE 146.— **Polyrrhiza Lindenii.** Plant, in natural habitat on bark of tree, approximately natural size. *Drawn by Blanche Ames.*

This species is found on trees in hammocks, cypress swamps and swampy depressions in pine woods. It has been collected on Pop-ash (*Fraxinus caroliniana*), Custard-apple (*Annona glabra*), Live Oak (*Quercus virginiana*) and Royal Palm (*Roystonea regia*). The Palm-polly flowers from February to July.

GEOGRAPHICAL DISTRIBUTION: Florida (Collier and Lee counties); also Cuba.

CULTURAL NOTES: The Palm-polly of the Florida swamplands can best be collected by sawing out a section of tree trunk or branch upon which a colony thrives. This log may then be wired to a lath-house post or greenhouse pipe. Like most Florida epiphytes, the Palm-polly requires a high humidity and an abundance of water at its roots during its growing season, but since it has no pseudobulbs for the storage of water, it cannot endure long periods of drought. Judicious syringing throughout the year is necessary, but care must be observed when the flower buds appear lest the blossoms rot or spot because of excessive moisture.

If it is not feasible to bring in a whole log, the plant can be carefully pried from its original substratum and then transferred to a pecky cypress board. If it is held in place with waxed cord for a while it will soon attach itself and, except for watering, will grow without further attention.

In the early spring well-grown specimens may send out short scapes which possess one or two flower buds. The blossoms, when fully expanded, are delightful to look at and they are a distinctive addition to any collection of "botanical" orchids. Visitors to Florida are unanimous in their praise of the Palm-polly, and it has been suggested that the flowers of this species might have possibilities for use in corsages as their keeping quality is excellent. (J. V. W.)

Glossary

Abortive. Imperfectly formed or rudimentary.

Abbreviated. Shortened.

Acauline. Stemless or apparently so, or with the stem subterranean.

Acid. A chemical condition of water or moist soil capable of producing certain chemical and physiological effects. Acids turn the commoner indicator dyes red or yellow, and when concentrated enough, taste sour.

Acidity. The condition characterized by the presence of acid substances.

Acidulous. Weakly acid.

Acinaciform. Scimitar-shaped.

Acuminate. Gradually tapering to a point.

Acute. Ending in a point.

Adherent. The union of dissimilar parts which are usually separated.

Adnate. Having one organ attached wholly or in part to another.

Adventitious (roots). Arising from some other part of the plant other than the rootstock or base of the stem.

Aerial (roots). Borne above the surface of the ground or water.

Alkaline. A chemical condition of water or moist soil capable of producing certain chemical and physiological effects opposed to those produced by acids. Alkalies turn the commoner indicator dyes blue or green and when concentrated enough taste "soapy."

Alluvial. Of or pertaining to soil, sand, etc., deposited by running water.

Alpine. Of or pertaining to high mountainous regions.

Ancipitous. Compressed or flattened, two-edged.

Annulated. Ring-shaped, rounded.

Anterior. On the front side of a flower or organ; the under side.

Anther. The part of a stamen containing the pollen.

Anthesis. The time of expansion of a flower.

Apex. The tip of an organ.

Aphyllous. Without leaves.

Apical. At the tip of any structure.

Apiculate. Ending in a short pointed tip.

Apicule. A short pointed tip at the apex of a leaf or floral segment.

Appressed. Lying flat against another organ.

Approximate. Close together, but not united.

Arcuate. Moderately curved.

Aristate. Tipped with a bristle-like appendage or awn.

Articulate. Jointed.

Ascending. Rising somewhat obliquely or curving upward.

Attenuate. Slenderly tapering; becoming very narrow.

Auricle. An ear-shaped appendage.

Auriculate. With a basal lobule; furnished with auricles.

Autophyte. A green plant capable of manufacturing its own food, neither saprophytic nor parasitic.

Axil. The angle formed by a leaf or branch with the stem or rachis.

Axillary. Situated in an axil.

Barranca. Spanish for a gorge or ravine.

Barrens. Usually level tracts of "waste land," poorly forested with scrub oaks and pines, and commonly having a light sandy soil.

Bi-. A prefix, meaning two or twice.

Bifid. Two-cleft.

Bifurcate. Two-forked or two-pronged.

Blade. The expanded portion of a leaf or floral segment.

Bog. Wet areas where the surface soil is organic (peaty) and the soil water is acid in contrast to habitats that have a mineral soil. They are usually designated by the dominant species growing in them, such as sphagnum, Spruce and Tamarack bogs.

Bracteal. Of or pertaining to bracts.

Bracted (-eate). Having bracts.

Bracteiform. Of the shape and form of a bract.

Bracteose. With numerous or conspicuous bracts.

Bulbous. Having the character of a bulb.

Bursicle. A pouch-like receptacle.

Caespitose. Growing in tufts.

Calcareous. Containing an excess of available calcium, usually in the form of the compound, calcium carbonate. "Limy" is essentially a synonym.

Calceolate. Slipper-shaped.

Callose. Having a hard protuberance or thickening.

Callus (-osity). A hard protuberance or thickening.

Calyptrate. Having a small cap-shaped hood.

Calyx. The outer of the two series of floral leaves.

Campanulate. Bell-shaped; cup-shaped with a broad base.

Canaliculate. Longitudinally channeled.

Capillary. Hairlike.

Capitate. Shaped like a head; collected into a head or dense cluster.

Capsule. A dry dehiscent fruit composed of more than one carpel.

Carina. A keel or projecting longitudinal median line on the lower surface of a leaf or floral segment.

Carinate. Having a keel or carina.

Carpel. A simple pistil, or one member of a compound pistil.

Cartilaginous. Hard and tough.

Cataphyll. A rudimentary scalelike leaf which precedes the foliage leaf.

Cauda. A slender tail-like appendage.

Caudate. Having a cauda.

Cauline. Borne on the stem.

Cellular. Composed of cells.

Cereus. Waxy.

Chaparral. A dense almost impenetrable thicket of thorny or stiff shrubs or dwarf trees; characteristic of semiarid regions of the southwestern and western United States.

Chartaceous. Having the texture of writing paper.

Chlorophyll. The green coloring matter in plants.

Ciliate. Marginally fringed with hairs which are usually stiff.

Circumboreal. In boreal regions around the world.

Circumneutral. A chemical condition of water or moist soil such that neither acidity nor alkalinity are present in amounts sufficient to influence plant growth.

Clavate. Club-shaped.

Clavellate. Diminutive of clavate.

Claw. The narrowed base of a floral segment, especially the petal.

Clay. The fine grained mineral matter making up the active part of a soil. In composition it is usually a hydrous aluminum silicate.

Cleistogamous. Self-fertilized in the unopened flower.

Clinandrium. The anther-bed, that part of the column in which the anther is concealed.

Cm. (centimeter). A measure of length equal to .3937 inch (2.54 cm. = 1 inch) or ten millimeters.

Cochleate. Shell-shaped; as used here, shaped like one valve of a clam shell.

Coherent. Having similar parts united.

Colloid. A substance in such a fine state of division that chemical forces on the particle surfaces exert a strong influence; two important phenomena in the clays constituting soil colloids are the ability to become plastic when wet and to adsorb plant food substances.

Column. The organ formed by the union of the stamens and pistils.

Complicate. See *Conduplicate.*

Compound. Composed of a number of similar parts or divided into a number of similar parts or divisions.

Compressed. Flattened, especially laterally.

Conduplicate. Folded together lengthwise.

Confluent. Merging into each other; blended into one.

Coniferous. Cone-bearing; evergreen trees, such as pines, spruces, cedars, etc.

Connate. Similar organs more or less united.

Connective. That portion of the column which connects the two cells of the anther.

Connivent. Coming into contact; converging.

Convex. Having a more or less rounded surface.

Convolute. Rolled up longitudinally.

Coquina. A soft whitish limestone formed of broken shells and corals cemented together, found in the southern United States.

Coralline. Resembling coral in appearance.

Coralloid. Coral-like, somewhat brittle; usually much branched.

Cordate. Heart-shaped.

Coriaceous. Leathery in texture.

Corm. Bulblike but solid; the enlarged fleshy base of a stem.

Cornucopiate. Shaped like a cornucopia.

Cornute. Horned.

Corolla. The inner of the two series of floral leaves.

Corrugated. Wrinkled or in folds.

Corymb. A flat-topped or convex open flower-cluster.

Crenate. Scalloped with rounded teeth.

Crenulate. Finely crenate.

Crested. Bearing an elevated appendage or protruding fringes.

Cucullate. Hooded or hood-shaped.

Cuneate. Wedge-shaped; triangular with the acute angle downward; applied to leaf bases and the base of floral segments.

Cuspidate. Tipped with a sharp rigid point.

Cuticle. The outermost layer of the cells of the epidermis.

Cymbiform. Boat-shaped.

Deciduous. Falling away at the close of the growing season; not evergreen.

Decumbent. Reclining but with the growing end or summit erect or ascending.

Decurrent. Extending down the stem or ovary below the point of insertion.

Dehisce. To split into definite parts by valves, slits or pores, as the capsule (fruit) of orchids.

Deltoid. Broadly triangular.

Dentate. Toothed, usually with the teeth directed outward.

Denticulate. Minutely toothed.

Dichotomous. Forking regularly into two nearly equal branches.

Didymous. Twin; found in pairs; somewhat two-parted.

Dioecious. Unisexual, with the male and female flowers on separate plants.

Disc. In orchids, the face or upper surface of the lip.

Distal. Remote from the place of attachment.

Distant. When similar parts are not closely aggregated.

Distichous. In two vertical ranks.

Divaricate. Separated by a wide angle; widely spreading.

Dm. (*decimeter*). A measure of length equal to 3.937 inches or 10 centimeters.

Dolabriform. Hatchet-shaped.

Dorsal. Upon or relating to the back or outer surface of an organ.

Duplicate. Double, as the two similar sides of a leaf.

Ebracteate. Without bracts.

Ecallose. Without a callus.

Ecology. The study of plants in relation to their environment.

Ellipsoid. A solid with an elliptic shape.

Elliptic. Oblong with regularly rounded ends.

Elongated. Drawn out in length.

Emarginate. Having a shallow notch at the apex.

Endemic. Confined to a given region, as a country or island.

Ensiform. Sword-shaped.

Entire. Without toothing or lobing, in reference to the floral segments and leaf-blade.

Ephemeral. Lasting for only one day; transitory.

Epidermis. The outer layers of cells of an organ.

Epiphyte. A plant growing on or attached to other plants but not parasitic, occasionally on posts, buildings or other objects.

Epseudobulbous. Without pseudobulbs.

Equitant. Used of conduplicate leaves which overlap each other in two ranks, as in *Oncidium.*

Erose. As if gnawed; a ragged edge.

Erostrate. Without a beak.

Evergreen. Bearing green foliage all the year, as pines, spruces and hemlocks.

Excrescences. Small warty outgrowths.

Excurrent. Running out, as a nerve of a floral segment or leaf projecting beyond the margin.

Exserted. Projecting beyond a common point.

Extine. The outer coat of a pollen grain.

Falcate. Scythe-shaped; curved and flat, tapering gradually.

Family (*of plants*). A group of related genera.

Farinose. Covered with meal-like powder.

Fasciation. A malformation caused by several stems becoming fused into one.

Fasciculate. In close bundles or clusters.

Fecundation. Fertilization of the female by the male to form a new individual.

Fibrous. Composed of or resembling fibers; the texture of roots as in *Listera.*

Filament. The threadlike support of the anther; threadlike.

Filiform. Threadlike.

Fimbriate. Fringed.

Flabellate, flabelliform. Fan-shaped.

Flatwoods. Any low-lying dry timber lands; in Florida, the level pinelands occupying most of the peninsula, its characteristic tree being the Longleaf Pine (*Pinus palustris*).

Flexuous. Bending alternately in opposite directions.

Floral. Of or pertaining to the flower.

Foliaceous. Resembling a leaf in texture and appearance.

Foliage. Leaves.

Foot (of column). An extension of the base of the column beyond its point of attachment to the receptacle.

Forest (coniferous). Composed of trees in the order Coniferales, such as pines, spruces, balsams, hemlocks and cedars.

Forest (hardwood). Composed of broad-leaved deciduous or non-deciduous trees as distinguished from coniferous trees.

Forest (mixed). Composed of both deciduous and evergreen (coniferous) trees.

Forcing. To hasten flower production by artificial means.

Fractiflex. Zig-zag.

Fruit. The seed-bearing organ of a plant.

Fugacious. Falling away or fading very early.

Fusiform. Spindle-shaped; swollen in the middle and narrowing toward each end.

Galeate. Helmet-shaped.

Geniculate. Bent abruptly, like a knee.

Genus. The smallest natural group containing distinct species.

Gibbous. Protuberant or swollen on one side.

Glabrous. Smooth; devoid of hairs.

Glandular. Bearing glands or of the nature of a gland.

Glaucous. Covered or whitened with a bloom.

Globose. Nearly spherical.

Glutinous. Covered with a sticky exudation.

Granulose. Composed of or appearing as if covered by minute grains.

Guttate. Dotted.

Habit. General appearance of a plant.

Habitat. The type of locality in which a plant grows, as woods, field, etc.

Hammock. A slightly elevated area, typical of southern peninsular Florida, supporting a hardwood vegetation and possessing a deeper more humus-rich soil than that of the surrounding flatwoods.

Hastate. Like an arrowhead but with the basal lobes pointing outward nearly at right angles.

Heath. A tract of waste land, usually level or gently rolling, supporting a low shrubby vegetation, especially members of the family Ericaceae.

Herb. A plant with no persistent woody stem above ground.

Herbarium. A collection of dried and pressed plants, usually mounted or otherwise prepared for permanent preservation, and systematically arranged.

Hermaphroditic. With the stamens and pistils in the same flower.

Hirsute. Pubescent with rather coarse or stiff hairs.

Hispid. Beset with rigid or bristly hairs or with bristles.

Humus. Decomposing organic matter in the soil.

Hyaline. Thin and translucent, rarely transparent.

Hybrid. A plant obtained by placing the pollen of one species on the stigma of another; the progeny of dissimilar parents.

Hyphae. The branched cylindrical thread-like structures which constitute the vegetative body of a fungus.

Imbricate. Overlapping either vertically or spirally.

Incumbent. Resting or leaning upon another organ.

Indehiscent. Not opening by valves, etc.; remaining persistently closed.

Indigenous. Native to a country or region, not introduced.

Inflorescence. The flowering part of a plant.

Internode. That portion of a stem between two nodes.

Intra-. A prefix, meaning within.

Involute. Rolled inward.

Irregular (flower). Showing inequality in the size, form or union of its similar parts.

Keel. A central dorsal ridge, like the keel of a boat.

Labellum. The lip or modified petal in an orchid flower.

Laciniate. Slashed; cut into narrow pointed segments.

Lamellae. Thin flat plates or laterally flattened ridges.

Lamellate. Provided with lamellae.

Lamina. The expanded portion of a leaf or floral segment.

Lanceolate. Several times longer than wide, tapering at both ends, widest about a third above the base.

Lanuginose. Woolly or cottony.

Lateral. Fixed on or near the side of an organ.

Ligulate. Strap-shaped.

Limb. The expanded portion of any petal, lip or leaf.

Linear. Long and narrow, with parallel margins, like a blade of grass.

Lingulate. Tongue-shaped.

Lip. A modified petal in the orchid flower, usually differing markedly in size, coloration and form from the other two petals.

Lithophyte. Plants which grow on rocks but derive their nourishment from the atmosphere and from accumulated humus.

Littoral. Belonging to or growing on the sea-shore or near the sea.

Loam. A type of soil commonly found in woodlands consisting of a friable mixture of varying proportions of clay, sand and organic matter.

Lobe. Any division or segment of an organ.

Lobulate. Having a small lobe.

Lobule. A small lobe.

Lucid. Shining, referring to the surface of an organ.

M. (meter). A measure of length equal to ·39.37 inches or ten decimeters.

Maculate. Spotted.

Mammillate. Having nipple-shaped processes.

Marcescent. Withering but persisting.

Marginal. Placed upon or attached to the edge.

Marginate. Furnished with a margin of distinct character.

Marl. An earthy crumbling deposit consisting chiefly of clay mixed with lime (presumably derived from shells) in varying proportions.

Marsh. A tract of wet or periodically inundated level treeless land, having a mucky soil and covered mostly with grasses and sedges.

Meadow. A tract of moist (not inundated) land usually characterized by grasses and wild flowers, but without trees or shrubs; some meadows are used as hayfields.

Mediacid. The relatively high degree of acidity met with in the more typical acid soils, peats, and similar materials. (In the pH system, 4 to 5).

Membranaceous. Thin and semitransparent.

Mentum. A chin-like projection formed by the sepals and extended foot of the column.

Mesophyte. A plant which requires an average amount of water only.

Minimacid. The minimum degree of acidity met with in soils. (In the pH system, 6 to 6.9).

Mm. (millimeter). A measure of length equal to .03937 of an inch. (1/25 of an inch).

Moniliform. Resembling a string of beads.

Monocotyledoneae. One of two subclasses of the angiospermous (seeds in a closed ovary) plants having but one cotyledon (seed-leaf), a stem which rarely exhibits secondary growth in thickness and is without annual rings, leaves generally parallel veined, and the flowers trimerous (having parts in threes); composed of such families as the orchids, lilies, irises, palms, sedges and grasses.

Monoecious. With stamens and pistils in separate flowers on the same plant.

Monopodium. A main or primary axis that continues its original line of growth, giving off successive axes or lateral branches.

Monotypic. Having only one exponent, as a genus with but one species.

Montane. Pertaining to or living in mountains.

Moor. In Europe, an extensive area of waste land overlaid with peat and usually more or less wet.

Morphology. The study of form and its development.

Mucro. A short and small abrupt tip.

Mucronate. Tipped with a mucro.

Muskeg. A sphagnum bog, especially one with tussocks in it, common in boreal regions.

Naked. Wanting its usual covering or lacking certain organs as leaves, pubescence, etc.

Nervose. Prominently nerved.

Neutral. A chemical condition of water or moist soil in which acid and alkaline constituents are exactly balanced. (In the pH system, 7).

Node. The place upon a stem which normally bears a leaf or whorl of leaves; a joint.

Ob-. A prefix, meaning inversely or oppositely, as in "obovate."

Oblanceolate. Lanceolate with the broadest part toward the apex.

Oblique. Unequal-sided or slanting.

Oblong. Longer than broad and with nearly parallel sides.

Obsolescent. Becoming rudimentary.

Obtuse. Blunt or rounded at the end.

Opaque. Dull; neither shining nor translucent.

Operculate. Lid-like, as some anthers, or furnished with a lid.

Orbicular. Circular.

Organic. Descriptive of compounds formed by the aid of life, containing carbon, hydrogen, and often a few other non-metallic elements.

Orifice. An opening.

Osmundine. The cut up stout fibrous root masses of ferns of the genus *Osmunda* which are used as a substratum upon which to grow epiphytic orchids in greenhouses.

Oval. Broadly elliptic.

Ovary. The part of the pistil that contains the ovules (young seeds).

Ovate. Shaped like the outline of an egg with the broader end downward.

Ovoid. A solid with an ovate outline; shaped like an egg.

Palmate. Lobed and radiating like the fingers.

Pandurate, panduriform. Fiddle-shaped.

Panicle. A loosely arranged compound inflorescence with pedicellate flowers.

Paniculate. Resembling a panicle.

Papillae. Minute nipple-shaped projections.

Papilliferous, papillose. Bearing papillae.

Parasite. A plant which grows on and derives part or all its nourishment from another plant.

Peat. Any mass of semicarbonized vegetable tissue formed by a partial decomposition in water of various plants, especially species of the moss genus *Sphagnum*.

Pedicel. The stalk of a single flower.

Pedicellate. Borne on a pedicel or like a pedicel.

Peduncle. The stalk of an inflorescence.

Pedunculate. Borne on a peduncle.

Pellucid. Wholly or partially transparent.

Peloria. An irregular flower become regular by a suppression of the irregular segments, a malformation which is often hereditary.

Perianth. The floral envelope, consisting of the calyx (sepals) and corolla (petals), whatever their form.

Persistent. Long continuous, as the perianth upon the fruit or the leaves on the plant.

Petal. One of the divisions of the corolla.

Petaloid. Resembling a petal.

Petiolate. Having a petiole.

Petiole. The stalk or support of a leaf.

Photosynthesis. The formation of carbohydrates, in constructive metabolism, from water and the carbon dioxide of the air in the chlorophyll-containing tissues of plants exposed to light.

Phylogeny. Ancestral history deduced from development.

Pilose. With long soft hairs.

Pistil. The seed-bearing organ of the flower, consisting of the ovary, stigma and style when present.

Pitted. Marked with small depressions or pits.

Plateau. A considerable tract of elevated land (a tableland), which is distinctly above adjacent land on at least one side, and may vary in altitude from a few hundred feet to thousands of feet above sea level.

Plicate. Folded (usually lengthwise) into prominently ribbed plaits.

Pocosin. A bog or swamp characteristic of the Coastal Plain in the southeastern United States, which may or may not be sphagnous and supports various broad-leaved non-deciduous trees and shrubs, especially members of the heath, magnolia, olive, and maple families.

Pollen. The fecundating grains contained in the anther.

Pollinate. To apply pollen to the receptive surface of the stigma.

Pollinia. Masses of waxy pollen or of coherent pollen grains.

Polygamous. With hermaphroditic and unisexual flowers on the same plant.

Polymorphic. Having more than one form.

Porrect. Directed outward and forward.

Posterior. On the back side of a flower or organ; the top side.

Potsherd. A piece or fragment of a broken earthen pot.

Prairie (coastal). Flat wet or periodically inundated intracoastal lands covered primarily with grasses and sedges, somewhat intermediate between coastal marshes and savannahs, without trees.

Prairie (interior). Extensive tracts of level or rolling treeless land in the Mississippi Valley, characterized by a usually deep fertile soil and a covering of coarse grasses.

Proboscis. A tubular sucking organ of an insect.

Proliferation. To produce offshoots.

Prostrate. Lying flat on the ground.

Proximal. The part nearest the axis.

Pseudobulb (-ous). Thickened and swollen stems, usually with only one internode.

Pteridology. The study of ferns.

Puberulent. Finely pubescent.

Pubescent. Provided with soft hairs.

Punctate. Dotted with translucent glands or spots.
Pyramidal. Pyramid-shaped.
Pyriform. Pear-shaped.

Quadrate. Four-sided.

Raceme. A simple inflorescence of pediceled flowers upon a common more or less elongated axis.
Racemose. Resembling a raceme or in racemes.
Rachis. The axis of an inflorescence.
Radical. Belonging to or proceeding from the root or base of the stem near the ground.
Ranks. The arrangement of flowers in an inflorescence, as one or several rows or ranks of flowers in *Spiranthes.*
Raphides. Needle-shaped crystals in the cells of plants.
Reaction (soil-). The general term comprising acidity and alkalinity.
Receptacle. The summit of the flower stalk bearing the floral organs.
Recurved. Curved downward or backward.
Reflexed. Abruptly bent downward or backward.
Regular (flower). Uniform in shape or structure.
Remote. Scattered; not close together.
Reniform. Kidney-shaped.
Repent. Creeping; prostrate and rooting at the nodes.
Resupinate. With the lip on the lower side of the flower in respect to the rachis.
Reticulate. In the form of a network.
Retrorse. Directed back or downward.
Retuse. With a shallow notch at a rounded apex.
Reversion. A change backward to an earlier condition.
Revolute. Rolled backward from the margins or apex.
Rhizome. A rootstock or underground stem, usually rooting at the nodes and becoming erect at the apex.
Rhombic. Top-shaped; an equilateral figure having oblique angles.
Ribbed. With the veins of the leaf prominent, or the longitudinal ridges of the capsules.
Ringent. Gaping.
Root-shoot. An above-ground shoot apparently springing from the roots.
Rootstock. See *Rhizome.*
Rosette. A cluster of leaves or other organs in a circular position.
Rostellum. A little beak; a slender extension from the upper edge of the stigma.
Rostrate. Having a beak.
Rudimentary. Arrested in an early stage of development.

Saccate. Pouch- or bag-shaped.
Sac. A pouch or bag.
Sagittate. Shaped like an arrowhead, with the basal lobes directed downward.
Saprophyte. A plant growing in and deriving most of its nourishment from dead organic matter, often apparently lacking in chlorophyll.
Savannah. A level grassy plain of the southeastern United States, without trees or with few scattered trees, supporting numerous flowering herbs and some low shrubs, with a noticeably fluctuating water-level.
Scabrous. Rough to the touch.
Scalloped. Crenate, with rounded teeth.
Scape. A peduncle rising from the ground, naked or without normal foliage, as in *Cypripedium acaule.*
Scapose. Bearing or resembling a scape.
Scarious. Thin, dry and membranaceous, not green.
Scobicular. In fine grains like sawdust.
Scrotiform. Pouch-shaped.
Scurfy. Scaly.
Sectile. As though cut up into partitions, as the pollen divisions.
Secund. Borne along one side of an axis.
Segment. A part of the perianth, as the petal, sepal or lip; any division or part of a cleft or divided organ.
Semi-. A prefix, meaning half.
Sepal. One of the divisions of the calyx.
Sepaline. Belonging to or consisting of the sepals.
Serrate. Having sharp teeth pointing forward.
Serrulate. Finely serrate.
Sessile. Without a stalk, or apparently so.
Setaceous. Bristlelike.
Sheath. A tubular envelope, as the lower part of the leaf, which clasps the stem.

Sigmoid. S-shaped.
Simple. Not compound; of one piece.
Sinuate. With the outline of the margin strongly wavy.
Sinus. The cleft or recess between two lobes.
Spathaceous. Resembling or like a spathe.
Spathe. A large stiff leathery bract or pair of bracts subtending or enclosing an inflorescence.
Spatulate. Gradually dilated upward to a rounded apex.
Species. The aggregate of all those individuals which have the same constant and distinctive characters.
Spicate. Arranged in or resembling a spike.
Spike. A simple inflorescence with the flowers sessile or nearly so upon an elongated common axis, as in *Spiranthes*.
Spinulose. Having small spines.
Spur. A hollow sac-like or tubular extension of the lip, usually nectariferous.
Stalk. Support of an organ.
Stamen. One of the pollen-bearing organs of the flower.
Staminode. A sterile stamen, or any structure (without anther) corresponding to a stamen.
Stele. An axial cylinder of vascular tissue.
Stellate. Starlike.
Stigma. That part of a pistil receptive to pollen.
Stipe. The stalk-like support of a pseudobulb or pollinium.
Stipitate. Having a stipe.
Stomata. Orifices in the epidermis of a leaf or stem communicating with internal air-cavities.
Stolon. A basal branch rooting at the nodes and usually giving rise to new individuals.
Stoloniferous. Producing or bearing stolons.
Striate. Marked with fine longitudinal lines of color or ridges.
Strict. Very straight and upright.
Strobile. An inflorescence with imbricate scales like a cone.
Style. The narrowed portion of the pistil which connects the ovary and the stigma.
Sub-. A prefix, denoting an approach to the condition designated, as "subacute," meaning somewhat acute.
Subacid. The moderate degree of acidity met with in many soils so rich in bases that mediacid conditions cannot build up. (In the *p*H system, 5 to 6).
Subalkaline. The moderate degree of alkalinity met with in the more calcareous soils. (In the *p*H system, 8 to 9).
Subulate. Awl-shaped.
Succulent. Soft and juicy.
Sulcate. Grooved or furrowed longitudinally.
Swale. A slight depression or small valley as in a plain which is marshy and rank with vegetation.
Swamp. A tract of land, seasonally dry or inundated, and dominated by trees and shrubs.
Symbiosis. The living together of dissimilar organisms, with benefit to both.
Symmetrical (flower). Regular as to the number of parts and as to their arrangement in the perianth.
Sympodium. An apparent main axis not developed from a terminal bud, but made up of successive secondary axes, each of which represents one fork of a dichotomy, the other being of weaker growth or is suppressed entirely.

Talus. Rock debris at the base of a cliff or slope, chiefly as the result of gravitational roll or slide.
Taxonomy. The classification of plants or animals in systematic order.
Teratological. Monstrous; relating to a monstrosity.
Terete. Cylindrical; circular in cross-section.
Terrestrial. Growing on the ground and supported by soil.
Tetrads. A structure formed of four cells, as in the pollen mother-cells.
Tomentose. Densely pubescent with matted hairs.
Tomentum. Densely matted hairs.
Translucent. Transparent to light.
Transversely. Broader than long; at right angles to an axis.
Trapeziform. An unsymmetrical four-sided figure.
Tri-. A prefix, meaning three.
Trichome. Any hairlike outgrowth of the epidermis, as a hair or bristle.
Trulliform. Trowel-shaped.
Truncate. Ending abruptly as if cut off transversely.
Tuber. A thickened and short subterranean branch having numerous buds or eyes.
Tubercle. A small tuber or tuber-like body, not necessarily subterranean.
Tuberculate. Beset with knobby projections.
Tuberoid. A fleshy-thickened root, resembling a tuber.

Tuberous. Having the character of a tuber; tuber-like in appearance.

Ubiquitous. Growing in all types of habitats.

Umbel. An inflorescence in which the peduncles or pedicels of a cluster spring from the same point or essentially so.

Umbellate. In or like an umbel.

Undulate. With a wavy margin or surface.

Uni-. A prefix, meaning one.

Unifoliate. One-leaved.

Unguiculate. Contracted at the base into a claw or narrow stalk.

Urceolate. Hollow and cylindrical or ovoid, and contracted at or below the mouth like an urn.

Variegated. Irregularly colored in patches, blotched.

Variety. A plant having minor characters or variations which separates it from the type species.

Vein. A thread of fibro-vascular tissue in a leaf or other organ.

Vegetative. That part of the plant not directly concerned with reproduction, as the stem and leaves.

Velamen. A parchment-like sheath or layer of spiral-coated air-cells on the roots of epiphytic orchids, capable of rapidly absorbing moisture.

Velamentous. Resembling or having a velamen.

Venose. Having veins.

Ventral. Belonging to the anterior or inner face of an organ; the opposite of dorsal.

Vernal. Appearing in the spring.

Vernicose. Shiny, as though varnished.

Verrucose. Covered with wart-like elevations or excrescences.

Verticillate. Disposed in a whorl.

Vesicle. A small bladder or air-cavity.

Villous. Bearing long and soft hairs.

Viscid. Glutinous; sticky.

Waste (*land*). Uncultivated, especially barren, land often having a sterile soil.

Xerophyte. A plant which can subsist with a small amount of moisture, such as a desert plant.

Zygomorphic. Flowers which are divisible into equal halves in one plane only (usually the anterior-posterior) as irregular flowers of orchids.

Explanation of Abbreviations of Authors' Names

(Unless otherwise noted, the years represent
dates of birth and death.)

Ait.—WILLIAM AITON, 1731-1793—Great Britain
All.—CARLO ALLIONI, 1725-1804—Italy
Ames—OAKES AMES, 1874-1950—United States.
Anderson—JACOB PETER ANDERSON, 1874-   —United States
Andrews (A. ANDREWS)—ALBERT LEROY ANDREWS, 1878-   —United States
Andrews—HENRY C. ANDREWS, actively engaged 1794-1830—Great Britain
Aublet—J. B. C. F. AUBLET, 1720-1778—France
Austin—COE F. AUSTIN, 1831-1880—United States

Banks—Sir JOSEPH BANKS, 1743-1820—Great Britain
Barker (M. BARKER), actively engaged about 1900—United States
Barker (P. BARKER), actively engaged about 1900—United States
Barnh.—JOHN HENDLEY BARNHART, 1871-1949—United States
Bartlett—HARLEY HARRIS BARTLETT, 1886-   —United States
Bauer—FRANZ ANDREAS BAUER, 1758-1840—Great Britain
Beck—LEWIS CALEB BECK, 1798-1853—United States
Benth.—GEORGE BENTHAM, 1800-1884—Great Britain
Bigel.—JACOB BIGELOW, 1786-1879—United States
Bl.—KARL LUDWIG BLUME, 1796-1862—Netherlands
Blake—SIDNEY FAY BLAKE, 1892-   —United States
Blankinship—JOSEPH WILLIAM BLANKINSHIP, 1862-1938—United States
Bolander—HENRY NICHOLAS BOLANDER, 1831-1897—United States
Bongard—AUGUST HEINRICH GUSTAV BONGARD, 1786-1839—Russia (German-born)
Britton—NATHANIEL LORD BRITTON, 1859-1934—United States
Brongn.—ADOLPHE THÉODORE BRONGNIART, 1801-1876—France
Br. (R. Br.)—ROBERT BROWN, 1773-1858—Great Britain
BSP.—N. L. BRITTON; EMERSON ELLICK STERNS, 1846-1926; JUSTUS FERDINAND POGGENBERG,
    1840-1893—United States

Camp—WENDELL HOLMES CAMP, 1904-   —United States
Cham.—ADALBERT VON CHAMISSO, 1781-1838—Germany and Russia
Chapm.—ALVAN WENTWORTH CHAPMAN, 1809-1899—United States
Chat.—JEAN JACQUES CHATELAIN, published work in 1760—Switzerland
Cockerell—THEODORE DRU ALISON COCKERELL, 1866-1948—United States
Cogn.—CÉLESTIN ALFRED COGNIAUX, 1841-1916—Belgium
Conrad—SOLOMAN WHITE CONRAD, 1779-1831—United States
Correll—DONOVAN STEWART CORRELL, 1908-   —United States
Coulter—JOHN MERLE COULTER, 1851-1928—United States
Crantz—HEINRICH JOHANN NEPOMUK VON CRANTZ, 1722-1797—Austria
Curtis—JOHN THOMAS CURTIS, 1913-   —United States

DC.—AUGUSTIN PYRAMUS DE CANDOLLE, 1778-1841—Switzerland
Don (D. Don)—DAVID DON, 1799-1841—Great Britain
Douglas—DAVID DOUGLAS, 1799-1834—Great Britain
Drejer—SALOMON THOMAS NICOLAI DREJER, 1813-1842—Denmark
Druce—GEORGE CLARIDGE DRUCE, 1850-1932—Great Britain
Dryander—JONAS DRYANDER, 1748-1810—Sweden and Great Britain

Eames—EDWARD A. EAMES, contemporary—United States
Eaton (A. Eaton)—AMOS EATON, 1776-1842—United States
Eaton (A. A. Eaton)—ALVAH AUGUSTUS EATON, 1865-1908—United States
Eaton (H. H. Eaton)—HEZEKIAH HULBERT EATON, 1809-1832—United States
Ell.—STEPHEN ELLIOTT, 1771-1830—United States
Engelm.—GEORGE ENGELMANN, 1809-1884—United States
Engl.—HEINRICH GUSTAV ADOLF ENGLER, 1844-1930—Germany

Farwell—OLIVER ATKINS FARWELL, 1867-1944—United States
Fawc.—WILLIAM FAWCETT, 1851-1926—Great Britain
Fernald—MERRITT LYNDON FERNALD, 1873-1950—United States
Fisch.—FRIEDRICH ERNST LUDWIG VON FISCHER, 1782-1854—Russia

Franklin—Sir JOHN FRANKLIN, 1786-1847—Great Britain
Frappier—CHARLES FRAPPIER, actively engaged 1853-1883—France?
Frye—THEODORE CHRISTIAN FRYE, 1869-   —United States
Fuller—ALBERT MORSE FULLER, 1899-   —United States

Gal.—HENRI (GUILLAUME) GALEOTTI, 1814-1858—Belgium
Godm.—FREDERICK DU CANE GODMAN, 1834-1919—Great Britain?
Goldie—JOHN GOLDIE, 1793-1886—Great Britain
Gray (A. Gray)—ASA GRAY, 1810-1888—United States
Greene—EDWARD LEE GREENE, 1843-1915—United States
Greenm.—JESSE MORE GREENMAN, 1867-   —United States
Griscom—LUDLOW GRISCOM, 1890-   —United States
Griseb.—AUGUST HEINRICH RUDOLF GRISEBACH, 1814-1879—Germany
Gron.—JOHANN FRIEDRICH GRONOVIUS, 1690-1762—Netherlands

Hall.—ALBRECHT VON HALLER, 1708-1777—Switzerland
HBK.—FRIEDRICH WILHELM HEINRICH ALEXANDER VON HUMBOLDT, 1769-1859—Germany;
    AIMÉ JACQUES ALEXANDRE BONPLAND, 1773-1858—France; KARL SIGISMUND KUNTH,
    1788-1850—Germany
Heller—AMOS ARTHUR HELLER, 1867-1944—United States
Hemsl.—WILLIAM BOTTING HEMSLEY, 1843-1924—Great Britain
Henry—JOSEPH KAYE HENRY, 1866-1930—Canada
Holz.—JOHN MICHAEL HOLZINGER, 1853-1929—United States
Hook.—WILLIAM JACKSON HOOKER, 1785-1865—Great Britain
Hook. f.—JOSEPH DALTON HOOKER, 1817-1911—Great Britain
House—HOMER DOLIVER HOUSE, 1878-1949—United States
Howell—THOMAS JEFFERSON HOWELL, 1842-1912—United States
Hubbard—FREDERIC TRACY HUBBARD, 1875-   —United States
Huds.—WILLIAM HUDSON, 1730-1793—Great Britain
Hult.—ERIC HULTÉN, 1894-   —Sweden

Jacq.—NIKOLAUS JOSEPH VON JACQUIN, 1727-1817—Austria
Jennings—OTTO EMERY JENNINGS, 1877-   —United States
Jepson—WILLIS LINN JEPSON, 1867-1946—United States
Johnston—IVAN MURRAY JOHNSTON, 1898-   —United States
Juss.—ANTOINE LAURENT DE JUSSIEU, 1748-1836—France

Karst.—GUSTAV KARL WILHELM HERMANN KARSTEN, 1817-1908—Germany
Kellogg—ALBERT KELLOGG, 1813-1887—United States
Ker-Gawl.—JOHN BELLENDEN KER (né GAWLER), 1765(?)-1842—Great Britain
Knight—ORA WILLIS KNIGHT, 1874-1913—United States
Ktze. (O. Ktze.)—CARL ERNST OTTO KUNTZE, 1843-1907—Germany

L.—CARL VON LINNÉ (CAROLUS LINNAEUS), 1707-1778—Sweden
La Llave—PABLO DE LA LLAVE, 1773-1833—Spain and Mexico
Lam.—JEAN-BAPTISTE ANTOINE PIERRE DE MONNET, Chevalier DE LAMARCK, 1744-1829—France
Lex.—JUAN JOSÉ MARTÍNEZ DE LEXARZA, 1785-1824—Mexico
Lindl.—JOHN LINDLEY, 1799-1865—Great Britain
Lodd.—CONRAD LODDIGES, 1732-1826; GEORGE LODDIGES, the son, 1784-1846—Great Britain

Macbr.—JAMES FRANCIS MACBRIDE, 1892-   —United States
MacM.—CONWAY MACMILLAN, 1867-1929—United States
Macoun—JOHN MACOUN, 1831-1920—Canada
Makino—TOMITARO MAKINO, 1863-   —Japan
Maxim.—CARL JOHANN MAXIMOWICZ, 1827-1891—Russia
Michx.—ANDRÉ MICHAUX, 1746-1802—France
Mohr—CHARLES THEODOR MOHR, 1824-1901—United States
Morong—THOMAS MORONG, 1827-1894—United States
Morris—FRANK MORRIS, 1869-   —United States
Mousley—HENRY MOUSLEY, 1865-1949—Canada
Muhl.—[GOTTHILF ERNST] HEINRICH MUHLENBERG, 1753-1815—United States

Nash—GEORGE VALENTINE NASH, 1864-1919—United States
Nelson—AVEN NELSON, 1859-   —United States
Nevski—S. NEVSKI, contemporary—Russia
Niles—GRACE GREYLOCK NILES, actively engaged 1904-1912—United States
Northrop—ALICE BELLE (RICH) NORTHROP, 1864-1922—United States
Nutt.—THOMAS NUTTALL, 1786-1859—United States

Oakes—WILLIAM OAKES, 1799-1848—United States

Paine—JOHN ALSOP PAINE, Jr., 1840-1912—United States
Parish—SAMUEL BONSAL PARISH, 1838-1928—United States

Parl.—FILIPPO PARLATORE, 1816-1877—Italy
Pavón—JOSÉ ANTONIO PAVÓN, 17(?)-1844—Spain
Peck—MORTON EATON PECK, 1871-   —United States
Pfitz.—ERNST HUGO HEINRICH PFITZER, 1846-1906—Germany
Piper—CHARLES VANCOUVER PIPER, 1867-1926—United States
Porter—THOMAS CONRAD PORTER, 1822-1901—United States
Prantl—KARL PRANTL, 1849-1893—Germany
Pursh—FREDERICK PURSH, 1774-1820—United States

Raf.—CONSTANTINE SAMUEL RAFINESQUE [-SCHMALTZ], 1783-1840—United States (mostly)
Rand—EDWARD LOTHROP RAND, 1859-1924—United States
Redfield—JOHN HOWARD REDFIELD, 1815-1895—United States
Reichb. f.—HEINRICH GUSTAV REICHENBACH, 1824-1889—Germany
Rendle—ALFRED BARTON RENDLE, 1865-1938—Great Britain
Rich. (A. Rich.)—ACHILLE RICHARD, 1794-1852—France
Rich. (L. C. Rich.)—LOUIS CLAUDE MARIE RICHARD, 1754-1821—France
Richards.—Sir JOHN RICHARDSON, 1787-1865—Great Britain
Ridley—HENRY NICHOLAS RIDLEY, 1855-   —Great Britain
Rigg—GEORGE BURTON RIGG, 1872-   —United States
Robins.—BENJAMIN LINCOLN ROBINSON, 1864-1935—United States
Rolfe—ROBERT ALLEN ROLFE, 1855-1921—Great Britain
Rothr.—JOSEPH TRIMBLE ROTHROCK, 1839-1922—United States
Ruiz—HIPÓLITO RUIZ [-LOPEZ], 1764-1815—Spain
Rydb.—PER AXEL RYDBERG, 1860-1931—United States

St. John—HAROLD ST. JOHN, 1892-   —United States
Salisb.—RICHARD ANTHONY SALISBURY, 1761-1829—Great Britain
Salvin—OSBERT SALVIN, 1835-1898—Great Britain
Schltr.—FRIEDRICH RICHARD RUDOLF SCHLECHTER, 1872-1925—Germany
Schum. (K. Schum.)—KARL MORITZ SCHUMANN, 1851-1904—Germany
Schweinf. (C. Schweinf.)—CHARLES SCHWEINFURTH, 1890-   —United States
Sims—JOHN SIMS, 1792-1838—Great Britain
Small—JOHN KUNKEL SMALL, 1869-1938—United States
Soland.—DANIEL SOLANDER, 1736-1782—Great Britain
Spreng.—KURT SPRENGEL, 1766-1833—Germany
Standl.—PAUL CARPENTER STANDLEY, 1884-   —United States
Stone—WITMER STONE, 1866-1939—United States
Sw.—OLOF SWARTZ, 1760-1818—Sweden

Thompson—ZADOC THOMPSON, 1796-1856—United States
Thouars—AUBERT DUPETIT-THOUARS, 1758-1831—France
Tidestrom—IVAR TIDESTROM, 1864-   —United States
Torr.—JOHN TORREY, 1796-1873—United States

Victorin—Frère MARIE VICTORIN (CONRAD J. KIROUAC), 1885-1944—Canada

Wall.—NATHANIEL WALLICH, 1786-1854—India
Walt.—THOMAS WALTER, 1740-1788—United States
Wats. (S. Wats.)—SERENO WATSON, 1826-1892—United States
Weatherby—CHARLES ALFRED WEATHERBY, 1875-1949—United States
Wherry—EDGAR THEODORE WHERRY, 1885-   —United States
White—MARCUS W. WHITE, actively engaged about 1900—United States
Wiegand—KARL McKAY WIEGAND, 1873-1942—United States
Wight (W. F. Wight)—WILLIAM FRANKLIN WIGHT, 1874-   —United States
Willd.—KARL LUDWIG WILLDENOW, 1765-1812—Germany
Wms. (L. O. Wms.)—LOUIS OTHO WILLIAMS, 1908-   —United States
Woot.—ELMER OTTIS WOOTON, 1865-1945—United States

Selected Bibliography

ABRAMS, L.:
  1940. Illustrated Flora of the Pacific States 1: 469-484.
AMES, BLANCHE:
  1947. Drawings of Florida Orchids (with explanatory notes by OAKES AMES), pls. 1-63.
AMES, O.:
  1904. A Contribution to Our Knowledge of the Orchid Flora of Southern Florida, pls. 1-12.
  1905. Orchidaceae, fasc. 1.
  1908. Notes on *Habenaria*. Rhodora 10: 70-71.
  1910. Orchidaceae, fasc. 4 (The Genus *Habenaria* in North America).
  1924. An Enumeration of the Orchids of the United States and Canada.
——, HUBBARD, F. T. and SCHWEINFURTH, C.:
  1936. The Genus *Epidendrum* in the United States and Middle America.
AMES, O.:
  1937. *Zeuxine strateumatica* in Florida. Orch. Zeyl. 4: 89-90, fig.
  1938. *Zeuxine strateumatica* in Florida. Bot. Mus. Leafl. Harvard Univ. 6: 37-45, pl.
  1938A. Resupination as a Diagnostic Character in the Orchidaceae, etc. Bot. Mus. Leafl.
      Harvard Univ. 6: 145-183, pls. and figs.
  1947. Commentaries on *Spiranthes,* I. Bot. Mus. Leafl. Harvard Univ. 13: 17-31, pls. 1-3.
——, and CORRELL, D. S.:
  1943. Notes on American Orchids. Bot. Mus. Leafl. Harvard Univ. 11: 1-28, pls. 1-3.
  1943A. Studies in *Habenaria* and *Dichaea*. Bot. Mus. Leafl. Harvard Univ. 11: 57-80, pls.
      4 and 5.
BALDWIN, H.:
  1884. The Orchids of New England.
BARKSDALE, L.:
  1936. Some Notes on Orchids of the Piedmont and Western North Carolina.
BARTLETT, H. H.:
  1922. Color Types of *Corallorrhiza maculata* Raf. Rhodora 24: 145-148.
BASTIN, E. S.:
  1881. Note. Bot. Gaz. 6: 269.
BINGHAM, M. T.:
  1939. Orchids of Michigan. Cranbrook Institute of Sci. Bull. 15.
BLAIR, K. R.:
  1909. The Orchids of Ohio. Ohio Nat. 10: 24-35.
BLOMQUIST, H. L. and OOSTING, H. J.:
  1940. A Guide to the Spring and early Summer Flora of the Piedmont, North Carolina.
      3d ed. (Orchidaceae contributed by D. S. CORRELL), pp. 45-48.
BRITTON, N. L.:
  1901. Manual of the Flora of the Northern States and Canada, ed. 1, pp. 289-306.
——, and BROWN, A.:
  1913. An Illustrated Flora of the Northern States and Canada, pp. 547-577, figs.
BROWN, R. (*in* AITON, W. T.):
  1813. Hortus Kewensis, ed. 2, vol. 5: 188-223.
BRYAN, M. M.:
  1917. A Spurless Variety of *Habenaria psycodes* (L.) Sw. Ann. Mo. Bot. Gard. 4: 37, pl. 5,
      figs. A-C.
BULHART, V.:
  1927. Orchids of Utility. Orch. Rev. 35: 234-236.
BUSWELL, W. M.:
  1937. Orchids of the Big Cypress. Am. Botanist 43: 147-153, fig.
  1945. Native Orchids of South Florida. Bull. Univ. Miami (Coral Gables, Florida) 19,
      No. 3, pls. 1-7.
CAMP, W. H.:
  1940. A New Variety of *Triphora*. Rhodora 42: 55-56.
CHAMISSO, A.:
  1828. Linnaea 3: 34.
CHAPMAN, A. W.:
  1897. Flora of the Southern United States, ed. 3, pp. 477-491.
COCKERELL, T. D. A.:
  1916. A New Form of *Corallorrhiza*. Torreya 16: 230-232.

COPELAND, H. E.:
1876. Some notes, etc. Bot. Gaz. 1: 33.
CORRELL, D. S.:
1937. The Orchids of North Carolina. Journ. Elisha Mitchell Sci. Soc. 53: 139-172, pl. 15.
1938. *Cypripedium Calceolus* var. *pubescens*. Bot. Mus. Leafl. Harvard Univ. 7: 1-18.
1939. A New Status for × *Habenaria Andrewsii*. Bot. Mus Leafl. Harvard Univ. 7: 57-72, pls. 1 and 2.
1940. A Contribution to Our Knowledge of the Orchids of the Southeastern United States. Bot. Mus. Leafl. Harvard Univ. 8: 69-92.
1940A. *Epidendrum conopseum* in the Southeastern States. Am. Orch. Soc. Bull. 9: 58-59, pl.
1940B. Some Southern Orchids. Am. Orch. Soc. Bull. 9: 79-83, 7 figs.
1941. Notes Concerning Some West Indian Orchids. Bot. Mus. Leafl. Harvard Univ. 10: 41-58.
——, and CORRELL, H. B.:
1941. A Collection of Plants from Louisiana. Am. Midl. Nat. 26: 44-45.
CORRELL, D. S.:
1943. The Genus *Habenaria* in Western North America. Leafl. West. Bot. 3: 233-247.
1944. Flora of Texas (Orchidaceae), 3, pt. 3: 151-196, 34 pls. (C. L. LUNDELL and Collaborators).
1944. Vanilla: Its History, Cultivation and Importance. Lloydia 7: 236-264, pl.
1946. The American Species of "Leafless" Vanillas. Am. Orch. Soc. Bull. 15: 328-333, figs. 1-2.
COULTER, J. M.:
1894. Contrib. U. S. Nat. Herb. (Botany of Western Texas) 2: 422-425.
——, and NELSON, A.
1909. New Manual of Botany of the Central Rocky Mountains, pp. 122-127.
CUNNINGHAM, A. M.:
1896. Distribution of the Orchidaceae in Indiana. Proc. Ind. Acad. Sci. 1895, pp. 198-202.
CURTIS, J. T.:
1932. A New *Cypripedium* Hybrid. Rhodora 34: 239-242.
1941. Peloric Flowers in *Cypripedium reginae* Walt. Am. Midl. Nat. 25: 580-583.
1941A. Some Native Orchids of the Lake Superior Region. Am. Orch. Soc. Bull. 9: 191-194, 4 figs.
DARLINGTON, H. T.:
1920. Distribution of the Orchidaceae in Michigan. 21st Rept. Mich. Acad. Sci., pp. 239-261.
DARWIN, C.:
1877. Various Contrivances by which Orchids are fertilized by Insects.
1884. On the Fertilization of Orchids by Insects.
DEAM, C.:
1940. Flora of Indiana, pp. 335-351.
DOIG, J. S.:
1941. Orchids in Bloom. Am. Orch. Soc. Bull. 9: 334-335.
DORMAN, CAROLINE:
1934. Wild Flowers of Louisiana.
ELLIOTT, S.:
1824. Sketch of the Botany of South-Carolina and Georgia 2: 482-510.
FARR, EDITH M.:
1907. Contrib. Bot. Lab. Univ. Pa. 3, No. 1: 27-29.
FARWELL, O. A.:
1917. New Species and Varieties from Michigan. 19th Rept. Mich. Acad. Sci. 247-249.
FERNALD, M. L.:
1921. The Gray Herbarium Expedition to Nova Scotia. Rhodora 23: 223-245.
1926. The Ragged Orchis of Newfoundland. Rhodora 28: 21-22.
1926A. Two Summers of Botanizing in Newfoundland. Rhodora 28: 161-178.
1946. Rhodora 48: 4.
1946. Technical Studies on North American Plants. Rhodora 48: 5-13, pls. 993-994.
1946A. Some Orchids of the Manual Range. Rhodora 48: 161-162, 184-197, pls. 1045-1048.
1947. Additions to and Subtractions from the Flora of Virginia. Rhodora 49: 121-142, pls. 1057-1063.
FITZPATRICK, T. J. and M. F. L.:
1900. The Orchidaceae of Iowa. Proc. Iowa Acad. Sci. 7: 187-196.
Fox, H. G.:
1895. On the Genus *Cypripedium*, L. with Reference to Minnesota Species. Minn. Bot. Studies, Bull. 9: 423-449, figs.

FULLER, M. A.:
1932. A Natural *Cypripedium* Hybrid from Wisconsin. Rhodora 34: 97-101.
1933. Studies on the Flora of Wisconsin. Part I: the orchids; Orchidaceae. Bull. Publ.
    Mus. Milwaukee 14, No. 1: 1-248, pls. 1-54.
GATTINGER, A.:
1887. The Tennessee Flora, pp. 83-84.
1901. The Flora of Tennessee, pp. 62-64.
GIBSON, W. H.:
1905. Our Native Orchids.
HENKEL, A.:
1907. American Root Drugs. U. S. Dept. Agric., Bureau Pl. Ind. Bull. 107.
HITCHCOCK, A. S. and STANDLEY, P. C.:
1919. Contrib. U. S. Nat. Herb. (Flora of the District of Columbia) 21: 127-132.
HOLM, T.:
1904. The Root-structure of North American Terrestrial Orchideae. Am. Journ. Sci. 18:
    197-212, figs. 1-4.
HOUSE, H. D.:
1924. New York State Mus. Bull. 254: 234-252.
JEPSON, W. L.:
1911. A Flora of Western Middle California, ed. 2: 112-116.
KEARNEY, T. H. and PEEBLES, R. H.:
1942. Flowering Plants and Ferns of Arizona, pp. 207-214.
KNUDSON, L.:
1922. Nonsymbiotic Germination of Orchid Seeds. Bot. Gaz. 73: 1-25.
LINDLEY, J.:
1830-40. Genera and Species Orchidaceous Plants.
LINNAEUS, C.:
1753. Species Plantarum, ed. 1, 2: 939-954.
LOWE, E. N.:
1921. Plants of Mississippi. Miss. State Geo. Surv. Bull. 17: 123-126.
MACDOUGAL, D. T.:
1895. Poisonous Influence of Various Species of *Cypripedium*. Minn. Bot. Studies, Bull. 9:
    450-451.
MICHAUX, A.:
1803. Flora Boreali-americana 2: 155-161.
MOHR, C. T.:
1901. Contrib. U. S. Nat. Herb. (Plant Life of Alabama) 6: 452-460.
MORRIS, F. and EAMES, E. A.:
1929. Our Wild Orchids.
MOUSLEY, H.:
1920. Further Notes on the Orchids of Hatley, Stanstead County, Quebec, 1919. Can. Field-
    Nat. 34: 44-47.
1940. Peloria and Other Abnormalities in Orchids. Can. Field-Nat. 58: 73-76, fig. 1.
1940. *Listera australis* Lindl. in the Province of Quebec. Can. Field-Nat. 54: 95-96, pl.
1941. A Distinctive New Variety of *Orchis rotundifolia* from Canada, etc. Can. Field-Nat.
    55: 64-65, fig.
1941A. Two Orchids New to the Province of Quebec and the Dominion of Canada, etc.
    Can. Field-Nat. 55: 79-80, pls. 1-2.
NILES, G. G.:
1904. Bog-trotting for Orchids.
NUTTALL, T.:
1818. Genera North American Plants 2: 188-199.
NYLANDER, O. O.:
1935. Our Northern Orchids.
PECK, M. E.:
1941. A Manual of the Higher Plants of Oregon, pp. 217-222.
PFITZER, E.:
1889. Orchidaceae *in* A. ENGLER and K. PRANTL, Die natürlichen Pflanzenfamilien, pt. 2,
    Abt. 6: 52-220.
PIPER, C. V.:
1906. Contrib. U. S. Nat. Herb. (Flora of the State of Washington) 11: 205-211.
——, and BEATTIE, R. K.:
1914. Flora of Southeastern Washington and Adjacent Idaho, pp. 67-72.
1915. Flora of the Northwest Coast, pp. 106-112.
POLUNIN, N.:
1943. Contributions to the Flora and Phytogeography of South-Western Greenland. Journ.
    Linn. Soc. Bot. 52: 379.

PURSH, F.:
  1814. Flora Americae Septentrionalis, pp. 585-595.
RAFINESQUE, C. S.:
  1833. Herbarium Rafinesquianum.
RAND, E. L. and REDFIELD, J. H.:
  1894. Flora of Mount Desert Island, Maine, pp. 150-154.
ROBINSON, B. L. and FERNALD, M. L.:
  1908. GRAY's New Manual of Botany, ed. 7, pp. 304-319.
      (Orchidaceae revised by OAKES AMES).
ROLFE, R. A.:
  1892. CCLXIII.—New Orchids: Decade 3. Kew Bull., pp. 208-211.
RYDBERG, P. A.:
  1901. The American Species of *Limnorchis* and *Piperia,* north of Mexico. Bull. Torr. Bot. Club 28: 605-643.
  1906. Flora of Colorado, pp. 87-90.
  1922. Flora of the Rocky Mountains and Adjacent Plains, ed. 2, pp. 176-184.
  1932. Flora of the Prairies and Plains of Central North America, pp. 232-245.
SMALL, J. K.:
  1903. Flora of the Southeastern United States, pp. 309-330.
  1913. Flora of the Southeastern United States, ed. 2, pp. 308-331.
  1913. Flora of Miami, pp. 49-59.
  1933. Manual of the Southeastern Flora, pp. 363-399.
STEMEN, T. R. and MEYERS, W. S.:
  1937. Oklahoma Flora, pp. 69-72.
STEVENSON, J. A.:
  1926. Foreign Plant Diseases. U. S. Dept. Agric., pp. 120-124.
STEYERMARK, J. A.:
  1940. Spring Flora of Missouri, pp. 93-100.
STREET, J. F.:
  1929. The Orchids of the New Jersey Pine Barrens. Year Book Acad. Nat. Sci. Phila., pp. 20-25, 3 pls.
TAYLOR, L. A.:
  1940. Plants Used as Curatives by Certain Southeastern Tribes.
TIDESTROM, I.:
  1925. Contrib. U. S. Nat. Herb. (Flora of Utah and Nevada) 25: 129-131.
——, and KITTELL, T.:
  1941. A Flora of Arizona and New Mexico, pp. 729-733.
TRACY, C. M.:
  1869. The Orchids. Am. Nat. 2: 342-351.
VEITCH, J.:
  1887-1894. Manual of Orchidaceous Plants, vols. 1-5.
VICTORIN, FRÈRE MARIE:
  1929. Deux Épibiotes Remarquables de la Minganie. Trans. Roy. Soc. Canada, ser. 3, 22. Sect. 5: 163-176, pls. 1-3.
WALLACE, JEAN E.:
  1949. The Orchids of Maine. Mss. in press, Univ. of Me. Studies.
WALTER, T.:
  1788. Flora Caroliniana, pp. 220-223.
WATKINS, JOHN V.:
  1942. Orchids in Florida. Univ. of Florida, Agric. Ext. Serv. Bull. 116. 47 pp., 35 figs.
WELLS, B. W.:
  1932. The Natural Gardens of North Carolina.
WHERRY, E. T.:
  1918. The Reaction of the Soils Supporting the Growth of Certain Native Orchids. Journ. Wash. Acad. Sci. 8: 589-598.
  1927. The Soil Reaction of Saprophytic Orchids. Journ. Wash. Acad. Sci. 17: 35-38, fig. 1.
  1928. Northward Range-extensions of Some Southern Orchids in Relation to Soil Reaction. Journ. Wash. Acad. Sci. 18: 212-216.
  1938. Notable Pennsylvania Orchids. Proc. Penn. Acad. Sci. 12: 42-45.
WIEGAND, K. M.:
  1899. A Revision of the Genus *Listera.* Bull. Torr. Bot. Club 26: 157-171, pls. 356-357.
——, and EAMES, A. J.:
  1926. The Flora of the Cayuga Lake Basin, New York, pp. 151-161.
WILLIAMS, L. O.:
  1937. The Orchidaceae of the Rocky Mountains. Am. Midl. Nat. 18: 830-841.
WOOTON, E. O. and STANDLEY, P. C.:
  1915. Contrib. U. S. Nat. Herb. (Flora of New Mexico) 19: 148-154.

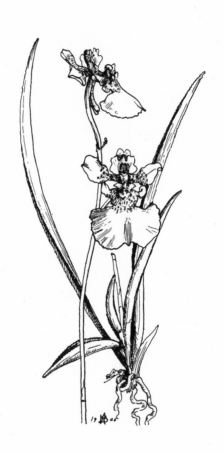

INDEX of SCIENTIFIC NAMES

(The first page cited, in **bold face**, is where the subject is treated in detail; page numbers with an asterisk (*) indicate illustrations; names in *italics* are those of synonyms.)

INDEX *of* COMMON NAMES

(The page cited is only where the orchid is treated in detail.)